HONEY BEE
BIOLOGY
AND BEEKEEPING

THIRD EDITION

DEWEY M. CARON AND LAWRENCE JOHN CONNOR

HONEY BEE BIOLOGY AND BEEKEEPING, Third Edition

Text written by Dewey M. Caron and Lawrence John Connor.

Artwork by Jon Zawislak.

Photos provided by Dewey M. Caron unless otherwise credited.

Anatomy photos by Ian Stell, M.D.

Front cover and front page (L): a honey bee forager on a basswood flower. C. Burkhead

Front page (R): Seasonal views of an apiary. C. Burkhead

Published by Wicwas Press, LLC, 1620 Miller Road Kalamazoo, MI 49001

www.wicwas.com

ISBN (10) 1-878075-62-4 (13) 978-1-878075-62-8

Published in the USA

Dedicated to Ann Harmon and Robert Cole, two EAS Master Beekeepers who spread their knowledge of bees and beekeeping around the world with their outreach and teaching.

Our heartfelt thanks to an amazing group of people who have reviewed this textbook and selected chapters.

Entire book: Charlotte Hubbard, Randy Kim and Dr. Jon Zawislak

Selected sections: Dr. James Tew, Steve Repasky, Dr. Ernesto Guzman, Dr. Ramesh Sagili, Dr. Priya Chakrabarti, Judy Scher, Dr. Meghan Milbrath, Tammy Horn Potter, Rich Weiske, David Priebe, Dr. Tom Seeley, Ana Heck, Dan Wyns, Morris Ostrofsky, Ellen Tophithoper, Carolyn Breece, Shaana Way, Becky Tipton, Mike Connor, Todd Smith.

ABOUT THE AUTHORS

Dewey M. Caron

A native of Vermont, Dewey Caron received a B.S. from University of Vermont (Zoology), a M.S from University of Tennessee (Ecology) and completed his Ph.D. in 1970 at Cornell University under Dr. Roger Morse in Apiculture. He was Cooperative Extension and teaching faculty at University of Maryland (11 years) and University of Delaware (29 years). He served as acting Department chairman in Maryland and as Department Chair at University of Delaware. He is currently Emeritus Professor of Entomology & Wildlife Ecology.

With retirement in 2009 he moved to Portland, Oregon to be closer to grandkids. He remains active in bee education, writing for newsletters, giving bee short courses, assisting in several master beekeeper programs and giving presentations.

Dewey represents the Western Apicultural Society on the Honey Bee Health Coalition and is principal author of *HBHC Tools for Varroa Management and Best Management Practices*. He has over 100 research publications, over 200 popular articles and is regular contributor to bee club newsletters and bee magazines. He has been author of more than 15 book chapters, including most recently *Bee Medicine, a Practical Guide to Veterinary Practitioners*. He authored *The Complete Bee Handbook* for Rockridge Press in 2020.

Lawrence John Connor

Born in Kalamazoo, Michigan, Larry Connor earned his doctorate in honey-bee pollination of crops at Michigan State University, working with Dr. E.C. Martin. He worked as Extension Bee Specialist at The Ohio State University, President of Genetic Systems, Inc. (producing tens of thousands of instrumentally inseminated queens honey bees and the Starline and Midnite breeding stock). He is the founding member of Wicwas Press LLC, specializing in publication of quality bee books.

Connor relocated from Connecticut to Michigan in April 2007 to continue growing his teaching, writing and publishing activities. He has authored, edited and published over two dozen books: *Increase Essentials*, *Bee Sex Essentials*, *Queen Rearing Essentials*, *Bee-sentials: A Field Guide*, *Swarm Essentials* (with Steve Repasky), *Honey Bee Biology and Beekeeping* (Revised Edition with Dewey Caron), *Increase Essentials* Second Edition and *Mating Biology of Honey Bees* (with G. and N. Koeniger and J. Ellis). New titles include *Keeping Bees Alive* and *Package Essentials*. He has contributed many articles to beekeeping magazines and publications.

For further information about Dr. Connor's books, journal writing, and teaching, consult the website: www.wicwas.com.

Chapter Quick Finder

Table of Contents

HONEY BEE BIOLOGY AND BEEKEEPING

SECTION 2 BEEKEEPING

HOW TO USE THIS BOOK

Many readers and diverse applications

We spent most of the 2020-2021 Covid-19 confinement working on the third edition of the popular beekeeping book, *Honey Bee Biology and Beekeeping*. We maintained its popular features and have expanded many areas. We are aware that earlier editions have been used in a variety of situations, from a personal starter book to a method of reviewing for master beekeeping examinations. We are honored that many college and university instructors have selected this text for their classrooms. Bee clubs also use the book for their intensive beekeeping classes, perhaps spanning a year or two in Beekeeping 101, 102 and 103 classes.

Our goal has been to make this book as complete as possible without oversimplifying complicated science or advanced beekeeping practice. We sought to update the book and have include topics not found in earlier editions. We have expanded the book and added new chapters that reflected the constantly evolving focus of beekeepers and bee research.

We added a set of terms at the end of each chapter where they are addressed. We expanded the Glossary at the end of the book. At the end of each chapter we added a listing of references, both publications and web-based, to guide the reader.

This book can serve as a powerful reference for the beekeeper based on relevant activities of the bee season. For instance, if you have just purchased a nuc or package, read the chapters on Getting started (Ch. 12), Spring (Ch. 15) and Management basics (Ch. 13). Manage your time to read Honey production (Ch. 16) and Bee Mites (Ch. 21) in summer to anticipate your next moves. Stay ahead of the curve by reading Fall and winter (Ch. 14) in late summer to plan your preparations. Use your free time during the winter off-season to study anything you missed.

The book teaches using the printed word and the visual image. We strive to use clear and helpful photos throughout the book. Most of the graphics, both redrawn and new, have been developed in cooperation with Dr. Jon Zawislak, University of Arkansas. Jon also contributed to the written part of the book, and we appreciate his efforts.

There is no wrong way to use this book. Each chapter is a comprehensive introduction to the subject. This explains some minor redundancy and duplicate photos. We feel this helps tell a complete story without extensive page flipping.

If you read this book from front to back, or from back to front, you will obtain a great deal of useful information about bee biology and beekeeping. If you are interested in a particular topic, you may reread certain sections over and over and peal away, layer by layer, the knowledge onion of beekeeping. As you do, you will be enriched with the fascinating and beautiful world of the honey bee.

We welcome any and all feedback you feel you wish to supply. Contacting us initially via email is recommended. We are all learning and the beekeeping industry is constantly evolving and changing. Good luck and happy beekeeping!

DEWEY M. CARON, PH.D. dmcaron@udel.edu
LAWRENCE JOHN CONNOR, PH.D. ljconnor@aol.com

2021

Photo on opposite page shows a honey bee forager on a basswood flower. C. Burkhead

SECTION 1
BIOLOGY

HISTORY
TAXONOMY
BEE SCIENCE

Chapter 1
Introduction

Figure 1.1
Smoke from a bellows-type smoker. Smoke interferes with bee communication and calms bees during hive inspection. New beekeepers need to learn proper smoker lighting and use. G. Hansen

Concepts

Our insect ally

What is beekeeping?

Association of bees and humans

Development of managed colonies

Learning bee culture

Saving the planet's pollinators

Our insect ally

The honey bee is our insect ally. This is ironic because 'ally' is not a word we usually use when referring to insects. Wherever social bees exist, humans have exploited them for their resources, hunting wild (feral) nests for honey and wax. Initially hunter-robbers, humans eventually learned to care for honey bees. Beekeeping (apiculture or bee culture) is the care and maintenance of bee colonies for fun and profit. Today, honey bees are managed for pollination and honey production worldwide.

Many people know something about honey bees and their products. Bees have been admired, studied, cultured, feared and valued, but not always well understood. This book is dedicated to improving human understanding of our complex interactions with honey bees.

Beekeeping can be rewarding. Beekeepers are compensated for their efforts with revenue from honey sales and hive rental fees. It is not an easy way to make a living. There are countless risks in successful care of honey bee colonies. The vast majority of beekeepers are small-scale operators, commonly termed backyard beekeepers or hobbyists. Many hobbyist beekeepers simply receive satisfaction learning bee culture, harvesting little in return.

There is no 'one size fits all' when it comes to beekeeping. Honey bees do not need daily care or husbandry. While colonies can be managed to increase return on investment, humans vary in their management intensity. Owners of a few colonies may provide extensive colony care, while those keeping larger numbers of hives manage bees as livestock, providing the same level of per hive attention. Intensive managers examine their colonies frequently to observe and learn colony secrets, while commercial beekeepers employ uniform management of many hives.

What is beekeeping?

At a basic level, beekeeping is simply providing honey bees a convenient domicile, a hive, that allows them to rear young (brood) and store honey in abundance. Swarming (reproduction of the social colony) is discouraged and the bees' natural instinct to visit flowers to gather and store food is encouraged (Figure 1-2). Skillful beekeepers manage their colonies by anticipating colony growth and timing their manipulations according to the normal bee seasonal cycle and biology. We have not fully domesticated the honey bee, but increasingly use genetic selection programs to produce stocks that are easier to manage, produce more honey and have tolerance against diseases and parasites.

Figure 1-2
Worker honey bee foraging for pollen on *Datura*. L. Connor

Beekeeping can be defined as **applied bee biology**. Beekeepers should learn biology—what bees do—and then use this knowledge to help improve harvest potential and/or enjoyment of bee culture. Beekeepers apply bee biology to efficiently manage colonies by encouraging bees to follow their natural instincts. Colony management is less effective when we ignore critical biological information and details.

Successful beekeeping is characterized as **anticipation, not reaction**. Knowledge of bee biology permits beekeepers to anticipate bee responses to environmental conditions and internal biological cycles. When a beekeeper only reacts to what bees are currently doing, the beekeeper is being managed by the bees! Skillfully applying biological information allows beekeepers to anticipate colony development and needs.

Beekeeping is **colony population management**. As a social organism—a large family—the bee colony increases its population in a predictable, seasonal manner. Colonies do this with or without beekeeper intervention, instinctively growing stronger to take advantage of the resources offered by their environment. Skillful beekeepers support this growth so bee populations peak at the start of the nectar flow. Experienced beekeepers boost weak colonies and prevent swarming by strong colonies.

Beekeeping—both science and art?

It would be a mistake to say that beekeeping is exclusively knowing bee biology. There is a lot of science in beekeeping, yet good beekeepers also practice their beekeeping art. Skillful beekeepers combine bee biology, bee-flower interactions and natural history to form the art of beekeeping.

Experience can be one of the best teachers for beekeepers. Honey bee colonies are not like uniform bottles of ketchup. Each hive is unique. Bees are natural creatures and both new and experienced beekeepers alike ponder what bees do. Individual honey bee colonies do not always respond in the same way, nor as the beekeeper wishes! Beekeepers find individual colonies have a personality of their own. However, colonies often respond similarly to environmental cues with predicable and seasonal variations allowing multiple colonies to be husbanded with the same or similar management tools and techniques.

Beekeepers discover they cannot learn all they need to know about bee management and colony care in one season. The artful application of a growing body of colony knowledge makes it unlikely that individuals will become bored or disinterested in honey bees after exposure to them. Beekeeping is expansive and captivating. Enter the world of the honey bee with caution—it is likely to entertain, enrich and fascinate for many years.

The real key

If bee biology can be summed up in a graph to demonstrate how beekeeping management can be understood, then Figure 1-3 represents the essence of

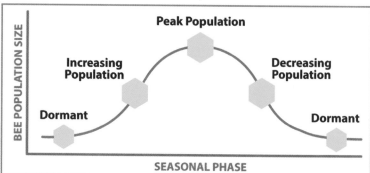

Figure 1-3
Typical bell-shaped curve relationship between time of the season and the number of bees. Population is at lowest over the winter, grows rapidly in spring to peak late spring/early summer and then declines in fall.
J. Zawislak

Ah Mucen Cab - A bee god

Figures 1-4, 1-5
Images of Spanish rock painting of about 7000 BC from Spider cave, Bicorp, (near Valencia) Spain. L: Actual painting and R: reproduction.

Figures 1-7, 1-8
L: Mayan Bee God entering his beehive, expressed as a thatched building. Carved in slate by the Garcia Sisters, San Antonio, Cayo District, Belize, Central America. M. Burgett.
R: Contemporary rendition of Mayan Bee God in pottery.

beekeeping. The figure illustrates that a bee population grows rapidly after a seasonal low point (winter in temperate climate areas or the wet/dry period in the tropics). As the population expands, there is a strong impulse for the population to naturally divide by swarming. Strong colonies will store a surplus of food reserves during a period referred to as nectar flow. After

peak population, colonies decline in size, reaching a low point in population before the next season begins again.

Figure 1-3 illustrates that adult bee populations change throughout the season. Similar graphs can be constructed for brood population (during the lowest point, this may be at zero as no brood is present) and for drone population (zero during the lowest point then rapid spring growth followed by sharp decline in the early fall). Good beekeepers, after one or more seasons of experience, recognize major seasonal events and subsequently adjust their colony care to account for seasonal variations.

Beekeepers also seek to overlay on this basic seasonal fluctuation other events such as the flowering times of major floral sources, swarming season, mite treatment times, when bees expand brood capacity and when to add or remove supers. Such details are presented in subsequent chapters following further discussion of bee biology.

Unlike other animals under human stewardship, bees do not need daily care. Swarms that escape simply add to the natural or feral bee colony population of an area. As interest and skills develop, beekeepers learn to work more efficiently for the benefit of the colony and themselves.

Human association with bees
What can be learned by trying to understand the life of another living organism, especially one as small as a honey bee? To humans, honey bees have been an

Figure 1-6
Two *Apis dorsata* nests in a coconut tree. M. Burgett

important source of honey and beeswax since ancient times. Prior to widespread cultivation of sugar cane, honey was the most readily available sweetener in the human diet.

Rich and poor alike, humans worldwide use honey, beeswax and other bee products as a powerful medicine cabinet and tool box. Beeswax is valued as a sealant, a lubricant and polish, for candles, and as a currency.

Honey bees fascinate humans. Bees are a convenient and interesting social animal to study. Although not closely related, humans have sought to draw comparisons between insect social life and human society. Being 'busy as a bee' is desirable. We seek to avoid being labeled 'lazy as a drone.' From early Greek and Roman times, humans have sought to emulate the honey bee queen, even to the practice of using royal jelly in the belief that it can help make one regal.

Prior to becoming beekeepers, humans, like other primates, were robbers of bee colonies. Chimpanzees use sticks pushed into a bee nest to remove and lick the honey. The earliest human record of interaction with bees, dating to about 7000 BC (Figures 1-4, 1-5), shows a human robbing a wild bee nest in Spain. Isolated cultures still hunt wild colonies, climbing high cliffs or tall trees, often at considerable risk of being stung. Figure 1-6 shows two *Apis dorsata* nests in a coconut tree. Harvest of honey from this largest bodied honey bee can lead to many painful stings.

Wasps, bees and warfare

Bees, and their close wasp relatives, have been deployed as biological warfare weapons for centuries. The Old Testament documents the use of hornets to vanquish enemies. During the Middle Ages, colonies were located inside castle walls to provide food and to use as a last resort to rout the enemy climbing over or tunneling under the castle walls. Later warriors hooked trip wires to release stinging bees on their enemies. In Vietnam, hill tribes used this tactic to discourage invasion.

Bees have been released into concealed mines/tunnels to expose the enemy. Today, honey bees are used to determine locations of land mine fields, plastic explosives, and nuclear and chemical weapon stocks by training individual bees. By using Pavlovian techniques, bees learn to associate the specific odors of such weaponry with food. Field bees are electronically tracked as they forage.

One American Revolutionary War story credits honey bees with saving the American forces from British capture. In 1780, Colonial troops were encamped outside Philadelphia. A young girl on a path to visit her family's beehives came upon a wounded British soldier who told her about the British enemy troop movement. She rode

Figure 1-9
Stingless bee *Tetragonisca* tunnel entrance.

ahead to the Continental Army encampment to warn General George Washington of the troop movement after first stirring up the bees to slow British soldier advance.

Probably the best description of social insect warfare comes from the Mayan story of creation:

And then the gourds were opened...and the yellowjackets and wasps were like a cloud of smoke when they poured out of each of the gourds. And the warriors were done in, with the insects landing on their eyes and landing on their noses, on their mouths, their legs, their arms. The insects went after them wherever they were. There were yellowjackets and wasps everywhere, landing to sting their eyes. They had to watch out for whole swarms of them, there were insects going after every single person. The yellowjackets and wasps dazed them. No longer able to hold onto their weapons and shields, they were doubling over and falling to the ground stumbling. They fell down the mountainside.

The Mayans have a Bee God, Ah-Muzen-Cab (Figures 1-7 and 8). The meso-American Mayans and Aztecs kept colonies of stingless bees (Figure 1-9), a social relative of honey bees (Chapter 2).

In 401 BC, the Greek general Xenophon was leading his army of mercenaries back home after several years of fighting the Persians. As they journeyed along the shores of the Black Sea, the soldiers noticed large numbers of bees so they set about searching for wild bee nests and that evening feasted on honey raided from the abundant nests they found.

The soldiers soon became ill. Fierce warriors who had been so valiant in battle were too ill to stand and defend themselves. Most recovered in a few days and eventually they continued their westward journey to more friendly territory. Unknowingly, the soldiers had consumed a toxic honey produced by bees collected as nectar from rhododendron blossoms. The native inhabitants of the Black Sea region knew all about the potentially dangerous rhododendron honey, but had not told the soldiers, strangers in their land, to test the honey before eating it. In North America, honey bees rarely collect rhododendron nectar.

Nearly four centuries after the passage of Xenophon, the Roman general Pompey passed through the same region. The Romans were fighting King Mithridate to gain domain over the trade routes of the area. Three Roman squadrons were offered delicate, sweet-tasting honey by the locals and were then slaughtered in the morning, as they were too ill to fight.

The region where Xenophon and the Greek soldiers and later Pompey with his Roman legions fell sick was known in legend as the home of Dionysus, god of wine and drunken revelry. Is it a coincidence that honey is central to this legend?

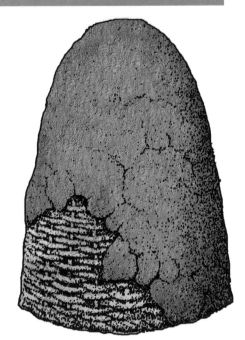

Figure 1-11
Clomed bee hive is built over a reed or wicker frame and covered with a mixture of mud, dung and ash. Redrawn by J. Zawislak.

Figures 1-12
Greek inverted skep with slat top bars for comb construction. G. Wheler

Only in the Twentieth Century would we discover **grayanotoxin**, the compound responsible for these human reactions. It is present in plants like oleander and ericaceous plants like rhododendron. It is known locally by such names as 'cattle destroyer' and 'horse killer.' Symptoms depend upon dosage and include tingling sensations and numbness, dizziness, psychedelic optical effects, giddiness, impaired speech, nausea, respiratory difficulty, low pulse rate, muscle paralysis and even death. The chemical is used by some for its mind-altering effects.

Figure 1-10
Gathering Honey, Tomb of Rekhmire, ca. 1479-1425 B.C. Drawn by Nina de Garis Davies. Original from Egypt, Upper Egypt, Thebes, Sheikh Abd el-Qurna, Tomb of Rekhmire (TT 100). The standing figure is holding a smoker and is fanning the bees with smoke. The kneeling figure is removing honey from clay hives similar to Figure 1-15. Digitally restored by J. Zawislak from image held at the Metropolitan Museum.

Pliny, the great Roman naturalist, described the excellent honeys of the Mediterranean region. He warned others (but not apparently General Pompey) about the 'mad' honeys of the Black Sea region. He determined that this honey was toxic only during springs that are wet and cold, and that symptoms appear only before the honey is fully ripened. Pliny reported that fermented mead made with this honey was consumed for its psychedelic properties to intensify the alcoholic effect.

Figures 1-13 and 14
L: Temperate area honey bee colonies require large nest cavities. R: Tropical and subtropical bees seek cavities about one-half the volume of temperate area bees and can nest successfully outside the hive with limited protection, as this colony in Panama.

Box 1

Temperate versus tropical seasonality

The development and behavior of bee colonies is predictable as bees have an annual cycle, though the length of the seasons may vary (See Chapter 4). The majority of bee colonies are kept in temperate climate latitudes between 34-65° N. This climatic area, 39% of the total land area of Planet Earth, includes all of the United States (except very southern portions), Canada, Europe, Russia, the countries of the former USSR, and most Asian countries including Japan and China. It does not include four major honey producing regions of the world (southern Brazil, northern Argentina, Yucatán of Mexico, and Australia).

The seasonal cycle of a bee colony is more predictable in temperate areas than in tropical/subtropical regions of the world. In more northerly areas of the temperate zone, bee colonies halt brood rearing, for a short time at least, during shorter winter days, and must cluster together to survive. Farther south, and in subtropical/tropical areas, clustering does not happen.

Proper beekeeping management employs activities which consider bee biology and take the annual colony cycle into account. Bee colonies are most productive when they reach their maximum population at the start of the bloom of the major nectar producing plants, whether bees are kept in temperate or tropical areas. Management practices thus are similar wherever bees are kept and vary only in timing and intensity. This book focuses on beekeeping in a temperate climate.

Figure 1-15
Cylindrical Egyptian mud bee hives. G. Kritsky *Tears of Re*

Honey is truly a unique and distinctive product. It is as highly prized today as when humans first discovered and robbed wild bee nests. Rhododendron is but one source of honey in the world. Under special circumstances, such as reported in this region, it is a rarity—a toxic honey. Closely related plants, including blueberry, heather or sourwood, are highly prized, non-toxic and sought-after honey sources.

Apiculture beginnings

No one knows when the first human became a beekeeper seeking to maximize the honey harvest from colonies. The transition from honey hunter to beekeeper was natural and probably occurred many times in many places. The best early records of beekeeping come from Egypt where honey played an important spiritual, social and economic role for both the living and the dead. Carvings and paintings (Figure 1-10) in Egyptian temples and tombs show bees and honey in the comb with humans caring for bees and harvesting honey from beehives.

Nile River beekeepers of ancient Egypt used elongated clay cylinder domiciles similar to hives which still can be found in use in the Middle East today (Figure 1-15). This is a hive of horizontal design. Bees organize their brood nest inside the entrance at one end and store honey toward the back. Modern beekeepers follow the ancient Egyptian custom and use smoke to drive the bees away from the back of the cylinder so they may harvest honey-filled combs until they reach brood.

The Middle East has a long beekeeping tradition. Hives were made mostly of pottery (such as large grain or water storage pots) or woven vines/reeds as vertical cylinders sometimes covered in mud mixed with dung (Figure 1-11).

Figures 1-16
Vertical woven "Greek Beehive" used by early Greeks and Romans. Institute of Agricultural Science

The clomed hive shown in Figure 1-11 starts as a reed or wicker frame that is then covered with mud, dung and ash. Generally such domiciles were small in size and easily handled for harvesting.

The Bible contains over 60 references to bees and their honey. It is not clear if honey was merely collected from wild nests or from managed colonies of beekeepers. The Qur'an also frequently mentions honey and also use of beehives in date palm plantations, the first reference to bees used in pollination.

Greek and Roman civilizations have many records of bees and beekeepers. Aristotle and many other Greek and Roman scholars wrote about bees. Aristotle used an observation hive to learn about bees. Greek and Roman athletes believed honey improved their performance. Honey was considered to be part of the formula for long life. The Romans used honey to sweeten wine. Beekeeping changed little during this time. Hives continued to be both vertical and horizontal. In some locations, hives of wood, wicker and cork

Figure 1-17
Bee gum with a rain/snow/sun shade. D. Skrypek

replaced pottery hives (Figure 1-16 plus illustrations in Chapter 9).

Bee gums and skeps

In forested areas, reproductive bee swarms settled in tree hollows (Figure 1-13). Beekeepers discovered these feral nests and marked them as their property. One tree might house several colonies. Some trees would be 'topped' and/or the cavity enlarged to provide a larger nest space. Soon, beekeepers learned to construct appropriate-sized tree hollows for their bees, termed **gums** (Figure 1-17), or they transferred the bees to lighter, easier to handle hives constructed from bark or twigs, sealed with animal dung.

In areas of fewer forests, hives of woven vines/straw, termed **skeps**, became common bee domiciles (Figure 1-18). Often, property-defining stone walls were provided with openings (**bee boles**), or indentations built into house and barn walls to house the skeps.

Colonies in trees, gums and skeps were vertically managed hives in which the bees

Figure 1-18
Woven skeps were made of straw, reed, or vines, sewn together with thin strips of softened wood (ash).

reared brood in lower sections and stored honey in upper portions. With time, some beekeepers added an extra hollow gum or wicker basket above (superior to) the brood nest which the bees tended to use just for storage of honey. This management, termed **supering**, led to larger honey harvests and greater profitability.

Fundamental discoveries

Strides were made in beekeeping development in the late 1500s and 1600s. The scientific basis of beekeeping was established and fundamental discoveries about bees were made, such as knowledge that the large bee was not a king, as Aristole believed, but rather a female queen. Beekeeping knowledge and colony care expanded through parts of Africa, Europe and the Middle East.

Bees on the move

Honey bees are not native to the Americas. We do not know precisely when the first colonies of honey bees were brought to North America. Ships crossing the Atlantic in the winter carried bee colonies to Virginia, arriving in 1622, and to Massachusetts prior to 1638. The honey bee did very well in the forest clearings of the early settlements, using the abundant nectar and pollen available from the trees and shrubs native to the Eastern U.S.

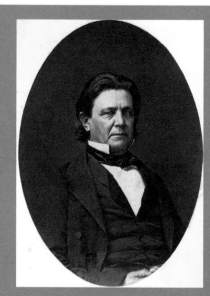

Figure 1-19
The Rev. L. L. Langstroth.

Box 2

FATHER OF MODERN BEEKEEPING

The Rev. Lorenzo L. Langstroth (Figure 1-19) is considered the Father of Modern Beekeeping. He developed the modern movable-comb hive that still bears his name, though his design was simplified and streamlined in the late 1800s by the A. I. Root Company. Langstroth explained his hive and beekeeping management in a book, The Hive and Honey Bee. This venerable tome, though not well-received initially, has had many revisions and today is one of the most useful references on bees and beekeeping. In his own words:

'This treatise on the hive and the honeybee is respectfully submitted by the author to the candid consideration of those who are interested in the culture of the most useful as well as wonderful insect in all the range of animated nature. The information which it contains will be found to be greatly in advance of anything which has yet been presented to the English reader. The present condition of practical beekeeping in this country is known to be deplorably low. From the great mass of agriculturists, and others favorably situated for obtaining honey, it receives not the slightest attention. Notwithstanding the large number of patent hives which have been introduced, the ravages of the bee-moth have increased, and success is becoming more and more precarious. Multitudes have abandoned the pursuit in disgust. In the present state of public opinion, it requires no little courage to venture upon the introduction of a new hive and system of management; but I feel confident that a new era in beekeeping has arrived, and invite the attention of all interested to the reasons for this belief. A perusal of this Manual will, I trust, convince them that there is a better way than any with which they have yet been acquainted...'

— L. L. Langstroth — Preface and Introduction, Langstroth on *The Hive and Honey-Bee*, 1853

Figure 1-20
Model of the original Langstroth hive design. Root

As Europeans settled the U.S., they took beehives with them. Bees were recorded in Florida by 1763 and west of the Mississippi by 1800. Russian settlers carried bees to Alaska in 1809 and to California by 1830. The Spanish may have brought bees from Mexico into the Southwestern U.S. before that date.

A new hive

The 1800s were a period of great development in beekeeping, both in Europe and the United States. Numerous beekeepers sought to improve the design of the beehive and adopted management to increase average colony harvest. By 1820 most beekeepers were using wooden boxes of various sizes and shapes to hold their bees.

The greatest discovery of all completely changed beekeeping. In 1851, Philadelphia minister L.L.

Langstroth patented the first practical movable frame hive. He followed in 1953 with his book *The Hive and the Honey Bee* to explain how to properly use it (See Box 2).

The top-loading, movable-frame hive revolutionized beekeeping. It allowed a person to be a beekeeper rather than just handling the domiciles of bees and robbing them of their honey. It was quickly adopted by large and small beekeepers in the U.S. and around the world.

Additional practical beekeeping devices were invented in the last half of the 1800s, referred to by some as the **Golden Age of Beekeeping**. Examples include the **extractor,** a device that removes honey from combs without destroying them (the evolution is shown in Figures 1-21-23); **shouldered frames** and **beeswax foundation** — to ensure frames remain truly removable; **the smoker** (evolution shown in Figures 1-24 to 1-28),

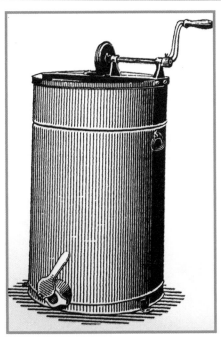

Figure 1-21
An early hand-turned honey extractor.

Figure 1-22
Belt-driven extractor by Root as used at Buckfast Abby, UK.

Figure 1-23
Contemporary motor-driven extractor by Maxant.

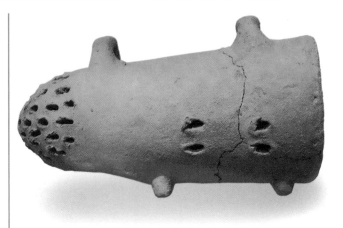

Figure 1-24
Primitive Greek smoker in museum in Herakion, Crete. The beekeeper blew air into the open space on the right to pass over burning embers and produce smoke released on the left. amyhenrybooks.com

Figure 1-25 and 1-26
L: Bellows smoker produces smoke used to move bees from one skep into another.
R: Intermediate smoker design, the Clark Cold Blast Smoker. B. Strauser

Figure 1-27 and 1-28
L: Modern smokers with plastic bellows and
R: battery-operated electric blower which replaces the bellows.

Figure 1-29
The queen excluder allowed beekeepers to confine the queen to one part of the hive, keeping honey clear of brood. It is also used in queen rearing. A. Connor

which permits better manipulation and harvest of honey without harm to bees; and the **queen excluder** (Figure 1-29), a device ensuring separation of brood and honey regions in the hive.

And today . . .

Management systems, and eventually understanding and controlling bee diseases, have been additional important advances. Within the authors' lifetimes, honey bees have become highly valued for the pollination service they provide. Workers tirelessly forage on flowers in all but darkness and the most extreme weather conditions. With clean cultivation, reliance on pesticides, intensive agriculture, monoculture and many other changes 'down on the farm,' growers have an increasingly long list of crops that have become more dependent on honey bees to fill the role once-plentiful native pollinators no longer perform. These bees often lack undisturbed land used for nesting sites.

The literature on honey bees may be highly technical, completely practical or full of 'gee whiz' and 'oh mys.' Honey bees have intrigued philosophers, inspired artists and challenged writers for centuries. Honey bees are a 'must do' for the nature photographer, allowing

seasoned practitioners and neophytes alike to find and preserve much about colony organization and bee social life. Video photographers include segments on honey bees since they are colorful, interesting, and available year-round for a video shoot.

Honey bees have been studied for what they can teach us about ourselves. Bees make excellent biological study subjects as their secrets are both fathomable and interesting. It is relatively easy to keep one or a few bee colonies and have research/study subjects readily available when needed. Their social life is fascinating and a challenge to understand, helping humans appreciate the thread of biology connecting all life.

Dance language communication is a well-documented honey bee behavior that many individuals know something about (Dance language is covered in Chapter 8). It is included in all standard text books on biology. Perhaps because bees can tell sister workers something specific about where food sources are located, humans feel a closer connection to bees. Their language is simple yet precise, basic, yet elegant. It permits honey bees to exploit the best resources available near their nest. That simple behavior makes them valuable to humans. We put them to work for us and rob their excess product.

A honey bee colony is an interesting study in evolution. How has it come to be that workers are willing to give up their life to sting a hive intruder or remain exposed and vulnerable to death or injury by scenting to aid sisters rather than quickly running into the safety of the hive? Stinging and scenting are but two behavioral decisions individual worker bees make that are for the good of the colony but detrimental to the individual.

For many, the connection of honey bees to the flowers they visit is of great interest. Flowers change and so do bees and we see how one complements the other in attractiveness and reward. It is a story of co-evolution we marvel at and can use to apply to our practical animal and plant breeding activities. It is not known which came first—bees with color vision or flowers in colors. We marvel at both.

Honey bee culture

Honey was and still is highly prized by humans (Figure 1-30). Bees and honey were endowed by the ancient Greeks with religious and poetic symbolism. Honey bee colonies were part of early human **medicine cabinets.** Honey is antibacterial and a mild laxative. The sweet flavor and smooth texture of honey helped make natural medicines palatable. Honey is still used medicinally, especially in developing countries. Manuka honey from New Zealand is commercially available as a wound dressing, for sore throats and other ailments.

The natural honey container, **beeswax**, is equally as important. The infrastructure of the beeswax comb

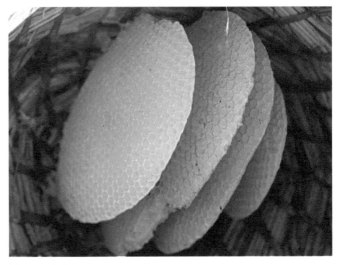

Figure 1-31
This view shows the attachment of honey comb to a skep basket. R. Williamson

Figure 1-30
Honey is a distinctive product sold in many different varieties and containers. L. Connor

is strikingly uniform and functionally efficient, a repeating patterned sheet of hexagonal cells, organized into parallel combs. These precise constructions are made entirely by workers without evidence of advanced construction or engineering tools (Figure 1-31).

Beeswax was combined with honey to embalm the important Egyptian dead. Alexander the Great's body was returned to his native Greece embalmed in honey and coated in beeswax. Beeswax was used to waterproof and seal letters and official documents. It enabled metal to be cast into figures through the lost-wax technique. It was used as an adhesive, mixed with pigments for paintings, and served as a clean burning, long-lasting lighting source (Figure 1-32).

The **beeswax combs** function as the platform for intricate behavioral interactions between colony members. Complex chemical messages deposited on the comb by bees as they travel across and work the cells convey the presence of a queen, as well as a myriad of other information. These chemicals, called pheromones, function and prompt unique responses depending on their context within or outside of the hive. Pheromones are discussed in Chapter 7.

Figure 1-32
An array of beeswax candles. Wax varies in color based on the floral source the bees use to produce the wax, plus the amount of processing by the beekeeper. J. Zawislak.

Figure 1-33
Pollen, once processed by bees and stored in the bee hive, is called bee bread. D. Morgan

Figure 1-34
Newly collected propolis on new bee equipment. Bees use the resin to seal the equipment with a moisture and pathogen barrier. L. Connor

Apitherapy, general term designating use of bee products in medicine, is as modern a medicine as it is old. Honey, propolis, royal jelly, bee-collected pollen and venom are all attributed with medicinal values. Long-suffering multiple sclerosis patients testify how bee venom therapy has given them back use of their body. Arthritis sufferers claim relief in bee venom. Allergy sufferers get benefit from bee pollen and local honey.

Some argue that bee-collected **pollen** (Figure 1-33) is a potential source of protein that might supplement feeding the planet's rapidly growing human population. As with honey, pollen is trapped (trap shown Chapter 17, Figure 17-20) with a hive entrance grid (Chapter 17, Figure 17-21). Inside the hive, bees convert pollen to **bee bread** which can be eaten when the combs are naturally harvested. (Figure 1-33).

Bees collect the resins produced in tree buds to line the inside of their nest. Bees add saliva to the resin

Figure 1-35
Contemporary instructional field session in beekeeping. Note the variation of protective gear.

to form **propolis**—a product beekeepers collect for home remedies and herbal use. This provides a natural moisture barrier. Of greater consequence, however, is that propolis has antibiotic properties. It has been linked to anti-viral activity, including HIV and Covid-19 viruses. It also helps bees combat varroa mites.

The **bees** themselves are another product sold to make new colonies and as replacement queens. Queen rearing and package bee production follow honey production and pollination as essential beekeeping activities

Bees are used in education—a quick glimpse inside a beehive leads to wonderment and fascination with the intricacies of honey bee social life (Figure 1-35).

Learning beekeeping

While the honey bee has been extensively studied from many scientific perspectives, we have much to learn about these insects. Bee culture has been explored from every conceivable angle and yet we still have not exhausted the possibilities to learn and profit from honey bee care. Both authors of this book continue to teach beekeeping to persons of many ages and backgrounds. It is just as new and interesting a topic as when we first started back in the 1960s. It is truly energizing to encounter individuals eager and willing to learn about honey bees and who plan to start their own beehive. As much as this book will help, it will be the bees who will be your best teachers (Figure 1-35).

One of the best uses of this book has been when coordinated with one or more beekeeping classes that

Figures 1-36 and 1-37 (inset)
Colony that has experienced Colony Collapse Disorder (CCD). Once strong, the bee population dropped sharply. Inset: *Time* Magazine cover on *A World Without Bees*.

Figure 1-38
The endangered rusty-patched bumble bee. USFWS.

integrate lecture and demonstration activities with field sessions with hives of bees. Many community colleges, bee clubs, nature centers and others have used this text for their 101, 102 etc. series of beekeeping courses. Regardless of the situation you find, please pay careful attention to what the instructors are saying and learn from them. They are often local beekeepers who have learned how to balance bee biology with local beekeeping conditions.

Selected universities and colleges offer courses in beekeeping. Most beekeepers learn beekeeping by attending beekeeping short courses. Such courses are often offered by beekeeping organizations and via master beekeeping programs. They may offer a mentoring program where new beekeepers are paired with more experienced beekeepers. The person who wants to learn about bees and their care to become better informed and/or a better beekeeper should learn both biology and practice. Experience still remains one of the best ways to learn.

Are bees going extinct?

For over a decade headlines have warned of an insect/bee Apocalypse. The Time Magazine, August 13, 2013 cover highlighted a report entitled **A World Without Bees** (Figure 1-37).

Although insects are the most common organisms on our planet (two of every three animal species is an insect) people are concerned that some insects are disappearing. Due to several factors, beekeepers are experiencing extensive annual losses. The term Colony Collapse Disorder or CCD, is the yet unexplained condition where colonies of bees suddenly die. It has gained much media attention (Figures 1-36 and 37); see Chapter 21 for further discussion). Are honey bees becoming extinct?

Scientists have documented that fresh-water stream insects, butterflies, moths, and tropical insect populations are in apparent decline. Pollinators like native bees and monarch butterfly populations have suffered some decline, although we lack 'bench-mark' studies to conclusively define how many species are threatened. Three bumble bee species are extinct and one bumble bee species, the **rusty-patched bumble bee**, is on the Endangered Species list (Figure 1-38). It was once widely distributed in 28 states from Maine south to Georgia, west to Dakotas and into Ontario and Quebec.

Feral bee colonies (natural colonies in tree cavities) initially disappeared with varroa mite invasion in North America but their numbers have started to rebound. Feral populations of European bees in much of the Americas (Argentina to southern U.S.) have been replaced by Africanized bees. While beekeeper-managed bee colonies are currently suffering annual overwinter losses double what beekeepers once considered acceptable, colonies are being replaced through intensive management to meet crop pollination demand. Small-scale hobby beekeepers have the highest levels of colony losses, double the level of the larger-scale commercial beekeepers.

What are the factors in bee decline?

Extensive research has shown that no one single factor is responsible for the reduction in bees, pollinating insects and insects in general. Our human footprint is so extensive that we continually modify natural habitat to make our lives more comfortable. Farmland is converted to housing and areas of vacant unused lands that

Figure 1-39
Large planting of soybeans limit bee forage and increase insecticide and herbicide use. L. Connor

will support bees are reduced. This is usually a one-way change, but cities like Detroit have reversed this situation.

Agriculture is constantly changing. Intensive crop and animal agriculture reduce the nesting sites for native pollinators while also eliminating the flowering plants they depend upon for food. Monocultures may be a feast if they are attractive to pollinators, but only when in bloom. The rest of the year these areas are a desert for flower visitors (Figure 1-39). Intensive agriculture relies on chemical pesticides and herbicides to eliminate insect pests and weeds. They also may kill flower visitors, contaminate soil and water may run off to nearby streams, endangering soil dwellers and insects that need clean fresh water.

Figure 1-40
Zika virus control by mosquito spraying. Human need for mosquito control exposes bee colonies to toxic insecticides whenever a dangerous disease or virus is a threat to human health. 633rd Civil Engineer Squadron Pest Management flight

Figure 1-41
Strips of selected flowering plants provide pollen, nectar, nest sites and beneficial pest predators within large agricultural fields. The *Applied Ecologist*

The nature of farming is rapidly changing as well. Yes, there are more organic and sustainable farming initiatives, but most farms are becoming larger and less diverse. Family farms are disappearing because investors see farmland as a good opportunity for profit. Absentee owners and farm managers making decisions on behalf of equity fund or investor groups are more remote from long-term sustainable land care.

Current public policy greatly impacts these changes. Crop insurance and fund incentives are not evenly distributed and tend to be more favorable for intensive, larger farms. Programs for farmers to set aside areas for pollinator nesting and flowering plants are too poorly utilized (Figure 1-41). To date the argument that more flowers will promote more pollinators has been tough to inspire all but a few landowners to create such habitat.

Meanwhile, climate change is having significant impact on all of agriculture. As water resources decline agriculture suffers.

Saving bees

Individuals become beekeepers for a variety of reasons. They find bees fascinating and they can provide income through pollination rentals to growers, the harvesting and sale of honey, and other bee products. There is a heightened interest in keeping bees in towns and cities. Communities are no longer banning bees, and in many instances have removed restrictions on keeping bees within cities, on city rooftops, on small suburban lots and community properties such as abandoned city properties. Some individuals become beekeepers as a means of saving bees.

Programs to promote more flowering plants/changes in pesticide practices are easier to implement in the suburban/urban environment. Gardeners, property managers, community park and recreation personnel, roadside agencies, corporations and others are adopting general practices to promote better pollinator health. This includes planting more bee-friendly flowering plants, reducing general broadcast pesticide use in favor of targeted pesticide applications of chemicals that are less toxic to pollinators, and setting areas aside for native pollinator nesting and reproduction.

Native bees, honey bees, and other pollinators are keystone species in many habitats on planet earth. This means that their demise means loss of the critical ecological interconnectedness of the environment. Their loss would mean less shelter and food for birds and other wildlife. They pollinate the trees and shrubs we enjoy for their flowering and fragrance and the myriad ecological processes flowering plants foster. Without bee pollination our typical diet would be less colorful and diverse, removing as much as one third of the foods we commonly consume.

For the past 25 years there has been a program of tax incentives in the Conservation Resource Program (CRP) of USDA to set land aside to establish plantings for pollinators. However participation has been declining in favor of fence-to-fence planting that includes field margins.

A new USDA program, the **Pollinator Habitat Initiative** (CP-42), offers landowners the opportunity to create long-lasting meadows of high-quality native wildflowers to support pollinators and other wildlife populations throughout the growing season. The new initiative includes fast-blooming forage legumes along with wildflowers that have traditionally been a part of CRP plant mixes. The land must be suitable for growing crops and needs be managed for a minimum 10-year period. Growers receive annual rental payments, cost share payment covering up to 50 percent of the eligible cost of establishing the pollinator patch and one-time $150 per acre Signing Incentive Payment (SIP).

Ancient scripture (Leviticus 19: 9,10) says:

And when you reap the harvest of your land, you shall not make clean riddance of the corners of your field when you reap, neither shall you gather any gleaning of your harvest: you shall leave them to the poor, and to the stranger.

While this speaks to helping our fellow citizens who are less fortunate, it could also apply to our efforts to help our pollinators by providing them a harvest as well. By helping them we will be helping ourself.

Ten things to save bees and pollinators

1. Plant for pollinators. Not all flowers offer bees comparable rewards. Choose long-blooming plants that have colorful, aromatic flowers. Utilize plants with high numbers of flowers, even if flower size is small. Plant in groups, as large as your space will allow. Keep an eye on what's blooming in your garden and make notes on where you see bees (Figure 1-42). Find websites for recommendations of flowering plants appropriate for your area. Ask the master gardener specialists at your local Cooperative Extension Office (each county has one) about appropriate plants.

2. Plant for every season. When does your garden lack flowers? Bees need flowers for their total adult life. Research the entire flower season and fill in any gaps when there are fewer flowering plants in your garden.

3. Think like a bee. What do bees need? Food, of course, but also shelter. To encourage bumble bees, provide

Figure 1-42
Planting pollinator-supporting flowers, trees in shrubs in lawns and open spaces increases food diversity for a wide range of beneficial species. T. Horn

Figure 1-43
Provide water for bees in clay pots, and other containers that allow the bees to collect water without drowning. L. Connor

overwintered queens a place to nest. Mining bees need dry soils, so make a berm and don't over-water it. Grow or distribute hollow reeds or bamboo, or place drinking straws (no plastic, please!) and/or holes drilled in wooden blocks in shelters for mason bee nest sites. Alternately, you might purchase commercial mason bee houses and even buy some bees to stock them.

4. Water, Water, Water. Plants need water but so do bees. Include some type of water feature in your garden. Bees like water with a smell so allow flowering water plants to decay. Bees also need to perch, so include stones or plant features they can use (as opposed to simply a big pool, Figure 1-43).

5. Nature may be messy. For the benefit of the bees, allow their favorite flowers to remain in the garden or the lawn, even if they are called weeds. Lawns with a variety of flowering plants provide foraging opportunities, while carpets of a single grass variety are food deserts and take

considerable gardening time and chemicals to maintain. Reduce lawn size and plant large beds and borders in vegetative layers, with the lowest adjacent to the lawn, increasing in height in subsequent layers (Figure 1-42). Small and medium size trees can offer great numbers of pollinator-friendly forage.

6. Cut out the chemicals. Minimize your use of insect-killing pesticides and plant-killing herbicides. Don't ignore pest outbreaks but seek to spot treat early before pest populations build—and only when necessary. Like humans, unhealthy plants don't look as well as healthy ones, and when they're ailing, they may have little to offer bees. Seek alternatives to hard pesticides, such as organic chemicals, or eco-pesticides, like soaps or oils. And don't be afraid to welcome and foster beneficial creatures, including frogs, snakes, ladybugs, lacewings, and other wildlife, to your yard.

Seek to work with communities where large-scale spraying might be necessary for public health pest control reasons

Figure 1-44
Bee colonies may be kept most anywhere when certain basic precautions are followed. Here Kerry Owens is inspecting small colonies maintained for mating queens on a rooftop in Cochabamba, Bolivia.

(Figure 1-40). For bees in agricultural areas seek to work with farm owner/pest control advisor or applicators on plan to protect bee colonies (See Chapter 23 for more on **pesticides).**

7. Consider landscape variety. Ground nesting bees need well-drained soils, such as a berm. Piles of rocks or wood piles are great potential nest sites. Leave areas less heavily mulched so ground nesting bees can better access the soil surface. If you find ground nesting bees, protect and expand that area, providing continued maintenance.

8. Think long term. Make this a fun project. Purchase something to transplant immediately and then make a wish list for follow up. Seeds take longer to produce flowers but there's joy watching the plants develop. Start small, but start now!

9. Spread the word. Individual actions multiplied across a community increase the speed of progress. Spreading the word returns many rewards benefiting the whole community. Sometimes all that's needed is the spark. Be that spark! Become a Bee Ambassador to take the conservation message to your community. Assist local/regional/national groups that support bee habitat improvement. It takes a community to affect real change, but it all starts with passionate individuals.

10. Start a bee hive. Learn how to manage it to ensure overwintering success (Figure 1-44). If that is not feasible, encourage cavity nesting bees, such as mason bees, to visit your garden by buying or building mason bee houses. Also support your local beekeeper, by purchasing local honey and/or beeswax. Local honey is better for you, anyway!

key terms

anticipation/reaction	clomed hive	grayanotoxin	nectar flow
apitherapy	colony	gums	pesticides
applied bee biology	colony management	hive	pollen
artisanal propolis	colony population	honey	propolis
bee apocalypse	combs	honey as weapon	save the bees
bee boles	essential management	honey bees	skeps
bee space	evolution	hunter-robbers	supering
beekeeper	Father of modern beekeeping	insect ally	superorganism
bees	feral hives	keystone species	swarming apiculture
beeswax	gardening for bees	medicinal honey	toxic honey
cave paintings	golden age of beekeeping	monoculture	

discussion questions

Why do we speak of the honey bee as an insect ally? If toxic honey from rhododendron is possible, why is honey so readily harvested and consumed? What is your perception of past/present bee culture/beekeeping?

Reflect back to the Middle Ages. How would you use honey bees if you were the wealthy elite in the castle? Why would the working class benefit from bee culture? Return to the current time and answer the same questions.

When was the last time you, a relative, or someone you know used a product from honey bees? Was it part of the diet? Did you use it as a medicine? Do you know of bee products in foods or how bee products are used medicinally? Do you know of someone who believes that honey, or another hive product, is a medicine?

How conscious are you of honey bees? When was the last time you read about honey bees? Or heard references to honey bees? Or thought about honey bees? What previous experience(s) do you bring to this book about bees and how will that influence what you will seek from the material? Why study honey bees?

What have you heard about the bee/insect apocalypse? Have you noticed fewer insects? How can losses be better documented? What might be done to change the current trends?

Are honey bees in danger of going extinct? Why are some pollinator populations in peril? What do you understand are the major reasons for changes in agriculture and how do they impact numbers of pollinators, including honey bees?

Ten things were listed as possibilities of what one could do to Save the Bees. What are some other things that might be done? What else might one individual do to spark a change? What have you been doing/ will consider doing to Save the Bees?

exercises

Choose a topic (bees in warfare, toxic honey, etc.) and determine what is available on the topic. Alternately, check general sources of information (world data book, encyclopedia, general biology text, Internet, etc.) and determine what is written about honey bees. Prepare a general statement about the status of information available on honey bees.

Check your local library for information on honey bees. Inquire if a beekeeper or bee club in your area or region has a library of bee books and determine if you can utilize that private collection as a resource to learn more about bee biology and beekeeping.

Bees have been a common subject in literature, art, music and photography. Search for references, statements or illustrations of bees in one (or more) of these areas. How has the human reaction to bees changed over history as evidenced in human artistic expression?

How often does the honey bee or beekeeping get mentioned in print or video media? Survey newspapers, magazines or television news shows for honey bee and insect information. Categorize the coverage—is the honey bee more positively viewed compared to insects in general? View print and video cartoons to determine how honey bees and other insects are viewed by the artists.

Develop a plan for increasing bee/pollinator-friendly plants using your available space or at some site within your community.

references

Internet links by topic

Apocalypse-bee/insect: Bees: Time Magazine August 13, 2013; Insects: https://www.nytimes.com/2018/11/27/magazine/insect-apocalypse.html. Bee colony losses documented with annual surveys: www.beeinformed.org and www.pnwhoneybeesurvey.com

Gardening for Pollinators: Accessed via: https://www.fs.fed.us/wildflowers/pollinators/gardening.shtml

Grayanotoxin: Jansen, Suza A. et al. 2012. Grayanotoxin Poisoning: 'Mad Honey Disease' and Beyond. Cardiovasc Toxicol. 2012 Sep; 12 (3): 208–215. doi:10.1007/s12012-012-9162-2

Honey harvesters: https://www.metmuseum.org/art/collection/search/544626

Honey hunters: Gurung (Nepal) Accessed via: https://www.nationalgeographic.com/magazine/2017/07/honey-hunters-bees-climbing-nepal/

Importance of bees: Ellis, Rebecca A. et al. 2020. From a free gift of nature to a precarious commodity: Bees, pollination services, and industrial agriculture. Jour. Agrarian Change. Accessed March 25 via: https://doi.org/10.1111/joac.12360

Pollinator Habitat Initiative: https://www.fsa.usda.gov/Internet/FSA_File/pollinator_fact_sht.pdf

Rusty-patched bumble bee. Accessed via https://www.fws.gov/midwest/endangered/insects/rpbb/factsheetrpbb.html

Greek beehive: https://en.wikipedia.org/wiki/Horizontal_top-bar_hive#/media/File:Sir_George_Wheler's_The_Greek_Beehive.jpg

Publications by author

Berenbaum, M. et al. 2007. Declining pollinator populations: Status of Pollinators in North America. National Academy Science

Caron, D.M. 2020. The Complete Bee Handbook. Rockridge Press, Emeryville, CA

Connor, L.J. 2019. Keeping Bees Alive. Wicwas Press. Kalamazoo, MI

Crane, E. 1999. The World History of Beekeeping and Honey Hunting. Routledge, New York

Hoopingarner, R. 2014. The Hive and the Honey Bee Revisited. Wicwas Press. Kalamazoo, MI

Kritsky, G. 2015. The Tears of Re: Beekeeping in Ancient Eqypt. Oxford Press, London

Seeley, T. 1989. The Honey Bee Colony as a Superorganism. American Scientist 77 (no 6, November-December) pp. 546-553

Tedlock, D. 2013. Popol Vuh: The Mayan Book of the Dawn of Life. Touchstone.

Chapter 2
What's in a name?

Figure 2-1
A leafcutter bee on blanket flower in Idaho. These solitary bees nest in hollow twigs or stems. They line their nests with pieces of leaves and create pollen balls and deposit one egg on each cell. L. Connor

Concepts

Understanding classification
Hymenoptera
bee taxonomy

Types of bees
Genus *Apis* — honey bees
races
Africanized bees

Improved bees
varroa-mite tolerant stock

Wild-caught queens

The classification system

Humans have had a long association with the honey bee, which has been well recorded in history. While there has been much uncertainty about the exact identity of some animals or plants, the honey bee has escaped confusion with other organisms.

Our more complete knowledge of the honey bee is undoubtedly due to the fact that recorded history has largely been European history and there is only one honey bee in Europe. As is the case with many animals, we have found that other parts of the world have honey bees that are similar, yet sufficiently different that they cannot interbreed. Each of these different kinds of honey bees is considered a separate species.

In the 1700s scientists began concentrating on the identification of plants and animals. The Swedish biologist Carl Linnaeus (Carolus Linnaeus) started the system we now accept for naming living organisms. Under this system, plants and animals are given a scientific name with two parts (binomial). The first is the genus name, and the second the species name. Our honey bee (Figure 2-2) is called *Apis mellifera* L.

NOTE: The genus name is capitalized and the species name is lower case. The scientific name is always underlined or italicized. The 'L' stands for Linnaeus, because scientific names carry the name of the individual who first described the species. The honey bee's scientific name was just one of some 9,000 species that Linnaeus designated. The name itself is a combination of the Latin word for bee, *Apis* and the Greek *mellifera* which means "honey-bearing."

The common name, honey bee, is correctly written as two words although it frequently appears as a single word. By convention of the Entomological Society of America, an insect's common name is two words if the insect is

Figure 2-2
Apis mellifera L. worker bee with pollen on her hind leg (corbicula).

classified in a taxonomic grouping to which the name applies. Thus honey bee, bumble bee and house fly are two words because the first two are bees and the house fly is a true fly. However, the dragonfly is not a true fly and the ladybug is a beetle so they have one-word common names. Frequently, honey bee is hyphenated when used as a compound modifier placed before the word it modifies (i.e. honey-bee physiology).

All living things which feed, grow, respond to stimuli and reproduce are classified into an orderly system. For the honey bee, *Apis mellifera* L., the classification system of major sub-divisions is shown in Table 2-1. The classification systems we use are human-made and often not exactly the same, but they are usually logical.

All divisions, except that of species, are made primarily on the basis of anatomical features (morphology). Each division contains organisms that are more similar in appearance than higher classifications. Appearance, behavior and biochemical relationships are frequently

used to help classify organisms. In addition to the main categories of classification, intermediate categories also exist — often aided by genome sequencing. Suborder and superfamily are frequently used in classification of the honey bee.

The broadest classification is that of **Kingdom**. Modern classification systems recognize five or six kingdoms. The most familiar are the Plant and Animal Kingdoms.

Kingdoms are divided into major groups, called **Phyla**. Each phylum is a grouping of organisms whose members have certain structural characteristics in common. The principle animal phyla are as follows:

Porifera — sponges

Cnidaria — jellyfish, corals, sea anemones, etc.

Platyhelminthes — flatworms, flukes, tapeworms, etc.

Nemathelminthes — roundworms

Mollusca — clams, snails, squid, etc.

Annelida — earthworms, leeches, etc.

Arthropoda — spiders, insects, lobsters, etc.

Echinodermata — starfish, brittle stars, sea urchins, etc.

Chordata — fish, birds, mammals (including humans), etc.

Phylum Arthropoda

The honey bee (Figure 2-2), along with all insects, is classified in the Phylum Arthropoda (jointed-footed animals). All arthropods (common name) have a segmented body of two or three regions, paired segmented appendages, and an exoskeleton. Additionally, all are bilaterally symmetrical with a tubular alimentary canal (digestive tract). Arthropods have an open circulatory system consisting of a dorsal blood vessel, or heart, and an open body cavity in which blood circulates freely within the body, not within arteries or veins as in humans. Arthropods lack a backbone and are therefore also called invertebrates in contrast to humans and other animals with backbones (vertebrates) which are grouped in the Phylum Chordata.

Arthropods are the most common type of animal on Earth. Three of every four animals is an arthropod, as shown in Figure 2-3. Within the arthropod phylum, the members are grouped into classes. Insects, all in one class, comprise the majority of arthropods. Major classes in the Phylum Arthropoda include:

Crustacea — lobsters, crayfish, shrimp, etc.

Diplopoda — millipedes

Chilopoda — centipedes

Merostomata — horseshoe crabs

Pycnogonida — sea spiders

Arachnida — spiders, mites, ticks, etc.

Insecta — insects

Table 2-1

Classification of the honey bee

Kingdom: Animalia
Phylum: Arthropoda
Class: Insecta
Order: Hymenoptera
Suborder: Apocrita
Superfamily : Apoidea
Family: Apidae
Genus & Species: *Apis mellifera* L.

Class Insecta

All insects possess the characteristics of arthropods but are further distinguished and recognized from other arthropods by the following anatomical features:

- three body regions (head, thorax and abdomen)
- one pair of antennae
- normally three pairs of legs
- usually one or two pairs of wings

Members of other arthropod classes lack this combination of characteristics, although some members of other classes might have one or more characteristics.

There are an estimated one million different insect species in existence. Insects are the most dominant group of animals found on earth today. Insects occur practically everywhere but are uncommon in the oceans where crustaceans are dominant. Over a thousand different species of insects might be found around your home, most of which are quite small and occur in or close to the soil.

Not only are there large numbers of insect species, but insects also frequently occur in large populations within a specific habitat. Social insects are one of the types of insects frequently found in large numbers.

Scientists differ on their organization of the insects, dividing it into 26 to 31 orders. Body shape, wings, appendages and types of mouthparts are the main characteristics used to distinguish between the orders. Four large orders contain the majority of the insect species as shown in Figure 2-4. These four are:

Diptera – true flies such as house flies, horse flies, mosquitoes

Coleoptera – beetles

Lepidoptera – butterflies and moths

Hymenoptera – sawflies, ants, wasps, bees

Order Hymenoptera

The Order Hymenoptera is a large, diverse group of over 100,000 species that, from a human standpoint, is the most beneficial in the entire insect world. The name Hymenoptera refers to the clear membrane-like (*hymen-*) features of the two pairs of wings (*-ptera*).

The majority of social insects, except for one group, the termites (Order Isoptera), are classified in the Hymenoptera. Because of great diversity in hymenopterans, it is difficult to provide a listing of characteristics that are shared by all members.

The hymenopteran order is divided into two suborders, Symphyta (sawflies) and Apocrita (ants, wasps and bees). Members of the second suborder, including the honey bee, have a constricted (wasp-waist) abdomen, wings that are membrane-like (not all adults have wings), larvae that do not resemble caterpillars and generally do not damage plants by directly feeding on them. Adult bees and some wasps are specialized herbivores that feed on nectar and pollen. Some wasps, but not bees, may cause minor plant damage with their biting mouthparts.

The Apocrita are further subdivided into two major groups, the Parasitica, which are quite diverse, mostly parasitic insects and the Aculeata characterized by females having the ovipositor modified into a sting. Two large aculeate superfamilies are the Vespoidea (wasps and ants) and Apoidea, the bees and sphecid wasps.

Superfamily Apoidea

It is estimated that there are over 18,000 species of bees in the world. Of this number, perhaps 4,000 are found in America north of Mexico. Bees are unlike all other insects in that:

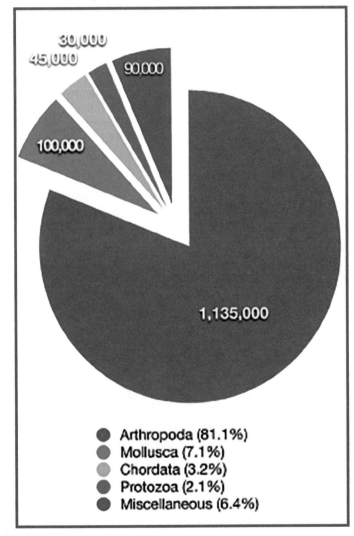

Figure 2-3
Pie chart illustrating the major animal phyla. L. Connor

30,000
45,000
90,000
100,000
1,135,000

- Arthropoda (81.1%)
- Mollusca (7.1%)
- Chordata (3.2%)
- Protozoa (2.1%)
- Miscellaneous (6.4%)

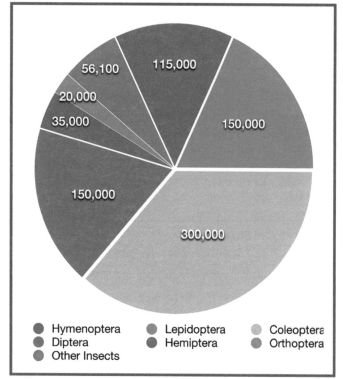

Figure 2-4
Hymenopterans are one of the four major orders of insects. Numbers are estimated species. L. Connor

- their bodies are variously covered with plumose (branched) hairs

- they have special body hairs for pollen transport on hind legs or lower abdominal surface

- they use pollen and nectar from plants as a sole source of food

While the oldest fossilized honey bee is about 40 million years old, scientists have determined that the first bees evolved perhaps 130 million years ago from pollen-feeding wasps (see next chapter). Bees speciated and diversified with flowering plants, and likely drove each others speciation and evolution–and continue to do so. The classification Apoidea includes some wasps (Family Sphecidae, the thread-waisted wasps) but most bee species are hairy. A few bees are parasitic on other bees' nests—called **kleptoparasites**—utilizing their host's food provisions, not feeding on the bee body, per se. They have lost all, or nearly all, of their body hairs.

Families of bees

Of the seven commonly recognized families of bees, six are found in North America (The seventh family is confined to Australia). Following is a short description:

Family Colletidae (plaster bees). This group is considered to be the most primitive of all the bee families. One large genus, *Hylaeus* (yellow-faced bees), is quite wasp-like in appearance. Members of this genus are parasitic with few pollen-collecting hairs; pollen is mixed with nectar and carried in the honey stomach. Most are black with yellow markings and few are much bigger than the honey bee head. The second major genus in this family, *Colletes*, are large, robust and quite hairy bees. They are ground-nesting but seldom abundant except at nesting sites. At some nest sites (lawns, golf courses, etc.) it may be desirable to control their numbers but they will not cause any harm if left alone. Most species are adults during either spring or fall.

Family Halictidae (sweat bees). The halictids numerically represent 60 to 70% of the Apoidea. Different family members exhibit various degrees of social development. Genera include the green bees *Augochlora, Augochlorella, Agapostemon* (Figure 2-5); the large genera *Halictus, Dialictus, Lasioglossum*; and the parasitic *Sphecodes*. Also included are *Nomia* and *Dufourea*. One species, *Nomia melanderi* (the alkali bee), is highly efficient at pollinating alfalfa. In western states farmers construct protected nesting sites for them. Many species have narrow flower foraging preferences.

Family Andrenidae (sand or digger bees). This family has many species in North America. Members are not very diverse in habitats or appearance and are difficult to identify. Most are soil nesting. The Genus *Andrena* is the largest genus and individuals are the same size as and closely resemble honey bees. Many species have a very short flight season that is correlated with the type of flower to which the species is confined. Two other genera, *Perdita* and *Calliopis*, are smaller-bodied and generally associated with drier habitats.

Family Melittidae. This is the smallest family of just a few species. Little is known of these soil-nesting bees, with hairy hind legs and limited floral source foraging preference. They also collect floral oil.

Figure 2-5
Agapostemon, a green bee, one of a wide range of colorful members of the Halictidae. R. Weber

Family Megachilidae (leafcutting, carder, resin and **mason bees**, Figures 2-1, 2-7). This is a large family but members are quite uniform in appearance. Most members nest in existing cavities using non-secreted materials such as petals, resin and cut pieces of vegetation. Females have pollen-collecting hairs (the scopa) found on the underside of the abdomen in this family (Figure 2-1). Main genera include *Megachile, Osmia, Anthidium, Hopilitis* and *Heriades*.

One species of leafcutting bee, *Megachile rotundata*, is a useful pollinator of alfalfa. 'Mega-nests' (holes drilled in wood blocks) are available commercially (Figure 2-7). Mason bees are effective pollinators of several early flowering fruit tree species and a bucket of mason bee straws can pollinate the same number of trees as a colony of honey bees. Mason bee nests are popular with gardeners who often provide nesting sites.

Family Apidae

Family Apidae (long-tongued bees), includes the honey bee and bumble bee and a wide range of genera formerly classified as Family Anthophoridae. Three common subfamilies include the Apinae (stingless bees, orchid bees, bumble bees and honey bees), the Nomadinae (cuckoo parasitic bees) and Xylocopinae (carpenter bees). *Bombus* species (bumble bees, Figure 2-6) occur from the

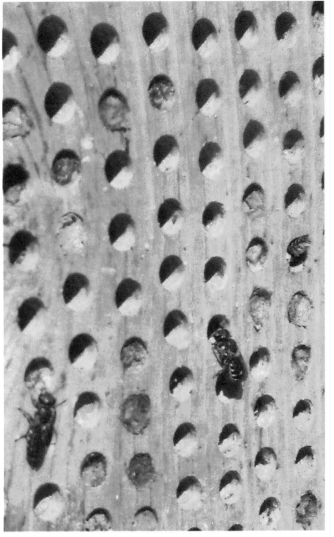

Figure 2-7
Leafcutter bees at boards containing new cells sealed with leaves and flower petals.

tropics to the Arctic, with more species in colder climates. The orchid pollinating bee genus (*Euglossa*) is most common in the tropics. The stingless bees of Central and South America, *Melipona* (Chapter 1, Figure 1-9) and in SE Asia, *Trigona*, have been kept by humans as long as honey bees. These most interesting bees are still kept for honey production in the New World tropics. Their honey is highly valued as a medicine.

Some Apidae are **eusocial**. They have a social structure of worker (a female lacking full development of reproductive organs), queen (fully-developed female) and drone (the male reproductive). Worker bees are distinguished from all other bees by the presence of **pollen baskets** (corbiculae), which are flattened, smooth, shiny areas surrounded by a fringe of hairs. The **corbicula** is located on the exterior surface of the hind leg tibia (Figure 2-2). Queens, drones and some parasitic and solitary Apidae (none in North America) lack the

Figure 2-6
Bombus (bumble bee) on raspberry flower. L. Connor

Box 3

BUMBLE BEES

If there is one bee we recognize other than the honey bee, it is probably the large, noisy bumble bee (sometimes called humble bee). They are robust and hairy; their body hair is dense and colored with bold yellow or orange markings, contrasting with black. Like honey bees, they are common flower visitors and pollinators (Figure 2-8).

Bumble bees appear each spring as the weather warms and spring flowers open. Overwintered females (queens) search for a suitable ground cavity, often an unoccupied mouse nest, to build a nest, gathering nesting material to line the chamber. She will make repeated foraging trips to flowers to collect nectar and pollen. Nectar is stored in special wax honey pots (Figure 2-8).

Figure 2-8
A colony of nesting bumble bees. The nest is in an abandoned mouse nest. The large queen sits on top of a cluster of cocoons inside of which are worker pupae. The smaller chambers contain larvae. Larger pots hold honey. The cluster of cells on the upper right are used cocoons. J. Free

The queen molds the pollen she collects into a ball, and lays several eggs alongside it. This is covered with a wax envelope produced from wax glands. She continues to forage for nectar for the energy she needs to generate heat to warm the developing bees. After the eggs morph into larvae, she feeds the larvae from the honey pot containing honey and freshly collected nectar. She will not lay more eggs until the first larvae reach the pupal stage.

The first daughter workers to emerge are usually the smallest of the season, taking two to three weeks from egg to adult. They assist their mother in nest duties and, within a few days, begin collecting nectar and pollen from flowers. As the colony grows in size the queen increases her egg laying. The workers become larger in body size with a better diet. Within the worker population, body size greatly influences individual duties. Larger bees forage at an earlier age and spend more time guarding the nest. Smaller bees work less.

At the climax of the colony population (which ranges from 50 to 400, depending upon species) stable nest temperatures, sufficient food availability and decreasing day length lead to the production of males and new queens. It is not known precisely why a colony stops rearing workers and turns to rearing reproductives (gynes) for overwinter preparations.

Male bees emerge before the queens and establish territories. Male and newly-emerged females mate in the fall before cold weather. Mated males die; mated females may return to the nest to engorge on honey. They seek a protected site to hibernate. The old queen and any remaining workers and males use up nest reserves and die with the cold nights. Mated females survive over the winter and start the cycle anew the next year. We term their social structure seasonally eusocial.

Figure 2-9
Bumble bee on dandelion. L. Connor

> *Full merrily the humble-bee doth sing,*
> *'Till he hath lost his honey and his sting.*
> *And being once subdued in armed tail,*
> *Sweet honey and sweet notes together fail.*
> *-William Shakespeare, Troilus & Cressida*

corbiculae. *Apis* species have hairy eyes, a long narrow marginal cell of the front wing and no spurs on the tibia of the hind legs.

Genus *Apis*

The Genus *Apis* fossil record dates to a honey bee fossil found in Baltic amber that is approximately 40 million years old. Fossils from 30 million years ago are very similar to the present species suggesting the genus has not undergone great evolutionary changes for some time.

Currently, there are eight recognized species of honey bee with a total of 44 subspecies, though historically, anywhere from six to eleven species have been recognized, including an extinct species that existed in North America, *Apis nearctica*, known from a single 14-million-year old fossil specimen from Nevada.

The four most widely distributed species are: *Apis mellifera*, the common western honey bee; *Apis cerana*, the Asian or eastern honey bee; *Apis dorsata*, the giant honey bee; and *Apis florea*, the dwarf honey bee. There are as many as three larger-bodied species in addition to *Apis dorsata* (*A. laboriosa*, *A. binghami* and *A. brevilaca* (these last two more likely subspecies). *Apis andreniformis* is a second small-sized honey bee, closely related to *Apis florea*. In addition to *Apis cerana*, *A. koschevnikovi*, *A. nigrocincta* and *A. nuluensis* (the last likely a subspecies) are closely related species.

Apis florea, the dwarf wild honey bee, builds exposed single combs (Figures 2-10, 2-11) in trees or bushes in Oman, Iran, Pakistan, India, Southeast Asia, and Indonesia. People rob its nests for a small yield of honey and wax. Their stings are usually unable to penetrate human skin. The color of the abdomen of this house-fly-sized bee varies from all black to bright chestnut brown. Two transverse abdominal bands of short pale hairs are usually present. The relatively sparse, short thoracic hair is grayish. *Apis andreniformis* is slightly larger, hairier, darker, and somewhat more defensive.

Apis dorsata, the giant wild honey bee, builds large, single comb exposed nests on high branches, buildings, or cliffs in Pakistan, India, Southeast Asia, Indonesia, Philippines, and southern China (Figures 2-14, 2-16). The bees are very defensive and have never been managed, though they are robbed for their honey, brood and wax by honey hunters (Chapter 1, Figure 1-6). Unfortunately, nests are frequently destroyed during harvest.

A. dorsata has an elongated yellowish to black abdomen with transverse bands of short pale hairs, long dusky wings, and a thorax covered with dense black and tan hairs. A related species, *Apis laboriosa* (Himalayan honey bee) is slightly larger and hairier. Attempts to bring this species into the U.S. were unsuccessful.

Apis cerana (*A. indica* is an older name), the Asian or eastern honey bee, has been kept by Indian and Chinese

Figure 2-10
Apis florea nest. This is the smallest honey bee, with the entire nest confined to one small comb. M. Burgett

Figure 2-11
Apis florea nest with bees removed, showing brood area. Honey and pollen are storaged in the larger cells at top. M. Burgett

beekeepers for centuries (Figures 2-12, 2-13). It closely resembles the common western honey bee but is somewhat smaller. Hives designed for this bee are scaled down to suit its smaller size. It is gentle and a fairly good honey producer. It is found in India, Sri Lanka, Southeast Asia, Indonesia, the Philippines, China, Taiwan, and Japan. Three related species (sometimes termed subspecies) are more narrowly distributed as island populations in Southeast Asia. It has been suggested that this bee would be a useful backyard bee for U.S. beekeepers; importation poses the potential risk of introducing additional pests and parasites to the already established *Apis mellifera*.

Figure 2-12
Apis cerana, the Asian or eastern honey bee. R. Morse

Figure 2-13
Apis cerana hive in hollowed log. Indonesia. M. Burgett

Apis mellifera, the common western (European) honey bee, has been intensively managed by humans for many millennia—including hybridization and introductions throughout the world by beekeepers. It has many well known morphologically different subspecies. The common honey bee has long been kept in managed domiciles, termed hives. Feral colonies, often originating from swarms, occupy cavities in cliff cavities, hollow trees or in other open structures.

The honey bee is considered "predisposed" to domestication as observed by L.L. Langstroth in *Langstroth on The Hive and the Honey-Bee* and reviewed by Thomas D. Seeley in the *Lives of Bees: The Untold Story of the Honey Bee in the Wild*. Through time, there have been extensive breeding efforts to obtain desirable characteristics for beekeepers, yet escaped swarms

Figure 2-14
Apis dorsata nest aggregation in a tall tree in Thailand. M. Burgett

establish wild (feral) colonies which survive well on their own for many generations.

Subspecies (races or ecotypes) of honey bees

Apis mellifera most logically originated in Asia and then spread to Africa before spreading northward into Europe. An alternative explaination places origination in eastern tropical Africa and spread from there to Northern Europe and eastwards into Asia. The natural range of the honey bee includes areas that are tropical, the dry Mediterranean region, and the cold northern temperate habitat. With such a range and variety of climates, regional differences have developed in the species.

Due to geographic isolation, differing floral resources and natural selection, several distinct and recognizable geographic subspecies (races or ecotypes) of honey bees have developed over time. These changes occurred as natural selection molded honey bees to the unique characteristics of their environment. Different ecotypes adapted to dissimilar environments (temperate to tropical) and isolation resulted in the changes becoming more pronounced over time. Bee races can be considered to be similar to breeds of cattle or varieties of plants, except that the initial differences in bees resulted from natural selection rather than human selection. All subspecies are capable of interbreeding.

Some of the features that can be distinguished when comparing bees of different races are body size, size of different anatomical features (such as tongue length),

Box 4

Do honey bees predate Europeans in North America?

Beekeeping historians have found records in the ship's log of European honey bees being shipped to the Virginia Jamestown colony in 1621, arriving in 1622 as cargo on one of three possible ships, including the *Discovery*. That document is cited as the evidence of the initial introduction of honey bees to the Americas.

"Wee haue by this Shipp and the Discouerie sent you diurs [divers] sortes of seedes, and fruit trees, as also Pidgeons, Connies, Peacockes Maistiues [Mastiffs], and Beehives, as you shall by the invoice pceiue [perceive]; the preservation & encrease whereof we respond vnto you..."

But a shale rock fossil from Nevada, given the name *Apis neartica*, has been dated to 14 million years ago. This species is considered extinct. It is related to *Apis* fossils from Germany. So were honey bees here in North America much, much earlier than 1622?

With the greatest biodiversity of *Apis* species in Asia, the origin of honey bees of genus *Apis* has been considered to be in Asia. Another explanation has been proposed that honey bees actually originated in Europe, migrating to Asia and then moving east to North America (via Siberia and Alaska) and westward to the Middle East and eventually Africa.

The strongest evidence suggests that *Apis mellifera*, our Western honey bee, originated in Asia and then spread to Africa followed by migration to Europe, not once but twice. The northern bee group *Apis mellifera mellifera*, the same subspecies of bees arriving in Jamestown, spread, it is theorized, via the Iberian peninsula to western Europe. The second spread into eastern Europe resulting in the population (race) we identify as *Apis mellifera carnica*, the carniolan bee.

Figure 2-15
Apis neartica in shale rock from Nevada, dated to 14 million years ago. California Academy of Sciences

Carniolan bees were not introduced to North America until late 1800's; they are the second most popular bee in the U.S. after the Italian bees (*Apis mellifera ligustica*) first successfully imported by The Rev L.L. Langstroth in 1860.

Ellis, J. Stocks of Bees in the United States. https://americanbeejournal.com/stocks-of-bees-in-the-united-states/

Engel, M.S., I. Hinojosa-Díaz and A.P. Rasnitsyn 2008. A honey bee from the Miocene of Nevada and the biogeography of Apis (Hymenoptera: Apidae: Apini). Proc CA Acad Sciences 60(3): 23-38

Kotthoff, U., T. Wappler and M.S. Engel 2013. Greater past disparity and diversity hints at ancient migrations of European honey bee lineages into Africa and Asia. Jour of Biogeography. https://doi.org/10.1111/jbi.12151

body color and coloration patterns, hair coverage on the body, wing vein differences and behavior.

There are as many as 44 subspecies of honey bees described (Figure 2-17). Today distinguishable races of bees are divided into five major groups—northern and Western European, north Mediterranean, Middle eastern, African and Ethiopian subgroups. Four out of twelve race introductions have been successful in the U.S.

Hybrid bees have been developed within the U.S. but are no longer available for beekeepers. In addition, an accidentally introduced subspecies, the Africanized bee or *scutellata*, has spread to the U.S. from South America.

Movement of bees from one area to another, selection within (and mating between) races, and mass rearing from prized stocks (as done by queen producers and commercial beekeepers) have made the distinctions between bee races less distinct today. Because of this blending of subspecies or genetic lines, some go as far as calling the bees in the U.S. 'American or Western bees,' although they are largely Italian-derived stock in some, but not all, areas.

Figure 2-16
Apis dorsata nests in a mango tree in Thailand. M. Burgett

Dr. Jamie Ellis at the University of Florida speaks to the status of U.S. bee stocks:

It technically is incorrect to claim that we use one race or another in our beekeeping operations. We have stocks of honey bees that originated from multiple European races and one African race, or crosses between the races. Granted, some of the bees available for purchase may exhibit characteristics principally associated with a given race, but they almost certainly are not pure, unadulterated descendants of the original bees of that race. For example, you might purchase Italian-derived honey bees that are yellow in color, produce large colonies, are relatively gentle, and are prolific honey producers. However, they almost certainly are not "pure" Italian honey bees, descended from the original stocks imported into the U.S. Genetic analyses of honey bees across the U.S. support this assertion.

The bee stocks popular in the U.S. include:

German (or black) bee — The bee race of northern Europe, the German or black bee (*Apis mellifera mellifera*)

was the original bee carried to North America in the early 1600s by Virginia and Massachusetts settlers. As the pioneers spread westward across the continent so did the bee, where it became known by Native Americas as the 'white man's fly.' The bee is dark in color (Figure 2-18) and known to be defensive. It builds slowly in the spring. The workers are nervous when their hive is opened and they tend to become excited and even boil out of the opened hive when disturbed.

The German bee is not common today and may exist only as feral colonies. It was susceptible to the bacterial disease EFB (European foulbrood) and in the early 1800s EFB became serious and spread rapidly throughout the U.S. Since most of the bees in the U.S. at that time were German bees, beekeeper colony losses were extensive. Commercial beekeeping was then gaining prominence

Figure 2-17
Distribution of the subspecies or races of *Apis mellifera* L. Only a few of them are used in North America.

and the defensiveness of the black bee was a major disadvantage. Once queen breeding using Italian bee stock became established in the southern U.S., along with the shipping of bees through the mail, Italian-derived bees predominated and the black bees quickly disappeared.

Carniolan bee—This race (*Apis mellifera carnica*), originated in the southern part of the Austrian alps and in present day Slovenia. It is dark gray to almost black in color (Figure 2-19). Carniolans are a gentle and quiet bee. They overwinter with low numbers and build up rapidly in the spring, but unless given sufficient room for expansion, tend to swarm. They have fewer disease problems than other races and are good house cleaners. Their only real disadvantage, swarming, has been selected against by beekeepers. Introduced in the late 1800s, genetic purity of the stock has seriously degraded in the U.S. There is renewed interest in this bee because of problems with bee diseases and mites. There have been recent introductions of new genetic material and selection for stock.

Caucasian bee—The Caucasian bee, (*Apis mellifera caucasica*), originated in the high valleys of the Caucasus Mountains near the Black Sea. It is a dark bee, with short gray body hairs (Figure 2-20). They are gentle and calm when their hive is opened. Young foragers drift and are prone to robbing behavior. Some beekeepers think the greatest drawback of Caucasians is their extensive use of propolis, the resin-based material bees use to seal their hive and reduce the colony entrance, often to bee-sized entry holes. Introduced in the late 1800s to early 1900s, there is no pure stock source in the U.S.

Italian bee—Italian-derived bees (*Apis mellifera ligustica*) are the dominant bee race in North America and Europe today (Figure 2-21). It is a yellowish-brown bee with an abdomen of light yellowish-brown and black bands. There has been selection for queens of reddish-gold color (golden Italians) and workers with five color bands on the abdomen (five-banded Italians). Otherwise they are more reddish with workers having three distinct abdominal color bands—the common **three-banded Italian**.

Italian bees were originally imported into the U.S. in 1859. L.L. Langstroth was one of the first to champion the race and offer Italian queens for sale. The original Italian bee has a long list of desirable characteristics and is well suited for most of the U.S. and world beekeeping. It is not overly defensive, it overwinters quite well, has a low tendency toward swarming and is not excessive in use of propolis. It was an excellent bee for the U.S. comb honey producers who were in the majority in the late 1800s because it caps honey cells with white wax making an extremely attractive finished comb product.

If Italian bees have a negative trait it is their tendency to over-brood during the year. They respond well to pollen

Figure 2-18
The German bee, *Apis mellifera mellifera*.

Figure 2-19
The Carniolian bee, *Apis mellifera carnica*.

Figure 2-20
The Caucasian bee, *Apis mellifera caucasica*.

Figure 2-21
Queen and worker Italian bees. R. Snyder

Figure 2-22
Apis mellifera scutelatta, or the African honey bee.

availability in the spring and build up well, but tend to maintain large, populous colonies during the summer and into the fall by consuming stored honey to continue brood rearing. Italian-derived bees are the bee of choice for many beekeepers.

Middle eastern bee races—There are a number of differences in the native bees occurring in the Middle East from Turkey to Iran. Less is known about these races. Those from the largest islands of the Mediterranean and the two major races of Northern Africa (Figure 2-17) have been introduced into the U.S. The remaining stock maintain small colonies, rear many queens and swarm repeatedly—making them poor bees for beekeeping.

African races—Two major races, along with several others, inhabit Africa below the Sahara Desert. In eastern Africa, *Apis mellifera scutellata* (Figure 2-17) occurs over a wide area of savanna and subtropical climate area from Ethiopia south to South Africa. This defensive and migratory bee has been hived and managed in a destruct-harvest system for centuries. In Western Africa, *Apis mellifera adansonii* is a yellow-colored bee that occupies more tropical conditions. Its nests have been robbed by human and ape relatives probably as long as *scutellata*. Other African bee races occupy the tip of South Africa (Cape bee), Madagascar (*A. m. unicolor*), narrowly along the eastern coast of Africa (*A. m. littorea*) and at higher elevations of eastern mountain ranges (*A. m. monticola*) (Figure 2-17).

Africanized bee—Many people have heard about the Africanized, or 'killer,' bee (Figures 2-22, 2-23). After accidental escape from colonies with introduced queens, this bee population has spread naturally throughout most of South, Central and into North America. Although originally thought to be a hybrid of African queens breeding with drones of European colonies in the São

Paulo area, (hence the name Africanized), the population is essentially pure African genetic material despite efforts to incorporate European generic stock.

The original 26 surviving queens were in excluder-protected hives, but the breeding colonies swarmed when the excluders were removed. Then, without further improvement, queens were bred and distributed to beekeepers. Subsequently, a feral population spread rapidly via swarming and migratory absconding movement.

The African stock, originally called *A. m. adansonii*, is now known to have originated from *A. m. scutellata*. It reproduces readily by swarming, and is overly defensive. The new population, well adapted for the climatic conditions of Brazil, then did the unexpected—it multiplied and spread as a distinct population rather than hybridizing with the existing European bees in the region. Colonization of a feral population with the objectionable defensiveness of the African bee was evident within the first five years in Rio de Janeiro. Populations were discovered in neighboring Paraguay (1964), Northern Argentina (1965) and Bolivia (1967) within ten years.

It was thought that perhaps the population would be diluted in the Amazon basin but instead it spread at a faster rate of 250-400 km/year (150-250 miles/year). It crossed the Amazon River in 1971. Expansion slowed in Venezuela to 160 km/year (100 miles/year), during 1975-1980. In 1978, at the height of colonization, an estimated 100 persons died in Venezuela from bee stings.

The bee continued its spread northward—southward spread was much slower as was colonization of higher Andes mountain elevations. The first confirmed Africanized bee swarm was collected in Panama in 1982, in Mexico in 1986 and in the U.S. in 1990. Efforts

Figure 2-23
Inspecting colony of Africanized bees, Panama. NOTE: 'Running' behavior of bees as they quickly move from frame surface to lower left of frame.

to slow the population included increasing beekeeping and beekeepers in Venezuela (genetic dilution plan), discussion of a physical barrier at the Panama Canal (that did not get organized, although a bee swat team removed over 7,500 bee swarms/colonies in a three-year time span) and a biological barrier at the coastal lowland narrowing of Mexico's Isthmus of Tehuantepec in 1987. Over 80,000 swarms/colonies were destroyed in this region during this failed attempt to halt or slow the spread of the population northward into the major beekeeping areas of Mexico and the U.S.

The initial Africanized bee swarms were captured via swarm traps in the lower Rio Grande valley of Texas. The first accidental stinging death was in 1991. Africanized bees colonized Arizona and California directly from Mexico. They remained west of the Mississippi River until 2005, when they were detected in the Tampa Bay area of Florida, probably due to swarms/colonies accidentally transported by ships. Southern and middle

Figure 2-24
Suitability index predicting eventual spread of Africanized bee population (yellow, orange and red) in United States. USGS graphic.

Florida were rapidly Africanized. The reason they failed to rapidly spread eastward from south Texas along the Gulf Coast of the U.S. remains a mystery.

As of 2020 they occupy the southern border states and marginally into the next tier of states in the U.S., except Georgia and Colorado. The population continues to slowly move northward in California and Florida. Highly defensive colonies have been reported in several additional states, largely attributed to movement of migratory colonies, queens and/or packages.

Using climatological data and based on their present spread, U.S. Geological Survey biologists, in collaboration with Sigma Science Corporation using a NASA supercomputer, developed a map predicting eventual distribution based on their current colonization (Figure 2-24). This predicted spread includes areas where most of the commercial queen breeders operate.

Beekeepers carried Africanized bees over the Andes Mountain chain to coastal Peru where they have spread northward to Ecuador but not yet (as of 2021) southward into Chile. Ships have carried them to the major islands of the Caribbean.

Something interesting has happened in Puerto Rico. Africanized bees first arrived in Puerto Rico in 1994, the first large oceanic island to be colonized. The human and animal loss from defensive bee stingings is one of the highest in the Americas. Over time a more docile, yet hardy bee has been developed throughout the island. A team from the University of Illinois and the bee specialist in Puerto Rico have discovered that although they retain most of the genetic traits of their African honey bee ancestors, a few regions of their DNA have become more like those of European honey bees. They surmised this evolution toward gentleness is a result of living on a very densely populated island from which they could not easily escape and through individuals, including beekeepers, killing the most aggressive bees, aiding the genetic selection toward more docile bees. Beekeepers report that colonies not under selection remain highly defensive.

Since 1986, further spread southward in Argentina has stalled. There is an apparent transition zone roughly at latitude 32-34° in Argentina with European bees remaining in the southern region. In the Western Hemisphere, only Canada, Chile and several small islands are free of this population.

Because the Africanized bee is of nearly pure African material (owing to the limited number of original queens brought from Africa), its genetic mix is not representative of the total population of *scutellata* in Africa. This suggests the population of Africanized bees has experienced a genetic 'bottleneck' in the Americas and does not fully reflect the full genetic mixture of the parent population in Africa.

The press name for this bee population, 'killer bee,' has unfortunately been widely used. The press in Brazil initially dubbed them the 'assassin' bee which was translated by the North American press as 'killer bee.' The highly expressed defensiveness trait of this bee led to animals and people, especially in the countryside, dying from receiving too many stings (toxic sting reaction) as the bees defend their feral and beekeeper hive home sites. Whatever its name, it has retained the tendency to run off brood comb (Figure 2-23) and exit the feral home or

beekeeper hive and defend a perimeter around the nest, readily stinging moving animals or people, a behavior it also exhibits in its native Africa.

The problem with this bee in the Americas is really fourfold: (1) the defensiveness of the bee resulting in human or animal mass-stinging accidents, (2) the lack of competitiveness of European-based genetic material alongside Africanized bee colonies, 3) Africanized bee heightened swarming, usurpation and absconding and (4) the difficulty in managing the bees, especially attempting to use management techniques developed for less defensive European-race bees. Urban apiary locations near humans, animals and congestion are not practical with Africanized bees unless carefully selected for gentler colonies. The Africanized bees are usually highly productive, hygienic and resistant to certain mites and pests. Despite their defensiveness, they have some traits that can be cultivated by skilled beekeepers.

The bee in Africa is not extensively manipulated or moved by beekeepers as is standard practice with honey bee colonies in North America. Swarming in Africa and capturing absconding swarms is a useful means of increasing colony numbers. With their defensiveness, African beekeepers locate colonies well away from homes and animals.

What the full extent of this spread may be is cause for considerable speculation. Beekeepers in Brazil and elsewhere in the Americas have learned to adjust to the bee. State-financed breeding programs have developed selected strains of the bee that are productive and somewhat less defensive. Beekeepers in the Southern U.S. are making adjustments by using competitively

Figure 2-25
University of Guelph's Paul Kelly examines a colony with a pure Buckfast queen open mated on an island in Ontario. L. Connor

Figure 2-26
After being frozen with liquid nitrogen, this patch of brood was cleaned out by hygienic bees. Univ. Minnesota Bee Lab.

Figure 2-27, 2-28
Left: VSH breeder queen. Right: Pol-line hygienic queen.
Both Glenn Apiaries

productive replacement European-stock queens. They are not in more semi-tropical regions of the Americas and have avoided the negative impact experienced in countries farther to the south and in South America. Stinging accidents have increased, largely due to accidental disturbances to feral Africanized colonies, but most U.S. beekeepers, except for those in urban areas, have adjusted and continue beekeeping.

Hybrid bees

Two methods are used to create hybrid honey bees. The first involves the crossing of two races, using concentrated (and ideally isolated) breeding areas or with instrumental insemination. The second involves intensive inbreeding and crossing unrelated inbred lines using instrumental insemination.

Dadant and Sons, Inc. geneticist Dr. G. H. 'Bud' Cale Jr, undertook a major bee breeding program after World War II to produce two hybrid bees. The Starline bee was first introduced in the late 1940s as a highly vigorous bee developed from four inbred lines. The breeding program was cutting edge for the 1940s, modeled after corn breeding programs. Due to heterosis (hybrid vigor) the resulting bees were slightly bigger in size and better honey producers. Their uniformity and productivity reduced apiary visits because manipulations could be done to all colonies at once. The bee was popular with large-scale beekeepers.

A second hybrid, the Midnite hybrid, followed in 1952. It was a cross of dark lines of bees, developed primarily as a gentle bee for the hobbyist (backyard) beekeeper. The Midnite hybrid tended to use propolis more than Italian

bees (but less than pure Caucasian bees). They were good bees and popular—unfortunately, neither hybrid is available today.

Whenever a pure line of bees open mates with unrelated drones the resulting bees are often considered hybrid colonies. The bees express a combination of the genetics and behaviors of both lines.

Improved bees

Brother Adam (Chapter 21, Figure 21-7), a monk at Buckfast Abbey in England, developed the Buckfast bee by making test crosses (hybrids) and selecting daughters for use in his breeding program. Developed to survive tracheal mite infestations, this mainly Italian and Carniolan strain is considered a better bee for the cool damp English summer. There is an active Buckfast breeding program in Ontario, Canada that coordinates with European Buckfast breeders (Figure 2-25).

Other beekeepers in Denmark, Ireland and Scotland consider their 'native' dark honey bees as the best bee for their conditions. The concept that we need to go elsewhere for a better bee is no longer in vogue. We can develop a better bee with what we have already, using local bees pre-selected for local conditions.

Varroa mite tolerant bees

The discovery of the varroa mite (Chapter 21) stimulated the selection of lines (closely related queen families) of honey bees possessing resistance or tolerance to the mites. Earlier, selections were made for American foulbrood-resistant bees (a line of bees that more readily detected and removed diseased brood), and a line of bees that were greater pollen collectors. Unfortunately, neither of these lines survived the attack of mites and propagation programs were lost.

Since then, one line, **Varroa Sensitive Hygienic (VSH)**, (Figure 2-27), originally labeled Suppressed Mite Resistance (SMR), was developed from mixed-origin survivor queens by Drs. John Harbo and Jeff Harris of the USDA Baton Rouge Bee Lab. It is widely used to reduce varroa mite levels. Unfortunately, the use of any tolerant bee stock does not eliminate the mites entirely—colonies must be sampled for mite levels and treatment applied if needed.

The **Minnesota Hygienic** was developed by Dr. Marla Spivak and Gary Reuter at the University of Minnesota. It is a hygienic, Italian-derived bee that both detects and removes mites from developing brood cells (Figure 2-26). The strain is maintained by commercial beekeepers.

The Pol-line Hygienic queens (Figure 2-28) have a combination of the best traits required for pollination and high honey production. They were developed by the USDA. to express VSH traits to an optimum degree

Figure 2-27
Russian queen. USDA Baton Rouge

Figure 2-28
Bee biting a varroa mite. Purdue University

to control mites and brood disease, while maintaining the high productivity needed by commercial beekeepers. Hilo queens are the newest VSH line.

Selected **Russian queen bees** (Figure 2-29) were introduced into the U.S. from far eastern Russia by Dr. Tom Rinderer, USDA Bee Lab, Baton Rouge. His team documented that they were a varroa tolerant population. Now, the **Russian Honey Bee Breeders' Association (RHBA)** employ a broadly based closed breeding population selected for resistance to varroa and increased honey production.

Queens are bred and DNA tested to be genetically pure Russians. RHBA currently has 17 lines of Russian genetic stock. Russian colonies winter with small bee clusters, but build rapidly when pollen and nectar are abundant. They must be monitored for swarming. Testing has shown that they are more tolerant or resistant to tracheal mites and varroa mites. There is evidence that they also possess hygienic behavior and grooming behavior.

Mite Biting Bees (Figure 2-28), also called ankle biters or simply biters, are a selection by Dr. Greg Hunt and Krispn Given of Purdue University. Beginning in 2007 they have enhanced Italian-derived bees with **grooming behavior.**

To assess grooming they used sticky boards beneath colonies to catch fallen mites. Mites on the boards are examined for chewed legs and other damaged body parts. Initially, an average of 3% of fallen mites had chewed legs but after selecting for this behavior for over a decade, now 50% of fallen mites have chewed legs.

Locally adapted survivor stock. Breeding of selected lines has been shown to offer an opportunity to reduce the harmful effects of disease and mites. Individual beekeepers and beekeepers of several bee clubs are seeking to improve their bees by going treatment-free and using locally adapted survivor stock. Losses might be extremely high at first, but some of these efforts report improving survival over several seasons.

One constant challenge to developing localized stock is beekeepers purchasing packages, queens, nucleus colonies. This is also challeged by migratory commercial beekeepers who have apiaries nearby. Such colonies produce drones that mate with the locally adapted queen offspring, negating the selection of local bees by introducing non-adapted genes (see Chapter 18 for discussion on queen rearing).

Local stock selection might be feasible in some isolated instances. Cornell University's Dr. Tom Seeley established an apiary in an isolated valley near Ithaca, NY that contains only local bees collected from swarms caught in bait hives, which he called **wild caught** (Figure 2-29) found in areas some distnce from package, nucleus and commercial hives. In 2018 he lost 31% of the colonies; in 2019, 29% and in 2020, 24%.

Seeley compared two other selected stocks with his locally adapted swarm offspring colonies. In 2019 he set up three apiaries in the same area. In addition to his locally selected wild caught colonies, he introduced Russian queens produced by Kirk Webster, a commercial beekeeper in Vermont, and VSH Italians queens from a large queen producer in California.

These queens were initially installed into five-frame nucleus colonies and later moved to eight-frame hives. On April 7, 2020 he found the wild caught colonies had five out of six colonies alive (83%); four out of five Webster Russian colonies were alive (80%) while only one out of seven VSH Italian colonies was alive (14%).

While Seeley cautions that we *"cannot draw sweeping conclusions from this study"* these data are *"suggestive of where a beekeeper who wishes to pursue treatment-free beekeeping should get his or her queens."*

Because the colonies with the highest mite numbers in the summer were the colonies that died in the fall or winter, Seeley suggests that such colonies might be culled (or treated and requeened) and only colonies with low mite numbers overwintered.

Figure 2-29
Wild caught queens obtained in isolated areas may be a source of locally adapted survival stock.

key terms

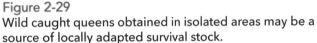

African honey bee	class Insecta	Italian bees	pollen transport
Andrenidae	Coleoptera	Kingdom	race (of bees)
andrenid	destruct harvest	kleptoparasite	Russian bee
Apidae	digger bee	leafcutter bee	seasonally social
Apis	Diptera	Lepidoptera	species
Apis subspecies	dwarf honey bee	mason bee	Starline hybrid
Apocrita	eastern honey bee	mellitidae	stingless bees
apoidea	eusocial	Midnite hybrid	stocks of bees
Arthropoda	German (black) bee	Minnesota hybrid	survivor stock
binominal	giant honey bee	Mite biting bees	sweat bee
Bombus	grooming behavior	Orders	three- and five-banded Italians
Buckfast bee	Halictidae	Phylum	VSH bees
bumble bee	heterosis (hybrid vigor)	plaster bee	wax pots
Carniolan honey bee	hygienic bees	plumose hairs	western honey bee
Caucasian honey bee	Hymenoptera	pol-line hygienic	wild caught queens

discussion questions

The classification system may sometimes seem tedious but it is specific and logical. Review the classification of the honey bee observing how at each successive level organisms more closely resemble each other. Give the common characteristics of each level. If you could devise a different type of classification scheme what would you change or modify in your system?

What is a bee? Is identifying bee families the "best" way to discuss the diversity of bees in North America? How do other species in Genus *Apis* differ from *Apis mellifera*? Why do we sometimes say non-*Apis* or 'wild' bee to designate a bee? Discuss similarities and differences between different bees. The term race is less politically acceptable these days and subspecies is not in favor so how would you describe the diversity in *Apis* to someone who wants to know what kind of bee you have? Variety? Breed? Ecotype? Queen Family?

What honey bee would you prefer to use for beekeeping? Where would you obtain them? What are the risks in bringing bee species/races from one area or county to another? Why would it be safer to breed a distinct bee with the characteristics you desire from within an existing population versus bringing in genetic material from another region?

What is the African or Africanized bee? Why is it labeled the 'killer bee?' What is the origin of this bee? What can be done about the 'problem' it has created for beekeepers and the general public?

What would you do to find/select/breed another bee? What characteristics would you use to develop a superior bee? Discuss how you might do this. What might be the possibility of you or your club using wild caught stock in a breeding program?

exercises

Make a field trip to a flower and observe the bees found foraging at the flower. Capture representative bees and prepare a collection for identification. Include as many different flowering plants as possible and visit flowers several times during the season. Identify the bees by family. Compare the numbers (species and number of individuals) of non-*Apis* bees to the number of honey bees you observe on the same flower.

Gain practice in recognizing the families and major genera of bees by use of taxonomic keys. Start with *Bombus* (bumble bees) since ID is possible using body color patterns to separate the species.

A marvelous resource to help identify bee genera is the Discoverlife.org website (click on bees). It covers all U.S. bees. Search for other aids on the Internet. Evaluate the top three for how they were able to help you identify a bee. Evaluate the top three for how easy they were able to use.

Research the literature for references to different bee races. If available, look in the literature for the 1800s to see the interest in the U.S. leading to importation of Italian bees in 1859. Other bee races were also imported until stopped with passage in 1922 of a U.S. law banning importation. Consult issues of *Gleanings in Bee Culture* and *American Bee Journal* from the early 1900s to determine the sentiment for and against such a ban. Find references to bees and beekeeping in ancient and modern literature and compare and contrast human attitudes towards bees. Can you find examples of how bees are represented in literature, art, children's books or other media?

references

Internet links by topic

Africanized bees: Lin, Wei, et al. 2018. Africanized bees extend their distribution in California. Plos One Accessed via https://doi.org/10.1371/journal.pone.0190604 Bee names, biologies, families: Accessed via: Https://bugguide.net/node/view/475348

Russian stock: http://www.russianbreeder.org/

Varroa sensitive hygiene bees: http://www.glenn-apiaries.com/vsh.html (This site is no longer being updated)

Publications by author

Avalos, A., et al. 2017. A soft selective sweep during rapid evolution of gentle behaviour in an Africanized honeybee. Nature Communications 8:1550

Card, A. 2019. VSH-Pol line Bees. Bee Culture. September 2019

Caron, D.M. 2001. Africanized Honey Bees in the Americas. A. I. Root, Co. Medina, Ohio

Hatfield, R. et al. 2012. Conserving Bumble Bees. Xerces, Portland, OR

Jarnevich, C.S. et al. 2013. Regional distribution models with lack of proximate predictors: Africanized honeybees expanding north. Diversity and Distributions, (Diversity Distrib.) (2013): 1–9

Koeniger, N.G. Koeniger and S. Tingek. 2010. Honey Bees of Borneo: Exploring the Centre of Apis Diversity. Natural History Publications, Borneo. Available through Wicwas Press, Kalamazoo, MI

Meixner, M.D. et al. 2013. Standard methods for characterising subspecies and ecotypes of Apis mellifera, Journal of Apicultural Research, 52:4, 1-28, DOI: 10.3896/IBRA.1.52.4.05

Pellett, F. 2013. History of American Beekeeping, Wicwas Press, Kalamazoo, MI

Seeley, T. 2019. The Lives of Bees: the untold story of the lives of bees in the wild. Princeton Univ. Press, Princeton NJ

Seeley, T. 2020. Progress report on three years of treatment-free beekeeping, including a test of three types of queen: Wild Colony, Webster Russian, and VSH Italian. August American Bee Journal.

Ulrich K., T. Wappler and M.S. Engel. 2013. Greater past disparity and diversity hints at ancient migrations of European honey bee lineages into Africa and Asia. Jour of Biogeography. https://doi.org/10.1111/jbi.12151

Williams, P.H. et al. 2014. Bumble Bees of North America. Princeton University Press Princeton, NJ

Wilson, J.S. and O.J.M. Carril. 2015. The Bees in your Backyard. Princeton University Press, Princeton NJ

Chapter 3
Sociality

Figure 3-1
More than an aggregation, eusocial worker caste honey bees collectively lap liquid honey from broken comb. L. Connor

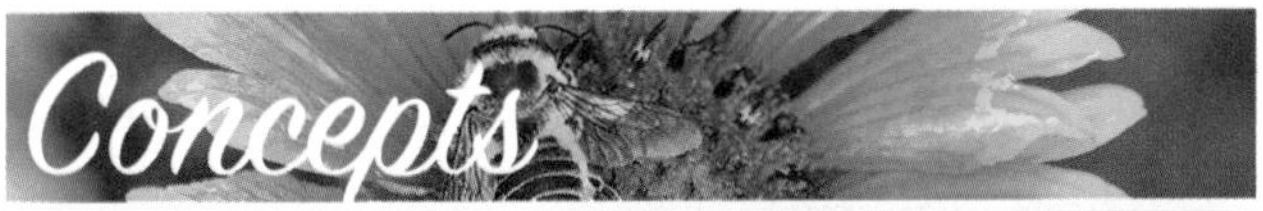

Concepts

Superorganisms
- **bee wasps and ants**
- **similarities and differences**
- **a bit about control**

What are insect societies?

Bees, wasps and ants
- **how they differ**
- **how they are alike**

Why do the Hymenoptera have so much sociality?

Stinging wasps and bees
- **how to control them**

Insect societies

Social life has evolved repeatedly in the Animal Kingdom. 'Social' is defined here as a group of individuals of the same species who are organized in a cooperative manner. Animal societies can be grouped into four distinct types. Two social organization styles are found in invertebrates and two among the vertebrates.

Invertebrate societies are characterized by individual cells or organisms that together function like a single organism. Corals and the bryozoans are basically individual cells that function in concert with others. The social insects are basically large families; some term them **superorganisms**.

Some members become physically modified and sterile. They exist to serve the female reproductive or queen. The social system is maintained by complex **chemical pheromones** and behaviors that spread the chemical messages to all individuals in the colony. Some aggression and conflict occurs in some social insects, particularly for the raising of replacement reproductives.

Vertebrate societies are not as rigid as those of invertebrates but can be more complex. The vertebrates are not solely family-based societies. Aggressiveness is more common. Selfishness rules and sterile castes are not present, though not all members capable of reproduction may do so at all times. Dominance hierarchies are established and when an individual is lost from the society, the ranking or pecking order of the survivors must be reestablished.

The human society is the most complex in the Animal Kingdom. Selfishness is not reduced but larger brain capacity means that humans learn from past experiences and plan for the future. Young spend a long time learning before they reach reproductive age. Language has become very important in maintaining social interactions and reasoning/insight means leadership is more flexible.

Figure 3-2
Milkweed bug nymphs and adults aggregate at a feeding site. L. Connor

Honey bees are totally social creatures (Figure 3-1). In fact, an honey bee cannot survive alone. A queen bee needs a minimum of several hundred workers in order to survive. Although organically separate, individual honey bees are inseparably united by behavior and chemistry. Honey bees represent a highly-evolved society among insects. Social insects are organized into large families. This type of social organization is different and distinct from the more familiar vertebrate mammals and birds in which social organization revolves around dominance hierarchies (chickens), territory (many birds), and/or leadership (apes).

As we examine insect biologies we can find various degrees of social organization. The most complex social organizations are termed eusocial (truly social). Honey

bees, bumble bees, stingless bees, yellowjackets, hornets, paper wasps, ants, and termites are all eusocial. Eusocial insects exhibit three common characteristics:

- cooperative care of young
- reproductive division of labor (caste system)
- overlap of generations caring for young.

While many insects gather together—for example, male and female to mate, some individuals of the same species congregate at a common food or nesting site. Such gatherings may be an **aggregation**. An aggregation is a group of individuals (more than a reproductive pair) gathered in the same place but who do not construct nests or rear offspring in a cooperative manner. Aggregations occur for mating (dancing flies), for hibernation (ladybird beetles), for defense (sawfly larvae), at food sites (milkweed bugs, Figure 3-2), or for other reasons. Aggregations are temporary social interactions.

We might find a primitive form of social behavior when members of a species share a common nest or gather at one site for rearing of young. Some insects (such as tree hoppers) are **subsocial** with adults caring for their nymphs for a period of time. Instead of mass provisioning, the adults provision growing offspring daily. Other insects are **communal**—adult members of one generation sharing the same nest or nest site area to rear their young—but do not otherwise cooperate in care of brood. A number of bee and wasp species exhibit communal behavior.

Bees, wasps and other insects may have one or two of the three characteristics of eusociality but not all three, a condition termed **parasocial**. Depending on which combination of traits they share, parasocial insects may be further classified as either **quasisocial or semisocial**. Table 3-1 shows one classification for social interaction.

Sociality in the Hymenoptera

Large numbers of mining bees and digger wasps are not eusocial but still have a degree of social interaction. Here are some examples:

- **Aggregations**—Bee and wasp females often nest in close association with each other due to favorable nesting conditions. There is no interaction and each female provisions her own nest. Many Halictidae, Colletidae and Andrenidae aggregate in areas of favorable soil conditions (Figure 3-7). Leafcutting (Figure 3-3) and carpenter bees (Figure 3-8) aggregate nests where appropriate wood structure exists. Males often patrol territories, hovering and fighting among themselves in such situations.

- **Parental care**—Some female insects extend care to their eggs or immatures. This occurs in some plant-feeding hymenopterans (sawflies).

Box 5

EVOLUTION OF SOCIALITY

Eusociality has evolved many times. It is estimated that sociality evolved at least eight times in bees alone. Nine percent of the species of Hymenoptera are social. However, in sheer numbers, social insects are truly impressive. Insects that are eusocial constitute over 50% of the total weight (biomass) of all the insects occupying Earth. Being common, sociality has been demonstrated to have evolved in more than one way.

In a quasisocial insect, brood care is cooperative. If an insect species cooperates in brood care, it is possible to develop a reproductive division of labor. Species with both cooperative brood care and reproductive castes are labelled semisocial. By a lengthening of life, the third evolutionary stage of eusociality might be achieved whereby adults live long enough so there is an overlap of generations.

This overlap is by no means the only possible evolutionary route to eusociality. Overlap of generations may occur initially when long life occurs in an insect species. The longer-living adults may then begin to share responsibility for brood care. Eventually reproductive division of labor evolves into a caste system and the species exhibits eusociality.

Another evolutionary route toward sociality may be through common nesting sites. Individuals in a communal species sharing a common nesting area may begin to share a nest like an inverted Y with one female having one branch and another the other branch, both sharing a single common entrance. This may lead, over time, to specialization in duties. Perhaps one female digs the nest while the other guards more frequently. This might eventually evolve to a species where most females do the work/nest guarding, and only one individual then considered a queen, lays eggs. With all three characteristics, the species is then considered eusocial.

Table 3-1

Relative stages of social interaction as the level of sociality

Social Degree	Cooperative Brood Care	Female Caste	Generation Overlap
Subsocial/Communal	−	−	−
Quasisocial	+	−	−
Semisocial	−	+	+
Eusocial	+	+	+

- **Quasisocial** — Several females cooperate to raise the brood of another female. This type of sociality is common in bees and wasps. It represents one of the evolutionary routes to eusociality. Euglossine bees, a number of Halictidae, as well as some *Osmia* bees show this social condition.

- **Semisocial** — This is another route to evolution of eusociality. A number of bees and wasp species exhibit this type of social structure. Several females may coexist but only one lays eggs while she and all others take care of young. There is no overlap of generations. Some Halictidae and Megachilidae show semisocial organization.

Eusocial

There are differences among the ants, social bees and wasps in social biology. In the Hymenoptera, one difference we see is in species with a **perennial life cycle** versus those with an **annual life cycle** (which some term primitively eusocial or seasonally eusocial).

In an annual life cycle such as in bumble bees, yellowjackets and paper wasps, only mated females survive over winter. These individuals seek a sheltered location in rotted logs, loose soil, in leaf litter or dig a hole to hibernate underground. Survivor queens, unaided, must establish and begin a nest in the spring.

Their first offspring are female worker daughters who then assume the sterile female caste duties of nest expansion, foraging and brood rearing. The overwintered female (the queen) then becomes only an egg layer. In the fall, the queen lays male (unfertilized) eggs and the last female brood develops into female reproductives capable of mating. The females will mate and overwinter while the queen, her worker daughters and males perish with the advent of cold weather. The cycle must be started anew next year by successfully overwintering females.

Figure 3-3
Manufactured nesting site for leafcutting bees. While these bees may aggregate at suitable domestic nest sites, they are not truly social.

Perennial life cycles are found in ants, *Apis* species and stingless bees. All maintain a sterile worker population throughout the year. During unfavorable weather (winter in temperate areas or wet seasons in the tropics), populations decline. With abundant resources, males (called drones in *Apis* species) and reproductive females are reared.

Apis colonies reproduce the colony unit when the old queen takes a portion of the adult population and swarms from the nest to a new nest site after new queens are started, but before they emerge as adults, in the original nest. In stingless bees, several reproductive females leave the parent colony to establish a new nest with a few workers. Workers may even prepare a new nest site several days in anticipation of the arrival of the new queens.

In both *Apis* and stingless bees, mating of newly reared reproductive females occurs soon after emergence. Males die in mating. Extra female reproductives are killed and a single mated queen lives to expand the nest with accompanying workers.

Ants have a large diversity of food habits and use a variety of sites for nests and different nest construction materials but their social structure is similar to bees. Their sterile female caste includes both workers (in more advanced societies as many as three or four adult sizes) and soldiers (sometimes two types of soldiers). Ant colonies swarm by generating winged males and females that leave the original nest site to begin a new nest without benefit of workers. New reproductives may also bud off from the parent colony using parent colony workers and soldiers to establish a new nest. Such satellite nests maintain contact with the original nests.

A common feature of the eusocial Hymenoptera is use of effective methods for defense of the individuals and the nest. They are masters of chemical defense, protecting themselves and nest mates via both biting and stinging. Nests must be defended in eusocial insects since they contain considerable stored reserves as well as constitute the home for the young and the reproductives. Table 3-2 compares several characteristics of bees, wasps and ants.

Termites — Order Isoptera (although a recent classification system includes them as an epifamily in the order of cockroaches) are a second major insect order that exhibit eusociality. All 4,000 termite species, as in ants, are entirely eusocial. They superficially resemble each other; termites are sometimes mislabeled as 'white ants.' There are some important differences between termites and the eusocial Hymenoptera due to the fact that termites have gradual or incomplete metamorphosis and the reproductive female cannot store sperm from the male within her body.

Eusocial termites differ from Hymenoptera in the following ways:

Table 3-2

Character Comparison of Bees, Wasps and Ants

Bees	Wasps	Ants
branched body hairs	few non-branched hairs	no branched hairs
pollen-collecting hair	no pollen-collecting hair	no pollen-collecting hair
pollen and nectar diet	meat eaters as larvae	omnivores
nest in hollows or ground	nest in vegetation or ground	primarily ground nesters
winged adults	mostly winged adults	wingless adults
hairy; constricted waist not always evident	angular body with long appendages	three prominent body parts; waist with three projections

• Termite workers and soldiers may be immature nymphs or adult sterile females and males.

• Reproductives are queen and king (there may be several pairs in large mature nests).

• Reproduction is by swarming whereby the parent colony produces large numbers of winged females and males (when conditions are favorable—often in a yearly cycle) which swarm or leave the nest, pair off and then attempt to establish a new nest by themselves without worker assistance.

Other eusocial species. There are eusocial aphids (Order Homoptera), thrips (Order Thysanoptera) and perhaps a beetle (Order Coleoptera) that have the three characteristics of eusociality. Presocial and some species with parasocial societies are found in these orders as well. Non insects include naked mole rats and *Synalpheus* coral shrimp.

Bees

Bees are generally hairy flower-visitors who use only nectar and pollen as food. Honey bees can be golden,

yellow-brown, grey or black. The natural nesting site of the honey bee is a sheltered, darkened enclosure. When honey bees are maintained by humans, their nests are a series of boxes called hives. 'Wild' or escaped honey bee swarms form colony nests in caves, tree hollows or in human-made structures such as attics, between the wall studs of houses, garages, or other buildings, within porch roofs or similar areas. Natural or wild nests are termed 'feral.'

Honey bee swarms consist of a mass of social worker bees with a queen that have temporarily clustered at some exposed location. Swarms may stay a few hours to a few days while the scout bees seek a new home location. Honey bees in a swarm are usually gentle because they have full honey stomachs. If left undisturbed, a swarm will locate new quarters and move into a new homesite. (Swarming in honey bees is covered in Chapter 10).

Bumble bees and carpenter bees are two other familiar bees. They are similar to each other in appearance but not in habitats. Both are robust, yellow and black, hairy bees with a loud buzz. There is a second, less well known, much smaller-bodied carpenter bee, *Ceratina* (Figure 3-5).

Figure 3-4
Osmia Mason bee sealing her completed brood cache.

Figure 3-5
Small carpenter bee, *Ceratina*.

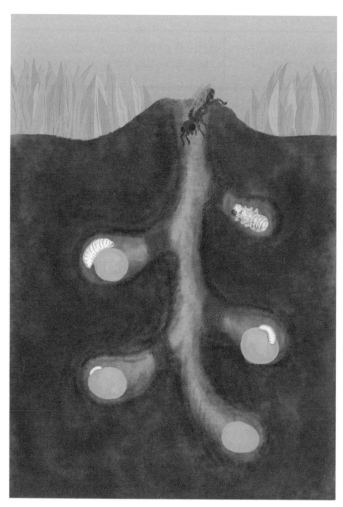

Above: Figure 3-6
Large carpenter bee (*Xylocopa*) chewing her nesting hole.

Left: Figure 3-7
A ground nest with side chambers. Both wasps and miner/digger bees build such nests. Key pollinator groups like squash bees build nests like this near squash and pumpkin plants. J. Zawlisak

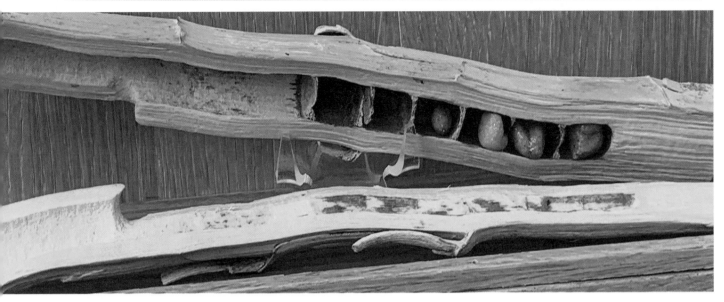

Figure 3-8
Carpenter bee cells in tunnels chewed into wood. Reproduced with permission of the Paleontological Research Institution, Ithaca, New York.

Bumble bees are ground nesters (Chapter 2, Box 3). They will occasionally nest in human-discarded trash, such as old furniture, little-used equipment and similarly protected sites. Adults are found foraging on flowers for nectar and pollen. Bumble bees are primitively (seasonally) eusocial.

The more familiar large-bodied carpenter bees bore holes in wood (Figures 3-6, 3-8). The males are territorial and can be very belligerent—however, like males of all bees and wasps, they cannot sting. Carpenter bees are most active in the spring. They are usually seen flying erratically near exposed wooden trim and overhangs of buildings. Porches, garages, shed ceilings, railings, wood on houses and outdoor wooden furniture are common nesting sites.

Carpenter bees are not social but they do aggregate, and often use the same nesting site from one season to the next. While the damage to the wood from a single bee is slight, the activities of numerous carpenter bees over a period of years may cause structural damage.

Carpenter bees overwinter in wood as young adults. The bees that survive the winter mate in the spring (April to June) and begin preparations for the next generation. Carpenter bees do not eat the wood they tunnel in, but use their tunnels for rearing young. The female begins the gallery by drilling an entrance hole (Figure 3-6). When the tunnel is about one inch deep (2.5 cm), she makes a right angle turn and tunnels with the grain of the wood. A completed gallery will be several inches (15-20 cm) long comprised of several partitioned cells, each with a developing larva (Figure 3-7).

Mining bees (Figure 3-7), leafcutting bees (Figure 3-3), and mason bees (Figure 3-4) bees may aggregate nests or exhibit degrees of social organization. Most females of these bees can sting but seldom will unless provoked. Mining bees can be troublesome because of their nest aggregation behavior. Hundreds will nest in one area where soil conditions are suitable for nest excavation.

Adult bees are most easily found foraging on flowers. Many bees are very specific and visit only one flower type. Most adult bees live only a short period of time. The majority, like sweat bees (Halictidae), are very tiny.

Wasps

There are many insects called 'wasps' in the Order Hymenoptera. Wasps can generally be grouped into three large subdivisions depending on their biology and use

Figure 3-9
Mud dauber wasp applying mud to a fresh nest. Each cell is provisioned with paralyzed insects or spiders and a wasp egg. L. Connor

of the ovipositor by the females. The three groupings are parasitizing wasps, paralyzing wasps, and the social wasps.

Parasitizing wasps. Most wasp species are solitary in life-style and parasitic on other animals—mostly insects and spiders. In this group, the female ovipositor (the portion of the reproductive system that aids in laying of eggs) is used to penetrate a potential host to insert one or more eggs inside the host's body.

Many wasps are **parasitoids** that lay eggs on a host, which their offspring eventually kill. Humans grow some of these wasps in large numbers and release them for biocontrol projects targeting specific crop pests. Two large families of parasitoid wasps, the ichneumonids and braconids, are members of the Superfamily Ichneumonoidae.

Paralyzing wasps. A second, even larger, group of wasps use the ovipositor to sting and paralyze a host. The immobilized spider or insect is carried back to a nest, or a nest is constructed on the spot around the immobilized-but living victim. When the host is secure, the female wasp lays her egg or eggs on the paralyzed host. The eggs hatch and consume the immobilized victim as their meal, kept alive and fresh for the larva to consume.

The mud dauber is a familiar example of a paralyzing wasp. Mud dauber adults go to stream banks or mud puddles to collect mud which they use to construct pipe-like mud tubes inside buildings, under eaves or shelters or in similar locations (Figure 3-9). Female adults find a suitable spider host, paralyze it with their sting and fly back with it to a partially completed nest. Before enclosing the paralyzed spider, the female wasp lays an egg on it, thereby providing her offspring with a fresh food source. Some additional examples of paralyzing wasps are the ground-nesting cicada killer wasps, spider-hunting wasps and potter wasps. Potter wasps make a nest which resembles a jug or pot.

Social wasps. Social wasps resemble bees—in fact they are commonly mistaken for bees. They generally have fewer body hairs compared to bees and the hairs they do possess are not branched (plumose). Many of these creatures have bright body coloration patterns—yellow and brown, (i.e. paper wasps Figures 3-10, 3-11), black and white, yellow and black—that serve as warnings of danger to potential predators (**aposomatic body coloration**).

In the social wasps, the ovipositor is modified to serve as a defense weapon. Social wasps build a nest from wood made into paper to rear young and, in a few species, to store food reserves. The slightest disturbance of their nest often leads to defensive behaviors and unwary intruders may be stung repeatedly. The sting is painful and may cause an allergic reaction in sensitive individuals.

Figure 3-10
Polistes 'queen' generates heat with her flight muscles to warm the eggs and larvae in a new nest made of chewed wood.

Figure 3-11
Polistes wasp nest showing paper nesting material and developing larvae.

Social wasps are the most serious stinging insect problem and by far the most likely creature to use their sting on humans. Wasps do not die after they sting, unlike honey bees, and they adapt very well to human-inhabited areas. Wasps are effective biological pest control agents until their nest reaches full size; then the adults of some species become scavengers and serious pests themselves.

Figure 3-12
Yellowjacket scavenging sweets on fruit.

Figure 3-14
European hornet, *Vespa crabro*.

Figure 3-13
Aerial yellowjackets working on the paper nest envelope.

Several familiar insects like yellowjackets (Figures 3-12, 3-13), hornets (Figure 3-14) and paper wasps (Figures 3-10, 3-11) are social wasps. The social wasps are meat eaters. Larvae spend their entire development in paper nest cells. Adult colony members feed the larvae chewed bits and pieces of insects which they often capture at flowers. Many adult social wasps do not eat meat, using only sugars as a carbohydrate energy source. One tropical species makes and stores honey in its paper nest.

Paper wasps are shiny, dark brown wasps that build an exposed nest of paper cells under the overhanging of buildings, in little-used equipment or debris of humans and occasionally in trees or shrubs (Figures 3-10, 3-11, 3-19). They will sting when disturbed and rarely become scavengers. In Texas, they are used as biological agents for some crops and their nests are encouraged in protected A-frames within the fields. Paper wasp nests remain small in population and members die quickly in the fall.

Yellowjackets (Figures 3-12, 3-13, 3-18) are the fiercest and the most common insects to sting humans. Most nest in the ground while others nest in vegetation (Figure 3-19), the sides of buildings or similar sites. One inside-nesting species, *Vespula germanica*, introduced from Europe, has increased dramatically in numbers the last few years and is a serious problem at parks, outside gatherings, backyards, etc., where it scavenges for food. *V. germanica* and other yellowjacket species can be troublesome for beekeepers as they invade bee colonies to steal honey or feed on adult worker bees. Yellowjacket workers create a pest potential when:

- their stings cause pain, swelling and discomfort.

- they nest in and around human habitation and recreation areas.

- they exhibit scavenging behavior, especially as nest duties become reduced in the fall months, and large numbers of wasps frequent areas where sugary fluids are spilled or discarded.

What are commonly called hornets are aerial-nesting yellowjackets, not true hornets. They make a nest of paper like the yellowjackets. The nests, which reach basketball size, are located in trees, shrubs and sometimes on buildings (Figures 3-20, 3-21). The nests grow in size during the season and often are not discovered until the foliage thins in the fall, long after the hornets are dead. A white and black species of yellowjacket in the East is the bald-faced hornet.

A true hornet, also eusocial, has been accidentally introduced into the eastern United States. This European hornet, *Vespa crabro*, is the largest of the species (Figure 3-14). It is a hornet that usually frightens people. It is large and has bright, contrasting, yellow and black markings, an excellent example of **aposomatic warning coloration**. It nests inside tree hollows, constructing a distinctive light brown paper nest. This hornet is attracted to lights at night and the adults hitting a door or window screen below a house light often startle the homeowner. When the hornets strip bark from certain shrubs like lilac and boxwood, to feed on sap, they may girdle and cause dieback of these popular ornamental plantings.

A related Asian *Vespa* species, *V. velutina*, is an expanding honey bee predator in the UK, France and Spain.

The Asian giant hornet (also termed murder hornet Figure 23-7) (*Vespa mandarinia*) is the largest hornet species. Like *V. velutina* it orginally was an Asian hornet, living in low mountains and forests. It feeds on larger insects, including honey bees. It was discovered in British Columbia, Canada in 2019, followed by its discovery in Washington state in December, 2019 and additionally in 2020 and 2021.

Ants

While ant social biology is fascinating and very complex, they are often confused with termites and misidentified. The major differences to distinguish between ants and termites include:

- ants possess a hardened exoskeleton
- termites are usually pale or colorless white, while most ants are darker
- elbowed antennae in ants, termites straight
- prominent wasp-waist in ants, not in termites
- ants have few, but obvious, body hairs
- ant wings unequal in size in reproductives
- wing stubs in termite reproductives but not in ants

While confusion in their identities persist, it is important to distinguish between the two (Figure 3-17) to properly determine the risks posed by their presence and the appropriate response from the beekeeper. Ants can be significant pests of bee colonies requiring the use of barriers to protect beehives (Figure 3-15) (also see Chapter 23 Figure 23-3). Also see Chapter 23 on how to reduce ant, termite and wasp pests around bees and beehives. Termites use wooden hive parts as their food source, causing great damage to wooden bee hives.

Figure 3-15
Tar or grease-covered legs keep ants out of a beehive, in Haiti.

Figure 3-16
Comparison of ant (left) and worker honey bee (right). Note level of constriction in body and degree of hair.
R. Weber

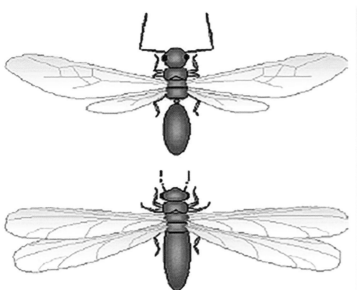

Figure 3-17
Differences between ant and termite. See Text.

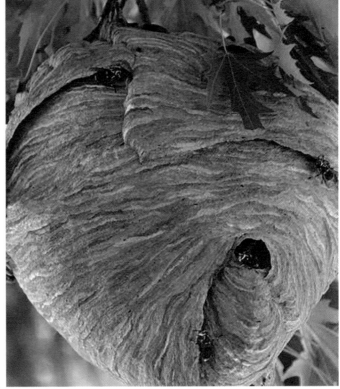

Figure 3-19
Bald-faced 'hornet' nest. T. Wessels

Figure 3-18
Yellowjacket feeding on a strawberry. L. Henrich

Why is sociality so common in Hymenoptera?

It is theorized that termites evolved in a social system because they must constantly pass the intestinal microbes they require to digest the cellulose (wood) they consume. But why is sociality so common in the Hymenoptera? Some general features considered as favorable characteristics toward evolving a social system in insects are:

• general food feeders—food source readily and easily available

• means of defense of a nest or food hoard

• food transmission or similar unifying behavior

• ability to store food for unfavorable conditions

• a method of reproducing the society more or less intact

• same or similar food habits of young and adults

• body structures and appendages adequate for manipulation

• selection of unifying characteristics of dispersion

• ability to evolve caste differentiation

• ability to generate and conserve heat

Box 6

CONTROL OF STINGING

WASPS AND BEES

Stinging wasps present a choice between the elimination of potential stinging pests and protecting insects that feed on caterpillars and other pests. Cicada killer wasps, spider-hunting wasps, and parasitic wasps are all beneficial. Most wasps hunt spiders, caterpillars, cicadas and other pest insects. Parasitic wasps are major biological agents in the battle against insect and arthropod plant pests.

While bees are valuable pollinators they may cause stinging episodes if in close proximity to humans and animals. Chemical control of bees and wasps is not often warranted and humans should be encouraged to leave them alone.

For ground-nesting aggregations of wasps or bees, you should weigh the economics of control with the beneficial work of the insects. Most bee and wasp aggregations are only temporary as their active flight season is usually very short.

Stinging insects must be correctly identified and the nest located. At the nest, beekeepers and pest control specialists must take proper precautions against stings and must work quickly and effectively to remove or eliminate the entire nest population to avoid a situation where humans and pets are stung.

To control yellowjackets, hornets, and paper wasps, locating and destruction of the entire nest population is often the only feasible control measure. In situations where the nest site is visually accessible, control is a relatively uncomplicated matter once precautions against stings are taken. There is no easy means of locating nesting sites except by careful examination of the surrounding area. Wasps tend to fly relatively short distances from their nest so efforts spent locating nest sites where they are troublesome pests may be worthwhile. Licensed and properly trained individuals can remove honey bee nests from buildings using special vacuum devices for a fee.

For wasps, after the nest is located and if an insecticide is going to be used, control should be done at night, approaching the nest as close as feasible to direct the insecticide into, not just on, the nest. For ground nests of yellowjackets, or aerial yellowjacket nests, apply the spray or dust to the entry hole. Make a loose dirt plug and spray or dust this plug well with the insecticide, closing the entry/exit hole with the plug. Repeat applications are frequently necessary. Apply

the poison quickly, within less than a minute, to avoid the aerial wasps escaping and stinging the applicator. For nests in buildings, spray as much into the opening as possible and soak the entrance area each time you spray.

If you only need to remove one or two nests, purchase insecticide aerosols formulated for hornets, wasps and bees. These aerosols spray up to eight feet in a stream rather than a fine mist and have compounds that ensure rapid knockdown. Do not use a water hose or flames to remove stinging insect nests as this may be extremely dangerous. Merely plugging the entrance without first killing the wasps is not adequate and potentially dangerous as they eventually chew their way out. For yellowjackets or bee nests in buildings, spraying the entry/exit area (or plugging it before adult removal) can lead to adults invading an interior room.

There are no effective area-wide control methods of wasps or bees though a number of approaches have been tried. Heptyl butyrate baits work moderately well in the western United States against the major yellowjacket species (*Vespula pennsylvanica*) but are not as effective in the east against other wasp species. Traps for bees do not out-compete flowers.

Commercial traps, using sweet food rewards, meat baits or fermenting mixtures are sold by manufacturers. Wasps are attracted and killed in large numbers, but control is only marginal at best. Traps attract yellowjackets to the area. If it is possible to locate the nest, control will be more effective. Unless a nest is built in an area where it will cause problems, it is usually best to leave it alone.

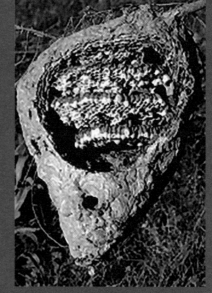

Figure 3-20
Cross section of aerial yellowjacket 'hornet' nest. Brood cells are vertical not horizontal.

Hymenopterans have such traits. Sociality is common in the order and is perhaps one of the reasons for the success of its members. It is staggering to think that one colony of driver ants contains more individuals than the number of lions and elephants on the entire planet or that there are more species of ants in a km^2 of Brazilian tropics than all the primates in the in the world. Sociality has indeed been a successful evolutionary route for the Hymenoptera.

Figure 3-21
Excavated ground yellowjacket nest, with paper envelope removed to show internal construction.
S. Repasky

key terms

aposomatic	dominance hierarchies	paper wasps	primitively/seasonally eusocial
branched hairs	eusocial	paralyzing wasps	quasisocial
carpenter bee	feral	parasitic wasps	scopa
caste differentiation	food hoarding	parasitoids	selfishness
caste system	food transmission	parasocial	semisocial
Ceratina	general food feeders	parental care	social wasps
chemical messages	heat generation/conservation	perennial life cycles	sociality
communal	hornets	plumose hairs	subsocial
cooperative care of young	meat eaters	pollen and nectar diet	termites aggregations
defense	*Osmia*	pollen-collecting hair	yellowjacket
defense with stings	overlapping generations		

review questions

Sociality occurs in many varieties and forms in the Animal Kingdom. Invertebrate societies are more rigid and defined than the vertebrate societies. Thus, while it is not possible to directly compare insects with humans in terms of their social structures, can you find similarities in how insect and vertebrate societies handle the necessities of reproduction, food acquisition, communication and how they maintain their social cohesiveness?

What are some of the reasons a social structure better equips a species to meet the requisites of life? Compare the chances for reproductive success of social insects compared to nonsocial species. Compare and contrast the eusocial termites, ants, bees and wasps. What differences exist between perennial and annual social organization?

There are eusocial bees and wasps and other bee and wasp species with other types of social interactions as well as solitary life styles. What are some of the differences and possible reasons for such differences? Identify the different terms used to classify insect societies. As hymenopterans, what characteristics do wasps possess that may facilitate evolution of sociality in the group?

Define wasp. Name some of the different wasps and describe their biology. Do the same for bee. If interested look up details on sociality of ants and termites.

exercises

Prepare a short essay or an outline for a group discussion about what evolutionary advantages social structure or specifically sociality in insects (or invertebrates/vertebrates) confers on success of a species. Alternately, focus on sociality in bees or wasps. Consult reference material and prepare an essay or an outline for a group discussion that includes features of the biology of species that are solitary, presocial, quasi-social and/or eusocial.

Examine adults, immatures and nests of social insects. This should include nests of bumble bees, wood drilled by carpenter bees, a mining bee or ground-nesting paralyzing-wasp nesting site (or above ground entrance), a yellowjacket nest, an aerial 'hornet' nest, a nest of the European hornet *Vespa crabro*, a paper wasp nest, potter wasp pots and mud tubes of mud dauber wasps. Not all will be available so some will need to be examined through literature or the Internet. During the season try to find as many nests and species of social wasps and bees as possible to observe their biology and nest construction and expansion (but be careful not to elicit nest defense behaviors). Prepare a reference collection or display of the social stinging insects and their nests.

Review the methods of bee, wasp, and ant nest/individual control. List some of the non-chemical control options. Interview a pest control operator (PCO) who controls such insects, or observe stinging insect control.

Using web sources follow the efforts in Washington and British Columbia to trap and eliminate the invader murder hornet *Vespa mandarinia*.

references

Hőlldobler, B. 1990. The Ants. Harvard Univ Press: Cambridge, MA

Hőlldobler, B. & E.O Wilson. 2009. The Superorganism: the Beauty, Elegance and Strangeness of Insect Societies. Norton, NY

Michener, C.D. 1990. The Ant. Harvard Univ Pres: Cambridge, MA

Michener, C.D. 1974. The Social Behavior of the Bees. Harvard University Press. Cambridge, MA

Ross, K.G. & R.W. Matthews. 1991 The Social Biology of Wasps. Cornell Univ Press, Ithaca, NY

Seeley, T.D. 2010. Honeybee democracy. Princeton Univ Press, Princeton, NJ

Squash Bee: Short animated link on Life cycle of squash bee https://ucanr.edu/squash_bees

Wilson, E.O. 1971. The Insect Societies. Harvard Univ Press: Cambridge, MA

Wilson, E.O. 1975 Sociobiology. Harvard Univ Press: Cambridge, MA

Figure 4-1
Worker bees festooning (hanging on to each other) while digesting honey, generating heat and eventually secreting beeswax scales from glands located on the underside of the abdomen (see Figures 4-6 to 4-8).
R. Williamson

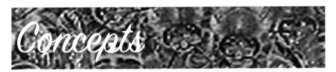

Concepts

Types of bees in a hive
 two sexes
 two female castes

Hive bees
 how they differ
 how they are alike

Field bees

Development of bees
 eggs
 larvae
 pupae

Seasonality

Queen, drone, worker

Ancient Greek and Egyptian mythology told of bees coming from cow or oxen carcasses while wasps originated from horses. This belief is often ascribed to Aristaeus, the rustic Greek God of beekeeping, honey and mead. In fact the scientific name *Apis* probably originated from the Greek 'oxen-borne bees.'

Aristotle believed bees obtained their young from plants such as reeds and olives and deposited them in the beeswax combs. Belief of spontaneous generation of these insects demonstrates that early observers of bees were aware of where insects might be found but had not yet discovered basic insect reproductive biology.

In order to understand reproductive biology, it is important to be able to distinguish between the adult members of bee society—the queen, worker and drone (Figures 4-3 to 4-5)—and their various developmental stages—egg, pupa and larva, collectively known as **brood** (Figure 4-2). The queen and workers are female, each with two sets of chromosomes. They are the members of the caste system characteristic of eusocial insects. The only males in the colony, with one set of chromosomes, are the drones.

The **queen** (Figure 4-3) is a fully-developed female whose two functions are to lay eggs and produce chemicals that help maintain colony cohesion and regulate colony reproduction. The queen is very specialized for these duties and cannot survive alone or perform her own feeding and grooming duties. She does not even leave the hive to excrete waste.

A colony typically has a single queen, although there may be short periods where this is not the case. Queens usually live two or more years when not stressed by parasites, diseases or environmental events.

Figure 4-2
A single nurse bee entering a brood cell of worker larva to feed it. Smaller larvae require fewer feeding visits than the larger larvae. R. Williamson

Another adult bee in a hive is the male bee or **drone**. The drone bee is bigger than workers and roughly barrel-shaped (Figure 4-4). He has very large eyes that meet at the top of his head. Drones are sometimes referred to as the drone caste, but they are a different sex, not a caste. The drone is a haploid adult, developing from an unfertilized egg, living an adult lifespan of a month.

Development of **haploid males** (through a process called **parthenogenesis**; possessing a genetic system called **haplodiploidy**) is unique to the Order Hymenoptera. Drones mate with virgin queens but do not work or assist in hive activities. As they mature, drones gather on pollen-filled frames outside the brood area to feed in preparation to mate, their primary function. They are active for two to four hours in the afternoon when they leave the hive to mate. They return every half hour, up to six times each afternoon, to refill their honey stomachs and return to mating. Few drones are successful, and those that mate die in the process.

Drones are an indication of plentiful incoming food resources. Worker bees monitor drone numbers, expelling drones from beehives as incoming food supplies dwindle as a dearth starts or as the weather cools before winter.

Most of the adult population in the beehive are **workers** (Figure 4-5). They are females but lack full development of their reproductive organs. Worker bees also differ in other anatomical aspects from queens. They are smaller

Figure 4-3
Queen bee on comb with worker bees. These are the two female castes.

Figure 4-4
Single drone bee on a comb of new beeswax. The drone is the male bee.

Figure 4-5
Worker forager bee with blue pollen from *Scilla*. All by L. Connor

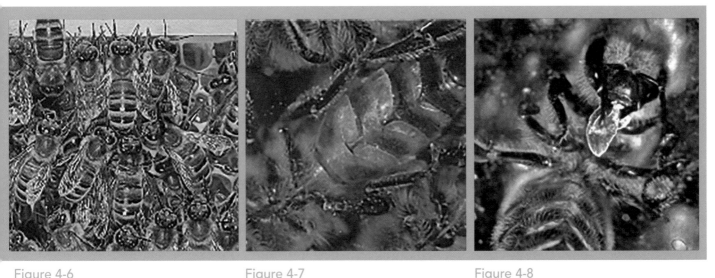

Figure 4-6
Workers festooning to secrete beeswax.

Figure 4-7
Four pairs of wax glands on the underside of the young bee.

Figure 4-8
Wax scale in the mandibles of a worker bee. All by R. Williamson

in size, possess corbiculae on hind legs, have more specialized mouthparts, and do not produce the same pheromones from internal glands as does the queen.

Hive bees

Unlike the other adult members of the hive whose functions generally remain the same through maturity, workers pass through a sequence of duties and behaviors. As they age, a hormone chemical **juvenile hormone (JH)** increases in their bodies, and their duties change.

When they emerge as adults, they initially remain in the brood area, avoiding light (**negatively phototactic**), feeding on the pollen stores nearby. As house bees, they function as the hive cleaners, cleaning the bottom and sides of the brood cells and nest.

After their initial feeding of the pollen stores, the **hypopharyngeal glands** in their head complete development. When these glands mature, they produce **royal jelly**, and the worker now functions as a **nurse bee**. They provision royal jelly to the youngest developing larvae (Figure 4-2). The older larvae are fed a mixture of pollen and diluted honey by slightly older nurse bees.

Nectar ripening is usually the next behavior a worker performs. At this point, a worker that is not feeding larvae leaves the brood area to position herself near the hive entrance to begin her next behavior. She meets

Figure 4-9
Guard bee at the hive entrance.

Figure 4-10
Nectar exchange between a field bee and a nurse bee (two pairs of bees are shown).

Figure 4-11
Bee fanning to cool hive and scenting to attract other bees. All by L. Connor

with field bees who have returned from foraging (Figure 4-10) and takes a partial load of nectar from their honey stomachs. She then carries the nectar to a quiet part of the hive above the brood area to begin active evaporation of the moisture content from the nectar. This nectar **ripening predigestion** begins the conversion of nectar into honey (Figure 17-2; also see Chapter 17).

Active evaporation consists of a bee regurgitating her honey stomach contents and blowing a series of bubbles to thoroughly mix the enzyme **sucrase** into the nectar. The bubble creates a large surface-to-volume ratio favorable to water evaporation in the warm, dry atmosphere of the hive. Next, she sucks the nectar back into her honey stomach. She repeats this process for 20 minutes or so and then hangs her bubble of now-ripening honey in an empty or partially filled cell where passive evaporation continues moisture reduction. Once ripened, the honey is finally consolidated into cells, and once filled, cells are capped with a thin layer of beeswax.

Meanwhile, other workers of this age are busy **processing pollen**. The field bees that have returned from foraging enter the pollen storage area, which is within or immediately outside the brood rearing area. Here, they reverse the packing action, freeing the pollen from their hind legs and dropping the pellets into a cell. As the pollen-collecting forager collects the pollen, she adds a small amount of honey to the pollen so it stuck together on her pollen basket. When each cell is about 3/4 filled and tightly packed, the adult worker preserves the pollen with a honey glaze over the top of the cell.

Other hive tasks of younger-aged workers include feeding the queen and removing her wastes, removing dead bees (**undertaker bees**), patrolling for invaders, resting, circulating air and scenting (Figure 4-11).

Bees 12 days of age are capable of wax secretion and can cap honey-filled cells as well as participate in the building of comb. Beeswax is produced in four pair of specialized wax glands on the underside of the worker abdomen (Figure 4-7). The wax scales are laminated and white when secreted. Using their legs, including the spine on the middle pair of legs, bees pass wax scales to their mouthparts. There, they add saliva and manipulate the scales into a pliable form.

Wax secretion and comb building are high priority tasks after swarming and when a colony is building new comb (as in package colonies and newly made nuclei). In a beekeeper's hive or when a colony is mature, the need for beeswax is generally low, so not all workers capable of producing wax do so.

Cells containing pupae (Figure 4-23) are capped with a mixture of reused wax (stored on the rim of the brood cells) and newly-secreted wax. The reused wax gives pupal cells their distinctive tan or brown color. Cell cappings over honey are usually entirely of new wax and therefore light in color (Figure 4-13). Capped honey cells do not usually show the distinct hexagonal outline whereas brood cells will.

After swarming and when a colony is building new comb (as in package colonies and newly made nuclei), wax secretion and comb building are high priority tasks.

By 18 days of age, adult worker bees become attracted to light (**positively phototactic**) and juvenile hormone and other chemicals trigger key behavioral changes. At this point, house bees can leave the hive entrance and perform outside activities such as orientation flights. Initially, a bee flies just in front of the colony's entrance. After some time, she progresses to circular flights around her home, eventually widening to flights in the surrounding area.

Figure 4-12
Worker bee using her proboscis (straw-like mouth parts) to gather water for the hive. S. Repasky

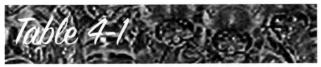

Table 4-1

Development time of the queen, worker and drone honey bee, in days.

Brood Stage	Queen	Worker	Drone
Egg	3	3	3
Larva	5.5	6	7
Pupa	7.5	12	14
Total	16	21	24

Home hive orientation is critical for individual bees. Some individual bees enter neighboring hives accidentally in a process called **drifting**. In an apiary, hives at the end of rows or adjacent to distinctive landmarks will usually gain bees from drifting, while hives in the middle rows tend to lose bees. Bees are generally accepted when they drift into other hives when they arrive with pollen and nectar. Guard bees can distinguish between disoriented drifting bees and **robbing bees**: enterprising foragers from other hives intent on robbing honey from the hive. The guard bee's role is crucial as an intense robbing frenzy may cause an entire colony to perish.

Guarding the entrance is an important activity for bees aged 18-21 days (Figure 4-9). Guard bees are usually present at the hive entrance at all times. They smell each individual that enters the colony, and they will challenge any individual that does not possess the distinctive odor characteristic of their hive.

Hive odor is a composite odor from both the queen pheromones and the food collected by the workers (see discussion of pheromones in Chapter 7). Guards are usually present all the time at a hive entrance.

Field bees

By 21 days of age, bees have performed a number of hive duties and are now ready to begin **foraging** (Figures 4-12, 4-14). Field bees forage for one of the four materials needed inside the colony — pollen, nectar, water and plant resins. Foraging is a hazardous duty as bees can get lost while out, may starve if they can't find their way back or be eaten by numerous predators along the way.

A field bee lives 10-21 days and then dies with exhausted flight muscles and torn wings. In winter, adult bees may live six months or more as their reduced hive and field duties impact hormone levels that delay the aging process, enabling the bees to survive longer through the winter and into spring.

It is not correct to assume that all the bees work nor that all bees do all duties. There is a great deal of learning involved to perfect some of the behaviors. Scientists have wondered how, in fact, all the tasks do get done because there is variation in individual bees. Some behaviors are strictly related to glandular activity (nursing and wax secretion for example) while others are not.

Conditions within the hive and in the forage situation outside the hive frequently change, and bees can modify their duties so all the work is done. For example, brood rearing dramatically increases in the spring when many adult bees are older. Some of the bees delay foraging to help provision the larvae as 'over-aged' nurses. Alternately, an abundant floral resource may suddenly become available, and hive bees may shorten their hive duties and become 'precocious foragers,' after only one

Figure 4-13
Worker bees capping honey. L. Connor

Figure 4-14
Forager gathering pollen. R. Williamson

Figure 4-15
Pollen storage. L. Connor

week of adult life. There is considerable flexibility within the hive and in field worker behavior.

Immature bees or brood

The three development stages in bees are collectively known as **brood** (Figure 4-19 to 4-23). Bees begin their life in the tiny white **egg stage** (Figures 4-19, 4-20). A queen will deposit one egg in each worker or drone cell (Figure 4-25 top). The eggs are deposited vertically, and with a diameter about the size of a pin, they are very difficult for a beekeeper to see upon inspection.

Worker eggs are fertilized (diploid) while those that will yield drones (haploid) are not. Queens selectively lay larger eggs in queen cups which influences both gene expression and the adult weight of the queen. We cannot tell the difference between fertilized and unfertilized

eggs but the bees can. When the queen places a fertilized egg in a drone cell, the egg or larva is removed and destroyed by worker bees.

The egg stage in bees lasts three days (Table 4-1). When an egg **ecloses** (often termed hatching but there is no membrane rupture, merely a melding of egg into larva) it becomes a larva (Figures 4-20, 4-22).

The **larval stage** of the bee has virtually no external and few internal features (Figure 4-27). It is a legless white grub whose body is a series of folds (Figure 4-20, 4-22). The digestive tract has only the single mouth opening; it does not complete development into a tube until just before the larva changes to the pupa. There are four Malpighian tubules that maintain salt and water levels. It is specialized to eat and never leaves its individual

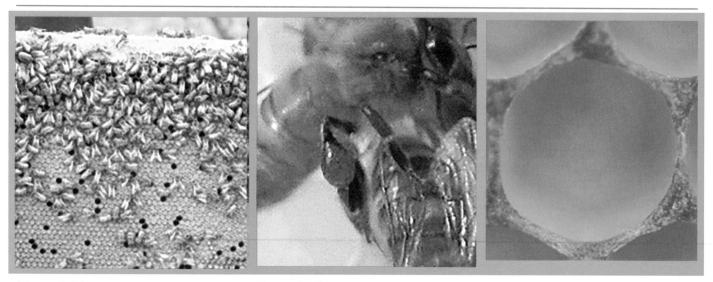

Figure 4-16
Brood frame with sealed brood. L. Connor

Figure 4-17
Forager with propolis on her hind leg. L. Connor

Figure 4-18
Propolis on the ends of brood cells strengthen cells and cappings. L. Connor

Figure 4-19
Eggs on a black wax comb. R. Burns

Figure 4-20
Eggs and larvae. Tucka Bee

Figure 4-21
Queen larva's silk threads. L. Connor

wax cell. Larvae grow at a rapid rate in a five instar or step development or metamorphosis, increasing 1,500 times its original size. During their development the larvae are visited up to 10,000 times by adult nurse bees for inspection, feeding and eventually capping of the cells. Larval food is placed in the cell—small larvae are not directly fed (Figure 4-25, middle bee).

Because their **chitinous shell** is soft, larvae swell is size until hormones trigger the molting of each **instar**. A new soft shell forms under the old one, but it is larger and allows for immediate growth and expansion of the larval body.

Once feeding and growth is completed, the digestive tract connects to the anus, and the larva defecates in the cell. The fecal matter defecated by the larva is

incorporated into a thin silk cocoon. This silk (Figure 4-21) is produced in the special silk (saliva) gland of the **prepupal stage**. The cocoon encloses the pupa and does not eat or move once it is completed. The last larval molt encloses the larva into a **pupa** (plural: pupae). The larval stage lasts seven days for drones, six days for workers and five and a half days for queens (Table 4-1). If brood nest temperature drops, development takes longer or stops altogether. The pupal stage is also termed the **capped brood stage**; after the larva defecates, worker bees will cap the cell using new and recycled wax (Figure 4-25 F).

The silk (Figure 4-21) is produced in a special silk (saliva) gland of the **prepupal stage**. Drones spend seven days as larvae, workers six days and queens five

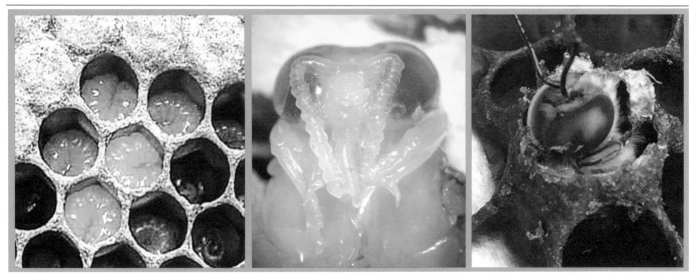

Figure 4-22
Larvae 72-96 hours old. Tucka Bee

Figure 4-23
Developing drone pupal head and legs. L. Connor

Figure 4-24
Emerging drone bee. L. Connor

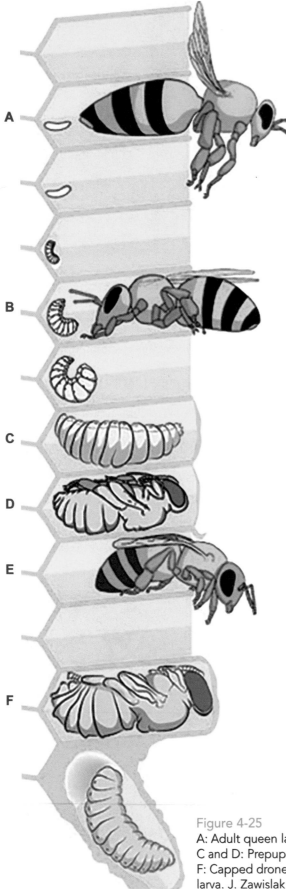

and a half days (Table 4-1). If brood nest temperature drops, development takes longer or stops.

The last larval molt (eclosion) to a **pupa (plural: pupae)** (Figures 4-25 D). The pupal stage is also termed the **capped brood stage**; workers add a protective capping wax. Juvenile and ecdysone hormones trigger such changes. Once feeding and growth is completed the digestive tract connects to the anus and the larva **defecates** in the cell. The worker bees cap the cell with new and recycled wax. The pupa does not eat or move once the cocoon is completed.

The pupa of the bee gradually assumes the features of the adult through cell division and differentiation. The early pupa does not resemble the adult while the final pupal stage clearly has all the major adult features. Once the pupa completely transforms, the adult bee emerges without help from her sister adults (Figure 4-5, E). During the final pupal stage the wings expand from **wing buds**, filling with **hemolymph** to expand the wings. After they reach full size, the hemolymph is forced out of the wings as they become thin and membranous. The cell pattern of the wings are unique for each subspecies of honey bee, and are used to identify bees by race. This cell pattern is the basis of a system used to identify the Africanized honey bees in North America.

While not all insects have a **four-stage development** termed **complete metamorphosis**, the majority (flies, beetles, butterflies and moths) do. Table 4-1 summarizes the length of development time for the two female castes and the drone brood stage for bees. Queens have the shortest developmental time. Is that because they are so essential to brood production and colony growth?

The transformation from egg to emerging adult requires 16 days for the queen, 21 days in the worker, and 24 days with drones (Figure 4-25). Notice the drone cell is bigger and capping is higher than the worker cell cappings.

Differentiation of queen and worker

Both female caste members—queen and worker—begin as fertilized (diploid) eggs. The transitional pupal stage follows the feeding of the larva to become the complicated adult form (Figure 4-24) within the capped beeswax cell. The differentiation of the two castes occurs during the few days of larval development. It is a biochemical process not completely understood.

All bee larvae (female and male) receive **royal jelly** after the egg encloses. Royal jelly is a protein-rich food

Figure 4-25
A: Adult queen laying egg. B: Nurse bee provisioning larva.
C and D: Prepupa above pupa (capped stage); E: Adult worker emerging head first.
F: Capped drone cell immediately above vertical queen cell with five-day old queen larva. J. Zawislak

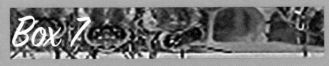

SEEING IS BELIEVING

The egg is the starting point in the life of the honey bee. It is incredible that the tiny egg contains all the genetic material that will yield the marvelous behaviors, intricate morphology and complex life of the adult. Which of the three hive adults the egg becomes is determined by both genetic and nutritional factors.

Honey bee eggs are tiny (Figures 4-19, 4-20, 4-26, 4-28). They are about 1.7 mm long by 0.4 mm wide (25 mm equals one inch). Length and width vary considerably, but interestingly, drone and worker eggs are essentially the same size. It is not known if egg size is a factor in adult size; it is likely that food quantity and quality during the larval stage and cell dimension are more important in determining final adult body size. At eclosure (hatching), larvae are very small and nearly impossible to see floating on a pool of royal jelly. They quickly grow to fill the cell.

Egg eclosure is a function of the temperature of the brood nest and the genetic makeup of the population. It's known that eggs of the Africanized bee in the Americas eclose into larvae in an average of 70-71 hours. The European bee averages 72-76 hours when the temperature is 94.6° F (35° C). Male (unfertilized) eggs require three additional hours. Temperatures lower than normal result in reduced egg eclosure; below 85.6° F (30° C), less than 1% of honey bee eggs will eclose. Eggs that do not eclose, such as when the brood is chilled on cold spring or fall nights, are removed by the workers.

Honey bee eggs are positioned upright at the bottom of the cell by the queen. Thus, we are looking at the diameter of the egg when we peer down into the cell (Figures 4-20, 4-26, 4-28). Since adult worker bees are plentiful in the brood area, seeing the eggs is often a real challenge. To improve chances of seeing these tiny eggs, look on a bright, sunny day. Position the sun or bright sky over your shoulder behind you, then grasp the brood frame firmly and turn it so the light penetrates to the bottom of the cell such that the surface is not in your shadow. Search carefully—after you see your first egg, it will be easier the next time.

Although it is not easy to see the eggs of honey bees, it is a necessary beekeeping skill. Develop the practice of checking to see if eggs are present every time you look

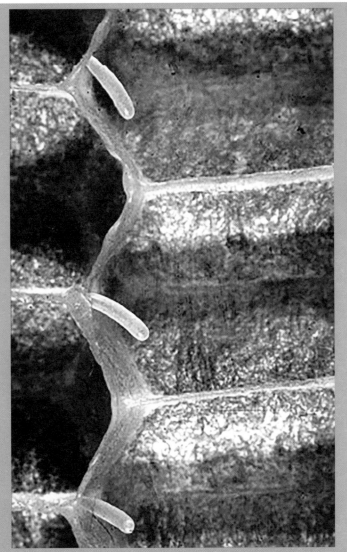

Figure 4-26
Cross-section of cells with eggs, which stand upright until eclosure. R. Williamson

in the brood-rearing area of the colony. If you have never seen eggs, ask a fellow beekeeper to point them out to you. Many local beekeeping associations have meetings in an apiary. This is an excellent time to get some help spotting eggs.

What do you do on a dark day or when the sun is not shining or it is too early or too late to see eggs and small larvae? Many beekeepers carry a headlight or a high intensity flashlight with them to the bee yard. Or use your cell phone's flashlight to see the eggs. Keep your phone handy, in an outside pocket, to see the eggs and larvae, or, in case of emergency, to call for help or 911.

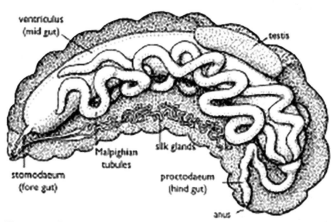

Figure 4-27
Drone bee larva internal anatomy. From H. Dade *Anatomy & Dissection of the Honeybee,* International Bee Research Association.

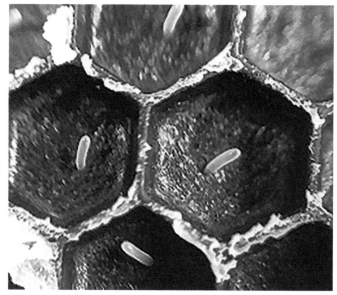

Figure 4-28
Eggs in worker cells, on black plastic foundation. L. Connor

made in the glands of worker bees and placed in cells just before eclosion. Initially the cell with a young larva is **mass provisioned**. A pool of royal jelly is kept replenished in the bottom of the cell, and the C-shaped larva simply lies in a pool of its food (Figure 4-29). After two and a half to three days, however, the diet of the worker and drone larva is changed to a mixture of pollen and nectar and food is not so generously supplied. This is called **progressive provisioning**. The queen larva is provided a diet of royal jelly, in generous supply, throughout her entire larval life.

Something in the different quality and quantity of diet results in differentiation of a queen from a worker. What exactly it may be is not known. Several conflicting theories attempt to explain the reason for the differences. Evidence is strong that **caste determination** is controlled by **juvenile hormone (JH)** levels. Worker larvae consume less food in response to lowered JH levels whereas queen larva continue high food intake leading to increased growth and differential gene expression necessary for queen development.

Figure 4-29
L: Egg. M: Larva floating on a bed of royal jelly. R: Older larva, about three days after egg ecdysis (hatching). J. Zawislak

Experiments have demonstrated that adults with both worker and queen characteristics (intercastes) can be produced in a lab when the royal jelly diet or JH levels are modified during the critical last three days of larval development. The longer a larva eats royal jelly, the more queen-like her adult form. One recent hypothesis is that a specific protein in royal jelly, called **royalactin**, is the compound that induces caste determination. When fed to fruit flies, individuals developed different body structures and lived longer. There are other competing theories, each with some supporting experimentation, but the exact factor or factors still remains to be shown.

An important difference leading to **worker-queen differentiation** for the bees is the type and orientation of the cell of developing larva and worker. Worker bees develop horizontally in hexagonal cells of approximately

Figure 4-30
Drone pupa at the purple eyed stage. L. Connor

and they feed the developing larva accordingly. How they detect the age of worker and drone larvae in order to change their diet from royal jelly to the pollen/nectar mixture is not known.

Superorganism

Jurgen Tautz, Tom Seeley and other researchers reason that a bee colony accomplishes its tasks far beyond the behaviors of the individual family members. They label the bee colony a **superorganism**. In this view, the bee colony functions more like a single complex organism possessing thousands of individual 'cells.' Cells are specialized in a complex organism to do things like see, digest, secrete chemicals, etc. Individual bees in the bee colony specialize to accomplish necessary tasks, joining nest mates to collectively guard the colony entrance, feed the specialized dietary material, royal jelly to the very young, clean, store reserves and make the beeswax cells, the food containers.

Perhaps the greatest 'cell' of all is the queen. By herself she is the sole reproductive 'organ' of the superorganism. She produces the eggs and holds the sperm to fertilize those eggs, stored from matings with multiple drones. When one bee dies, only one cell of the superorganism

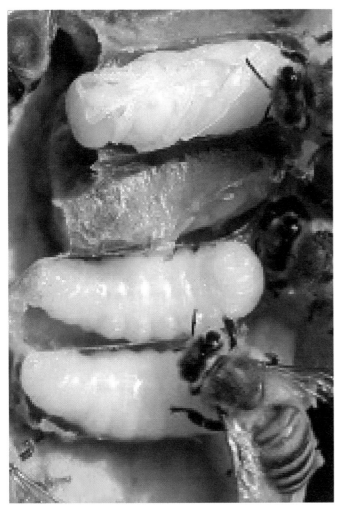

Figure 4-31
Four bees in the process of larval completion and pupation. Top bee is approaching the purple eyed stage as a pupa. Second bee has spun a cocoon and has pupated or is about to. Third and fourth bees are still in the late larval stage. These are apparently all drones. L. Connor

0.2 inch (5 mm) diameter (5 cells/inch). The queen measures the cell opening with her front legs as she inspects each cell prior to laying her egg. If a cell is 0.25 inch (6 mm) wide (4 cells/inch), she puts an unfertilized egg in the cell and a drone develops in this slightly larger sized cell. Drones, like workers, develop horizontally.

A queen develops in a vertically-oriented cell, appropriately called a **queen cell** (Figure 4-15 lowest cell). The existing queen herself lays fertilized eggs in special cup-like structures, called **queen cups**, oriented vertically on the face of the comb or, more usually, at the bottom margin of the comb. Upon hatching, the queen larva is vertically positioned. She is held inside the queen cell due to surface tension and a narrowing of the developing queen cell to an approximate peanut shape as the larva grows.

The orientation and different cell sizes are important to workers. They recognize what type of bee is in what cell

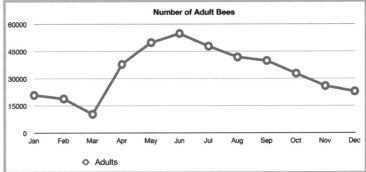

Figure 4-32
Typical seasonal fluctuation of the adult bee population of a bee colony. There is considerable variation based on local floral conditions, genetic stock of the bees and other factors. L. Connor

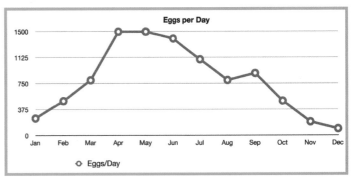

Figure 4-33
The eggs a queen lays per day reflects seasonal growth of worker brood population. There may be a spring sub-peak followed by a decrease in April. Other areas may have a sub-peak in September as shown here. L. Connor

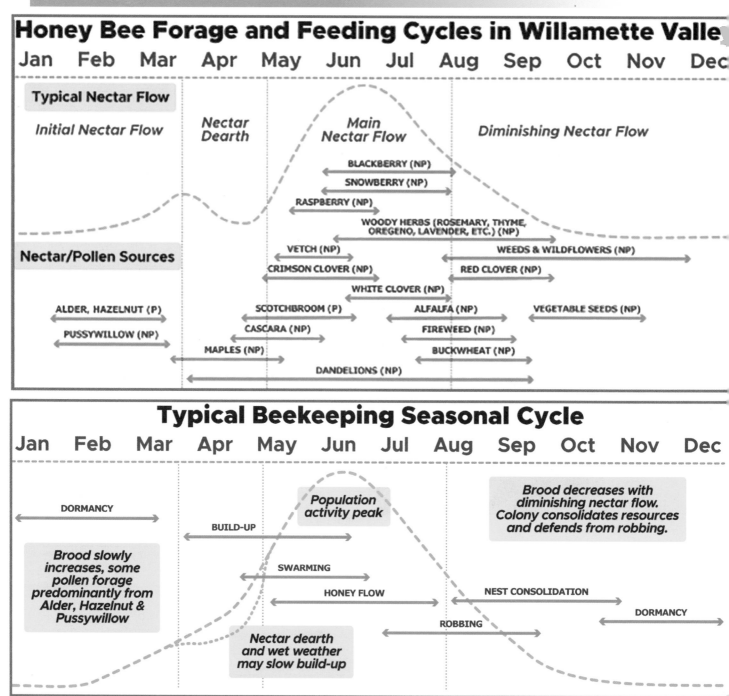

Honey Bee Forage and Feeding Cycles in Willamette Valle

| Jan | Feb | Mar | Apr | May | Jun | Jul | Aug | Sep | Oct | Nov | Dec |

Typical Nectar Flow

Initial Nectar Flow | Nectar Dearth | Main Nectar Flow | Diminishing Nectar Flow

BLACKBERRY (NP)
SNOWBERRY (NP)
RASPBERRY (NP)
WOODY HERBS (ROSEMARY, THYME, OREGENO, LAVENDER, ETC.) (NP)
VETCH (NP)
WEEDS & WILDFLOWERS (NP)
CRIMSON CLOVER (NP)
RED CLOVER (NP)
WHITE CLOVER (NP)

Nectar/Pollen Sources

ALDER, HAZELNUT (P)
SCOTCHBROOM (P)
ALFALFA (NP)
VEGETABLE SEEDS (NP)
PUSSYWILLOW (NP)
CASCARA (NP)
FIREWEED (NP)
MAPLES (NP)
BUCKWHEAT (NP)
DANDELIONS (NP)

Typical Beekeeping Seasonal Cycle

| Jan | Feb | Mar | Apr | May | Jun | Jul | Aug | Sep | Oct | Nov | Dec |

DORMANCY

Population activity peak

Brood decreases with diminishing nectar flow. Colony consolidates resources and defends from robbing.

BUILD-UP

Brood slowly increases, some pollen forage predominantly from Alder, Hazelnut & Pussywillow

SWARMING

HONEY FLOW

NEST CONSOLIDATION

DORMANCY

Nectar dearth and wet weather may slow build-up

ROBBING

Figure 4-34

A seasonal population graph. The orange lines show adult population. Top graph shows timing of major flowering plants (line length gives seasonal variation) with bee stewardship activity schedule added to lower graph. Appropriate for Willamette Valley of Oregon. Based on work of G. Hansen. Redrawn by J. Zawislak.

perishes, while the much larger organism is still buzzing with life. It is the whole that is more than the sum of its parts that characterizes a bee colony.

Dead bees

Often, dead adult and immature bees can be found in a colony, especially near the bottom. Worker bees produced during spring and summer die after five to six weeks as adults. Bees produced from late summer to fall will live

into the winter, ensuring the colony is strong enough to survive until spring. Most dead bee bodies are promptly removed from the colony—as as flight permits—by **undertaker bees** who fly the bodies a considerable distance away. Bees die during the winter and when a colony suffers loss from pesticide sprays, pests, a virus epidemic or due to high numbers of parasitic mites.

Figure 4-35
Two conflicting instincts are at work here. Forager worker bees are collecting and storing nectar in the cells at the top of the photo. At the same time the nurse bees producing royal jelly are stimulating the queen to lay eggs as seen at the bottom of the photo. This boundary is in constant flux, as the brood needs are balanced against the amount of food collected by the colony. T. Lane

Seasonality of brood and adult populations

Beehive populations fluctuate during the year according to the seasons and food resources (Figures 4-32, 4-34). The queen usually lives for a couple of years (in temperate areas at least) and is replaced during favorable foraging conditions during the season. The number of workers fluctuates considerably during the season. Drones are produced and eliminated in a seasonal pattern determined by resource availability.

There are seasonal fluctuations in worker adult and brood numbers in temperate climate areas. In January and February, the worker adult population has decreased to its seasonal low when a colony may have fewer than 10,000 bees. During April, May and June, the adult bee emergence rate exceeds the death rate, and the population grows rapidly. An average peak population of 40-60,000 bees is achieved sometime in June. Weaker colonies either have a lower peak population or reach their largest size later in the season.

The adult population remains high before dropping during July and August. Italian bee colonies stay larger than colonies of other races. The time of the nectar flow has a great influence on populations during the summer and workers may compete for empty cells with the queen's egg laying (Figure 4-35).

Some colonies show another increase in adult bees in the early fall before the numbers make their final decline for winter. The bees are stimulated by blooming periods of major fall nectar and pollen sources, fitting into the colony's need to produce well-fed fat bees for winter.

Bees in tropical or subtropical areas also have a seasonal cycle but their cycle is dependent on dry and wet seasons. Populations are largest when forage is abundant. In northern temperate areas, seasonality is more pronounced and linked to increasingly longer days. The whole cycle may be more concentrated into a shorter spring-summer fall season. Colonies in more northerly areas tend to grow faster and reach a larger population size than colonies in tropical or subtropical climates.

The brood cycle is also seasonal (Figure 4-33). In January, many colonies possess very little worker brood as this is often when the season begins. No drones or queens are raised at this time. With increasing day length and especially the availability of early pollen, the rearing of brood increases rapidly. Few eggs are cannibalized and the queen increases her egg output according to the behavior of workers (Figures 4-28, 4-33) who care for her and clean cells for egg deposition. A queen may produce 1,500 to 2,000 eggs/day — about her own body weight in daily egg production.

Figure 4-36
Swarm on a grape vine. R. Keller

Brood production continues at a high level during the summer months, although at a rate below spring levels. The number of brood cells in use can reach 40,000. There may be an early peak followed by a dip—when egg cannibalism increases or, in early fall, a second peak in brood rearing to rear fat bees when new pollen sources are available. Rearing of brood falls rapidly as food resources decline with colder weather.

Both drones and queens are also seasonally reared. Drone brood begins in the spring as food resources become reliable. Drone production is often a precursor to the development of swarm cells and swarm production. Some colonies rear more drones than others depending on colony resources, their genetic instincts and the availability of drone-sized cells. In feral colonies, bees raise more drones but only under favorable food conditions. Under normal circumstances, drone brood significantly slows or stops completely in the early summer. Late summer/early fall drones may be produced if resources become available. This is often linked with a fall swarming season.

The amount of drone brood reared varies. Drone adults appear 24 days after unfertilized eggs are laid by the queen. Depending on food availability, drones are usually present in colonies until the fall. Some colonies eliminate all their drones each fall as food resources dwindle, so adult drones decrease in numbers very rapidly from mid-September into October. Drones do not appear until next spring. Colonies that are without a queen retain drones for a longer period. Colonies with drones in the late winter are often queenless.

Queen replacement is seasonal. When weather and food resources allow, a colony may swarm or replace a queen by supersedure. Swarming is more common during population buildup in the spring from mid-April to mid-June (Figure 4-36). During the summer, supersedure is more common than swarming. Except under very unusual circumstances, a bee colony does not rear queens during the fall, winter or early spring months. Colonies manipulated to be queenless will produce queen cells at any time if food reserves are adequate (Chapter 10).

Fat (fall or winter) bees

In the fall workers need to suspend the aging process to live five or six months compared to five weeks of the normal adult life span experienced during the summer. We speak of these fall-reared bees as **fat, winter or long-lasting bees (diutinus)** and the colonies as fat (heavy) with stored honey and at least a frame filled with the equivalent of stored bee bread.

We cannot recognize a fat bee in the fall—they look the same as bees produced in the spring and summer. They have fat bodies with storage of **glycogen** and **vitellogenin** as a body reserve (Chapter 5 Figure 5-18 They also work much less, feed many fewer larvae, do not produce wax, mold it into comb, forage or convert nectar to honey.

Bee stewardship

Successful beekeeping is based on a solid understanding of bee activities. Being able to interpret the sequence of duties that worker bees pass through—overall bee development—is the key aspect of bee biology that forms the basis of bee stewardship.

Equally important is the understanding of the seasonal cycle of your specific area. Using local data and observations, you should be able to create graphs like Figures 4-32 to 4-34 for your own area so you can coordinate colony management with local pollen and nectar flows. Beekeepers will find the best results when they anticipate their local nectar and pollen flows.

It will take experience and requires practice.

key terms

active evaporation	drone	glycogen	larva
bee bread	ecdysone	guard bees	life cycle
brood stage	eclosure	haplodiploidy	metamorphosis
buildup	egg	haploid males	microbes
caste	egg laying rate	hemolymph	mortality rate
cocoon	fertilized/unfertilized egg	hive bee	nectar ripening
developmental time	field bee	hive odor	nest consolidation
dormancy	forage cycle	hypopharyngeal glands	orientation flights
drifting	foraging	juvenile hormone	oxen-borne bees

parthenogenesis	prepupa	robber bees	virgin queen
passive evaporation	progressive provisioning	royal jelly	vitellogenin
phototactic	pupa	sucrase	wax glands
pollen collection	queen	swarm season	wing buds
precocious foragers	queen cell/cup	undertaker bees	worker

discussion questions

How can you tell the difference between the three adult members of a bee colony? What are the differences in brood development in the three members of the hive? Why is understanding these distinctions so critical to successful beekeeping?

Explain the typical sequence of duties of the worker adult honey bee. How can you tell which activity an adult bee is performing? What are some of the factors influencing adult behavior? Make a list of words that modify honey bee (such as nurse, forager, guard, undertaker, etc.).

Both queen and worker bees are females but they look very different and they perform different functions. Describe some of the functional and behavioral differences between the two caste members. Sometimes the drone is incorrectly termed a third caste member—why is this designation incorrect?

Table 4-1 and Figures 4-25, 4-33, 4-34 summarize brood development. How else would you seek to illustrate brood development in honey bees? Are there other aspects of brood that should be included in these summaries? How might you illustrate adult worker duties?

Re-read Chapter 1 on seasonal population management as a key to successful beekeeping and then discuss how knowledge of adults, worker task sequence, brood development and seasonality all fit together to be important for successful beekeeping.

exercises

Visit a beehive or examine an observation beehive. Find the three adult members and differentiate between the three brood stages present. If weather does not permit, view one or more films or video clips about honey bees concentrating on the biology and behavior of the hive members and the rearing of brood.

Establish an observation beehive (see Webster and Caron, Observation Bee Hives, 1999). Using resource material determine how you can distinguish the behavior of worker bees as they perform different duties. Prepare a typical activity chart using the data you collect from observations of bee activities.

List at least 20 aspects of bee biology that can be described as fitting the 'rule of three' (i.e. three adult bees, three brood stages, three egg days, three weeks for workers to develop, etc.).

Develop a journal and follow the annual cycle of a honey bee colony or one of a social relative (bumble bee, paper wasp, aerial yellowjacket).You will need access to the nest to make your observations throughout a season. An observation hive can be used for honey bees. Be careful as all the social insects sting—you need to plan carefully so you can collect data without releasing stinging behaviors.

references

Ellis, J. 2015. The members of a honey bee colony. American Bee Journal 160 (6) June

Ellis, J. 2015. The tasks of a worker bee. American Bee Journal. 160 (8) October

Gary, N.E. 2015. Activities and Behavior of the Honey Bee. In The Hive and Honey Bee. Chapter 10. Dadant & Sons, Inc

Brood development video, National geographic: https://www.youtube.com/watch?v=f6mJ7e5YmnE

Schneider, S. 2015. The Honey Bee Colony: Life History. In The Hive and Honey Bee. Chapter 10. Dadant & Sons, Inc

Tautz, J. 2008. The Buzz about Bees: Biology of a Superorganism. Springer-Verlag

Webster, T. and D.M. Caron. 1999. Observation Bee Hives. A.I. Root Co. Medina, OH

Wei, H. et al. 2019. A Maternal Effect on Queen Production in Honeybees. Current Biology 29, 1–6

Winston, M. 1991. The Biology of Honey Bees. Harvard University Press, Cambridge, MA

Figure 5-1
Worker bee gathering water. You can see the head on the left (with eyes, antennae and mouthparts). Wings and legs attached to thorax. The abdomen is on the right. Note the bee is 'tasting' the water with both antennae. A. Connor

Concepts

Insect body plan
  three body regions

Honey bee anatomy
  head
  thorax
  abdomen

Queen/worker/drone differences

Internal anatomy by system

Gland system

Three body regions

The anatomy of any animal is the assemblage of structural parts that enables the animal to maintain its own existence and to reproduce. The adult honey bee follows the general plan of an insect, but is equipped with unique structures that enable it to live within its particular environment. The combination of both the fundamental insect parts, as well as the bee's specialized structures and anatomical modifications, help the honey bee adapt to its manner of living and differentiate it from other insects.

This chapter and the next discuss anatomy and physiology of honey bees. This chapter features adult and larval morphology (anatomy)—the physical aspects of the bee's body. Chapter 6 covers honey bee physiology, the functional workings of the bee's body.

The honey bee has the typical segmented insect body of three regions: head, thorax and abdomen (Figures 5-1, 5-2). The body appendages (one pair of antennae, two pairs of wings and three pairs of legs) are also segmented. The **open circulatory system** inside the body circulates blood freely in a large cavity, not within arteries and veins. The alimentary canal is a tube. Paired openings to the respiratory system, the **spiracles**, are evident on two thoracic and seven abdominal segments. The body is **bilaterally symmetrical** (a single cut through the body length results in two nearly equal halves).

Exoskeleton and body hairs

On the outside, the honey bee has a hard outer body covering or **exoskeleton**. This protective covering functions as the body skeleton. Insects do not have internal 'bones' as in humans. The exoskeleton consists of hardened plates connected by more flexible membranes between for movement, something like a medieval knight's suit of armor.

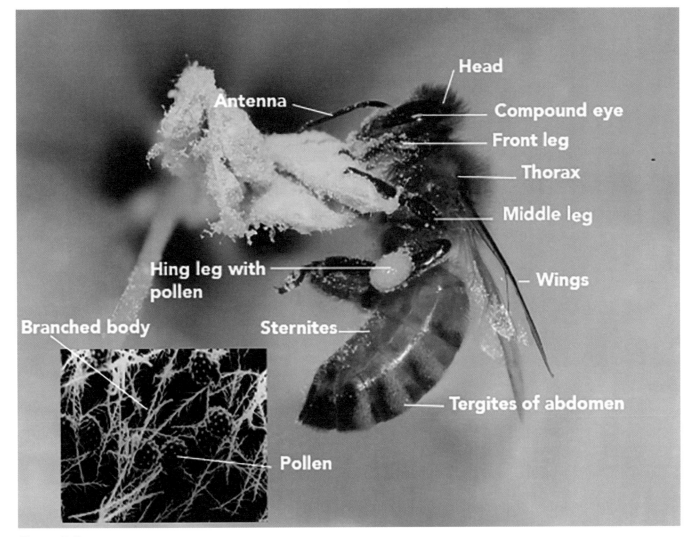

Figure 5-2
Honey bee worker on *Datura*. L. Connor photo. Inset. Branched body hairs holding pollen grains.

Often called the insect's 'shell', the rigid exoskeleton is resistant to physical and chemical harm. The exoskeleton also protects the animal from **desiccation** (drying out). Special ingrowths, called **apodemes**, serve as the anchor places for the bee's muscles.

The exoskeleton is made of **chitin**—a long-chain polymer comparable to cellulose in plants—and **sclerotin**, a class of protein molecules. During **metamorphosis** from pupa to adult, the bee's body darkens through a process called **sclerotization** that also strengthens the body. Even the wings of a bee are made of very thin layers of chitin and sclerotin. This protective layer extends internally within the bees's body to form the breathing tubes or tracheae and also lines the fore- and hind-gut.

Body hairs generously cover the exoskeleton of the bee. These are structured something like a feather with a main shaft and numerous side branches (Figure 5-2 inset). Such hairs, a bee exclusive, are termed **plumose hairs**. They give bees a hairy or fuzzy appearance. These hairs protrude from all portions of the exoskeleton, even between the facets of the compound eyes. Body hairs have sensory functions, enable the bee to collect and transport pollen, help protect the bee, help regulate body temperature and keep the exoskeleton free of dirt and debris.

Head

The head (Figure 5-3) of the honey bee contains major sense organs, structures that detect stimuli, such as rays of light or chemical odors. The major sense organs of the bee head are the ocelli, compound eyes, antennae, mouthparts, and body hairs. Each sense organ consists of millions of smaller receiving structures located on the exoskeleton. These are minute and most are not visible except under a microscope.

In addition to the regular body hairs, there are smaller hair-like structures, tiny pits, minute protruding pegs and flat, smooth disks. The flat disks are called **sensilla**, and contain openings that allow the bees to detect odors,

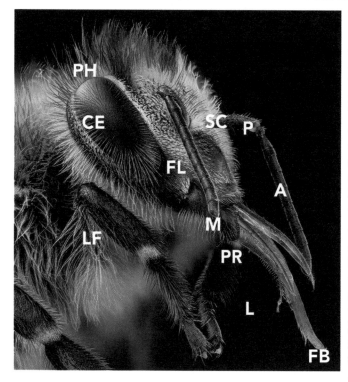

Figure 5-3
Parts of the worker's head (USGS Bee Inventory and Monitoring Lab). *Label Code:* A antennae, FL flagellum, L labial palp, LF leg, front, CE compound eyes, SC scape, FB flabellum, PH plumose hairs, P pedicel, M mandible, PR proboscis.

both good and bad (Figure 5-17). Sensory structures serve to inform bees about their environment.

Honey bees have three **ocelli** arranged in a triangle at the top of their head. The exact function of each ocellus is unknown. They respond to and receive light but these structures do not allow bees to 'see' as the transparent exoskeleton is not directly connected to the nerve area.

Ocelli help bees respond to light levels. Newly emerged bees are initially **negatively phototactic** but become attracted to light as they age. Bee species that fly under low light levels have large, prominent ocelli.

The honey bee has two **compound eyes**; workers have about 5,500 facets and drones have 10,000. Each **facet** is a lens of transparent exoskeleton capable of 'seeing' at a fixed focal length with only fair vision. They actually 'see' by assembly of a mosaic of hundreds of different facets from the large optic lobes of their brain. As the bee moves, and as things around the bee move, the view of each lens changes, improving visual ability. Bees can distinguish between patterns as long as they are sufficiently different in amount of brokenness. If bees could read, this type would need to be some 100 times larger for the bee to distinguish the different letters.

Bees have **trichromatic apoposition vision**, meaning that their eyes contain three types of photoreceptors (cone cells) just as ours do. Unlike humans who have blue, green and red cones, bees have blue, green and ultraviolet photoreceptors. This means that the vision of bees is shifted toward the ultraviolet compared to ours. Bees see in range 300-650 nanometers while human range is 400-700 nanometers (Figure 5-4). Many flowers with a uniform color pattern to humans have a distinctive bullseye or target patterns as a bee sees it. A comparison of the color vision of bee and humans is shown in Figure 5-5.

Each **antenna** (plural: antennae) consists of 12 segments. The first segment (**scape**) is the longest and the most flexible. It is positioned midway on the head, fitting into a **ball-and-socket joint**. The **pedicel** is a flexing elbow joint. The last 10 distal segments (**flagellum**) are of nearly equal size (Figure 5-6). Each antennae is completely covered with hairs (Box 8, Figure 5-17), pore plates, pits, pegs and other sensory structures that perceive stimuli. The antennae of bees are very mobile and in constant movement.

Antennae smell, taste (Figure 5-1), perceive humidity and temperature, feel (touch), monitor gravity, compute flight speed and even detect sound waves (vibrations) to help guide bees in their daily activities.

Mouthparts
The mouthparts of the bee are complex structures located on the bottom margin of the head (Figures 5-3

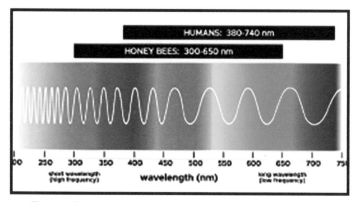

Figure 5-4
Top: Comparison of the visual range of humans; Below: with that of bees. J. Zawislak

Figure 5-5
Comparison of silverweed, *Potentilla anserine*. As we humans view it on the left and as bees view it on right. B. Roslett

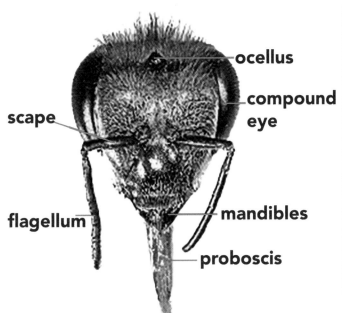

Figure 5-6
Worker head. From I. Stell, *Understanding Bee Anatomy.*

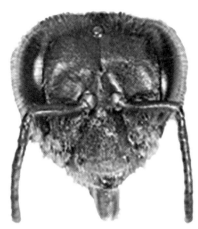

Figure 5-7
Queen head. From I. Stell, *Understanding Bee Anatomy.*

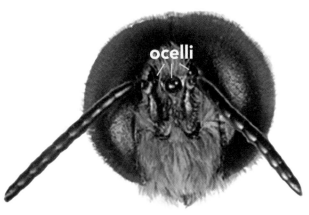

Figure 5-8
Drone head. From I. Stell, *Understanding Bee Anatomy.*

Figure 5-9
Honey bee worker using proboscis to collect a drop of honey. R. Williamson

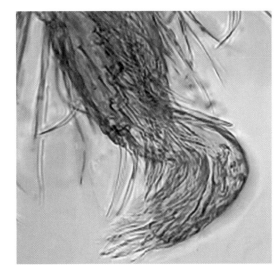

Figure 5-10
Spoon-shaped flabellum at the tip of the tongue. From I. Stell, *Understanding Bee Anatomy.*

and 5-6 to 5-9). Bees have **chewing-lapping mouthparts**, which means they can manipulate solids and lap up liquids (Figure 5-9). Basically, the mouthparts consist of four parts. The **labrum** is the front-most portion. It serves as a protective shield closing the mouth cavity, something like the upper lip of humans. The **mandibles**, one to a side, are the 'jaws.' They move laterally and are mainly used to form and manipulate wax. They have sharp edges but lack muscles strong enough to chew through or seriously bite anything. They are spoon-shaped, resembling cement trowels, better suited to smooth and carry rather than chew or cut. The remaining distinct mouthparts, the **maxilla and labium**, contribute to form the **tongue or proboscis**.

The proboscis is a sucking tube with an inner and outer chamber ending in the spoon-shaped **flabellum** (Figure 5-10). The labium has paired segmented **palpi** (singular: palpus) that resemble antennae but only have three small segments. Palpi and the **hairy glossa** have many taste, smell and touch sense organs. When not in use, the proboscis folds into an area beneath the head, so the mouthparts are not visible unless extended.

Internally, most of the head cavity is occupied by gland systems, muscles of the antennae and mouthparts, plus the bee brain. In the center, the proboscis ends in a muscular pharynx that sucks fluid up into the mouth and digestive tract. The various glands of the head discharge their contents via small ducts into the mouth cavity just before the pharynx. Major head glands are the mandibular, hypopharyngeal, post-cerebral and thoracic (salivary) glands, the last pair extending into the thorax.

Queen and drone head

The head of the queen (Figure 5-7) is similar to that of the worker (Figure 5-6), but theirs is a little rounder in shape when viewed from the front. They have about 1000 fewer eye facets, and their mandibles are toothed rather than spoon-shaped like the worker's. The toothed mandibles are used to chew holes into unemerged queen cells.

The drone head (Figure 5-8) is the largest, and their compound eyes are twice as large as the worker's, containing more (about 10,000 total) and larger facets. The ocelli are displaced downward to allow the compound eyes to meet at the top of the head. Drone antennae are one segment longer, for a total of 13, and slightly thicker than in the worker. Drone mandibles are smaller, not spoon-shaped and have teeth on the outer margin.

Thorax

The thorax (middle body region) is the locomotor section of the honey bee body (Figure 5-1). The thorax consists of three body segments, although on close examination it appears that bees have four segments. Anatomically the fourth segment is actually the first abdominal segment. The segments are labeled the **pro-, meso- and metathorax**. Attached to the meso- and metathoracic segments are the **two pairs of wings**. Each segment has a pair of legs, the norm in insects. The exoskeleton of the thorax, shaped like a box, consists of many plates (sclerites) that overlap and serve as attachment points internally for numerous muscles.

The wings of the honey bee are paired, with the first pair being the largest. Each wing has numerous hollow lines or 'veins' on its surface carrying nerves and through which blood circulates into the wing. The veins define a network of 'cells' that provide support and a framework to the wing. When the bee is in flight, the wings are

joined by a tiny set of hooks, **hamuli**, extending forward from the back wing (Figure 5-11). Joining the wings increases flight surface, helping give bees their great flight agility.

Bee flight is accomplished by indirect wing muscles. Flight muscles do not attach directly to the wing itself as one might expect because wing attachment points are very narrow. Rather, the flight muscles are located in the thoracic segments and occur as complementary pairs, one pair running front to back, and the other, top to bottom (Figure 5-12). Small direct muscles fold wings over the abdomen.

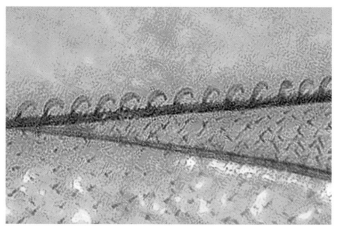

Figure 5-11
Hind wing of the honey bee, showing veins and the hamuli, the tiny hooks located along the upper edge of the wing. As flight begins, the hooks fasten onto the bottom of the front wing to prevent the wings from beating against each other.

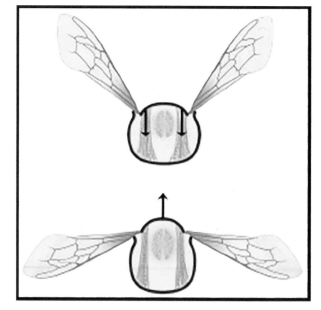

Figure 5-12
Diagram of indirect wing muscles. See text description.
Redrawn from R. Elzinga by J. Zawislak

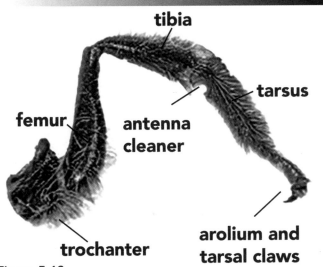

Figure 5-13
The front leg of a worker. From I. Stell, *Understanding Bee Anatomy.*

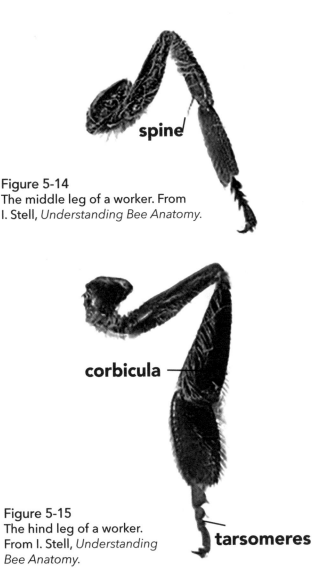

Figure 5-14
The middle leg of a worker. From I. Stell, *Understanding Bee Anatomy.*

Figure 5-15
The hind leg of a worker. From I. Stell, *Understanding Bee Anatomy.*

To fly, the muscles that extend from top to bottom contract while the front to back set of muscles relax. This results in the thorax being pulled from top to bottom and pushed out at the ends, causing the wings to be pulled upwards at their attachment points. Then the other muscles (those front to back) contract and the top to bottom set relax. The thorax is now pulled from the ends, and the top and bottom of the thorax pops outward so the wings go down. By alternating contraction and relaxation of the muscles, wings go up and down and flight result. The wings have a hardened anterior edge and are flexible posteriorly. They flex, roll and vary their surface exposure as they are moved up and down in a figure-eight pattern.

The honey bee, like all insects, has **three pairs of legs**. A pair of legs is attached to each of the three segments of the thorax. Legs obviously serve locomotion, but they also contain sensory structures for taste, smell and touch. Although six legs may seem awkward for walking, they are coordinated by the nervous system to operate as a pair of triangles. The first and third leg of one side work with the middle leg of the opposite side.

Each leg consists of five major segments: coxa, trochanter, femur, tibia and tarsus—with further segmentation of the most distal tarsal section. Legs end in a pair of claws with central **arolium**, a softer, pad-like structure. Legs have body hairs modified to groom the bee body.

The **forelegs** have the **antenna cleaner**, an indented area with special stiff hairs of the indentation that clean the antennae of debris when they are drawn through the hairs (Figure 5-13).

The **middle pair of legs** have a stout spine which is used to spear wax scales from abdominal wax glands to pass to the mouthparts (Figure 5-14).

The **hind legs** of workers have modified body hairs arranged in special patterns to help the bee collect pollen. Body hairs line the outside edge of the tibia, the fourth distal segment. The structure formed is called the **corbicula or pollen basket** (Figures 5-1, 5-15). Pollen is carried in this structure from flower to hive. On the inner surface of the next distal segment, the **basitarsus**, the body hairs are arranged in compact rows (combs). These hairs collect and accumulate pollen grains. Other hairs located at the top margin, the rake and auricle (the **pollen press**), push and pack pollen from the inner metatarsus to outer corbicula.

The **esophagus** (oesophagus) of the digestive tract and aorta of the circulatory system are thin tubes passing through the thorax (Figure 5-16). The ventral nerve cord consists of one large ganglion and a second smaller ganglion that receives sensory neurons from the wings and legs and sends impulses via motor neurons to wing muscles and legs to coordinate movement of the bee.

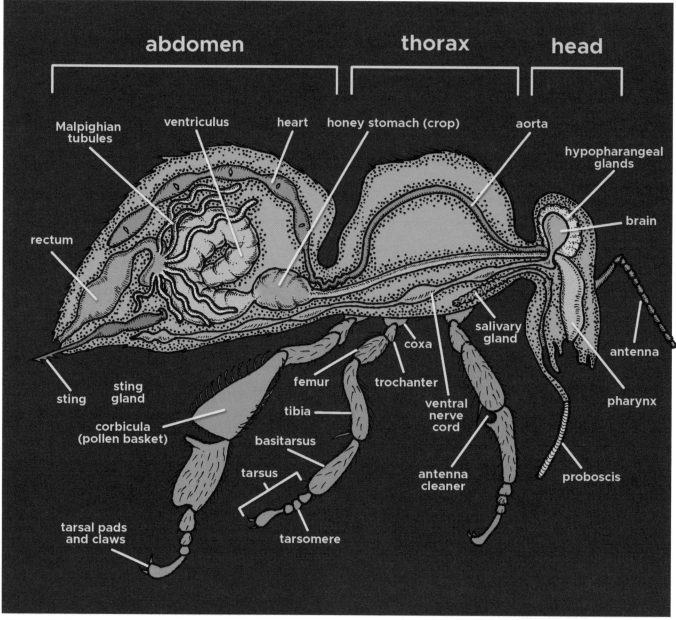

Figure 5-16
Section of honey bee worker showing major internal organs. J. Zawislak

Abdomen

A prominent feature of the honey bee body is the narrow segment, termed a **wasp-waist**. It does not represent separation of thorax and abdomen but rather it separates the first and second segments of the abdomen. Thus three thoracic and one abdominal segment are anterior to this 'waist,' followed by continuation of the segments of the abdomen termed the 'gaster'. The reason for this or the significance of such a body narrowing is not known.

Virtually all hymenopterans have a thin waist. In some hymenopterans (such as mud daubers) the restricted portion is very long, reaching 1/2 inch (1 cm) or more in length (Chapter 3, Figure 3-9). Portions of the internal systems that must fit through this narrowing are the

nerve cord, the esophagus and the aorta, which for unknown reasons, is coiled at this point (Figure 5-16).

The **abdomen** lacks external attachments. When closely viewed, the seven visible abdominal segments (three are hidden) consist of overlapping top (tergites) and bottom (sternites) sclerotized plates (Figure 5-2). Each abdominal segment has a pair of **spiracles**, the openings of the respiratory system connected internally with three on the thorax. The abdomen is continually moving due to flexible membrane joints between segments. Movement is side-to-side, up-and-down, and in-and-out (telescoping). Such movement aids breathing, digestion, excretion and circulatory functions. The hidden segments of the narrow posterior tip form the honey bee sting in the female and drone mating genitalia.

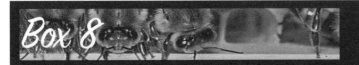

Box 8

BEE SENSES

Vision and chemical senses of smell and taste are important to honey bees. Touch or mechanoreception is also important. Bees have touch sensors on antennae, mouthparts, tarsi and elsewhere on the exoskeleton. They also have internal sensors. Using nerve impulses, mechanoreceptors perceive and transport mechanical energy to the nervous system. They can be very general, such as body hairs (setae) for touch, or very specific, such as proprioreceptors, that provide information on the relative position of parts of the body. These sense cells stretch from one body region to another or one body part to the next. They respond to pressure or changes in stress.

Special mechanoreceptors are used for measuring distances. On the antennae, specific hairs respond to wind as both air speed and air current indicators. As a bee flies through the air, these hairs, and perhaps other sense cells responding to energy use, provide the bee with a measure of flight distance. Bees also can measure distance by walking, which they use in measuring the internal dimensions of a potential cavity for a new nest site.

As the bee moves, hairs on different body regions change contact with hairs (called bristle fields) on an opposing body region. Bees use this touch information to detect gravity. Bees need excellent gravity-detection ability. Other uses of gravity information are not certain. In a NASA space study, a small colony of 3,400 bees and a queen were able to construct comb and survive without apparent ill effects for seven days without gravity.

Other specialized mechanoreceptors on the bee's body detect vibrations which pass through a substrate. This is how bees hear. We now know they are capable of perceiving airborne sound waves. Specialized hairs in the pedicel of the antennae (Johnston's organ) detect air pressure oscillations over a very short distance. It is thought this is how bees gather information from dancing bees. The bees 'hear' a bee's waggling in the wagtail dance and can measure how long it lasts. Bees perceive substrate vibration very well. Most beekeepers avoid jarring or bumping movements when working around bees to help reduce the chances of alerting bees and being stung.

The sense of time is understood in bees as an internal mechanism. Bees accurately time the waggling of dancing bees. They know sun passage time; they have been observed to return to an experimental feeding station at the same time each day to collect sugar syrup fed only at that time. Remarkably, if bees are imprisoned on their way back from a foraging trip, they accurately compensate for the passage of time, giving the correct sun time in their dance, even if not allowed to see the sun's new position when released to dance.

Two of the newest discoveries in bee senses are the realization of their ability to detect magnetic and electrical fields. Bees have special iron deposits in their fat bodies that perceive magnetic force fields and pass this information on to the nervous system. This sense may be used in flight (by birds at least); bees probably use it to align their parallel beeswax combs. How they detect or use electrical field information is not well understood.

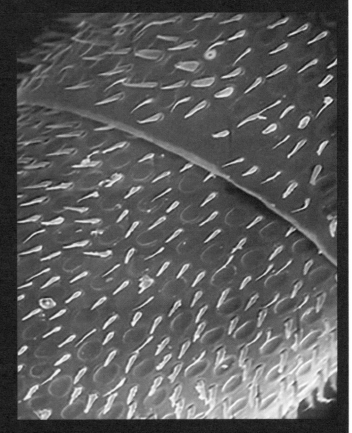

Figure 5-17
Close-up of sensory hairs and oval plates on bee antenna.

Digestive and excretory systems

The major internal body systems of the bee are located in the abdomen. The digestive and excretory systems are shown in Figure 5-16. After food enters the body at the mouth, pulled inward by a **muscular pharynx**, it passes through the thorax and wasp waist within the **esophagus**.

The first section in the abdomen is called the **honey stomach**, but it is not a true stomach. There is no consumption or digestion; the honey stomach simply stores and transports nectar collected at flowers before it is converted to honey. Nectar stored here can be returned (regurgitated) back into the mouth then given to another bee in the hive. This action has earned the name 'bee spit' for honey. The actual eating of food is a different behavior completely separate from the collecting of food.

The honey stomach is closed by a muscular valve called the **proventriculus**. When the bee eats food (versus when it collects nectar from a flower), the valve is opened and the food (honey or pollen) passes immediately to the mid-portion—the ventriculus, mid-gut, or stomach. **Digestion**, the process of breaking complex foods down into their simpler components, occurs in the **ventriculus**. The ventriculus is coiled and averages about twice the length of the bee body (Figure 5-16).

The digestive tract expands with the **posterior intestine or rectum**. The rectum reclaims reusable products and reabsorbs water to make a semisolid excretion. **Rectal pads** aid in reclaiming and recycling water. The digestive tract tube ends at the **anus** through which semi-solid wastes are excreted. Bees usually void wastes while in flight.

There are around 100 **Malpighian tubules** connected to the digestive tract between the ventriculus and intestine. These are the main excretory organs. They are long, tube-like structures that are suspended in the body cavity to take waste matter from the blood. Wastes are accumulated in each tubule and then dumped into the digestive tract as uric acid. These wastes then pass into the rectum where any valuable ions, minerals and water are reabsorbed before excretion.

Fat body

The top of the honey bee abdomen contains the **fat body**, a specialized section of tissue that holds fat cells, as well as glycogen, protein, and high concentrations of mitochondria and enzymes. The fat body functions much like the human liver and fat storage. The fat body develops by the end of the larval stage, when nutrients needed during pupation are stored under the outer layer of the larva's body. When the adult emerges, the fat body is only in its abdomen. During the winter the fat body stores energy and nutrients needed over several months.

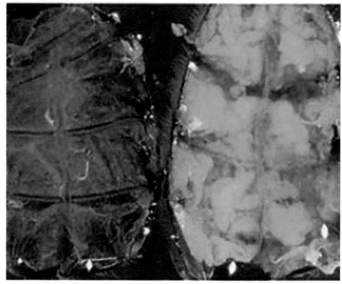

Figure 5-18
The fat body is the tissue immediately under the dorsal abdominal sclerites. The bee on the left is a forager, and has used most of the fat body. The bee on the right is a bee ready for winter, called a fat bee. I. Keller et al. *Bee World*

During the summer the fat body is smaller or even non-existent.

Our appreciation of the fat body came about with the discovery by Dr. Samuel Ramsey while at the University of Maryland that the varroa mite feeds on the fat body and not on the hemolymph or blood of the adult worker bee. The fat body contains more nutrients than the hemolymph and speeds varroa growth and development. Heavy mite feeding helps explain colony weakening and collapse. This also explains some of the abrupt colony collapses that beekeepers find by the end of fall when stronger hives (big in numbers and resources) end up dying before even getting to winter (See Chapter 19).

Nervous system

The nervous system includes a **two-part brain,** with **optic and antennal lobes** in the head and a series of seven ventral ganglia in the thorax and abdomen (Figure 5-19). The honey bee has a large brain and ganglia relative to its body size. The brain coordinates overall functions and has nerve centers for vision, smell, taste and touch perception.

Nerves from each ganglion extend to the major organs of the respective body segment to regulate their activities. As in all insects, each ganglion of the nervous system is capable of coordinating functions for the segment in which it is located. It can also send information to other ganglia and to the brain to unify the behavior of the whole individual. The last ganglion coordinates the complicated behavior of stinging. Headless bees can still walk and sting, although not as well as with intact brain.

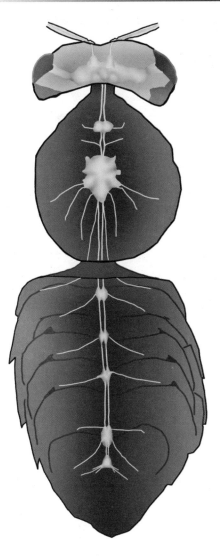

Figure 5-19
Brain, thoracic and abdominal ganglia of the honey bee. These are the major components of the nervous system in the honey bee. I. Stell, *Understanding Bee Anatomy.*

Circulatory system and hemolymph

The circulatory system is very simple in the bee, as in all insects. The major organ is a **five-chambered heart** and a single tube, the **aorta**, that carries blood, hemolymph, forward to the head (Figure 5-16). The heart, positioned dorsally in the abdomen, has a series of muscular chambers, each with a pair of openings. When the heart muscle is relaxed, blood enters the five chambers from the abdominal body cavity. These openings close when the heart muscle contracts forcing blood forward through the aorta to the head. Once in the head, the blood is free in the body cavity. It sloshes around percolating backward to the abdomen, aided by breathing and abdominal movements, to be sucked into the heart to repeat the circuit.

Insect blood carries nutrients to the body cells and removes cellular wastes. It also carries hormones, blood cells and other substances. The nutrients enter the blood

when absorbed from the digestive tract. Blood contains a large variety of cells but not oxygen-carrying red blood cells. The blood, therefore, is not red, nor must it circulate rapidly. This type of circulatory system, called an **open circulatory system**, serves the needs of the bee even though it is much simpler than the closed human circulatory system with arteries and veins.

Respiratory system

The respiratory system of the bee is considerably different from the human system. Insects have three thoracic and seven abdominal air openings, called the **spiracles**, and internally many air sacs that lead to branching tubes or **tracheae** (Figure 5-20). Oxygen moves through **tracheal air sacs** and into and out of tracheae with wing and abdominal muscle activity. The tracheal system branches into even finer tubes, the **tracheoles**. A **tracheal tube** runs alongside each and every living cell

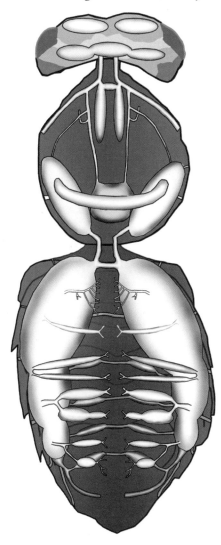

Figure 5-20
Tracheal tubules and sacs oxygenate internal organs I. Stell, *Understanding Bee Anatomy.*

Figure 5-21
Queen honey bee. There are no pollen-collecting structures on the legs. USGS

Figure 5-22
Drone honey bee. Note large eyes, large antennae and barrel shaped body. No pollen-collecting structures on legs. USGS

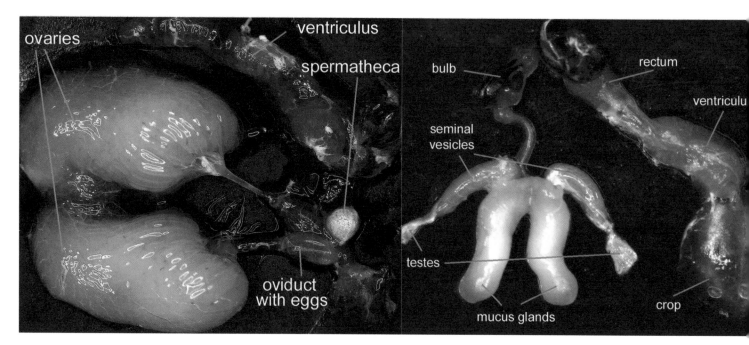

Figure 5-23
Paired ovaries in a laying queen honey bee: Each ovary consists of up to 200 ovarioles, the egg-producing structure of the bee. Eggs pass down the lateral and median oviduct to the spermatheca where sperm are released through the spermathecal duct for the female castes.
A. Collins, USDA

Figure 5-24
Mature, sexually active drone: The digestive system (right: crop, ventriculus and rectum) has been spread out separately from the reproductive system. The white mucus glands are very distinct from the tan seminal vesicles filled with semen. The testes have shrunken following sperm migration to the seminal vesicles. A. Collins USDA

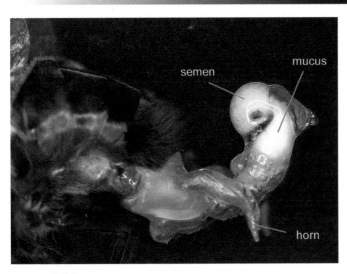

Figure 5-25
Ejaculated drone endophallus showing semen, mucus and horn. A. Collins, USDA

of the bee to carry the oxygen to each site. Waste carbon dioxide returns through the same tubes. Thus oxygen and carbon dioxide travel in the gaseous state to and from the cells rather than being bound in red blood cells as in humans. Cellular metabolic activity in bee and human is otherwise similar.

Reproductive structures

The reproductive organs are also located in the abdomen. The female worker bee's ovaries are undeveloped and appear threadlike under normal colony conditions. In laying workers, ovarioles are evident. In the queen, the reproductive organs are very large and occupy a much larger amount of space (Figure 5-23). The eggs of mated queens develop in hundreds of thread-like **ovarioles** in the **ovary** and, when mature, pass into the oviduct where they are fertilized by sperm which are stored in the round **spermatheca**. When ready, the queen deposits eggs into comb cells.

The male drone have two testes and a large sperm delivery organ, the **aedeagus** (Figure 5-24, 5-25). After emerging from their pupal cells, young drones require about 12 days for the sperm to migrate from the testes to the seminal vesicles where they are stored prior to ejaculation. During this time, the drones must feed on pollen to provide the energy for this sperm migration.

Sting structure

The sting is a highly modified portion of the reproductive system (Figures 5-16, 5-27, 5-28). The sting is anatomically an ovipositor. While in most female insects the ovipositor is used to lay eggs, in the female honey bee the ovipositor has lost this function.

Sting glands produce a protein chemical, **apitoxin** injected into the victim accompanied by the release of

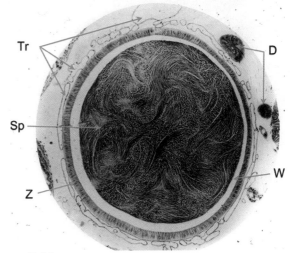

Figure 5-26
Cross section through a spermatheca, showing sperm with their long tails. D, spermathecal duct, Tr, trachea, Sp, sperm Z, membrane and W for spermathecal wall. G. Koeniger

alarm pheromones which serve to attract other worker bees to assist in defense.

Muscles attached to the sting help drive it into the victim. In worker honey bees strong barbs on the stinger lodge in thicker materials like human or animal skin, which cause the sting to tear loose from the bee's abdomen leading to the bee's death in minutes. Queen honey bees, bumble bees and some wasps like yellow jackets have smoother stings with smaller barbs permitting the stinging of and removal of the sting from insect or mammal skin without killing the insect. Queen honey bees use it to eliminate rival queens.

Gland systems

Glandular activity is extremely important to honey bees. The gland systems of the bee are complex and well developed. **Endocrine glands** secrete hormones that are key to the functioning of chemical processes. **Exocrine glands** open to the outside and produce **pheromones** that strongly influence many aspects of bee behavior. Other glands produce products that bees use in their nest while others regulate various metabolic processes. Bees could not survive without glands. The major glands are shown in Figure 5-29.

The bee head has several important glands. The **hypopharyngeal** (or maxillary) **glands** are above the pharynx. They secrete a sticky, milky fluid that we call **royal jelly** or 'bee milk.' The secretion is high in sugar, protein and vitamin content and is a complete food. Worker and drone larvae receive royal jelly the first two to three days of development while developing queens receive it their entire larval life.

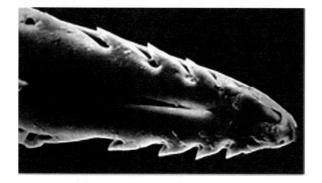

Figure 5-27
Worker sting showing barbs along two of the three sting shafts.

As with other gland systems, the hypopharyngeal glands are not completely developed when the adult bee emerges from her brood cell. Also called **brood food**

glands, they resemble miniature strings of onions or grapes (acini) and develop after the bees feed on pollen. They secrete **royal jelly** for a few days and then become less active. These glands only develop in workers; they are absent in drones and rudimentary in queens.

There are two pairs of **labial (salivary) glands**. The first pair is sometimes called post-cerebral glands, referring to their position in the head. They produce a watery saliva that is used to dilute food and hold pollen grains together. Their primary function is in the digestive processes. They secrete **sucrase** (sugar breakdown), lipase (fat digestion), amylase (starch digestion) and other enzymes. These enzymes convert the carbohydrates of nectar and the fat of pollen into substances useful for the bee.

The **mandibular glands** of queen bees are a major source of the **queen substance pheromone**. This pheromone is the key substance responsible for the social cohesiveness of the bee society. This material is only secreted by queens. In workers, the mandibular gland secretions helps with wax molding and also secretes **2-heptanone**, a material used in alarm communication. In drones, these head glands are rudimentary.

The main glands in the abdomen are dorsal abdominal **tergite glands, ventral wax glands, the scent gland and sting glands** (Figures 5-28, 5-29). The wax glands are found on the inner surfaces of four ventral sternites of the bee abdomen (Figure 5-30). Each is paired and secretes wax. The wax forms as scales that protrude from the overlapping sternite of the previous segment. Very young or old bees do not secrete wax. Bees 12 to 16 days of age have the greatest degree of wax gland development. Only worker bees have wax glands. After manipulation with their mandibles, the bees use the wax to make beeswax combs or cap brood or honey-filled cells.

The **scent or Nasonov gland** (Figure 5-31) is on the dorsal side of the abdomen connected by a tiny groove to a membranous area. Bees fan their wings and depress the tip of the abdomen to disperse the scent when they release the pheromone. The secretion is a mixture of terpenoids; two of the chemicals, citral and geranic acid, are most attractive to bees. Newly-emerged bees have little to secrete; maximum levels are reached in foraging-aged bees. In winter, the level of secretion is low.

The scent-gland **pheromone** is used to attract workers to food and to help lost and/or disoriented bees locate home or food. It is released most frequently at water sources, around a hive (especially in disorderly or confusing conditions), during swarm movement and at the swarm settling site. New nest sites are also marked with the pheromone. It may be released at flowers, but apparently this is not frequently done.

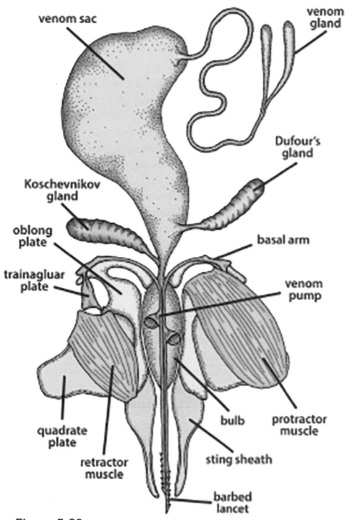

Figure 5-28
Sting structure. The venom sac stores the venom, while the muscles drive the barbed lancets into the skin, as the venom pump continues to inject venom. Compiled by J. Zawislak

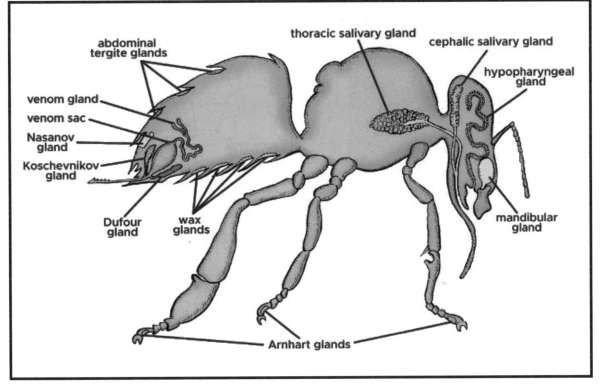

Figure 5-29
Glandular system of the worker bee. Redrawn from M. Winston by J. Zawislak

The worker has a series of glands associated with the **sting** (Figure 5-28). Two are individually termed **Dufour's** and **Koschevnikov glands**. A pheromone is released when a bee stings a hive intruder. The pheromone that causes **alarm behavior** is **isopentyl acetate**. Young bees have little of this material while older bees have 1-5 mg. In addition to release on stinging, workers elevate the tip of the abdomen and protrude the sting with a droplet of venom towards the disturbance on a cold winter day.

The **venom or acid gland** is the largest of the four sting glands. It produces a mixture of enzymes and proteins that result in the release of **histamine** in a victim and, in allergic individuals, a more serious allergic response. Other glands have unknown functions, perhaps connected with egg laying or sting lubrication. Queens have sting glands but produce no alarm pheromone

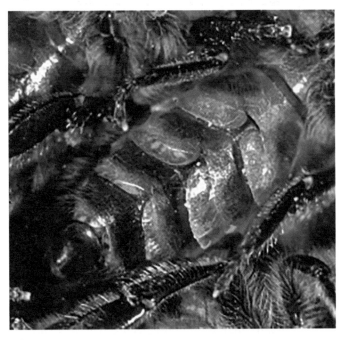

Figure 5-30
Wax glands. R. Williamson

Figure 5-31
Scenting with Nasonov gland at tip of abdomen. R. Williamson

Box 9

GLAND AND BEE DEVELOPMENT

Growth and development of the glands in the honey bee's body are regulated by three main organs. Hormones originate in endocrine glands. Neurosecretory cells in the brain release brain hormone in response to both internal and external stimuli. The hormone travels to small glands, the corpus cardiaca, where it is released into the hemolymph (blood) of the bee. The brain hormone from the corpus cardiaca acts on the prothoracic gland, a small area of glandular tissue in the thorax that is hard to identify. These glands produce ecdysone (molting hormone). This hormone travels in the blood and ends at epidermal cells of the exoskeleton. Ecdysone is the message to begin the process of molting. Another brain gland, the corpus allata, secretes juvenile hormone into the hemolymph. Juvenile hormone also travels in the blood to the epidermis cells of the exoskeleton. It suppresses the expression of adult characteristics.

Juvenile hormone and ecdysone together control growth and development. Whether the larva molts to a larger larva or proceeds to the pupal stage depends on the balance between ecdysone and juvenile hormone.

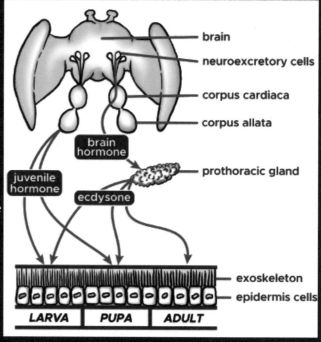

Figure 5-32
Interaction of structures in the endocrine glands.
J. Zawislak

Prior to the molt to pupa, juvenile hormone production ceases so its level in the blood goes down and the next molt produces the adult bee from the pupa. Juvenile hormone production returns during the adult stage when it regulates egg development, worker duties and queen aging.

and their venom gland contents are different from the workers.

Bees have glandular tissue on the thorax, lower tip of the abdomen and probably elsewhere on their bodies. One pheromone chemical bees utilize is called **footprint substance**. It is from the **Arnhart (or arolium) gland** of the tarsi of the ultimate segment of each leg, deposited as the bee walks and moves about. This pheromone is attractive to other bees who can smell and perhaps also taste it. It is used to mark home and food sources.

There are other pheromone-producing glands. Internally, other neurosecretory and endocrine glands produce hormones to regulate physiological, developmental, and behavioral events in honey bees. Enzyme-producing glands connected with the epidermal cells and internal systems function in digestion, development and detoxification.

Other queen and drone differences

The queen and drone bee differ somewhat in body details. The queen has a longer abdomen due to the large ovaries and the drone has a large barrel-shaped abdomen to house his reproductive organs. The queen has a long, smooth, curved sting which has tiny barbs that do not remain in victims. The drone is stingless. Both drone and queen lack the specialized body hairs on the legs since neither collects pollen. Their mouthparts do not work as well as those of the worker, and they have smaller honey stomachs. They take their food from workers in the hive (older drones feed themselves). They do not need the well-developed food collecting hairs or mouthparts of the worker.

Drones and queens lack wax and scent glands. The head glands differ and, in the queen, the differences are important. The queen's mandibular glands are very critical as they produce a complex series of chemicals that serve to coordinate and organize the colony. In the queen, the hypopharyngeal glands are not important as the queen does not feed the developing young. In drones, mandibular and hypopharyngeal glands are not developed. The role of these glands and the molecules they produce are explored in Chapter 6.

key terms

abdomen

acanus (acani)

aedeagus

air sacs

alarm chemical

anatomy (morphology)

antenna(e)

antennal cleaner

anus

aorta

apitoxin

apodemes

arolium

ball-and-socket joint

'bee spit'

bilaterally symmetrical

brain

bristle fields

chewing-lapping mouthparts

chitin

compound eye

corbicula (pollen basket)

coxa

esophagus

exocrine glands

exoskeleton

facet (of eye)

fat body

femur

flabellum

flagellum (of antenna)

forelegs

ganglia

gaster

gravity-detection ability

hairy glossa

hemolymph (haemolymph, British) (blood)

hamuli

heart

hind-legs

honey stomach (crop)

hypopharyngeal gland

indirect flight muscles

Johnston's organ

labium

labial (salvary) gland

labrum

leg pairs

locomotor

malpighian tubules

mandibles

mandibular gland

maxilla

mechanoreceptors

metamorphosis

mid-legs

Nasonov (scent) gland

ocelli

ocirculatory system

optic lobe

ovarioles

oviduct (lateral & median)

ovipositor (sting)

palpi

pedicel (of antenna)

pharynx

phototactic

plumose hairs

pollen press

postcerebral gland

proboscis

proprioreceptors

proventriculus

rectrum

regurgitation

royal jelly (bee milk)

scape (of antenna)

scent gland

sclerites

sclerotin

sensilla(e)

spermatheca.

spiracles

sucrase

sternites

sting

sting gland

tarsus

tergites

tergite glands

thorax (pro-, meso-, meta-)

thoracic (salivary) glands

tibia

trachea(e)

tracheoles

trichromatic (vision)

trochanter

ventriculus (stomach/mid-gut)

wasp waist

wax gland

wing veins

2-heptanone

discussion questions

Draw a bee and label important external features. Diagram the position of structures inside the bee. As you familiarize yourself with external and internal morphological features of honey bees, determine reasons honey bees are small. Consider how well-adapted bees are to their environment and how their anatomy goes hand in hand with this adaptedness. What systems both internally and externally would not be adequate if honey bees suddenly became giant monsters?

The exoskeleton would be a major limiting factor in insects like honey bees growing to be monsters but it is vital for their survival on Earth. What are some of the unique features of the bee exoskeleton? How do bees solve the problems of their being encased in body armor? How do they sense the environment through the exoskeleton?

Insect systems of digestion/excretion, respiration and circulation are very different from human systems for the same functions. Explain the major differences (consult a biology text or human anatomy/physiology books if you are unfamiliar with these systems in the human body).

How do you prefer to learn the parts of the bee? Earlier books labeled every part and to learn you learned lots of terms. More recent approaches have been to link form with function. Make the pieces (anatomical parts) mean something in how they might bend or digest or solve their problems for a successful life. Now the stories of how they find flowers and return or support a population of mites is told as a "story" that includes the anatomical pieces and how they function. How do prefer to learn?

What is the distinction between endocrine and exocrine gland? Describe three major differences in the female caste in gland secretions? A pheromone concert is two glands working in conjunction - give 2-3 examples where a concert might be positive.

How can we explain why the barbs of the worker bee sting remains in enemies while those of other stinging insects (like the queen or bumble bees) do not? Provide details where another structure and pheromone releasing gland work closely together like the sting and ovipositor.

exercises

Draw or model (clay, paper, lego blocks) or sculpt a bee and label important external and internal features.

Make paper cardboard models of the hind legs of bees and demonstrate how they transfer pollen from body hairs to the combs on the basitarsi and finally to the pollen basket on the outside of the tibia.

Identify what you would need to determine the extent of fat body in a worker bee body. When would be the best season to do this? Select ten bees and find their fat body - can you see differences between different bees that you examine? How would you measure fat body to document individual bee differences?

You can train bees to forage at an artificial flower source (see the end of Chapter 7 on Dance Language for discussions on the technique of training bees). At the training site, you can conduct experiments on what colors bees see, what sugars they taste and even what smells bees detect. To demonstrate color and experiment on detection, train the bees to a feeder with a color and then offer them a choice of other colors and shades of gray. Can bees detect and return to the color they were trained to recognize with the food reward? You must be careful to keep choice sites exactly the same and you must control for odor release as the bees might mark their site with scent or footprint odors. Taste will be an easier sense to work with than smell. Try offering different sugars in an artificial flower with multiple openings. Can you confirm that bees don't detect saccharine? What sugars do they prefer? What level of concentration is preferred?

How would you demonstrate a bee behavior response to scent, sting or footprint pheromone gland? Why might there be a difference in individual bee response?

references

Bortolotti, L. and C. Costa. 2014. Chemical Communication in honey bee society. In Neurobiology of Chemical Communication. Ed by C. Mucignat-Caretta. CRC Press. Chapter 5.

Collison, C.H. 2015. A Closer Look: Endocrine Glands & Hormones. Bee Culture December

Dade, H. A. 2017 (reprint). Anatomy and dissection of the Honeybee. Northern Bee Books

Capaldi Evans, E. and C.A. Butler. 2010. Why do bees buzz? Rutgers Univ Press

Ellis, J. 2015. The External Anatomy of the Honey Bee. American Bee Journal, August

Grozinger, C. 2015. Honey Bee pheromones. In The Hive and Honey Bee. Ed by Joe Graham. Chapter 11

Ramsey, S.D. et al. 2019 Varroa destructor feeds primarily on honey bee fat body tissue and not hemolymph. Proc Nat. Acad. Sci. January 29, 2019 116 (5) 1792-1801; first published January 15, 2019 https://doi.org/10.1073/pnas.1818371116

Riddle, S. 2016. How Bees See And Why It Matters. Bee Culture. May 2016.

Stell, I. 2012. Understanding Bee Anatomy. Catford Press, London, UK

Bee sting: en.wikipedia.org/wiki/Bee_sting.

Zhao, Z.-L. et al. 2015. Structures, properties, and functions of the stings of honey bees and paper wasps: a comparative study. Biol open 4(7): 921-928 online doi: 10.1242/bio.012195

A bee made from Legos by Daniel, age 7.

Figure 6-1
Collected from flowers to meet the hive's nutritional needs, pollen is stored in cells near the brood area and converted into bee bread via the injection of microbes.

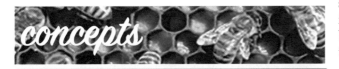

concepts

The honey bee as a living organism

Nutrition and food ecology
    carbohydrates
    amino acids
    fats and minerals
    food sources
    gut biome

Physiological changes to hive labor

Royal jelly

Physiological regulation
    respiratory
    osmoregulation
    thermal
    homeostasis

Comb as an organ of the hive

The living honey bee

Physiology is the branch of biology that deals with the normal functions of living organisms and their parts. It is the way in which a living organism functions. In this chapter we examine both how the honey bee individually functions and how the entire colony collectively functions in a coordinated fashion as a superorganism. We will focus on hive nutrition and food ecology, growth and development of individual bees, gas and liquid circulation and thermoregulation of the hive throughout the seasons.

Honey bee nutrition and food ecology

We understand a fair amount about honey bee nutrition. Vegetarians by nature, bees eat carbohydrates, fats and proteins that are changed by chemical digestion into units small enough to be absorbed from the digestive tract. The hemolymph (blood) of the bee then transports these components to all the cells of the body as **trehalose** or alternately is stored in the bee's fat body as **glycogen** until needed at a later time.

Carbohydrate intake is in the form of nectar or honey. Sugar content in nectar averages 40% but ranges from 5% to 75%; bees prefer higher concentrations. Enzymes such as **sucrase** and **invertase** break the nectar sugars into the simpler sugars of **glucose** and **fructose**. Some of the glucose is converted by another enzyme **glucose oxidase** into gluconic acid and hydrogen peroxide.

The simple sugars are used directly or converted into fat and glycogen. **Gluconic acid** makes honey acidic and hydrogen peroxide helps protect the nectar once processed into honey. Honey bees can live on a pure carbohydrate diet for a long time but without dietary protein, they are unable to continue raising brood and their glands don't develop.

Pollen needs of a colony

Bees use pollen to meet their protein needs. A single colony consumes 37 to 75 pounds (17 to 34 kg) of pollen on an annual basis. The nutritional value of pollen is determined by the absolute and relative content of essential amino acids. There are ten amino acids essential to the growth of the honey bee: arginine, histidine, leucine, isoleucine, lysine, methionine, phenylalanine, threonine, tryptophan and valine. Of these, the largest need is for leucine, isoleucine and valine. Bees need amino acids to synthesize tissues, blood proteins and enzymes.

Amino acids and minerals are needed for the development of muscles, glands and other tissues in the bee. Adult bees begin pollen consumption within two hours of emergence and quickly increase pollen intake to reach a maximum five days after emergence. Pollen consumption is negligible in bees older than ten days of age.

Colony nutrition directly impacts the colony's ability to produce high quality and adequate quantities of royal jelly to feed young developing bees. The young nurse bees serve as the nutritional center of the colony, consuming the pollen and producing royal jelly. Somehow they pass on whole colony nutritional needs to the forager bees. We do not know how these two different age-related functional groups share this information.

Since pollen grains are covered with a tough protein coat, termed the **exine** (Figure 6-2), honey bees need special microbial enzymes, produced in the midgut, to break the covering to allow digestion of the protein. Four endopeptidases, each different in their cleavage specificities, are involved. There is also evidence that the pollen grain is weakest at the germination pore (where the pollen tube grows out at germination),

and that is where enzymes enter to digest pollen grain contents. Examination of the pollen grains in the feces of bees shows that the exine often remains intact, not split open, but most or all of the internal protein has been removed.

Pollens vary widely from as little as 4% to as much as 60% in their **protein content**. Most pollens fall in the range of 18-22% crude protein. Some pollens are better nutritionally for bees while others lack essential amino acids. For this reason, bees collect pollen from a variety of sources. If pollen lacks any of the ten essential amino acids, or is insufficient nutritionally, brood rearing decreases, glands do not develop fully, and adult worker life is shortened.

Vitamins are necessary for the growth and development of bees. They are especially important in enzyme activity — bees lacking proper vitamins in the diet develop deficiency diseases. Bees obtain most of their vitamins from pollen, but nectar supplies some of their vitamin needs as well. Bees require several B-complex vitamins (biotin, folic acid, niacin, pantothenic acid, pyridoxine, riboflavin and thiamine) as well as inositol, and ascorbic acid (vitamin C).

Minerals needed by bees in their diet are also obtained from pollen. Pollen has been identified to have at least 27 trace elements. Phosphorus and potassium are important to the bee and the most common minerals in their bodies. Calcium, magnesium, sodium and iron are also common. Bees need some salt in the diet, but they probably retain it by recovering salt before it is excreted. However, if as little as 0.125% salt is added to sugar water and fed to bees, there is a reduction in longevity.

We know relatively little about the fat requirements of bees but pollen supplies this need as well. Fats are mostly stored and deposited in the abdominal fat body and then used in periods of food shortage. For normal growth, bees need a dietary source of cholesterol, usually as 24-methylene cholesterol.

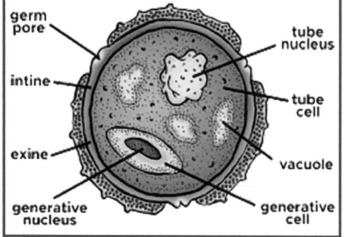

Figure 6-2
Structure of a pollen grain. J. Zawislak

Figure 6-3
While a forager probes for nectar, pollen grains are shown on the sticky pistil surfaces. L. Connor

Figure 6-4
Forager packing high-value pollen from almond flower.
L. Connor

Figure 6-5
While primarily collecting nectar, this bee has some dandelion pollen on her corbicula. C. Burkhead

Bees also need water in their diet. Water is specifically collected by foragers. Also, nectar is high in water content. When bees consume honey or sugar sources of 50% sugar content or higher, they dilute the sugar before use so there is a continual need for water in the diet. One estimate puts the annual water collection level at 44 lbs/colony (20 kg).

Analysis of pollen sources

Researchers have used various methods to measure the value of pollen: the growth and development of the fat body, the development of the hypopharyngeal glands, average bee life span, and the amount of brood rearing. When a small number of bees are put into laboratory cages, bees preferred protein-rich pollens and those containing certain phagostimulants; in the field, whole colonies may not be as discriminatory.

The weakness of small-caged bee studies is that they overlook the complexity of nutrition of the superorganism. Cage studies may show a certain result, but when applied to entire colonies over a period of months, the results may be quite different. This has been demonstrated in studies using artificial bee diets using small cages and long-term full colony feeding comparisons.

Certain 'showy' flowers like dandelion (Figure 6-5) and sunflowers are not able to satisfy the nutritional needs of bees compared to other sources, such as the wind-pollinated tree *Populus* spp. Pear flowers attract foragers for pollen, but nectar gatherers avoid the flowers because the sugar content of the nectar is extremely low.

Researchers have sorted pollen pellets by plant species and fed common single source pollen to bees. They determined that dandelion pollen is low in the amino acids valine, isoleucine, leucine and arginine, a **multi-amino acid deficiency**. Fortunately, dandelions usually flower when other attractive pollen sources are also

in bloom, like apples (*Malus*) which help balance dandelion's nutritional deficit. We can observe many nectar collectors visiting dandelion but not many will be collecting dandelion pollen.

When pollen pellets from other common pollen sources were sorted to determine their nutritional value to bees, they were grouped as follows:

Plants with high nutritional quality pollens include:
clover species (*Trifolium* spp.)
oilseed rape (*Brassica napis*)
pear (*Pyrus communis*)
almond (*Prunus dulcis*)
poplar, aspen and cottonwood (*Populus* spp.)
lupin (*Lupinus angustifolius*)

Pollen of lesser quality (minor nutrition) came from:
sunflower (*Helianthus annus*)
blueberry (*Vaccinium* spp.)
cattails (*Typha* spp)
dandelion (*Taxaxcum* spp.)
certain asters (*Haplopappus* spp.)
caltrop (*Kalistroemia* spp.)

In another cage feeding study of pollens collected from desert floral sources, researchers evaluated pollens and their impact on the length of life of newly emerged worker bees:

A few pollens decreased the life span of bees:
ragweed (*Ambrosia*)
Uromyces (a rust spore)
caltrop (*Kallstoemia* spp.)

Box 10

MICROBIOME

Honey bees, similar to all animals, have a diverse community of microbes in their digestive tract. Microbes are tiny and include bacteria, viruses, fungi, and single celled organisms like amoeba. The honey bee microbiome, as the community of microbes is called, might interact beneficially for the host bee commensally (the microbe is benefited without harm to the bee) or parasitically (the microbe harms the host bee).

The bee gut microbiome is currently of interest in bee health, in their defense against parasites and as a model to study human host defense against parasites. The USDA Tucson bee lab has initiated extensive studies on bee gut microbes, including contributions of bee bread to intestinal mirobes. Outside of a few harmful pathogens, such as foulbrood-causing bacteria and the *Nosema* microsporidian, studies of how exactly the gut microbiome might help maintain and/or protect worker and queen health are in their infancy.

The bee gut microbiome has been called "relatively simple but remarkably specialized." It consists of eight to ten bacterial species belonging to three different Phyla: Proteobacteria, Actinobacteria and Firmicutes. These bee gut bacteria are known to contribute to the digestion of macromolecules, breakdown of bee foods into absorbable nutrients, neutralization of dietary toxins, and defense against parasites. The majority of the bacteria occurring in the gut are not found elsewhere in the honey bee body. Interestingly, the gut biome is different in winter bees, summer foragers and nurse bees.

More specifically, species in genera of *Lactobacillus, Bifidobacteria,* and *Gilliamella* play a significant role in the breakdown of the polysaccharides of pollen and in honey and nectar metabolism—reducing them to be directly utilized by the bee host. Additionally, *Lactobacillus* and *Bifidobacteria* spp. can provide

protection against bee pathogens. *Frischella* sp. gain energy from anaerobic fermentation of carbohydrates and stimulation of host immune pathways. *Bartonella* sp. ferment carbohydrates and degrade plant metabolites present in pollen and nectar. *Gilliamella* and *Snodgrassell*a spp. work together to break down minor components of bee foods.

Honey and bumble bees have socially acquired microbes while the solitary species have only those environmentally acquired. Social life and individual behaviors such as mutual grooming and trophallaxis likely aid transmission of the microbes from parent to offspring and between colony members. Additionally, we know that beekeeping can influence the microbiome. For example, consider the acquired resistance of bacteria to oxytetracycline, a foulbrood antimicrobial. When two different bee races are put in the same location by a beekeeper, the oxytetracycline may have both positive and negative effects on the gut biome of our bees.

Pathogenic microbes that cause harm to bees appear to have synergistic activity with pesticides they ingest. This may make pesticide exposure more of a health risk. One negative view that was recently postulated involves the ubiquitous herbicide glyphosate (Roundup). Glyphosate targets an enzyme only found in plants and microorganisms. Unfortunately, it has been found that most bee gut bacteria contain the same enzyme targeted by glyphosate, putting bees exposed to glyphosate at a disadvantage in their defense against pathogens.

A. mellifera kept in managed (artificial) hives have a substantially weakened immune function when compared to feral hive bees. Compromised immune function can leave bees vulnerable to opportunistic infections that impact both rates of individual and colony survival, such as infections from viruses, protozoa, bacteria, and fungi. Environmental stressors have also been shown to alter the bee's indigenous gut microbiota. Diseased bees often show dysbiosis (microbe imbalance), reflecting a change in the dominant microbial taxa or change in level of transient bacteria not normally common in the gut.

See review by Raymann and Moran.

Figure 6-6
Stored pollen is fermented into bee bread by a combination of microbes present in the bee gut biome. L. Connor

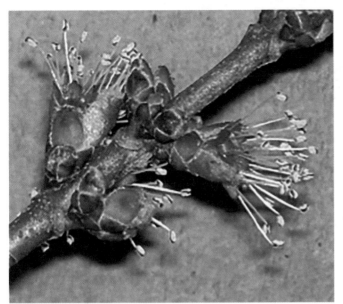

Figure 6-7
Many tree species, like this maple, produce early-season, high-protein pollen critical to colony nutrition. L. Connor

Pollen producing species that had no impact on the length of life of the bees:

Haplopappus, Baccharis (brooms)

dandelion (*Taraxacum*)

Pollen producing species that increased the life span of bees:

desert evergreen shrubs (*Ephedra*)

mesquite (*Prospia*)

blackberries and raspberries (*Rubus*)

popular (*Populus*)

In general, spring flowers produce higher levels of crude protein (20-25%) than summer flowers (15-20%) or fall flowers (19-23%). The amount and nutritional value of spring flowers benefits the bees during key brood feeding, colony growth, and swarm reproduction activities. Summer flowers produce the bulk of the honey crop, the carbohydrates the bees need for wintering. From middle summer on, fall flowers produce pollen with higher protein levels that fill a bee's fat body for winter.

Low-level pollen intake by a colony forces it to increase the percentage of pollen foragers. This reduces the number of bees collecting nectar, and may reduce overall honey production. When bees were given poor quality pollen reserves, colonies increased the proportion of pollen foragers but not the total forager numbers within their forager population. Colonies exposed to protein deficiencies increased the total amount of pollen they collected rather than specializing in higher protein-source flowers.

Physiological changes of the labor force

Adult worker bees undergo a major change in their physiology as they mature. Newly emerged worker bees focus on a diet of protein and fat, which they obtain from pollen and bee bread. As they age, their diet usually shifts to carbohydrates, which is obtained from nectar and honey.

Nurse bee nutrition

Compared to forager bees, nurse bees have highly developed hypopharyngeal glands, increased blood proteins and higher fat reserves in their fat bodies. The entire hive community seems to be involved in the conversion of nurse bees to foragers. Ordinarily, we think that nurse bees will become foragers at the three week mark in their adult life.

How this happens is viewed differently by different researchers. One group advocates that where there are large numbers of foragers present in a hive, they may use a primer pheromone that causes a social effect on the nurse bees that keeps them from developing into foragers. Another group advocates that the bee diet influences the balance of social signals and juvenile hormone has a major roll in passage from hive to field bee.

Colony-level nutrition

The nutritional needs of the honey bee superorganism are complex. Studying the effect of certain nutrients in the laboratory using small cages does not always agree with whole colony studies carried out in the field. For example, long-term feeding of artificial diets to colonies may cause greater queen losses and higher *Nosema* infection levels.

Bees clearly do better when given a **polyfloral diet**, one consisting of a mixture of pollens from different floral sources. When given such a mixed diet (vs. a monofloral diet), colonies experience better health, resistance to infections, and increased longevity.

There are some indications that scout bees select and preferably dance for pollen sources that supplement certain missing nutritional components, such as a specific fatty acid deficiency.

Bees also need cholesterol as a hormone precursor and may seek sources that have the most usable form 24-methylene cholesterol (24MC). Bees in cages consumed higher amounts of the provided artificial diets when supplemented with 24MC, and honey bee survival, head protein content, and abdominal lipid content were all significantly higher in bees with diets supplemented with higher concentrations of 24MC. Significantly higher head protein content in bees fed greater concentrations of 24MC, suggests its potential role in protein synthesis in the brood food-producing hypopharyngeal glands. The finding of higher content in abdominal lipids supports its importance in successful overwintering.

Forager bee nutrition

To leave the hive and to begin foraging, nurse bees must undergo a major shift in their physiology as they transition from nurse to forager. They experience a reduction of their hypopharyngeal glands that is prompted by changes in brain morphology, neurochemistry and gene expression.

Beekeepers widely use supplements to feed their bees. In fact, many beekeepers are being taught to 'always' feed their bees at certain times of the year regardless of the nutritional status of the colonies. Beekeepers need to keep in mind that there is no substitute for pollen, and all artificial feeding needs to be based on a balanced and mindful approach to the foraging ecology of the honey bee colony.

Careful record keeping of floral pollen production, even from the previous season, will help the beekeeper evaluate hive nutrition and help determine the need for protein feeding.

Royal jelly

One of the major evolutionary advances made by the honey bee colony is the refinement of pollen and nectar into colony stores and then digestively converting it into brood food in the form of **royal jelly**. This conversion is done by nurse bees, created in what is sometimes termed the "social stomach" of the hive. Few bee species convert their food into a nutritional substance before use.

Royal jelly is placed in worker, drone and queen cells by the nurse bees. Three days after egg eclosion (hatching), after the third larval molt, worker bees receive a different diet of glandular secretions, mixed with honey and pollen, while queen larvae continue to receive royal jelly.

How is a queen determined?

The royal jelly fed to workers and queens the first two days is the same. Prior to the third instar (third development day) larvae from fertilized eggs can develop into either a queen or a worker. Then the quantity and quality changes— larvae destined to be queens get more and higher sugar content royal jelly. It is believed the extra sugars have a phagostimulant (feeding) effect— queen larvae consume more food and this in turn leads to **stretch receptors** in the growing larva to key a higher juvenile hormone production. Juvenile hormone is a central regulator of queen phenotype.

There are additional differences besides sugar content in the food, including lipids, protein content and the vitamin B complex. Researchers have looked for a pheromone or some chemical that might be a queen determination factor. **Royalactin** was one such factor, one of nine major "royal" proteins. The problem is that worker jelly, after day three, contains more of this protein than does queen royal jelly. While considered a necessary protein component to differentiate a queen from a worker, it is not the determinate chemical. **Extra sugar content** remains the single greatest difference in larvae becoming queens vs. workers.

Both worker and queen larvae grow rapidly, with a 900- to 1,700-fold increase in weight. When worker larvae are

Figure 6-8
Queen larvae float on a bed of royal jelly, as seen through the base of these plastic grafting cups. L. Connor

fed royal jelly throughout their life, they become queens, indicating that diet is a key part of the formation of the queen (the amount of food and microRNAs—regulators of gene expression—are also likely involved). Studies of DNA methylation may well lead to answering the elusive question of what makes the queen different from a worker?

Royal jelly is generally uniform from location to location, with seasonal differences and protein source. It consists of an average of 63% water, 14% protein, 18% carbohydrates and 6% fats. It is commercially harvested for human consumption, used in cosmetics, and in queen rearing. Production for humans is usually found in countries where labor costs are low.

Workers secrete royal jelly from both the hypopharyngeal and mandibular glands. There are two primary fats in royal jelly—10-HDA (E)-10-hydroxy-2-decenoic acid) and 10-HDAA (10-hydroxy-decanoic acid). Both fats are components of queen mandibular pheromones. 10-HDA is an **epigenetic modulator** (turns genes on or off). Gene expression may play a role in caste determination.

Nutrition's specific impact

If a colony runs out of pollen, it will continue producing brood until the worker bee bodies deplete stored food reserves. At that point they cannibalize brood (drone brood first, if there is any) and thereby gain protein which they use to feed other larvae. Young larvae, in which less investment has been made up to that point, are cannibalized first, while older larvae are maintained. The bees will not produce new brood until the pollen reappears, or the bees are fed protein substitute.

Nutrition and queens

During a pollen shortage, the queen stops laying eggs and eventually her ovaries shrink in size. If queen cells are being produced during a supersedure event and a dearth occurs, the bees will attempt to keep the cells fed as well as they can — queen cells are usually the last to suffer from a protein depletion event. It is unlikely that bees would continue to produce swarm queen cells during an extended dearth because the swarming triggers of excess food, crowding and protein abundance would no longer be present in the hive.

When humans attempt to raise large numbers of queen cells in a colony, developing queens may experience poor protein feeding as evidenced by the amount of royal jelly available to queen larvae just prior to pupation (Figure 6-8). If allowed to complete development, the resulting queens may be small, possess lower numbers of ovarioles, and be less competitive in mating. The result will be a queen that produces fewer eggs, has fewer sperm stored in her spermatheca, and is fated to an early supersedure.

Nutrition and drones

Colonies that have been developing normally will terminate drone production when a pollen shortage occurs. If the dearth is prolonged, the bees consume the eggs and larvae, and pull out drone pupae from their cells. Colonies without abundant incoming pollen will eject adult drones if the dearth continues, especially at the end of the season.

Weak colonies rarely produce drones unless there has been a queen failure. In the absence of a queen, the worker bees are no longer receiving pheromone signals from the queen or the brood that inhibit ovary development. This creates a condition called **laying workers**, when a group of worker bees produce a flood of unfertilized eggs that result in a frame or two of all drone brood. Such a colony will eventually die unless requeened.

Drones produce sperm during their larval stage, so any drones that are poorly fed may develop fewer sperm. Also, these drones must feed heavily on pollen soon after emergence. This protein stimulates the sperm to migrate

Figure 6-9
Medium frame with comb added by bees below the bottom bar. Most of these cells are drone sized, and many, but not all, are occupied. L. Connor

from the testes to the seminal vesicles where it awaits the mating event. These two protein feeding events are critical to the production of healthy drones. It is not possible to identify poorly-fed drones from well-fed drones by either structure or behavior.

On rare occasions, queen failure and the production of 100% drone brood (termed **drone layer**) has been linked to poor queen mating during the prior season. When queens are mass produced during poor protein conditions, they may successfully mate, but the drones may posses fewer sperm. By the next spring these queens have used all their sperm and produce only drones.

This was witness in the 1978-79 season. Extremely cold weather in February, 1978 resulted in numbers of colonies producing only drones in early 1979. When the queens were dissected it was confirmed that their spermathecae were without sperm.

Nutrition and worker longevity

Colonies that experience a prolonged protein shortage may produce a cycle of bees that are poorly fed. The worker bees will appear full-sized, but they often die much earlier than well-fed bees. We expect workers to live for five to six weeks during the spring and summer. But when poorly fed as larvae, these worker bees may only live for three weeks as adults, reducing the colony's ability to collect pollen and nectar. We have seen this in regions of the country that do not experience a summer and fall nectar and pollen flow, reducing the number of bees produced, and weakening those produced so they die early.

Fat bee vs. skinny bee

Abdominal fat is a crucial indicator of bee fitness and performance in overwintering. We speak of **fat fall bees** with abundant fat body (and fat colonies with abundant honey stores) as critical for successful overwintering (Chapter 5, Figure 5-18).

The fat body regulates various aspects of insect physiology, including the synthesis and use of energy reserves, lipid storage, detoxification, synthesis of vitellogenin, and initiating foraging tasks in worker bees. The honey bee diet has been reported to influence gene expressions of the bee abdominal fat body tissues. Lipid content in abdomens was higher in bees from diets with higher 24 methylene cholesterol, suggesting this component of their dietary intact is significant in 'fatness'.

Low nutrition and synergism with diseases and pesticides

Scientists have examined the impact of poor nutrition on colony performance and observed that nutritional deficiencies may have synergistic effects with certain diseases and sub-lethal pesticide exposure. Studies have demonstrated that phytochemicals in pollen and nectar help bees combat viral infections, thus improving their longevity.

Improved protein nutrition protected nurse bees against *Nosema* disease. When pollens representing different nutritional levels were fed to young nurse bees exposed to *Nosema ceranae*, those fed protein-rich pollen survived

Figure 6-10
Bees in winter cluster between two frames. T. Smith

longer and experienced greater tolerance to the parasite. Bees infected with the organism lived longer when given a diverse mixture of pollen, or the protein-richest pollen.

Research has shown that by limiting food through nutritional restriction, a worker's queen pheromone response is affected. This is considered a behavioral indicator reflecting the investment in the entire hive vs. individual reproduction. Nutritional restriction during the worker larval stage has been shown to reduce worker ovary size and increase the adult bee's response to queen pheromone. But when nutritional restriction occurred during the adult stage, it led to reduced lipid stores and reduced queen pheromone response (Figure 6-11).

Individual worker honey bees may adjust both their behavioral and physiological traits in response to nutritional stress, causing them to invest their nutritional resources in either their own or their colony's reproduction. These results support the role of nutritional stress in the maintenance of cooperative behavior. It is thought that historical nutritional scarcity may have been an important contributor to the evolution of extreme forms of cooperation.

Gas, liquid and temperature regulation

Bees need to balance the colony's heat and cooling needs, breathing or respiration of individual bees, water regulation and temperature regulation. This section includes integration of ideas presented by J. Tautz in *The Buzz about Bees: Biology of a Superorganism.*

Respiratory activity and gas exchange

As explained in Chapter 5, bees have 10 pairs of spiracles—the first pair on the thorax works with a closing muscle, the second pair in the thorax has no muscles at all, and the last eight pairs (one on the thorax and seven on the abdomen) work with active closing and opening muscles.

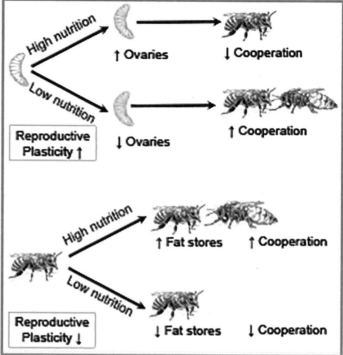

Figure 6-11
Low nutrition as a larva reduced worker ovary size and increase its response to queen pheromone. Low nutrition in the adult stage reduced lipid stores and reduced queen pheromone response. A. Walton

The bees have cycles of respiratory activity. During the open phase oxygen O_2 enters followed by a closed phase during which the spiracles are tightly closed. Carbon dioxide CO_2 is a waste product that builds in the body. In a following 'flutter phase' the spiracles partly open or close in rapid succession and the CO_2 is released in short, small pulses.

At low temperatures there are long periods between bursts of activity. Between 20 and 30 °C there are both small and large bursts of CO_2 release. Above 30° C the respiration patterns became increasingly cyclic. The rate of CO_2 production increased steeply with ambient temperatures.

It is thought increased CO_2 levels (and/or reduced O_2 levels) stimulate nervous system ganglia to increase air exchange, perhaps by monitoring acidity levels at the cellular exchange sites.

There is also a social respiration in a bee colony. A fanning colony can move air into and out of entrances and keep it circulating inside. During cooler weather, when the entrance guards might have to cluster, the entrance can be closed to small one-way entry/exit holes using propolis. The reduced entrance will assist with keeping air exchange reduced. The cluster itself is structured to keep the central core warm but avoid buildup of CO_2. See Chapter 10, Figure 10-20 for how

Figure 6-12
Bees with blurred wings are fanning to draw cool air into the hive. Other bees are foragers or guard bees.
L. Connor

a swarm cluster is organized — the winter cluster is thought to have a similar organization.

Osmoregulation

Osmoregulation is maintenance of **body fluid balance** and the concentration of electrolytes (salts in solution). It is necessary to keep the body fluids from becoming too diluted or concentrated. Salt and water both move by **osmosis** from higher to lower concentration. With their small body size, electrolyte and water balance is crucial to individual bees.

Malpighian tubules. The excretory structures Malpighian tubules are named for a 17th century Italian biologist Marcello Malpighi, the father of physiology and embryology. Along with the rectum, these organs function both in osmoregulation and waste removal. The Malpighian tubules remove nitrogenous wastes from the hemolymph and the rectum voids digestive tract wastes.

The Malpighian tubules are elongated structures that float in the abdomen (Chapter 5, Figure 5-6). Their function is analogous to the human kidney. They cleanse the blood of nitrogenous and sulfur wastes, phosphates, both acidic and basic ions, and convert the wastes into relatively non-toxic uric acid. The waste moves from the tubes into the digestive tract at the juncture of mid and hindgut. It will form part of the feces along with food wastes to be excreted from the **anus**, the termination of the digestive tract.

The last section of the digestive tract is the **hindgut**. The rectum section of the hindgut is important for the re-absorption of water and salt prior to waste excretion. Small areas on the rectum called **rectal pads** will reabsorb > 90% of the water, so the bees, like most insects, retain as much moisture as possible

from the food they eat. The final excretion is a semi-solid; primarily composed of the exine of pollen and uric acid from the Malpighian tubules. If the body has lots of water, the fecal discharge is more watery, but if desiccated then the final waste eliminated is more solid.

The bee exoskeleton is not very permeable to water loss, in large part to its waxy layer. Bees do not have sweat glands. Under hot humid conditions body water loss increases through the spiracles in respiration.

Thermal activity

While honey bees evolved in the topics, they are extremely successful in the temperate regions of the world. They are considered **heterothermic**, which means their body temperatures varies from being self-regulating to allowing the surrounding environment to affect it. Resting bees are present in a summer colony as well as in the winter cluster. They keep their temperature above 50° F (10° C) by increasing their body activity, specifically by performing **abdominal ventilation movements** and **generating heat in their muscles** through cellular metabolism in the wing muscles in the bee's thorax.

Most of the bee's muscles are in the thorax and associated with the legs for walking and wings for flight (See discussion in Chapter 5). Wing muscle activity can generate considerable heat — Heinrich recorded a body temperature as high as 47° C (116° F) during flight.

Unlike other muscular activity where a nerve impulse leads to activity, the indirect flight muscles of bees do not need direct stimulation for contraction — a condition termed **asynchrony.** Wing muscle contraction rate is much higher than nervous impulses.

The energy source comes from both **glycogen** stored in the muscle itself and **trehalose** from the hemolymph. Both potassium and calcium ions are involved in muscle activity, passing back and forth over the neuron cellular membranes with changes in membrane permeability.

Under colder temperatures bees generate heat in a method called **shivering thermogenesis**, where they use the metabolism of the skeletal muscles by shivering. The bees do not walk or fly during this process.

Heating the cluster

Honey bees use individual bee behavior to affect social temperature regulation. This 'shivering in place' behavior is dramatically observed in the winter cluster. The bees in the center of the tightly packed core of bees are **endothermic** (heat producing).

The cluster temperature is relatively constant, especially when brood is present, decreasing as bee density decreases towards the outside. Bees in this outer layer play an active role in thermal control of winter clusters by providing insulation to the warmer core. As bees in

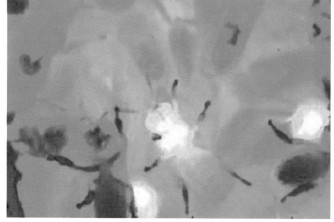

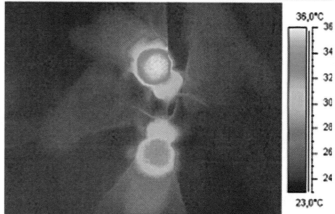

Figure 6-13
Thermal images of worker bees, warming brood and the hive. B. Sterk

the outer core move toward the cluster's center, bees from the core move to the outside. This provides overall **cluster thermal stability**.

Temperature on comb — thermography of single bees

Heat-producing bees were named **heater bees** by J. Tautz. Using thermographic images, Tautz showed that a brood comb reveals 'hot' heater bees with 'glowing' thoraxes within the capped brood cell region of the nest (Figures 6-13, 6-16). Heater bees enter head first into an empty cell or press their thoraxes onto the cell cap to transfer their warmth to the pupa inside. Heater bee bodies could rise to 109° F (43° C). The bees maintained this posture for up to 30 minutes, completely

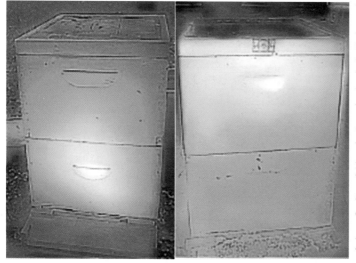

Figure 6-14 (left)
Thermal image shows the cluster is in the lower box of the hive; stored honey reserves occur above it for winter survival.
Figure 6-15 (right)
Thermal image shows the cluster is near the top of the upper box of the hive; bees may not have enough honey reserves for survival. T. Smith

Figure 6-16
'Heater bees' producing heat in their thorax muscles with heat radiating into the head. Public domain.

motionless. The antennae, which contain heat receptors, are held onto the surface of the cap, apparently measuring the temperature of the cell contents.

Heater bees concentrate on sealed brood; they were not observed on the open brood. Tautz reported that bees of all ages were heaters. Non-heater bees cover the heater bees to provide insulation and reduce heat loss by the density of their bodies.

Other than heater bees, the general body temperature of bees follows the surrounding air temperature. This is the normal endothermic state. When resting bees were observed using infrared thermography under carefully controlled laboratory conditions, researchers measured their body temperature as well as their activity.

At ambient temperatures the bees switched to the ectothermic state and relied entirely on the surrounding temperature for their heat supply. At 50° F (10° C), the bees fall into chill coma and stop all motor activity. Beekeepers have occasionally noted this chill coma after bringing apparently "dead" bees inside a warmer area and have them come "alive".

When the temperature was increased, the bees resting metabolic rate increases. At ambient temperatures between 59 to 86° F (15 and 30° C) bees other than the active foragers had a thorax temperature more or less equal to or elevated over ambient temperature.

At temperatures above 95° F (35° C) worker bees remain very active with short resting periods. Wet mouthparts cooled the head and part of the thorax with the abdomen the hottest part of the bee's body because it was not being cooled by the water droplets.

Homeostasis

The sophisticated method of producing heat is balanced by the colony's ability to provide ventilation by fanning of their wings.

On most days, bees must generate heat to warm the brood nest to a constant 95° F. This is the temperature at which bees optimally rear workers and drones as well as raise queen cells. There may be areas warmer than 95° F., such as in the areas where wax is being produced.

On very hot days bees will ventilate the hive. Bees align their bodies at the entrance of the hive and using their wings force air into a portion of the entrance and force it out at another location. This colony level behavior serves to help stabilize hive temperature and balance the heat of the brood nest, optimize wax production and avoid hive meltdown.

Ventilation also helps regulate the moisture content of the hive. Anytime the colony is ripening nectar into honey, the bees force drier air over the area where unripe honey is being reduced in moisture to an optimal 18% water content. The workers balance the heat of the brood nest, the moisture from their own respiration and honey ripening with outside temperatures by actively heating or cooling of the hive. The process is called **homoeostasis**.

The colony's ability to keep a balanced environment can be impacted by genetics (seen in heavily inbred stocks), pesticides and disease. Environmental exposure to high winds, high temperatures, heavy nectar ripening requirements or other extremes interfere with a colony's ability to maintain homeostasis.

Queen cell production occurs only within the brood area, where heater bees and wax producers are abundant. Natural queen cell production is optimized in the production of swarm cells, when the number of bees is elevated, drones are being produced, crowding occurs within the brood region, outside temperatures are more stable and there are abundant resources (stored honey and ripening nectar plus abundant stores of bee bread) both inside and being carried into the hive.

Queen cell production under either supersedure or emergency conditions may not occur under these optimal conditions. The bees might lack the best conditions to maintain stable temperatures around developing queen cells. Some started queen cells may be aborted in all three instances but it is not known if this is related to lack of proper temperature conditions. Smaller bodied queens with fewer ovarioles might be a consequence when a queen is reared under sub-optional hive conditions.

Comb as an organ of the colony

Perhaps the most important 'organ' of the honey bee superorganism is its **comb**. The comb performs many functions in the colony and is essential to the growth and well-being of the bees. The only time bees are without comb is during the swarming process. With honey stomachs filled, bees at a bivouac location begin to activate wax glands and are ready to begin construction of comb upon reaching a new home site—comb building becomes a priority.

Wax production

Comb wax is produced by four paired, smooth areas, called **wax mirrors** located on the underside (ventral) of abdominal segments four through seven (Figure 5-31). A layer of epithelial tissue called the **wax gland** forms the wax for part of the period in the life of the worker. The wax starts as a liquid released through the mirrors and hardens to small flakes in the pockets between the mirrors and the long underlapping parts of the preceding sterna.

Workers actively engaged in secreting wax engorge themselves with honey and hang in **festoons** at or near the site of comb building The beeswax is produced by metabolizing honey in wax gland fat cells; workers cannot produce beeswax unless they have access to pollen as newly emerged adults.

Bees start wax production when they are a week old, and continue until 12-18 days of age. After several days of wax production, the wax glands degenerate, so the bee that leaves the hive to forage no longer secretes wax.

The wax is a complex mixture of hydrocarbons, fatty acids, esters, hydrocarbons and proteins (lipophorins). Over 300 individual chemical components have been identified from pure beeswax. Beeswax consists primarily of monoesters (35%), hydrocarbons (14%), diesters (14%), triesters (3%), hydroxymonoesters (4%), hydroxypolyesters (8%), free fatty acids (12%), acid esters (1%), acid polyesters (2%), free alcohol (1%) and unidentified (6%).

Figure 6-17
New comb built between frames. Wax starts as white or light yellow and darkens with the addition of propolis, pigments from pollen and honey and the accumulations of cocoons in brood combs. L. Connor

Figure 6-18
As nectar is processed into honey, wax cappings are put on top of each cell, often with an air space between the wax and the honey, giving it a white appearance. L. Connor

To produce wax, the bees must metabolize honey, meaning there must be adequate honey stores present in the hive. Most wax production occurs during the warmer spring and summer when foragers are active.

Drones and queens do not have abdominal wax glands.

The colony is under great pressure to produce beeswax comb for honey storage and brood rearing. Over the season, colonies collect 660 lbs (300 kg) or more pounds of honey used for brood rearing, feeding foragers, providing drones with honey for mating, generating swarms, and to maintain the colony for these resources.

Comb use by bees

In a fully developed colony, there may be between 100,000 to 200,000 beeswax cells constructed in parallel sheets separated by the **bee space** (Figure 6-20). In the Western honey bees, bee space varies from 1/4 to about 3/8 of an inch, reflecting the thickness of two bees, each one working on the surface of two opposing combs. Bee space ensures adequate space to process incoming nectar into honey, feed their brood and perform other duties inside the hive.

The wax comb also provides space to place pollen when it is brought into the hive and kicked off the hind legs and into cells within or adjacent to the brood area (Figure 6-1). The nurse bees add honey to the pollen and press it into layers, often using their heads to do this. As they do this they moisturize the pollen with honey and introduce microbes (see Box 10). The enzymes and the microbes are thought to be responsible for the conversion of pollen into bee bread, working as a fermentation process.

The comb also serves as the nursery for the developing eggs, larvae and pupae. Combined with propolis that layers the top and sides of individual cells, the functional comb protects the developing bees against various pathogens. The addition of propolis strengthens the brood combs and provides a sounding board for bee dance language vibrations to pass from dancer to recruit.

Figure 6-19
Beeswax comb being used for worker brood rearing (center), drone brood production (lower edge) and honey storage (upper left and right corners). L. Connor

Brood rearing, honey storage and pollen fermentation are three activities that compete for the same cell space. The bees carry on a complicated dance, a 'tango' going back and forth over the same area, as the same comb area is used for pollen storage, then brood rearing, then honey storage and back again.

Contamination of the comb and pesticide exposure

Beeswax combs have been compared to the mammal liver, cleansing the bee stomachs of various environmental pathogens. The makeup of long-chain hydrocarbons make the wax a natural magnet for

Figure 6-20
Beeswax comb built in an open space above the hive. The bees maintained the bee space but the combs vary in thickness as used for brood production or honey storage.

Box 11

COMB EFFECT ON BEES

Empty comb, preferably drawn and previously used, stimulates bees to store honey. Colonies given more empty beeswax comb (drawn frames) stored 30% more honey compared to colonies given less empty comb. Bees hoard more sugar syrup in lab trials when supplied with three pieces of comb compared to only one piece. Passing a stream of air over drawn beeswax comb increases hoarding, suggesting a volatile pheromone is the stimulatory factor.

Comb containing brood is the major reason for inhibition of worker ovary development. Worker larvae secrete many chemicals. When deprived of food and cell visits, larvae become highly attractive to nurse-age worker bees which then visit and inspect such larvae more frequently than normal. Brood also stimulates pollen collection by adult foragers. If you artificially remove brood, the amount of pollen a colony collects decreases (28% in one experiment). Removal of both brood and an egg-laying queen doubles the decrease, showing how critically important it is to have an expanding brood area and healthy queens in colonies being used in pollination of crops. Giving colonies brood (transferred from other colonies) stimulates a colony to increase its pollen-collection behavior.

Figure 6-21
At the start of the nectar flow, the closest colonies received two supers of drawn comb, placed above two standard deep boxes. This stimulated the bees to gather up to 30% more honey than when given less comb.

---

various toxic molecules. Unlike the liver, however, there is no mechanism for the comb to purge toxins.

Bee specialists have pointed to the role of the proventriculus (Chapter 5) as a means of keeping honey free from pesticides and other contaminants. The reason for this is the structure allows pollen and honey to pass into the stomach (ventriculus) of the bee where it can be broken down. The nectar/honey is regurgitated and is stored in the honeycomb with the number of pollen grains greatly reduced.

Bees also have the Malpighian tubules, tube-like structures suspended in the body cavity that remove wastes from the bee's blood. The compounds are passed to the digestive tract as uric acid and stored in the rectum before voiding.

One would hope that this would protect the honey bee from contamination. Unfortunately, it is not that simple. Pollen is often exposed to pesticides, both those used by beekeepers to kill mites and other diseases and by agricultural chemicals that are applied to crops.

Dr. Clarence Collison reviewed the considerable research on bee health and pesticides that has taken place since Colony Collapse Disorder (CCD). This review shows that pesticide exposure has a strong negative effect on colony health. This includes the synthesis, transport and elimination of developmental hormones and enzymes.

More specifically, acaracides (mite-killing pesticides) have sub-lethal effects on bees; the bees are not killed, but their behavior is affected. Acaracides build up in the wax of a colony and contaminated comb impacts the development and immune response of bees reared on these combs. Low levels of acaracides reduce a colony's ability to produce queens and reduce sperm viability.

Several pesticides were found as residues in the hive. Some delay larval and pupal development of bees, reduce adult bee longevity, and lead to brood mortality and delayed bee emergence. Sub-lethal effects that interfere with larval development and adult bee longevity effects the premature shift in larval roles and foraging behavior.

Bees that were raised on pesticide-contaminated comb were more likely to become infected with *Nosema ceranae*, and at a younger age. As bees gather pollen and nectar, certain environmental toxins accumulate in the combs.

In a French study, beeswax samples were collected once a year over two years. There were 14 compounds found in the samples and beeswax contamination was the result of in-hive acaricide treatment. When the pollen was tested in these 125 colonies, 19 compounds were found out of the 36 molecules searched for.

A study of commercial beekeepers from 23 states and one Canadian province sampled pollen, beebread, broodnest wax, beeswax foundation, adult bees and brood and examined them for pesticide residues. Healthy colonies and those with symptoms of CCD were sampled.

The samples revealed that there were 121 pesticides found in 887 samples with 47% containing in-hive acaricides fluvalinate and coumaphos. Nearly all (98%) of the comb and foundation were contaminated with these miticides.

Other studies showed that honey bees can be exposed to several chemical agents at the same time. Also, the insecticide imidacloprid and the fungal pathogen *Nosema* can interact synergistically. Colonies treated with imidacloprid showed increased *Nosema* spore loads.

When honey from extracted honey supers were compared to honey sampled from the brood chamber of the same colony, pesticide residues found in honey contributed to the overall pesticide exposure to honey bees. Overwintered brood comb honey contributed more than honey stored in honey supers.

key terms

amino acid	exine	homeostasis	pollens
asynchrony	festooning	hydrogen peroxide	polyfloral diet
bacteria	fructose	hypopharyngeal glands	royal jelly
B-complex vitamins	glucose	juvenile hormone	royalactin
bee space	glucose oxidase	laying worker	shivering
cholesterol (24MC)	gluconic acid	lipophorins	social stomach
DNA methylation	glycogen	mandibular glands	stretch receptors
Dysbiosis	glyphosate	microbiome (microbes)	sucrose (invertase)
ectothermic	gut microbiome	monofloral diet	sucrose
endopeptidase	haemolymph (blood)	*Nosema* disease	theromographic
endothermic	heater bees	phagostimulant	trehalose
epigenetic modulation	heterothermic	physiology	trophallaxis

discussion questions

This chapter is pretty complex. What are the take-away messages that relate to bee biology needed to be effective beekeepers?

Bees need pollen but not all pollens are equal in what they can supply in the bee diet. What are the essential biologies of pollen intake? How can we determine if bees are getting a diversified pollen diet? Do we know enough about what pollens are most beneficial? How can we find that information?

What is the role of gut microbiome in bee healthfulness?

In this chapter we speak about both individual and colony level needs and differences. Identify some of these. Is the evidence of superorganism effects where the sum is more than the parts clearly evident? Consult Tautz reference for additional support.

Are the dietary needs of the three adults significantly different or more similar than different? How does nutrition potentially affect worker parasites/pesticides/pheromones?

What happens when the outside temperature gets colder? Or warmer? How do bees handle thermal differences?

Is there a super food equivalent to royal jelly in the human diet? Outline its importance to bee caste development.

Can you accept that beeswax comb is an "organ" of the superorganism? Give evidence to support this hypothesis.

exercises

Using bee dietary needs identified in this chapter draw correlations to our own diets.

Collect pollen at the hive entrance (See Chapter 17 for further information on pollen collection) at several intervals. How diverse (based on color separation) are the sources for your bees. Can you determine what some of the floral sources are?

Collect royal jelly (see Chapter 17 for more information on royal jelly harvest and uses) and determine if you might be able to utilize it as a bee product. Would mixing some royal jelly into your honey be significant?

Investigate the devices to help measure temperature in the bee hive? What interpretations might be made about bee colonies obtainable with temperature measurements?

Collect and examine various combs from colonies. Explain how they might differ and how they might be of such critical importance to the superorganism.

references

Brodschneider, R., and K. Crailsheim 2010. Nutrition and health in honey bees Apidologie 41(3). DOI: 10.1051/apido/2010012

Bernklau, E., et al. 2019. Dietary phytochemicals honey bee longevity and pathogen tolerace. (Nosema) Insects 10(1), 14; https://doi.org/10.3390/insects10010014

Burley, L.M. et al. 2008. Survival of honey bee (Hymenoptera: Apidae) spermatozoa incubated at room temperature from drones exposed to miticides. J. Econ. Entomol. 101: 1081-1087.

Chakrabarti, P. et al. 2019. Evaluating Effects of Critical Micronutrient (24-Methylenecholesterol) on Honey Bee Physiology. Annals of the Entomological Society of America, saz067, https://doi.org/10.1093/aesa/saz067

Chauzat, M.P. and J. P. Faucon 2007. Pesticide residues in beeswax samples collected from honey bee colonies (Apis mellifera L.) in France. Pest Manag. Sci. 63: 1100-1106.

Chauzat, M.P. et al. 2006. A survey on pesticide residues in pollen loads collected by honey-bees (Apis mellifera) in France. J. Econ. Entomol. 99: 253-262.

Chauzat, M.P. et al. 2009. Influence of pesticide residues on honey bee (Hymenoptera: Apidae) colony health in France. Environ. Entomol. 38: 514-523.

Collins, A.M. et al. 2004. Performance of honey bee (Apis mellifera) queens reared in beeswax cells impregnated with coumaphos. J. Apic. Res. 43: 128-134.

Collison, C.H. https://www.beeculture.com/a-closer-look-bee-health-and-pesticides/

Collison, C.H. A CLOSER LOOK: BEESWAX, WAX GLANDS: Beeswax is a complex substance made up of wax esters, fatty acids and hydrocarbons. Bee Culture

Desneux, N. et al. 2007. The sublethal effects of pesticides on beneficial Arthropods. Annu. Rev. Entomol. 52: 81-106.

Gregorc, A. and J.D. Ellis 2011. Cell death localization in situ in laboratory reared honey bee (Apis mellifera L.) larvae treated with pesticides. Pestic. Biochem. Physiol. 99: 200-207.

Gregorc, A. et al. 2012. Gene expression in honey bee (Apis mellifera) larvae exposed to pesticides and Varroa mites (Varroa destructor). J. Insect Physiol. 58: 1042-1049.

Heinrich, B. 1979. Keeping a cool head: honeybee thermoregulation. Science 205(4412):1269-1271 https://www.science.org/doi/10.1126/science.205.4412.1269

Hill, D. 2017. Honey bee nutrition. Amer. Bee Jour. May 2017. https://bee-health.extension.org/honey-bee-nutrition/

James, R.R. and J. Xu 2012. Mechanisms by which pesticides affect insect immunity. J. Invertebr. Pathol. 109: 175-182.

Johnson, R.M. et al. 2010. Pesticides and honey bee toxicity-USA. Apidologie 41: 312-331.

Kovac, H. et al. J Insect Physiol. 2007 Dec; 53(12): 1250–1261.Published online 2007 Jul 13. doi: 10.1016/j.jinsphys.2007.06.019

Motta, E. et al. 2018. Glyphosate perturbs the gut microbiota of honey bees PNAS October 9, 2018 115 (41) 10305-10310; first published September 24, 2018 https://doi.org/10.1073/pnas.1803880115

Mullin, C.A. et al. 2010. High levels of miticides and agrochemicals in North American apiaries: implications for honey bee health. PLoS ONE 5(3):e9754 doi:10.1371/journal.pone.0009754

National Geographic: YouTube of development: https://www.youtube.com/watch?v=f6mJ7e5YmnE

Ostiguy, N. and B. Eitzer 2014. Overwintered brood comb honey: colony exposure to pesticide residues. J. Apic. Res. 53: 413-421.

Owens, C.E. 1971. The thermology of wintering honey bee colonies. USDA Technical Bulletin 1429.

Pettis, J.S. et al. 2012. Pesticide exposure in honey bees results in increased levels of the gut pathogen Nosema. Naturwissenschaften
99: 153-158.

Pettis, J.S. et al. 2013. Crop pollination exposes honey bees to pesticides which alters their susceptibility to the gut pathogen Nosema ceranae. PLoS ONE 8(7):e70182 doi:10.1371/journal.pone 0070182

Sagili, R. et al. 2011. Division of labor associated with brood rearing in the honey bee: how does it translate to colony fitness? PLoS One https://doi.org/10.1371/journal.pone.0016785

Raymann, K and N.A. Moran. 2018. The role of the gut microbiome in health and diesease of adult honey bee worker. Curr Opin. Insect Sci. 26:97-104

Southwick, E.E. and G. Heldmaier 1987. Temperature control in honey bee colonies. Bioscience 37:395-399 (Also see 2015. Physiology & social physiology of the Honey Bee. Hive and Honey Bee Chapter 6. Dadant and Sons

Tautz, J. 2008. The Buzz about Bees: Biology of a Superorganism. Springer

Walton, A., et al. 2018. Hungry for the queen: Honeybee nutritional environment affects worker pheromone response in a life stage dependent manner Functional Ecology DOI: 10.1111/1365-2435.13222

Winston, M.L. 1987. The Biology of the Honey Bee. Harvard University Press, Cambridge, MA.

Wright, G.A. et al. 2018. Nutritional Physiology and Ecology of Honey Bees. Annu. Rev. Entomology 63:327-44

Wu, J.Y. at al. 2011. Sub-lethal effects of pesticide residues in brood comb on worker honey bee (Apis mellifera) development and longevity. PLoS ONE 6(2): e1472. doi:10.1371/journal.pone.0014720

Wu, J.Y. et al. 2012. Honey bees (Apis mellifera) reared in brood combs containing high levels of pesticide residues exhibit increased susceptibility to Nosema (Microsporidia) infection. J. Invertebr. Pathol. 109: 326-329.

Figure 7-1
Workers pick up the queen pheromone through antennal and proboscis contact with a queen or from each other.

Concepts

Pheromone communication

Queen pheromones functions

Alarm communication Nasanov scent gland colony odor

Brood and comb pheromones

Chemical coordination

Pheromone communication

The honey bee society is coordinated via effective communication. Dancing notwithstanding (covered in Chapter 8), most honey bee communication is chemically regulated by use of olfactory (smell) or gustatory (taste) receptors. Honey bees and other insects manufacture specific organic semiochemicals, termed **pheromones**, for communication. A pheromone is a chemical secreted to the outside by an individual which, when received by another individual of the same species, results in a specific behavioral response. A **kairomone** is a semiochemical that communicates between different species.

Pheromones differ from hormones in that they pass outside the body from one individual to another. Pheromones are secreted through **exocrine glands,** usually as a liquid, but may function in smell (gaseous stage) rather than in taste (liquid) form. Pheromones that cause rapid changes in the behavior of the recipient are termed **releaser pheromones**. Those that have slower, long-term effects (hours or even days) on the physiology and behavior of the recipient are called **primer pheromones.**

As early as 1926, it was observed that bees communicated using chemicals. Professor Karl von Frisch, while studying dance language, observed honey bee foragers using their **Nasonov scent gland** (Figures 4-11, 5-31, 7-15) to release an odor at dishes of sugar water he was using in his experiments. Von Frisch found that the scent a bee released was attractive to all bees, not just bees from the same hive. He initially thought that scent was the principle means by which bees informed hive mates of food resources.

In 1954 Dr. Colin Butler in England offered the hypothesis that the queen produces a **queen substance**, a chemical that helps maintain her status as the single reproductive female in the colony. In 1961, the specific chemical, **9-oxo- 2-decenoic acid (9 ODA)** was isolated from queen **mandibular glands**. A year later, Dr. Norman Gary at Cornell University identified the same compound as the sex attractant of the virgin queen honey bee.

At the same time honey bee pheromones were identified, sex attractant pheromones of the silkworm and the gypsy moth were also isolated and identified. Today, we recognize numerous insect pheromones and use many of these chemicals in insect survey and control programs.

Pheromones are extremely important as sex attractants, in aggregating behaviors, in alarm communication and in many other behaviors. They are found in most, if not all, insects. Pheromones are found in other animals too, including humans, although humans seek to cover their chemical emissions with artificial scents like perfumes.

Queen pheromones

One of the most active and vital chemical communication pheromones in the bee society is the **mandibular gland secretion** of the queen. Chemically, it is very diverse with at least 17 major components. The five most important chemicals from queen mandibular glands are:

- 9-oxodec-2-enoic acid (9 ODA)(sometimes written as 9-keto-2-(E)-decenoic acid or 9-oxo-2-decenoic acid)
- cis-9 hydroxydec-2-enoic acid (9 HDA)
- trans-9 hydroxy-2-enoic acid (9 HDA)
- methyl-p-hydroxybenzoate (HOB)
- 4-hydroxy-3-methoxyphenylethanol (HVA)

The first three are carboxylic acids and the last two are aromatic compounds. The first chemical listed, **9 ODA**, is by far the most common material but all five components are necessary for full efficacy. Removal of any one of the five chemicals reduces effectiveness by 50%.

Careful analysis has enabled us to determine the queen mandibular gland's daily output, or **Queen equivalent (Qeq)**. This has lead to a lure or **QMP (queen mandibular pheromone)** that can be used to stabilize a queenless unit or delay colonies from swarming.

Queen substance, Butler's original name of this mandibular gland secretion, has persisted since 1954. It is considered a **primer pheromone**, the major regulating factor of colony functions. It is the role of the queen caste to produce this chemical pheromone, a function as necessary as egg laying.

Newly emerged queens produce little of the pheromone blend, mainly lacking in 9 ODA. By the sixth day, the mandibular glands produce enough 9 ODA (and 9 HDA as well) to enable the queen to attract drones for

Figure 7-2
Marked queen without a well-defined retinue of workers. Retinue bees feed and take pheromones from their queen.

mating. Mature mated queens secrete double the combo on a daily basis with a daily peak from 11 a.m. to 5 p.m. Amounts of 9 HDA, HVA and HOB are initially low but increase as queens begin to lay eggs and age.

Figure 7-3
Clustered swarm on pine branch. C. Burkhead

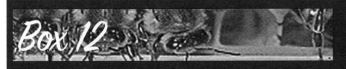

QUEEN SUBSTANCE SPREAD

Queen substance is not very volatile. Bees need to receive some level of the pheromone on a continuing basis or the inhibitory effects will not function properly. The message is spread by worker bees of the queen's retinue, and by food transmission behavior.

Some worker bees of the queen retinue touch her with their antennae but they pick up only a small amount of queen substance from her body. Queen substance can be passed to other bees by the antennating bee. Other retinue bees lick the queen with mouthparts (Figure 7-4) and touch her with their forelegs. Each of these bees receives a larger dose of pheromone, effectively passing the queen's pheromone message to hive mates.

The queen, as she travels over the beeswax combs, leaves a pheromone trail from Arnhart (tarsal) glands and tip of abdomen on the beeswax that workers apparently detect as they travel in the same area. Queens generally do not leave the brood rearing area and relatively few bees are members of her retinue. This means that some bees receive more information than others. Foragers are not often in the brood area, or even in the hive very long on a good day, so they receive less of the message. This suggests some bees have a need for larger quantities of queen pheromone than others and perhaps they, in turn, are more likely to be responsible for queen replacement behaviors.

One yet unexplained finding about queen pheromone distribution is why an apparently large amount of the chemical, as revealed in radioactive isotope studies of tagged queen substance, ends up inside the bodies of the queen and the worker (Table 7-1). The question arises as to whether it is possible for the pheromone to function like a hormone inside the body after it functions as a pheromone? It would be a unique example of efficiency—recycling and reuse of a pheromone as a hormone!

Figure 7-4
A retinue of attendants surround a honey bee queen, licking the queen's body while touching her with their antennae, picking up her pheromone. Tuckabee

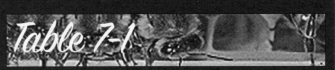

Percentage of radioactive bees after six foragers were fed 20 ml of radioactively labeled sugar

types of bees or location in the hive	after 4 hours (%)	after 28 hours (%)
top super	21	60
bottom super	16	53
brood chamber	18	43
returning foragers	62	76
drones	.	27

Nixon H.L., Ribbands C.R. 1952. Food transmission within the honeybee community. Proc R Soc London 140 (898): 43–50

There is considerable variation between queens. A queen's gradual decline in pheromone production as she ages may be a trigger that initiates her replacement through queen supersedure.

The chemicals are dispersed over the queen's body as she is **groomed** by workers. Workers pick up the pheromone by **antennal and proboscis contact** with a queen or from each other (Figure 7-4). Workers that touch the queen with their mouthparts are especially useful in further distribution. Using the behavior of **food transmission**, queen substance is passed from one worker to another.

When a queen is removed from her hive, worker bees become 'nervous' within an hour of her removal and begin behaviors of queen replacement within four hours of her absence.

Queen substance spreads by contact; scent perception alone is not sufficient. An experiment was set up where a queen was confined within a colony divided in half by two layers of screen that bees can not pass through or make contact with their antennae. A control colony was likewise divided but with a partition of excluder screen material that allowed workers, but not the queen, to pass through.

In a double-screened colony, the queenless worker bees become more active and begin to rear replacement queens. In the colony where worker bees passed through the excluder, there was no queen rearing in either portion. This demonstrates that odor alone was not effective in communicating the message that a queen is present or absent.

The greater the separation from the queen or larger the total bee population, the less effective the distribution of queen substance. Beekeepers use both separation distance and a large bee population to rear queens.

Figure 7-5
Beekeepers are able to take advantage of the power of the queen substance to keep even the smallest number of bees together during swarming. As long as the queen stays with the swarm, the bees are relatively easy to handle. C. Hubbard

All parts of the queen's body are attractive to workers. The queen substance is surprisingly persistent—bees respond to a cage that held a queen long after she has been removed. Dr. Butler found that the mast of his sailing yacht, contaminated with 100 μg of queen substance in 1963 during an experiment he was conducting, was still attracting drones six years later despite weather exposure over that time period.

Queen substance functions

Careful experiments over the years have revealed that queen substance has a number of functions. Queen substance is the major pheromone for these behaviors:

- inhibition in rearing of replacement queens
- swarm stabilization
- sex attraction
- queen retinue behavior
- stimulation of foraging and brood rearing
- hive functions like comb building, nectar and pollen foraging and food storage.

Inhibition of queen rearing

The queen substance pheromone effectively prevents worker bees from rearing queens until the supply of the chemical either stops (the queen is removed or dies), diminishes (as in supersedure) or there is serious interference in worker bee distribution of her pheromone (as in swarming).

When the queen of a colony is removed, emergency queen rearing begins in the colony. If colonies rearing queen cells in the spring are fed or sprayed with artificial queen pheromone (QMP), there is a delay in rearing replacement queens for a few days compared to untreated colonies that begin queen rearing immediately. The absence or reduced quantity of queen mandibular gland pheromone can thus be shown to be largely responsible for the initiation of queen rearing in bee colonies.

Swarm stabilization

A function of the queen mandibular gland pheromone outside the colony is to attract flying workers to the swarm and to reinforce the behavior of swarm stabilization (Figures 7-3, 7-5). Both of the two major decenoic acid compounds are necessary in normal swarm behavior. 9 ODA attracts flying workers to the queen and helps keep the bees flying in a swarm together as they move from hive location to cluster site. Then 9 ODA, in combination with the two forms of 9 HDA, stimulates bees to cluster around a queen and stop flying, resulting in **swarm stabilization behavior**. 9 HDA only works over a short distance, whereas 9 ODA has a wider effect.

Other stimuli contribute to clustering behavior besides queen substance. Vibrations produced by workers, the sight of other workers, and the smell of workers (not a specific chemical smell apparently) are all attractive to workers under swarming conditions. Workers do not apparently release their scent gland pheromone in this situation to prevent chemical interference and help their sisters orient to a queen who has landed after her flight. Scenting becomes key when beekeepers attempt to capture a swarm or when bees move into a new home.

Sex attractant

Outside the bee colony, 9 ODA is the main attractant chemical that attracts drones to a virgin queen during mating. This compound is the first communication between a virgin queen and a drone in the sequence of signal exchanges that occurs in mating behavior (Chapter 10). 9 HDA and material from abdominal tergal glands, along with 10 HDA (2E-10-hydroxydecenoic acid found in the virgin queen mandibular gland secretion) plus likely other as yet unidentified chemicals from the mandibular gland are also involved.

9 ODA only functions outside the colony as a sex attractant and needs to act in concert to ensure a successful mating. 9 ODA and the chemical mix communicate the presence of the virgin queen. Drones orient downwind to the chemical when it is at least four meters (4.4 yards) above the ground. Inside the hive, 9 ODA does not excite the drone, although it is obviously present there. The stimulus must work only when a few molecules are present at the receptor site—when large quantities are present, as in the beehive, there is no behavioral response.

Studies have shown that this same chemical, 9 ODA, is also the sex attractant for the southeast Asian species of *Apis*. Inter-specific attraction may potentially occur in regions where two or more *Apis* species coexist. Mating between different species does not occur because they mate at different times of the day. *Apis florea* mates earlier in the day than *Apis dorsata*. There are also significant anatomical differences in the genitalia of the drones that prevent mating and behavioral distinctions in the sequence of mating behaviors.

Flight time is apparently one adaptation that allows the Africanized bee (*Apis mellifera scutellata*) to successfully maintain its own distinctive identity from temperate bee races in South America. The Africanized bee queen flies late in the day after most European race drones have retired for the day. Drones of the Africanized bee fly for a longer period of time and are present to mate with the earlier-mating European queens. They are often the only drones left to mate with Africanized queens late in the day.

Queen retinue

Another behavior in which queen substance plays a role is queen retinue behavior (Figures 7-2, 7-4, 7-10). Although 9 ODA alone elicits a retinue response, four additional components serve to attract workers to the live

Figure 7-6
Food transmission between worker bees. R. Williamson

queen. In addition to the five queen substance chemicals, the four additional components of Queen Retinue Pheromone QRP are:

- methyl (Z)-octadec-9-enoate (methyl oleate)
- (E)-3-(4-hydroxy-3-methoxyphenyl)-prop-2-en-1-ol (coniferyl alcohol)
- hexadecan-1-ol (cetyl alcohol)
- (Z9, Z12, Z15)-octadeca-9,12,15-trienoic acid (linolenic acid)

Coniferyl alcohol is produced in the mandibular gland secretion while the remainder come from head and abdominal tergite glands. The 'footprint substance' from Arnhart (tarsal) glands is also involved. An artificial mixture of these nine compounds is not as effective as live queens, suggesting worker attraction to queens involves additional, but as yet unidentified, chemicals.

Younger-aged bees are more attracted to the queen than foragers. Worker bees with larger ovariole numbers have less contact with their queen, and they may actively seek to avoid her to reduce their exposure to her pheromones.

Hive functions

Queen pheromone, in concert with other pheromones, influences important colony activities such as comb building, nectar and pollen foraging and food storage. QMP modulates many aspects of worker physiology and behavior and is critical for colony social organization. It increases worker longevity by slowing down worker maturation through a shifting of brain gene expression. It increases lipid levels in abdominal fat bodies. It plays a role in synthesis of juvenile hormone by the corpora allatum, an endocrine gland.

Small colony units, with more queen substance per bee, may be stimulated to greater activity. Thus, small colonies, such as swarms, grow at a faster rate, an effect that may be important to ensure survival. Worker bees reared under queenless conditions have a higher attraction to a queen's pheromones compared to those reared during the queen right colony condition.

It is possible to breed lines that have higher QMP production. There are some racial differences; Cape and Africanized worker bees are less attracted to queen substance. There is also a seasonal variation in queen pheromone production, with spring and early summer production being highest.

It is unclear how the queen's pheromone production relates to her suitability as a queen. Can workers evaluate their queen, thus remaining sterile and rearing only the queen's offspring, as the best means to increase their own (and their colonies') fitness? Studies by Mark Winston and colleagues in British Columbia suggest the queen tergite pheromone, not queen mandibular gland pheromone, performs this important function. Ethyl palmitate, a primer pheromone, is apparently an active agent contributing to the queen's ability to inhibit worker ovary development.

By substituting the combination of chemicals, it is possible to trick bees into believing their queen is present. Recent work has demonstrated that bees not only recognize a queen, but they recognize — and prefer — their own queen when offered a choice. Queen substance undoubtedly plays a role in this recognition.

Worker mandibular glands illustrate a caste specific difference. Worker mandibular glands have 10 HDA (10-hydroxy-2(E)decenoic acid) and 10-HDAA (10 hydroxydecanoic acid), which are minor components of the queen secretion plus a trace of 9 HDA. Laying workers (pseudo or false queens) that develop in the queen's absence have the highest production of 9 ODA and 9 HDA which enable them to establish the queen dominance hierarchy. This is especially noted in *Apis mellifera capensis*, a bee population that frequently develop laying workers which can subsequently produce a parthenogenic egg in a process termed **thelytoky**.

Food transmission

The behavior of food transmission — **trophallaxis** — is extremely important in the distribution of queen substance. Trophallaxis is a two-way exchange of food and chemicals. Workers pass the pheromone obtained from the queen to other bees in the colony via food transmission (Figure 7-6) and antennation (Figure 7-4). Even bees on the periphery of a nest received the queen's pheromone in just 15 minutes.

To obtain an offering of food, one bee 'begs' from another by a combination of antennal touching, body posture and other signals. The solicited bee offers a droplet of food at the base of her mouthparts. The bee that solicits extends her proboscis and takes the offered droplet.

Food transmission keeps all bees supplied with carbohydrates. If a bee colony is starving, workers pass any remaining food among each other until there is no more to share. Then they all die together in a short time period. This situation may occur during winter when a bee colony runs out of honey stores. The entire colony suddenly collapses. Food transmission ensures that all bees share their food resources until all food reserves are exhausted.

To demonstrate the extent of food transmission behavior, two English researchers fed six bees 20 milliliters (about two tablespoons) of radioactive labeled sugar syrup. They sampled bees five and 29 hours afterwards in their experimental colony of 24,000 bees for the presence of radioactivity (Box 10, Table 7-1). After only five hours, over one-half of the foragers had shared the sample. One day later over one-half the entire bee population was radioactive, indicating extensive sharing. Additionally, when the researchers examined older worker larvae 48 hours after initial feeding, they found 85% of the larvae radioactive. Bees were sharing with each other and with their larvae as well. This extensive sharing behavior assists distribution of food and passage of pheromones.

Dufour's gland

The secretions of the Dufour's gland (named after the French naturalist Léon Jean Marie Dufour) have been somewhat of a mystery. The gland's opening is located near the opening of the poison sac and secretes its alkaline products into the vaginal cavity. This gland is

Figure 7-7
Multiple stings lodged in a bee veil. The sting apparatus (shafts, muscles and glands) are the source of pheromones that attract other bees who may also leave their stings.

much larger in queens compared to the workers, and their composition of at least 24 chemicals is more diverse as well. While the mated queen gland secretion is higher in hydrocarbon content, virgin queens have higher ester components.

The Dufour's gland secretion of laying workers is similar to a queens.

Dufour's gland secretions are found on the queen's abdomen and on eggs that the queen lays. One suggestion is that the secretions are involved in egg-policing behavior whereby workers eliminate eggs laid by other workers but not those of the queen. It may be important in the early stages of queenlessness leading to removal of eggs of some laying workers while sparing those eggs from workers with better developed ovaries. Selection might be based on higher ester amount.

Tergal glands

Tergal glands are on the dorsal (top) side of the first four abdominal segments of the **gaster** (the part of the body following the narrow waist). They produce fatty acids, esters and hydrocarbons. The major component is Z-9-octadecenoic acid (oleic acid). Both workers and queens have tergal glands, but queens have more of this chemical. Virgin queens also release unique esters including decyldecanoic acid and octadecenoic acid from their tergal glands. Ethyl palmitate (EP) has also been identified in the tergal gland secretion.

The queen tergal gland secretion elicits retinue behavior and also inhibits ovary development in workers. At short range, the secretions are a drone attractant during mating. It also seems that virgin queens might somehow use the tergal gland unique to them in the elimination of rival virgin queens.

Fecal pheromone

Young virgin queens produce **o-aminoacetophene** and at least ten additional compounds in their feces, spraying rival virgin queens when they emerge together into

Figure 7-8
Alert to intruders, these three guard bees are in character-istic defensive posture. R. Williamson

a colony. It is repellent to workers. It is likely used in combination with tergal gland pheromone to protect the victorious queen from being attacked by workers and mark loosing queens, ensuring workers don't protect them. Older queen feces may serve a role in nestmate recognition and assist workers to recognize their own queen.

Alarm communication

Beekeepers long ago noticed that they were more apt to get additional stings after the first sting (Figure 7-7). As early as 1814, Francoise Huber observed bees stinging in response to a sting removed from another bee. The honey bee is the only sting-possessing species known to have a strongly-barbed sting. When human skin, clothing or mammal hide is stung, the sting (Chapter 5, Figure 5-27) usually remains embedded in the victim and releases an alarm chemical, which marks the enemy. The odor remains effective up to five minutes, often leading to attack by other bees. Some wasp species also have barbs on their stings but lack the alarm chemicals.

Alarm pheromones are widely distributed in social insects. Honey bees have two different alarm pheromones, one from each end of the body. The mandibular glands of workers produce **2-heptanone**. The glands of the sting apparatus (**sting sheath gland** and **Koschevnikov gland**) produce low molecular weight, highly volatile **isopentyl acetate** (IPA) plus some 40 additional compounds including butyl acetate, 1-hexanol, n-butanol, 1-octanol, hexyl acetate, octyl acetate, n-pentyl acetate and 2-nonanol. The **sting pheromone**, with a banana oil fragrance, is the **major alarm chemical.**

The alarm chemical may also be released by extending the sting in the direction of an alarm-causing incident. Opening a hive in the winter causes bees on the periphery of the bee cluster to protrude the sting and release a **droplet of venom** with alarm pheromone. Likewise, a guard bee at a colony entrance may extend her sting and fan her wings to help alert sisters to the threat. Release of the alarm chemical recruits soldier bees, workers that respond to hive disturbances, to join in hive defense.

The major chemical in the sting that causes alarm is **isopentyl acetate (IPA)**, also called isoamyl acetate. IPA also acts as a **target-marking pheromone**, guiding other defenders to the sting site. Newly emerged workers have no isopentyl acetate whereas bees 15+ days of age have one to five µg. There are several other components of the gland such as acetates and alcohols, as listed above, and they probably work in conjunction with isopentyl acetate.

Actual stinging or defensive behavior is correlated with isopentyl acetate. This can easily be demonstrated by placing a tiny drop of this compound on a dummy target such as a felt 'mouse' that is placed at the hive's entrance. The bees will seek to remove and even sting the dummy target. Bees display a faster reaction time upon perception of the alarm pheromone, and, generally, bees will respond to alarm pheromone only at or near the colony, not in the field. Movement increases and targets guard bee response. Smoke in some way masks the pheromone.

Another alarm pheromone component, (Z)-11-eicosenol, induces stinging behavior but is less volatile. (Z)-11-eicosenol prolongs the activity of the more volatile IPA, presumably by slowing down the evaporation of IPA. The blend of IPA and (Z)-11-eicosenol is active for a longer time than IPA alone. Africanized honey bees may have two components, IPA and an unsaturated derivative of IPA (3-methyl-2-buten-1-yl acetate) which may improve recruitment of additional hive mates to targeted enemies. The queen honey bee has no isopentyl acetate. Drones lack a sting and neither produce nor respond to alarm chemicals.

The second alarm pheromone, 2-heptanone, is produced in worker mandibular glands. Also called the **mandibular gland alarm pheromone**. It, like isopentyl acetate, is absent in newly emerged workers but is present by foraging age. Bees respond to 2-heptanone at the nest entrance. Guard bees at a colony entrance have a characteristic stance with front legs, mandibles and antennae outstretched (Figure 7-8). This posture along with biting behavior may assist in marking hive intruders with 2-heptanone. This compound has a repellent effect, deterring potential enemies and robber bees. 2-heptanone is not always as effective in producing a response as it requires 20 to 70 times as much compound before bees respond. Queen and drones lack 2-heptanone.

Not all scientists agree that 2-heptanone is an alarm chemical. Some suggest it is used as a substance to warn bees to avoid a strongly-guarded colony or is used to mark foraging sites since 2-heptanone does repel foragers and foragers have the highest amounts of 2-heptanone. Alternately, it may be used by robber bees to avoid attack in the colony they are robbing or even used by workers to mark larvae that have been fed in the colony. One research paper suggests yet another possible function. 2-heptanone may be used to bite and paralyze small insects and mites. Such pests might be anesthetized by 2-heptanone (for up to nine minutes according to the study), so the bees can remove pests like wax moth larvae and varroa mites, which are too small to sting.

Nasonov scent gland

Located at the tip of the abdomen, the **Nasonov scent gland** (also Nasanov) is an extremely important pheromone-producing releaser gland for honey bee workers. Named after a Russian scientist, the scent gland (its most common name) is exposed at sources of water, artificial feeding stations, at flowers, at the hive in a confused situation, swarm cluster locations, and new home site entrances during swarming.

To release the chemical, bees fan their wings while standing high on their hind legs with their abdomen pointed upward and their last segment pointed downward. This posture is termed **scenting**. When in this position, it is possible to actually see the exposed gland between the sixth and seventh tergites of the worker's abdomen (Figure 7-15).

The chemical pheromone released from the Nasonov gland is a mixture of seven terpenoids: E and Z isomers of citral, nerol, geraniol, nerolic acid, geranic acid and (E, E) farnesol. These terpene derivatives contribute to the characteristic lemony odor of several plant species (for example lemongrass).

In honey bees, E-citral is the most active component. Geraniol, the most common compound, is converted by enzymes to citral and geranic acid. Like many other

Figure 7-9
Apiary at the University of Guelph, Ontario, Canada. Each hive in an apiary has an individual odor which provides identity and protection. L. Connor

Figure 7-10
Queen surrounded by antennating retinue bees. Tuckabee

Figure 7-11
Bees may mark flowers with their tarsal footprint to signal other foragers of their recent flower visit. L. Connor

pheromones, the Nasonov scent pheromone is produced when most needed. Newly emerged workers and bees in winter have little scent pheromone while foraging bees and bees that are swarming produce the greatest quantity.

During swarming, the pheromone interacts with 9 ODA from the queen during movement through the air and with 9 HDA and 9 ODA of the queen as bees settle into a single swarm cluster. Release of the scent gland pheromone may help coalesce the many small clusters of worker bees around the single location of the queen.

Queens and drones can detect Nasonov gland pheromone, but they lack the gland and cannot produce it. The evidence demonstrating that they can detect the chemical comes from both a bioassay experiment and electrophysiological recordings via an **electroantennograph** (EAG). In the bioassay experiment, adult drone response is measured in streams of air, some of which have the pheromone. The drones go toward the smell of the pheromone but not other odors, thus demonstrating a positive behavioral response to the pheromone.

In the EAG experiment, a recording electrode is inserted into an excised antennae of a drone. If the chemical is perceived, an electrical impulse is generated, which results in the recording electrode becoming temporarily negative. The change from positive to negative can be observed on an oscilloscope, confirming the passage of an electrical impulse. The amplitude of the response can be shown to be related to the amount of the odor.

Colony odor

Early on, beekeepers and bee scientists observed that bees could easily distinguish between individual colonies (Figure 7-9). At one time this was called colony 'morale' or 'spirit of the hive.' We now understand this social cement or signature mixture comes largely from the queen. Above and beyond the odors from their queen, each colony has an individual colony odor. Recent research suggest this common hive odor also comes from shared gut bacteria distributed via food transmission.

The waxy layers of the bee exoskeleton absorbs many of the odors of the hive, marking each bee and leading to individual colony differences. While foraging bees spend each day on several trips, their time in the hive at night reinforces the odor clinging to their body.

Colony odor and alarm odor function together in worker behavior to guard a hive. Honey bees, like all social insects, will attack an intruder threatening the safety of their colony. **Guards**, usually young foraging-age bees, position themselves near the entrance and stand with front legs off the ground and antennae forward (Figure 7-8). Mandibles and wings are closed but can be opened if the bees become further alarmed. The number of guards increases after an alarm pheromone alert prompted by robbing bees or other external intrusions.

Bees entering a colony are smelled to determine friend or foe. During favorable forage conditions, a colony has fewer guards; after the flow their numbers increase.

If a foraging bee enters the wrong hive by mistake (a behavior termed **drifting**), a guard may halt the incorrect-smelling visitor. If challenged, the invading bee may adapt a **submissive behavior**, move very little, turn away from examining guards and offer food so they may be allowed to pass. Guards may grab extremities such as wings or legs and attempt to push or pull the intruder outside. As long as the intruder remains submissive, no further response is evident. Usually, the guard bee gives up her actions or she succeeds in pulling the incorrect-smelling bee from the entrance.

If robber bees attempt to enter or if drifting bees become more aggressive in their attempts to enter a bee colony, guards seize the intruders and grapple with them. Guards usually assist each other in the expulsion of such intruders, who may also be stung. Bees stung in fights soon die, but the bee that stings another bee usually can withdraw the sting and function normally.

With individual colony odors and alarm pheromones, a colony can adequately and appropriately defend itself. Harmless intruders, such as young bees that have drifted to the wrong entrance by mistake or successful foragers that have done likewise, usually remain unhurt. They may succeed in joining the new colony and then obtain that new hive odor in a couple of hours. Bees that behave like robbers or different-smelling yellowjackets, bumble bees or other intruders are quickly intercepted and may be stung to death if they persist in hive entry.

Trail pheromones

As honey bees walk, they distribute an attractive chemical called ethyl palmitate (EP). Also called the footprint substance or trail pheromone, the major source of this chemical is the Arnhart or tarsal gland. The chemical is deposited by the terminal arolium between the tarsal claws as the bee walks about. In addition to the feet, it is deposited by the tip of the abdomen, which often trails over the surface as bees walk. Drones and queens also have a trail substance, distinguishable from the worker trail substance by guard bees.

The attractiveness of trail substance can be demonstrated by forcing a bee to walk in one of two glass tubes and then offering that tube, with an identical one not visited, to a group of worker bees. Given such a choice, bees will more likely enter the tube which has been previously visited. In the bee colony, footprint substance is used like a trail pheromone; bees follow it to the entrance (as when it is experimentally moved). Outside it serves as a longer-term marker to help foragers relocate flowers visited by bees after nectar has been replenished.

Figure 7-12
Worker bees constructing new comb cells. Comb serves as a pheromone sink for the bee colony. L. Connor

Figure 7-13
A section of brood of all ages, from eggs to sealed cells. Worker bees apparently can tell the difference in caste and developmental stage. R. Williamson

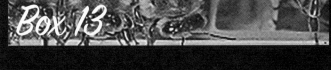

ODOR RECOGNITION

Insects perceive smell much the same as we do, except olfactory receptors are on the antennae of the insect. When a chemical smell is perceived by the smell receptor, it binds chemically to the sense receptor. The binding causes the receptor to change shape, which in turn causes an electrical change in the cell. This change is fed into the nervous system of the insect which can ignore the information, store it or react to it. When we observe a reaction, it is usually some type of behavior.

Some smell receptors are general while others receive very specific chemicals, such as food odors or pheromones. The surface of antennae have space for many receptors; over 700 floral scents have been tested to be detectable in the olfactory receptors of honey bees.

An example of a general sense is the aroma of decay. When a bee dies, chemical changes result in changes in the normal release of chemicals from a living organism. In bees, an identified decay odor is oleic acid. When a bee dies inside the hive, the body will begin to release this chemical. Hive bees smell it and begin the process of removal of their dead comrade.

Several bees may pick up and carry the dead body. Eventually the body is detected by a specialized group of bees we label 'undertaker bees.' Such bees will not abandon the body but instead carry, drag, or push it out of the hive itself. Usually, they fly off with the body and drop the remains away from the hive entrance.

If we dab a bit of oleic acid on the body of a living bee, she will be treated like a dead sister. Bees carry her about and eventually drag her outside the entrance, despite her struggling and other manifestations of protest over her treatment. Only when the chemical wears off will she be allowed to return.

Figure 7-14
Nest mate recognition by guard bees allows access to odor recognizable nest mates. L. Connor

Figure 7-15
Scent pheromone is produced by a gland at the raised tip of the abdomen. Bees fan their wings to spread the chemical. J. Zawislak

There is also some suggestion that tarsal footprints may help **short-term marking** of individual flowers as having recently been visited (Figure 7-11). It may combine to work with 2-heptanone to repel bees from revisiting such marked flowers. Bumble bees have such marking ability from their tarsal gland, and honey bees may additionally avoid flowers they have recently marked.

Footprint substance works in conjunction with the Nasonov gland pheromone but persists longer. Footprint substance, along with colony odor, probably helps bees find their own home entrance. It does not appear that bees distinguish a distinctive, individual hive-footprint substance at flowers or artificial food sources, but, rather they recognize the odor as 'bee smell.' Trail substances are extremely well known in ants and termites. It is how they find their way from home to food and back again. Marking in other animals (like dogs and cats) is well known too.

Queen footprint substance may assist in the important function of **to inhibit queen rearing**. Worker bees are the builders of queen cups for the queen to deposit fertilized eggs. There is some suggestion that her movement over these areas may slow or reduce queen cup building activity of worker bees. This response is in concert with the activity of QMP and/or QRP (queen mandibular and queen retinue pheromones discussed earlier) to inhibit queen rearing by the workers. We call this a **pheromone concert**.

Brood and comb pheromones

In addition to pheromones produced by workers and queens, there are stimulatory triggers from brood (Figure 7-13) and beeswax comb (Figures 7-17, 7-19). When brood is present, workers gather pollen, and when not present, their pollen foraging is greatly reduced. The brood itself produces a **brood ester pheromone** chemical (BEP) from their salivary gland that stimulates foraging behavior. It is not believed that bees need such stimulation to collect nectar.

BEP is a blend of ten fatty-acid esters (methyl palmitate, methyl oleate, methyl stearate, methyl linoleate, methyl linolenate, ethyl palmitate, ethyl oleate, ethyl stearate, ethyl linoleate and ethyl linolenate) and a volatile terpene E-ß-ocimene. Some components are more active than others, but all ten individual compounds show some releaser pheromone effect on adult bees. The esters are present in different amounts and proportions as a function of caste and larval age. Thus, nurses can recognize the egg and caste of larvae and provide them appropriately with optimal attention.

Four esters, methyl linolenate, methyl linoleate, methyl oleate, and methyl palmitate, induce the worker bees to cap the cell with a thin cover of wax. The esters are produced in large quantities by the larvae during their cocoon spinning activity. In addition to releaser effects on various aspects of brood care, BEP also has primer effects.

Methyl palmitate and ethyl oleate increase the activity of the hypopharyngeal glands of workers, where royal jelly is produced. Various components seem specifically to affect queen rearing—methyl stearate increases the acceptance of queen cells, methyl linoleate enhances the amount of royal jelly deposited by the worker, and methyl palmitate increases the weight of the larvae.

Brood ester pheromones, specifically ethyl palmitate and methyl linolenate and a third component E-ß-ocimene, also **inhibit ovary development in worker bees** in conjunction with the QMP pheromone. BEP additionally acts to regulate adult bee activities. High dosages of the methyl and ethyl esters slows down the progression of young bees towards the tasks typical of older bees. The young larvae who have a lower need for nurse-age bees (their cells are mass provisioned) promote foraging by emitting a low quantity of brood ester pheromone and a large amount of E-ß-ocimene. In contrast, older

Figure 7-16
Inspecting a bee colony may temporarily interfere with pheromone communication among the bees in the colony.

Figure 7-17
Using drawn, empty comb (in plastic hives), beekeepers stimulate honey gathering by utilizing the bees honey hoarding behavior. D. Morgan

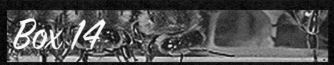

Box 14

COLONY DEFENSE

Great quantities of brood and often large stores of honey and pollen make the beehive a tempting target for intruders. Defense is needed to prevent entry and growth of organisms as small as bacteria and fungi that might cause sickness or disease to bees. A venomous sting is the ultimate weapon in a long line of defensive mechanisms for a colony of honey bees. Here are some weapons in the defensive arsenal of bees:

Protective nest site

Bees nest high and choose sturdy cavities with small entrances. Have you tried to find a bee tree? They are not easy to spot. Other visually-oriented predators probably have the same difficulties finding a nest site as humans do.

Large colony size

Many hive mates mean colonies can afford to lose members in defensive behaviors because there are others to take their place. More individuals means better protection throughout the animal kingdom. Honey bee colonies are much easier to examine and manipulate in spring and fall when populations are smaller. You get fewer stings too!

Guard bees

Guards challenge insects, including bees from different colonies, that smell or behave differently. They grasp and mark such individuals with mandibular gland pheromone, pulling and pushing the intruder away. Larger intruders, when moving about the hive site, are buzzed by guard bees. Such behavior is directed toward dark, different-appearing portions of an intruder's body. Bees buzz loudly and attempt to burrow into body coverings like fur or hair to sting flesh.

Nest mate recognition

Bees recognize their queen and nest mates on both an environmental and genetic basis. This recognition is both effective and rapid in establishing relatedness. Alarm recruitment pheromones—two specific glands produce two different pheromones to assist bees in calling for help.

Propolis

Propolis (Figure 7-18) is primarily a substance that aids defense of the nest against tiny microorganisms. Bees use propolis to cover bodies that can't be removed so they cover them in propolis. They also use propolis to cover surfaces to defend against harmful bacteria and fungi that may enter the colony. Propolis is the colony's major defense against ants.

Other protection mechanisms include a digestive tract that kills pathogens, leaving the hive to void wastes, high viscosity and enzyme protection of honey that inhibits pathogen growth, rapid recognition and removal of dead nest mates (both adult and brood), heightened nest-cleaning behaviors and finally an elevated, finely-regulated brood nest temperature. Nest defense is important and therefore highly redundant.

Figure 7-18
Worker bee carrying propolis on her hind leg. R. Williamson

larvae with a high need for nurse bee attention (they are progressively provisioned and with larger bodies need more food) keep nurses in contact with them for a longer time by producing a high quantity of brood ester pheromone.

Worker bees recognize each brood stage (age) of the different castes (Figure 7-13). Recognition of caste and brood is most likely due to a pheromone of unknown origin. Brood, transferred from one colony to another, is readily accepted. Perhaps brood pheromone masks colony odor so the transferred brood is accepted and not

rejected, whereas adult bees added from another colony with a different odor are often rejected.

It is possible to demonstrate a behavioral effect that seems to be related to beeswax comb pheromone. When bees in a cage (or an ordinary colony of bees) are offered more empty drawn comb, the bees **hoard** a greater amount of food stores. In the lab situation, this means the bees consume more sugar water. In a field test, honey bee colonies given twice the amount of empty comb stored more honey than the control (Figure 7-17, 7-19). The **beeswax comb releases a chemical pheromone** which bees perceive; they respond by continuing the collection of nectar to ripen into honey, leading to storage of a larger surplus when so challenged.

Pheromones in dance language

Dance language, discussed in Chapter 8, may include pheromone release. Waggle-dancing bees produce and release four cuticular hydrocarbons (two alkanes, tricosane and pentacosane, and two alkenes, Z-(9)-tricosene and Z-(9)-pentacosene) from their abdomens into the air. These compounds are produced subcutaneously; they are not stored within a gland and are present in only minute quantities in non-dancing worker bees. If these substances are injected into a hive, they significantly increase the number of foragers leaving the hive, suggesting these compounds play some sort of pheromonal role in worker recruitment along with the dancing.

Other pheromones

Honey bees can recognize their own individual queen. Pheromones play a role in this recognition. Bees can tell their queen even from closely related sister queens, although with greater difficulty the more closely related. This distinctiveness makes requeening management, the substitution of a new queen for the old established colony queen, a challenge. This individual odor is also important for guards to detect as a queen returns from mating flights and attempts to reenter the colony.

Queens must be physically contacted by bees to be recognized. Smell alone is not enough as several experiments have shown. The distinctive colony odor is not the recognition factor. All other things being equal, when their own queen is experimentally removed, bees will elect to cluster around a queen of similar age and reproductive status to their own their own queen over

Box 15

STIMULATORY EFFECT OF COMB AND BROOD

Empty comb, whether new or previously used, stimulates bees to store honey (Figures 7-17, 7-19). Colonies given more empty comb (drawn frames) stored 30% more honey compared to colonies given less empty comb. Bees hoard more sugar syrup in lab trials when supplied with three pieces of comb compared to only one piece. Passing a stream of air over beeswax comb increases hoarding, suggesting a volatile pheromone is the stimulatory factor.

Comb containing brood is the major reason for inhibition of worker ovary development. Worker larvae secrete many chemicals. When deprived of food and cell visits, larvae become highly attractive to nurse-age worker bees which then visit and inspect such larvae more frequently than normal. Brood also stimulates pollen collection by adult foragers. If you artificially remove brood, the amount of pollen a colony collects decreases (by 28% in one experiment). Removal of both brood and an egg-laying queen doubles the decrease, showing how critically important it is to have an expanding brood area and healthy queen in colonies being used in pollination of crops. Giving colonies brood (transferred from other colonies) stimulates a colony to increase its pollen-collection behavior.

Figure 7-19
Adding drawn comb at the start of the nectar flow stimulates the bees to gather up to 30% more honey than when given fewer empty comb. Place two supers above two standard deep boxes.

queens from queens from a different background or condition. Genetics are also important.

Ethyl oleate is a chemical produced in the worker digestive tract and appears to act in conjunction with queen mandibular pheromone and brood pheromone to inhibit adult worker division of labor. It is higher in forager bees than in nurse-aged bees, inhibiting younger-aged bees from becoming foragers. This effect occurs regardless of the amount of honey in the hive and even in absence of queen and or brood.

There are probably other pheromones to identify in the bee colony. For example, bees recognize drones. Drones use a pheromone to attract other drones to specific areas for mating (Chapter 9). Can bees recognize drones and workers as individuals as they do the queen or is the recognition of each a more generic colony odor?

Bees also recognize larvae from fertilized eggs versus those from unfertilized eggs because each receives a different diet. They also distinguish between a young

worker larva and an older one, in order to supply them each with a different diet. Chemicals, whether specific pheromones or not, play a major role in this recognition. Ethyl oleate is released by older forager bees to slow the maturing of nurse bees. This primer pheromone serves to keep the ratio of nurse bees to forager bees in the balance that is most beneficial to the hive (Figure 7-13).

It is evident that chemical communication is extremely important in bees. As we examine and manipulate bee colonies (Figure 7-16) using smoke or feeding scented sugar syrup, the beekeeper may unintentionally disrupt pheromone communication. We need to learn more about the chemicals and how they work. It may be possible to artificially introduce specific messages into hives at appropriate times (Figure 7-16) or use some of these chemicals to simulate natural effects to our benefit.

The bee world is chemically oriented—we need to learn more about chemical communication to become better bee stewards.

key terms

9 ODA (9-oxo-2-decenoic acid)	ethyl palmitate	pheromone concert	scenting
9 HDA (9 hydroxydecenoic acid (cis & trans)	exocrine gland	primer pheromone	semiochemical
	fecal pheromone	propolis	sex attractant pheromone
Antennae (& proboscis) contact	food transmission	pseudo or false queens	submissive behavior
Arnhart (tarsal) gland	footprint substance	queen equivalent (Qeq)	swarm stabilization
beeswax comb pheromone	grooming	queen mandibular pheromone (QMP)	supersedure
brood ester pheromone (BEP)	guard bees	queen rearing inhibition	thelytoky
colony odor	juvenile hormone	queen retine	trail pheromone
drifting	kairomone	queen retine pheromone (QRP)	trophallaxis (food transmission)
Dufour gland	laying worker		undertaker bees
electroantennograph (EAG)	mandibular glands	queen substance	waggle dance
emergency queen cell	Nasonov (scent) gland	releaser pheromone	
ethyl oleate	nest mate recognition	scent gland	
	pheromone		

discussion questions

Why are pheromones the 'social glue' and the principle communication method in a honey bee colony? Name some of the pheromones and how they work. Some pheromones may consist of multiple chemicals – do they all have equal roles to play in influencing the behavioral response to the pheromone?

Describe how pheromones define a queen/defend a hive/identify nest mates/stimulate honey storage/stimulate pollen foraging. What other behaviors do pheromones influence?

What is a pheromone concert? Can you give an example? If a pheromone such as 9 ODA could become a hormone what does that mean in conservation of energy resources to bees?

What is the role of food transmission in pheromone communication? Describe the behavior of food transmission. How else are pheromones spread in a colony? Or among bees?

Why is hive or colony odor not a pheromone? Could it be a kairomone?

Where do other possible pheromones likely serve the honey bee society? Why is pheromone function using the bioassay technique so difficult to interpret?

The beehive is a dark, smelly place. Are you more aware of smells in dark enclosures? Why are smell and taste probably the best means of communication in the dark, smelly beehive?

exercises

Duplicate, or modify as you feel appropriate, some of the experiments described here demonstrating how queen substance is distributed. Divide a colony so one portion has contact with a queen, or artificial queen substance and the other portion does not. Monitor each portion for queen cells and worker ovary development. Allow contact or exchange in separate experiments.

Demonstrate the presence and activity of a pheromone. You can do this by creating a confusing situation by dumping bees in front of a colony entrance and observing Nasonov scent gland use. How many bees scent? How long do they scent? Alternatively, place a piece of black felt cloth stuffed with cotton (i.e. a 'mouse') on the entrance and observe how the bees behave. Then put a small drop of isopentyl acetate on the 'mouse' and see if you observe a more definite response. What happens? Can you think of additional ways to demonstrate scenting or alarm communication?

Develop and design an experiment that will show the existence of and bee response to a pheromone such as trail substance, brood pheromone or other suspected pheromones.

Observe bee guarding behavior at a beehive entrance. Determine how many guards are present at different times of the day. Then do some tests of colony odor by putting bees from other hives, drones, or other insects at or just inside the entrance. Exchange the hive locations of two colonies during active flight and during drone flight in the afternoon and see if you can see changes from the 'normal' condition.

Demonstrate the stimulatory (or inhibitory) effect of a bee pheromone. Add or remove brood from a colony and see if you can measure a change in foraging behavior. Alternatively, add or remove beeswax comb to a colony or group of bees and determine if you can detect a difference in the amount of foraging and/or honey collected by two colonies during active flight and during drone flight in the afternoon. See if you can observe changes from the 'normal' condition.

references

Bortolotti, L. and C. Costa 2014. Chemical Communication in the Honey Bee Society. Chap 5 In Neurobiology of Chemical Communication. Ed by C. Mucignat-Caretta. CRC Press/Taylor & Francis, Boca Raton, FL

Free, J.B. 1987. Pheromones of Social Bees. Chapman and Hall, London

Grozinger, C.M. 2015. Honey Bee Pheromones. In The Hive and Honey Bee Ed by J. Graham. Dadant and Sons, Hamilton, IL

Papachristoforou, A. et al. 2012. The Bite of the Honeybee: 2-Heptanone Secreted from Honeybee Mandibles during a Bite Acts as a Local Anaesthetic in Insects and Mammals. PLOS ONE https://doi.org/10.1371/journal.pone.0047432

Tautz, J. 2008. The Buzz about Bees: Biology of a Superorganism. Springer

Winston, M.L. 1987. The Biology of the Honey Bee. Harvard University Press, Cambridge, MA

Figure 8-1
Dance language allows bees to concentrate foraging on the richest sources—here on a bee-bee tree.

Concepts

Dance language communication
- round dance
- waggle dance
- sickle dance
- dance floor
- dialects
- accuracy of dance language

Dance language controversy

Marking bees

Nest site selection

Dance communications

Imagine this common occurrence—a honey bee forager discovers a rich, new food source. She could be a scout bee or an experienced forager working a patch of flowers that is failing. After discovering the new food source, the bee fills her honey stomach with nectar and/or pollen baskets with pollen and flies back to her hive. Once home she makes a series of repeated, exaggerated movements, sharing a bit of the nectar with hive mates. We call the movements **bee dancing**. These dances recruit other bees to join her at these new-found riches.

Imagine a second bee, a scout bee in a swarm of bees hanging on a branch several hundred feet from the original colony they just departed. They must find a new home. Our scout bee searches for a cavity—an empty box or an unoccupied cavity in a huge tree—and returns to the swarm to dance about the potential nest site.

These food/home seeking, collection, and sharing behaviors allow bees to use sight, touch, movement, chemical signals and sound vibrations (although they lack ears) to communicate where to find a new food supply or a new home. With dancing, honey bees are able to communicate precise information on distance, source and especially direction to fly to forage (nectar, pollen or water) or to locate new food/home sites.

Honey bees are remarkable social animals. Through the work of Professor Karl von Frisch, Martin Lindauer and others, the dance language of honey bees has been decoded and interpreted. Frisch was honored for his studies on honey bee dancing as advancing the study of ethology (animal behavior) with the Nobel Prize in Physiology and Medicine in 1973.

Dance routines

Honey bees exhibit two basic behaviors or dances to communicate food resources and new home sites to other members of their colony. The two basic dances are the **round dance** and the **wagtail dance**. They may include an intermediate **sickle dance** as well, in some bee races. There are differences (dialects) among the various bee races in their dancing.

The round dance

A Carniolan race honey bee which finds food or water less than 80 meters (88 yards) from the hive will perform a round dance on the vertical beeswax combs in the hive. The dancing bee, with quick short steps, runs around in narrow circles on the comb, often changing direction (Figure 8-3). The bee may dance for several seconds or as long as a minute. Then she may stop, distribute some of the contents of her honey stomach and begin the same dance at a different place on the comb.

The round dance informs potential nestmates, called recruits, of a food source within 80 meters (88 yards) of the hive. The liveliness of the dance is influenced by source richness, with more vigorous and faster dancing for nectar of higher sugar concentration. Powerful food odors cling to the body of the dancing forager. These odor clues communicate the floral source of the food.

Additionally, the bee performing the round dance, by pausing occasionally to give hive mates a taste sample of the food, communicates information about the food source. Thus by **taste, odor and dance**, precise information is conveyed from dancer to recruit.

In summary, a round dance communicates:

- food close (< 80 m) of the hive
- smell and taste of food
- profitability of source (liveliness of dance)

The wagtail dance

Bees translate environmental clues such as the position of the sun's azimuth (the sun angle above the horizon which varies during the day) and gravity information, coupled with internal information of time of day and energy expenditure, to inform hive mates of potential food or home sites at greater distances. When the food source is greater than approximately 80 meters (88 yards) from the hive for Carniolan bees (each race or stock may show variation in their performance), foragers perform a **wagtail dance** (also termed waggle dance, waggling dance, figure-8 dance or sometimes hyphenated wag-tail dance, Figure 8-7).

In a wagtail dance, the dancing bee runs in a narrow half-circle to one side, then does a sharp turn and runs in a straight line while vigorously waggling her abdomen from side to side. She then makes a half-circle in the opposite direction completing a full circle (Figure 8-4). The straight portion is always performed with the bee orienting her body at the same position relative to gravity on the vertical comb in the dark hive.

Figure 8-2
Workers with tiny numbered tags on their thorax and painted abdomens, made during a communications study. T. Seeley

Figure 8-3
Round dance. J. Zawislak

Only the straight portion is characterized by vigorous side to side movement of the abdomen, waggling, and sound production. The bee may not start the waggling position of this dance at the same point each time due to varying distances of the half-circle position but there is little variation in the direction on the comb the waggling is performed or in waggling duration. Orientation to gravity encodes the direction to fly while the time of sound production in waggling informs how far to fly.

By means of the wagtail dance, bees are able to convey accurate distance and direction information. Using the information, recruits quickly locate the food source. The dancing bees also provide odor and taste clues in the wagtail dance as well as some estimate of richness by the vigor of the dance.

While dancing, bees produce a series of sounds with wing muscles and abdominal waggling at a **frequency of 250 Hz.** During the waggling segment, there is a direct correlation between the sound production time and the distance a bee must travel to a food source (Figure 8-6). The farther the distance to the food source, the longer the waggling segment of the dance.

Bees use their **Johnston's organ** in the pedicel of the antennae to pick up the sound vibrations, and successfully translate the time segment of waggling, converting such information into distance to fly.

Bees measure distance by energy expended in flight as an **optic flow pattern** of their outbound flight rather than in a linear measure. Flight conditions like a strong headwind or tailwind are automatically taken into

account since the bee conveying the information and the bee being recruited will encounter the same conditions outside while flying. Flight over water, without a varying bee-eye view, cannot be conveyed with precise accuracy.

Outside the hive, bees use the sun's azimuth position as their **compass for direction**. Their eyes can detect **polarized light** and, using planes of polarization, they can accurately fix on the location of the sun. Some internal mechanism helps them adjust to the movement of the sun from east to west throughout the day. Thus, at any time, they are able to fix the location of a food source from their home by using the position of the sun. As the sun's position moves, bees adjust the direction information so that they can still find food and their way back to their hive.

Inside the dark hive where the wagtail dance is performed on the lower vertical brood combs, bees cannot see the sun. The bees must convert the sun angle outside the hive to a **gravity orientation** on the vertical combs inside the dark hive. It is this necessity for conversion that makes dancing a **true language.** It is not possible to simply point recruits in the correct direction.

In bee language, the sun's azimuth is oriented directly upward on the comb (against gravity). Therefore if bees need to indicate a food/water/home source that is directly towards the direction where the sun meets the horizon, they orient their body upward, away from gravity for the waggling segment, as diagrammed in Figure 8-8 A.

Figure 8-4
Wagtail dance. J. Zawislak

Figure 8-5
Sickle dance. The center (solid arrow) indicates the direction to source while the dotted arrows show direction of waggling movements. J. Zawislak

Food may be anywhere in a radius of 360° from the hive for several miles. To indicate locations to the right or left of the sun's position, the dancing bees transpose the angle they need to fly relative to the sun by alignment with gravity in the dark hive. Thus, for a food source 60° to the left of the sun, bees dance 60° to the left of straight up on the comb. Illustration 8-8 B diagrams a situation 60° to the left of a straight line toward the sun and 8-8 C illustrates food 120° to right of sun.

If the food is in the opposite direction to the sun, the flight orientation of the bee in the field would be 180°(directly away) from the sun's azimuth. In the dark hive the body orientation of the dancer's body would be directly downward on the comb, 180° from the upward or 0° position. To solve dance language remember that the bees always use the hive location as the axis of angle to sun and food.

In summary, the wagtail dance communicates:

- distance to food source
- direction to food source
- smell and taste of food
- profitability of source

There are some excellent videos available that illustrate the waggle dance (Bienentanz GmbH - 1 minute, 2006) and that discuss and illustrate dance language and wagtail dancing (Georgia Tech https://www.youtube.com/watch?v=bFDGPgXtK-U - 77 min. 28 sec. 2011).

The sickle dance

Food or water sources found by Italian bees between 10 and 30 meters (11 to 33 yards) from the hive are conveyed by performing a crescent or sickle dance (Figure 8-5). This transition dance appears in the shape of a figure eight. The direction of the source is approximated by the bee estimating an imaginary line which runs from the middle of the crescent base through the middle distance between the ends of the crescent.

A dance indicating a food source just beyond 10 meters looks more similar to a round dance. The dance changes to a recognizable sickle dance as distance increases in observations made with Italian bees. The two lobes gradually close together to resemble the wagtail dance for sources over 40 meters (44 yards). Figure 8-9 compares movement patterns for the three dances.

Dance floor

Bees do the majority of their dancing on the lower comb surfaces. When bees dance on empty cells it is easier to transmit the sound clues compared to when they dance on capped cells. Examinations of plastic comb and foundation used by beekeepers indicate that the use of plastic does not interfere with the outcome of the bee dances.

Other scout bees follow her instructions of the direction and distance of the cavity she shares with the dance and fly to it. After walking the inside of the cavity they return to the hive and dance as well if they are motivated.

Bees in a swarm cluster also use dances to inform the clustered bees about potential new home sites. The swarm cluster doesn't transmit dance information

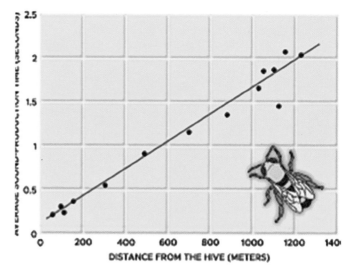

Figure 8-6
Relationship of sound production to distance in wagtail dance. J. Zawislak

Figure 8-7
Pollen forager performing a wagtail dance. Notice the number of hive mates observing the dance. C. Grüter

as readily as the beeswax comb surface. It seems temperature might alert others to follow a dancer in this situation. Additionally there is less reliance on information transfer as around 5% of scout bees dart back and forth to help lead the swarm cluster intact to their new home.

Taste and smell

As previously mentioned, during all dancing, potential recruit bees are able to smell the fragrance of flowers visited by dancing bees from odors clinging to the bodies of the dancers. Also, bees collecting nectar give samples to potential recruits during a dance. The odor of the flowers and nectar are very important in helping bees find specific flowers in the field. Tasting the gathered nectar informs bees of rich food sources.

Rich and plentiful food sources are communicated by the number of dancing bees in the hive and by the frequency of dances. If several kinds of plants are in bloom at the same time, sources with the most and sweetest nectar cause the liveliest dances. The largest number of recruit bees fly to blossoms where collecting is currently most rewarding. When a nectar supply diminishes, the dances for that source slow down or stop altogether. Foragers then turn to follow dancers indicating other sources for which dancing is livelier. This enables colonies to be able to exploit the most profitable and plentiful food sources.

Dialects

Different races of bees use different dialects of the dance language. Carniolan bees (*Apis mellifera carnica*) do not use the sickle dance at all. At approximately 80 meters

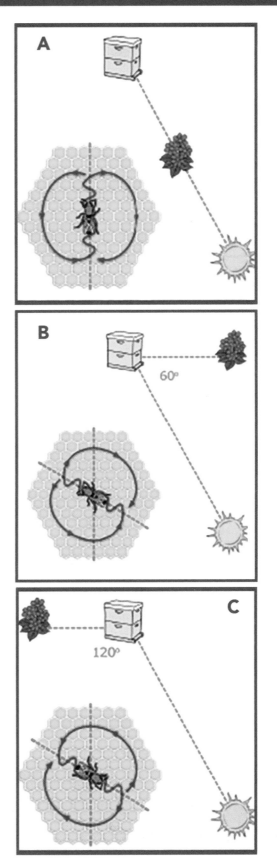

Figure 8-8
Diagrammatic representation of the dance corresponding in different field situations. J. Zawislak

Table 8-1

Comparison of distance communication in several bee races (in meters).

Races	Round	Sickle	Wagtail
Carniolan bees	0 - 80	none	> 80
German bees	0 - 20	20 - 64	> 64
Italian bees	0 - 10	10 - 40	> 40
Caucasian bees	0 - 10	10 - 35	> 35
Egyptian bees	0 - 5	5 - 10	> 10

(88 yards) they change from the round dance directly to the wagtail dance. Other strains (races) of honey bees also exhibit variations in dialect. The Italian and Caucasian races begin to perform the wagtail dance for food distances as close as 35 meters (44 yards) to the hive (Table 8-1).

It has been found that different races of bees will work together peacefully, but confusion arises when they communicate through dance language. For example, Carniolan bees recruited by the wagtail dance of an Italian bee will search for the feeding place too far away. The races have different distance communication, but direction information is conveyed the same way.

Different species of bees also use different dialects. The eastern (or Asian) honey bee, *Apis cerana*, employs the round dance for sources up to three meters away while in the giant bee, *Apis dorsata*, the round dance changes to the wagtail dance between four and five meters distance. Both species dance on the vertical comb; dance rhythm in *A. cerana* is slower.

The dwarf bee, *Apis florea*, dances on a horizontal landing place on top of the single comb nest (Chapter 2, Figure 2-11). They use a round dance for distances up to four or five meters and then the wagtail dance is done pointing

toward the food source. Interestingly, when *Apis mellifera* is forced to perform the wagtail dance in an experimental horizontal observation hive without vertical combs, their waggling portion also points towards the food source.

Additional recruitment dances

There are movement patterns that bees use that have also been described as dances. Bees run excitedly through the hive and the clustered swarm in what is called the buzz run 'breaking dance.' It is thought to be the signal to leave the hive to fly to a bivouac site or to leave from the swarm cluster to follow scout bees to a new home site.

A '**grooming dance**' (also termed 'shaking dance') is a side–to-side body movement, accompanied by wing vibrations. It is performed when a bee grabs another with her front legs and vibrates up and down for one or two seconds. It is thought this recruits assistance in body grooming and perhaps is used to recruit bees to perform a needed hive task. A '**tremble dance**' is similar to the wagtail dance as it is a rapid side-to-side body movement but in a stationary position. Returning foragers use this behavior to recruit house bees to take their nectar load.

Accuracy of the dance information

We can measure the accuracy of dance language in an experiment. All that is needed is a stop watch, protractor and an artificial food source. The watch will be used to time the waggling portion of dances and protractor to fix its gravitational orientation.

To conduct such an experiment, honey bees are first trained to an artificial food source. The artificial food source should be a scented sugar syrup dispenser or a simple dish of sugar syrup. The feeding source is initially placed adjacent to the hive entrance and when several bees begin to feed, it is gently moved away from the hive

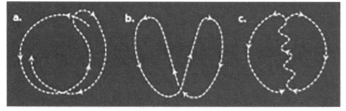

Figure 8-9
Comparison of bee dances:
a. round, b. sickle dance and c. wagtail dances. Arrows indicate the direction of movement. J. Zawislak

in a series of 10 to 15 meter stages (11 to 16 yards) until the desired distance from the hive is reached. With Italian bees, it should be 36 meters (40 yards) or more from the hive to obtain the wagtail dance. Fan, step or other experiments can now be performed after you mark your foragers (Figure 8-2).

The **fan experiment** (Figure 8-10) is an effort to measure the accuracy of the direction information conveyed from dancer to recruit. The data shown is from an actual experiment performed by Professor von Frisch on 27 September 1949 from 9:10 to 10:40 a.m. In this experiment, bees were trained to the location F from his experimental observation hive. Then the artificial source and marked bees were removed and seven identical sources separated at 15 degree angles from each other, were offered.

The recruited bees who were informed of the food location F were remarkably accurate in finding food in that direction. As the numbers show, 24 recruits visited the station F in a direct line with the training table. (During the experimental time period all individual foragers were collected at the 7 fan stations they visited so they did not have the opportunity to return to the hive and dance). A few bees visited identical stations 15° to either side, with the greatest number, eight, visiting the station upwind of the training table F (a slight wind was moving left to right during the experiment). Statistical analysis of the results showed that the number visiting the correct station (24 total) was significant and distribution at the 7 stations during the experiment was not random. The conclusion is that bees informed of location F could find the food in that direction from the hive and visited that specific location over other stations at the same distance.

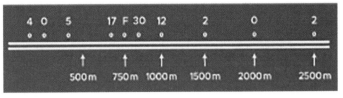

Figure 8-11
Step experiment. Numbers below line indicate distance to feeding stations; numbers above the double lines indicate number of recruited bees. J. Zawislak

The **step experiment** (Figure 8-11) was an attempt to measure the accuracy of the distance information conveyed in the honey bee dance. The figures shown are an actual experiment conducted 27 June 1949 from 11:15 a.m. to 12:45 p.m. by Professor von Frisch. In this experiment, bees were trained to location F, 750 meters from their hive. Then nine identical stations with sugar water scented with linalool were offered the bees at closer and farther distances from the hive along an abandoned railroad track.

The results demonstrated that although the bees were informed of food 750 meters (820 yards) from the hive, the recruit bees were not especially accurate in their foraging at the indicated distance. Nine bees stopped at closer distance stations and 16 bees flew beyond the feeding dish. Statistical analysis indicates that the number (47) going to the 700 and 800 meter location tracking the feeding station F was not significant, although the numbers do reveal a bell curve focused on the feeding station. Thus we cannot conclude that bees used the specific distance information specified to find food with this experiment.

The probable reason the step experiment fails to prove distance communication is because honey bees also communicate by chemicals. A powerful communication element is the smell of the flower (or in the step experiments, the smell of sugar syrup with linalool) on the body of the bee and the taste of the food given to recruits. We surmise that recruits flew from the hive with information to go 750 meters but nine individuals were apparently able to detect the food smell at closer stations (75 and 400 meters—82 and 437 yards) so they stopped to forage and were counted in the experiment as were 16 individuals that flew to stations beyond 750 meters.

The ability of the bee to select odor communication clues over dance language information is within bee capability. Bees are generalist foragers who tend to exploit available food sources, preferring to forage close to the hive rather than fly longer distances. Dance language communication allows a bee colony to concentrate its foraging on sources with the richest rewards, in the greatest quantity, at the nearest distance, while flying in a straight direction.

While dance language is very useful for ensuring a colony of bees concentrates on the richest, most

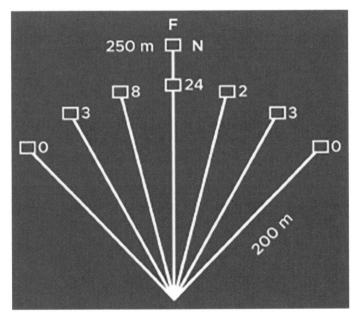

Figure 8-10
Fan experiment. J. Zawislak

profitable new home site, there are limitations in what they can communicate. Bees cannot communicate to recruits to search up within tree foliage or down at the ground level, though presumably flower odors can offer odor clues. A second limitation is they are unable to indicate a more favorable flight path to the food source.

A further limitation in dance language may be demonstrated by performing an experiment. First, an observation beehive is established in a building and then foragers trained to forage at a scented sugar water dish on the opposite side of the building at a distance of say 150-200 meter (170 or more yards). To do this we would move the training dish around the building and then away from it. The question we then ask the bees with this experiment is what direction information would the bees convey to recruit their sisters?

The dancing bees cannot tell recruits to go out and around the building and then fly a straight line to the food source nor can they tell the bees to fly through the building. The only distance information they can provide is the actual distance they fly when they go around the building and then directly to the feeding site. In their waggling orientation they can indicate only the straight line vector to the food, straight through the building, although they can't fly that route.

So what do the recruits do? They follow the sun angle provided and fly the sun compass angle by flying up and over the building and then on to the feeding station. You can station observers and see this flight path. Apparently however they remember the shorter distance they were told about in the dance because recruits soon seek the

shorter distance by flying out and around the building obstacle then return to the sun compass toward the feeding station. If the new recruits dance to recruit other bees they give the shorter distance and since they cannot relate to fly two directions, they must also provide the direction in a straight line to the food. Dancers and recruits soon learn to fly around the building rather than over it to reach the food.

Another experiment, conducted in the desert mountains near Tucson, Arizona, also demonstrates the way bees interpret information in their dance language. Honey bees usually fly a short distance (two meters or six feet) above the ground. Bees were trained from a hive on one side of a canyon to a feeding site on the opposite canyon wall (Figure 8-12). The trained foragers, although trained to fly down into the canyon OS-1, across the canyon floor and up the opposite side OS-2 (the path used to train them from one side of the canyon to the other), quickly found the shortest flight route from one canyon wall to the opposite (line A on diagram) and used this information in the waggling portion of their dances.

The experiment asked how quickly recruit bees following dance language information found route A. As expected, the recruits followed line B, initially, the longer route. Within a couple of trips they switched to the more direct flight line A which they used in seeking to recruit more new bees. They used the shorter distance, route A, apparently because they too were given such information by a dancing bee.

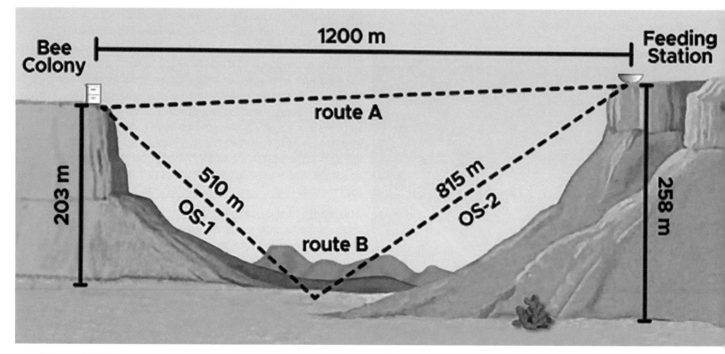

Figure 8-12
Desert experiment. Bees trained to fly route B quickly learn A is shorter which is what they communicate in their dancing.
J. Zawislak.

Box 16

MARKING BEES

In order to follow foragers at flowers or the queen and hive bees inside the observation hive, you should mark them. You can put a dab of paint onto the bee thorax (Figure 8-13), or glue a distinctively colored and numbered plastic tag on the thorax (Figure 8-2) to make it easier to follow one particular individual.

The easiest and cheapest way to mark bees is to put paint on their thorax. Model airplane paint is one possibility but queen marking pens are available at bee supply stores. Test them to see if they leak to prevent damage to the queen. To mark a bee, grasp her on the sides of the thorax with your fingers (Figure 8-13) or with a pair of 'soft' forceps. Be careful not to crush or injure her when you grasp or hold her. Once immobilized, apply a small amount of paint using the tip of the brush, blunted toothpick or the end of a straightened paper clip. Be careful not to put paint on the head or eyes. Paint on wings can distort flight and paint on the head or abdomen may disrupt pheromone distribution.

You can use different colors to mark additional bees or two colors on one bee so it can easily be differentiated from all the others (Figure 8-2). After applying the paint dab, hold the bee a few seconds to allow the paint to dry a bit before you release her. Professor Karl von Frisch devised a system to individually mark up to 599 bees using just 5 colors.

Today we can attach tiny numbered tags onto the thorax of bees (See Figure 8-2). The discs come in 5 colors to mark up to 500 bees. These discs are fixed onto the thorax with a fast-drying glue that is included with the numbered discs.

To apply, put glue on the lower surface of the disc just before catching the bee you wish to mark. Next grasp the bee firmly by the sides of the thorax and then use forceps to place the disc, numbered side up, on the shiny spot of the bee thorax. Allow the glue to dry momentarily before releasing her. Do not get glue, or discs, on the bee's head, wings, or abdomen.

Learn how to hold the bee while marking her to prevent stinging. Practice using drones before attempting to mark workers or the queen. If you handle a number of queens, one may react to the previous queen's pheromones and attempt to bite and sting your fingers.

Figure 8-13
Using a marking pen to mark a drone to practice the technique without being stung. L. Connor

Figure 8-14
INTERNATIONAL MARKING SCHEME OF QUEENS
It is useful to know when a queen bee was raised and introduced to a colony. To facilitate there is an international queen marking scheme. A common mnemonic used to remember the colors is: "Will You Raise Good Bees"

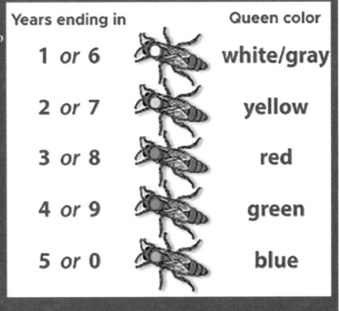

Years ending in		Queen color
1 *or* 6		white/gray
2 *or* 7		yellow
3 *or* 8		red
4 *or* 9		green
5 *or* 0		blue

Dance language controversy

Dance language has been studied by researchers in biology, psychology and other fields. It is a feature of nearly all biology text books. How can scientists prove that this behavior is a language? Because humans can correctly interpret a bee dance does not prove that bees can do the same.

Research in the late 1960s questioned the validity of interpretation of dance behavior. The contrasting evidence surmised that bees find their way using the following:

- past experience (recognize odors on dancer's body)

- odor clues in the field (Nasonov and footprint chemicals)

- visual clues such as other bees, flower pattern or a geometric pattern of experiments as in fan experiment

Experiments indicate that bees overwhelmingly favor odor cues to waggle dance information. Does this mean sufficient evidence exists to scrap the dance language hypothesis and elect the simpler biological explanation of olfaction? After considerable scientific analysis, the answer is no. The preponderance of evidence indicates that dance language theory is valid, but in part hinges on the definition of language. Robot bees even can provide accurate information. Four major points support the dance language hypothesis:

- As the food shifted from two to 100 meters (two to 110 yards) and round changes to waggle dance, the accuracy of finding the food greatly improves.

- On a horizontal surface, the waggle dance is still performed. When the sun's position is blocked, searching for food is random as is the direction of the waggle dance. When the sun's position is viewed, accuracy of dancing orientation and finding food by inexperienced foragers is very high.

- Detour experiments show that when a scout bee goes around building or mountain, she supplies information on the direct route. Recruits initially fly direct, going over the top of the building or down into the canyon floor and only later learn the detour.

- If an experiment is established that forces bees to walk through a tube to reach a food source, their dancing gives distance information on energy expended. Flying foragers using their distance information end up at correctly calculated distances in the field.

In an interesting recent study by L'Anson Price et al., Buckfast bee dancers were induced to give a confusing message to potential recruits. In experimental hives, frames were changed to a horizontal position so dancers

Figure 8-14
Closely look for scout bees dancing on the surface of the swarm, recruiting for a new home location. C. Burkhead.

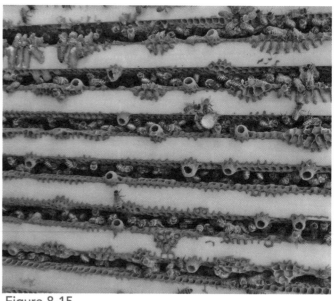

Figure 8-15
Queen cups and queen cells at bottom of frames.

could not orient to gravity and they were prevented from reverting to pointing toward food with light elimination. This created disoriented dances. The bees in the colonies with the confused messaging lost "interest" in dancers and "went on foraging flights that were eight minutes longer and yielded 29 percent more honey over the entire 18-day period" compared to colonies where dancers performed normal waggle dances. The authors suggest that bees in colonies where the disoriented dancers were giving mixed messages "did not waste time waiting for information" and stored more honey suggesting "the waggle dance language is not well adapted … [in] human created environments".

The evidence for dance language is indeed strong. Bees do use odor cues to find food. Bees may prefer certain pieces of information in the dance over others or could ignore the dancing entirely if the message was not understood. Therefore we can conclude that dance language does indeed exist and is used by honey bees.

Nest selection by honey bees

The use of the dance language behavior to find a new home site is very important to the future of a colony. The honey bees use of this adaptive decision-making process is a remarkable example of group function by a superorganism.

House hunting by honey bees was examined by German researcher Martin Lindauer in the early 1950s. Lindauer studied swarms from University colonies that settled across the street in the Botanical Garden in Munich, Germany. He described swarm behavior as a **decision-making process**.

He discovered that scout bees performed waggle dances on the surface of swarms, not promoting food locations, but potential nest locations. He spent hours looking at how many 'new' scout recruits danced to indicate a potential new nesting cavity originally discovered by a scout.

From the cluster other scout bees follow her instructions of the direction and distance of the cavity she communicates with the dance and they then fly to investigate the same cavity. After walking the inside of the cavity they too return to the swarm cluster and dance as well (if they are motivated).

Meanwhile, other scout bees have found other locations. They too return to recruit followers. Recruited follower bees also return to the swarm and dance. There may be two, three or a dozen groups of bees each promoting different potential nest sites. Lindauer found an average of two dozen potential nesting sites were discovered and evaluated.

The dances continue with scout bees evaluating the information being exchanged. Some stop dancing, deceasing support of their find. Eventually one site

Figure 8-16
A large swarm represents a huge resource investment by the parent colony and a potential loss of honey to the beekeeper.

becomes dominant receiving the majority of dancing. Only then do the bees break their swarm into the air and fly to this site to establish their home there.

Tom Seeley has been seeking further details since 1975, following up on studies by Martin Lindauer. He has found only a small group of the swarm bees are scouts. The scouts however are the deciders of the fate of the swarm.

Early in the spring, as the old winter bees die, colonies begin swarm preparations. As they refill empty combs with pollen and nectar, the colony gains weight, reversing winter's losses. Drone production begins as conditions improve. Queen cups, present year round, increase in number (Figure 8-15). The queen lays an egg in one and then in other cups to begin rearing of her replacement.

The initial preparations to swarm extends beyond just rearing of several new queens. Scout bees begin to look for new home sites before the colony issues a swarm. Once cells are sealed, the colony prepares to issue a swarm. A portion of a colony population will leave their home to form a temporary 'bivouac' cluster on a tree branch or other convenient clustering site.

The role of scout bees

Scout bees are older foragers that forsake foraging for resources. When their home colony begins to rear queens (the first step in swarming) they begin searching for a new home site. As such, scouts play an important role in triggering the departure to leave home and then subsequently in founding of a new home site.

Scout bees, flying in and out of the hive, have warmer bodies because of the necessity of warming thoracic flight muscles. Inside a hive, following research by Juliana Rangel and Tom Seeley, the scouts press their thorax against house bees, activate their flight muscles and produce a short burst of sound (200-250 hertz), a behavior termed **worker piping**. This is a message to hive bees that it is "time to warm up the flight muscles." Over an hour or so the frequency of piping increases.

Then the scouts will give the message it is time to leave. This is the **buzz-run** (sometimes **breaking dance**); scout bees excitedly run in zig-zag fashion among their hive mates, buzzing their wings, penetrating throughout the brood area, creating a hive of movement. The house bees, meanwhile, in response to the hive rearing queens, have been preparing by taking more food into their honey stomachs from hive stores, which then increases dramatically with the piping.

Figure 8-17
In a blur of activity, tens of thousands of bees blast out of a swarming hive. Drones and returning foragers are caught up in the flurry of activity. L. Connor

When the swarm leaves its parent home, there is a mad dash toward the entrance. The queen now gets pushed off the comb to the entry area by her daughters. She is now a slimmer version due to her daughters having kept her moving and feeding her less. The workers and the queen exit and fly in a circular pattern, like a cloud, approximately 30 to 60 feet diameter.

The cloud drifts from immediately in front of the entrance but they don't go far. Some workers eventually land on a convenient near-by location and expose their scent gland. The swirling bee cloud, along with the queen, settles into a beard-like cluster drawn by both scent and queen pheromones. The whole process from start to finish takes a mere 10-15 minutes.

Not all the workers that exit join the cluster – they go back home and if, on occasion, the queen is unable to fly, or doesn't exit, the clustered bees regroup back to the original home within 15-20 minutes of exiting. Pheromones are powerful communication tools for this critical behavior of formation of the temporary bivouac (the swam cluster).

Once clustered at this temporary bivouac, the swarm bees with their queen settle quietly, hanging on to each other. Only scout bees leave the cluster to continue their home searching. The swarm may remain a matter of minutes to a day or more.

Sometimes a colony may swarm again, this time with one to several virgin queens, formerly imprisoned in their cells by workers. We call this an **afterswarm**. It is not at all clear why a colony might cast off a primary swarm and then a couple days later produce an afterswarm. In addition to further reduction of the adult population of the original hive, the colony becomes at risk as afterswarms are usually smaller in adult numbers and are not as tightly organized.

Scout activity

Once clustered, scouts inform members of the swarm about suitable potential new home sites. What are they looking for? Tom Seeley was able to utilize digital recording equipment to follow the dancing of both the original scouts and their recruits. One very critical factor of a potential nest site is a cavity of about 40 liters volume (same as a 10 frame Langstroth box).

The scout bee determines the cavity volume of a prospective home site by walking the interior and making short flights from one position to the next. Initial inspection and measurements can take several minutes to almost an hour. A scout will return again after flying back to the clustered swarm, where she will likely dance if her initial inspection is favorable. Her subsequent trips and her walks inside the cavity are not as lengthy.

Scouts also evaluate the entry opening by flying in and out and hovering in front of the entrance. The position of the entrance at or near the bottom of the cavity is an

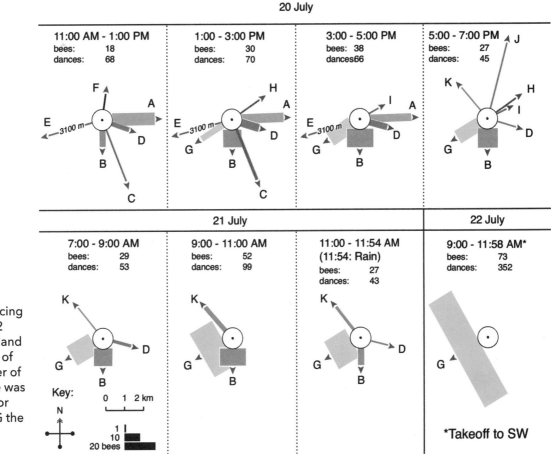

Figure 8-18
Record of scout dancing on swarm July 20-22 observed by Seeley and Buhrman. Thickness of bar indicates number of dancing bees. There was fierce competition for sites B and G, with G the eventual choice.
T. Seeley

important factor and entrances that face the sun also favorable. Bee smell from previous bee occupancy is a definite plus. If some beeswax combs are still present they are examined. When ants are present or the cavity is otherwise occupied, scouts lose interest. Draftiness or moisture is not important.

Nest site searching is generally at higher elevation in trees/buildings rather than ground level or lower cavities, especially if the bees come from a feral nest. All potential sites are examined. The type of tree, either for initial bivouac site or for an eventual home is not important.

Competition for favorable sites is often "fierce" according to Seeley. Scouts might number 300 to 500 individuals in a normal sized swarm, nearly 3% of the total population. That is a big investment befitting the enormous consequences of getting the correct cavity as a new home.

Scout bees might use inhibitory stop signals—a short buzz delivered with a head butt to the dancer—to inhibit the waggle dances produced by scouts advertising competing sites. This inhibitory signaling helps ensure that only one site is chosen when two sites are equally attractive.

To confirm scouts make the best choice, Seeley and student Susannah Buhrman used an artificial nest box in

which they could change the entrance size and interior dimensions (Figure 8-20, shown inside a shelter). They were able to change an "ideal" site (40 liter and small entrance) to make it an acceptable but mediocre one (15 liter and larger entrance). In four of five trials, artificial swarm bees chose the 40 liter nest box (the one with the larger dimension) over the smaller box with larger entrance size.

To independently demonstrate that the bees choice was advantageous to survival, Seeley established 15 colonies into hives of 40 liter size and 15 into hives of 15 liter size. Over three winters the bees in the larger sized boxes survived 73% of the winters of Ithaca while the smaller boxed hives had only a 27% winter survival rate. He concluded that bees were indeed making the best choice.

Figures 8-18 and 8-19 illustrate how scout bees arrive at a decision. Figure 8-18 shows a 3-day process of numbers of bees and their number of dances for competing nest sources as published in *Honey Bee Democracy*. The eventual new homesite was first indicated by dancers at the 1:00 to 3:00 PM monitoring period. Initial sites A and the site E, 3100 meters distant, lost favor among dancers by 5:00-7:00 PM. Site G gained dancer attention on July 20.

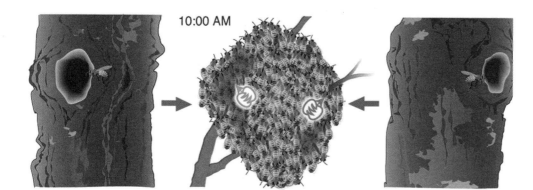

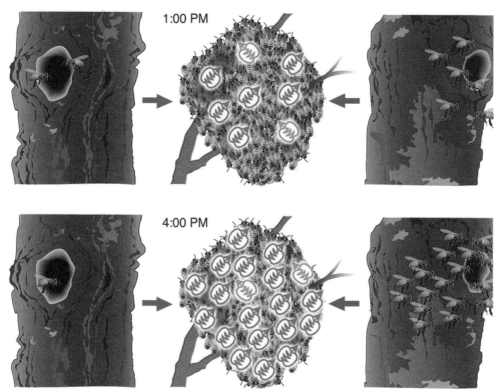

Figure 8-19
Activity at potential nest sites compared to dancing on the surface of the swarm. Through time, an increased number of dancers for the size entrances and opening direction are discovered by scouts. The best site, with smaller (defensible) southerly facing entrance resulted in the larger number of dancing scout bees. T. Seeley

The next day July 21, site dancing was down to 4 sites with the G location the most favored. However rain around noon cut off house searching activity. The next morning only the G site was advertised (73 bees, 352 dances total). The swarm left the bivouac for this new homesite just before noon.

Additionally Figure 8-19 illustrates how changes in scout bee dancing leads to the best choice. Two tree hollows of same approximate volume but different size entrances and opening direction are discovered by scouts. The favorable smaller southerly entrance cavity (on right) is investigated by more and more scouts, each which subsequently dance on the cluster to advertise their find. In this manner a consensus is reached and the best cavity is chosen.

Once scouts have determined the best location, those same scouts advise the bees in the outer insulating layer that they need to heat their bodies to get ready to leave the bivouac site (the bees at the core already have an elevated body temperature sufficient for flight). This is accomplished with the same worker piping behavior utilized to get the bees to leave their home initially. Then the buzz run (breaking dance) is used once again to tell the bees it is time to leave the bivouac site. As with home leaving, getting airborne takes but a few minutes.

Once in the air the swarm moves slowly with a larger size flying mass straight toward the site that the scout bees have indicated as the new home site. A queen must be present because the bees keep checking on her

Figure 8-20
Buhrman and Seeley used an artificial nest box to change entrance size and interior dimensions. T. Seeley

presence by her queen substance as they move in a circular flight.

The scout bees, a population of several hundred individuals who have actually previously visited and evaluated the newly found cavity, streak back and forth, at maximum flight speed (about 20 miles per hour) above the mass of bees pointing toward the correct direction. The swarm picks up speed (up to four miles per hour).

As they approach the actual site, the scouts land and expose their scent glands, allowing the mass of the flying swarm to settle quickly and rather efficiently into the new site.

Finding a home site is a critical behavior that helps ensure success in colony reproduction. Bees must make their decision on a variety of variables. The bees need to make their decision quickly. Food reserves are being consumed as the swarm decides its future home—and as time passes the swarm is often exposed to soaking rain and strong wind. The decision must be accepted by all the bees, or there may be a 'splinter group' of bees dividing the swarm and going to a different location. This would be a disaster for the swarm. A swarm of honey bees choosing its future home is one of the most impressive examples known of an animal group functioning as an adaptive decision maker.

LOOKING FOR A HOME

Have you ever needed to find a new home? A new apartment, a piece of property to develop or farm perhaps? Do you recall how you searched and then arrived at the final decision? You probably found you had numerous alternative sites available to purchase and sooner, or later, you settled on one.

Honey bee scouts on average visit two dozen potential sites, according to the research of Lindauer in Germany. Tom Seeley, in *Honeybee Democracy* equates how honey bees search for a new home site using a process similar to that humans take. Here, condensed from Chapter 5, Seeley discusses similarities between humans and bees in the task of finding, evaluating and then deciding on a new home:

"As is true for all decision-making problems, finding a good solution is a two-fold process: first identify the possible alternatives then choose among them. In an ideal world, the decision maker would be able to learn about all the alternatives and all the attributes of each, calculate the value of each alternatives in light of all its attributes and rationally choose the one with the highest value. Doing all these things will produce optimal decision making. In the real world however, truly optimal decision making rarely happens . . . someone hunting for an apartment in a large city would have to expend excessive time, money and mental effort to survey the entire market of available rental properties, evaluate them all and make the perfect choice."

Does that sound familiar if you have ever looked for new home/farm/land? Based on his own research Seeley says that a swarm cluster

". . . makes its decision only after its scout bees have discovered numerous alternative nest sites and have performed a multifaceted inspection of each site . . . a honey bee swarm pursues an unusually sophisticated strategy of decision making, one that involves nearly all of the information relevant to the problem of choosing the best place to build its new nest . . . its democratic organization enables it to harness the power of many individuals working together to perform collectively the two fundamental parts of the decision-making process: acquiring information about the alternatives and processing this information to make a choice."

Are not humans and bees so similar?

Seeley, T. 2019. Honeybee Democracy. Princeton University Press.

key terms

afterswarm	dialects	nucleus colony	scout bee
Apis cerana	decision making	package (of bees)	sickle dance
Apis dorsata	fan experiment	piping	step experiment
Apis florea	forager	polarized light	support hive
azimuth (of sun)	gravity orientation	queen cup	swarm(ing)
bivouac (swarm cluster)	grooming (shaking) dance	queen cell	tremble dance
breaking dance	house hunting	queen marking scheme	waggling (of abdomen)
buzz run (dance)	Johnston's organ	recruits	wagtail dance
dances/ing	marking bees	round dance	
dance language	optic flow pattern	scent gland	

discussion questions

What are the basic differences between the round dance and the wagtail dance? What are the similarities? How does the sickle dance seem to connect the two other dances?

There are differences in the dance among *Apis* species and the 'dialects' within different races. What are some of the important differences? What might happen if we mixed bees of two races in a single hive? What information might not be accurate? What would the likely response be of the bees?

Why can bees not tell sisters to fly two directions in one flight? How do bees reconcile differences in information they have and the real world they encounter?

Explain the dance language controversy. Can the fan and step experiment prove the hypothesis? What additional evidence can you find to indicate that Professor von Frisch was correct?

Finding a homesite using dances has been well studied by Professor von Frisch, his student Martin Lindauer and more recently by Tom Seeley. Review the sequences involved. How do pheromones and dances serve to get bees to leave, cluster and then move to a new homesite? Why is swarming such a critical biology to hone bees? Why discovering food?

What might be some important differences in dancing for food and for a homesite. Is there an interplay of dancing and pheromones in both? What are the similarities?

exercises

Some good materials are available to supplement dance language. Most introductory films and videos on honey bees have at least a short segment on dance language. A video 'Dancing for their supper' by Dr. Francis Ratnieks includes images of dancing and exercises students might perform. There is a wealth of material available on the web (do a search for 'dancing bees'). Georgia Tech and German videos (referenced in the text) should be compared for usefulness. 3M has an interactive CDROM learning software entitled 'What's the Secret' (based on Newton's Apple PBS TV show segment) for MacIntosh or Windows that features dance language in honey bees. Critique one of more of these films/videos/web-based sources.

By using an observation hive (see Chapter 9), and marked foragers, observe their dance. Executing some simple measurements and with use of a stop watch and protractor, you can determine the location of flowers from such observations. Consult the information on dance language from the book Observation Hives by Caron & Webster.

When you're confident you understand dance language communication solve three language problems.

A. Bees in a hive find food as shown in diagram below. Diagram the dance the bee would perform in her hive.

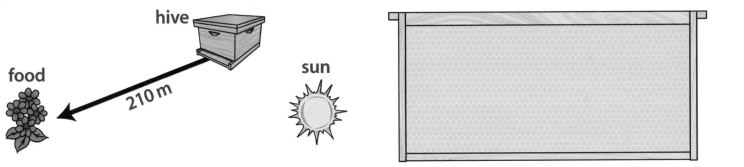

B. You see a bee doing the dance diagrammed below. Where is the food source?

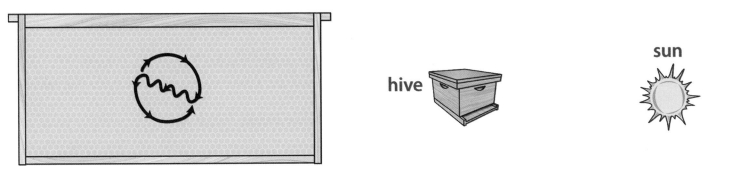

C. Bees find food directly east of their hive at a distance of 2000 m. The sun is in the Southwest as shown below. Diagram the dance you would expect to see in the hive. Diagram dance you would see if distance was 20 m.

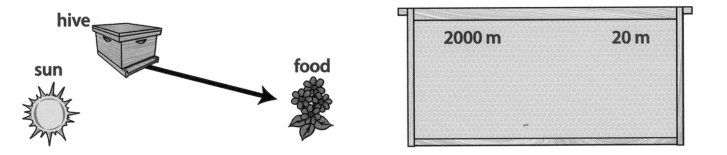

Observe a clustered swarm. Can you notice the one site of dancing bees? See if you can solve their language.

Establish and use an artificial swarm and the move it by removing the queen to another closeby site. Walk among the bees as they move from one site to another. There is no comparable experience.

references

l'Anson Price, R. et al. 2019. Honeybees forage more successfully without the "dance language" in challenging environments, Science Advances (2019). DOI: 10.1126/sciadv.aat0450

Connor, L.J. 2014. Increase Essentials, Second edition. Wicwas Press. Kalamazoo, MI

Connor, L.J. 2020. Package Essentials. Wicwas Press. Kalamazoo, MI

Esch, H.E. et al. 2001. Honeybee dances communicate distances measured by optic flow. Nature 411, 581-583

Kak, S.C. 1991. The honey bee dance language controversy. The Mankind Quarterly. 31:357-365

l'Anson Price, R. et al. 2019. Honeybees forage more successfully without the "dance language" in challenging environments, Science Advances (2019). DOI: 10.1126/sciadv.aat0450

Connor, L.J. 2014. Increase Essentials, Second edition. Wicwas Press. Kalamazoo, MI

Connor, L.J. 2020. Package Essentials. Wicwas Press. Kalamazoo, MI

Esch, H.E. et al. 2001. Honeybee dances communicate distances measured by optic flow. Nature 411, 581-583

Kak, S.C. 1991. The honey bee dance language controversy. The Mankind Quarterly. 31:357-365

Lindauer, M. 1955. House hunting by honey bee swarms. Zeitschrift für vergleichende Physiologie [Journal of Comparative Physiology] 37:263-324

Mangum, W.A. 2016. How to Mark Queen Bees with No Runs, Drips, or Errors. American Bee Journal. 156: (August)

Rangel, J. et al. 2010. An oligarchy of nest-site scouts triggers a honeybee swarm's departure from the hive. Behavioral Ecology and Sociobiology 64(6):979-987

Rosen, R. 1988. Do honey bees still have a "dance language"? American Bee Journal, 128:267-268

Seeley, T.D. 2010. Honeybee Democracy. Princeton Univ. Press

Seeley, T.D. 2019. The Lives of Bees: The Untold Story of the Honey Bee in the Wild. Princeton Univ Press

Seeley, T.D. and S.C. Buhrman 2001. Nest site selection in honey bees: how well so swarms implement the "Best-of-N" decision rule? Behavioral Ecology & Sociobiology 49:416-427.

von Frisch, K. 1953. The Dancing Bees: An Account of the Life and Senses of the Honey Bee (translation of Aus dem Leben der Bienen), First English ed. Harcourt Brace

von Frisch, K. 1967. The Dance Language and Orientation of Bees (translation of Tanzsprache und Orientierung der Bienen). Harvard University Press

Wenner, A.M. 1967. Honey bees: do they use the distance information contained in their dance maneuver?, Science, 155, 847-849

Wenner, A.M. and P.H. Wells. 1990: Anatomy of a Controversy: The Question of a "Language" Among Bees, Columbia University Press.

sealed honey

bee bread

sealed brood

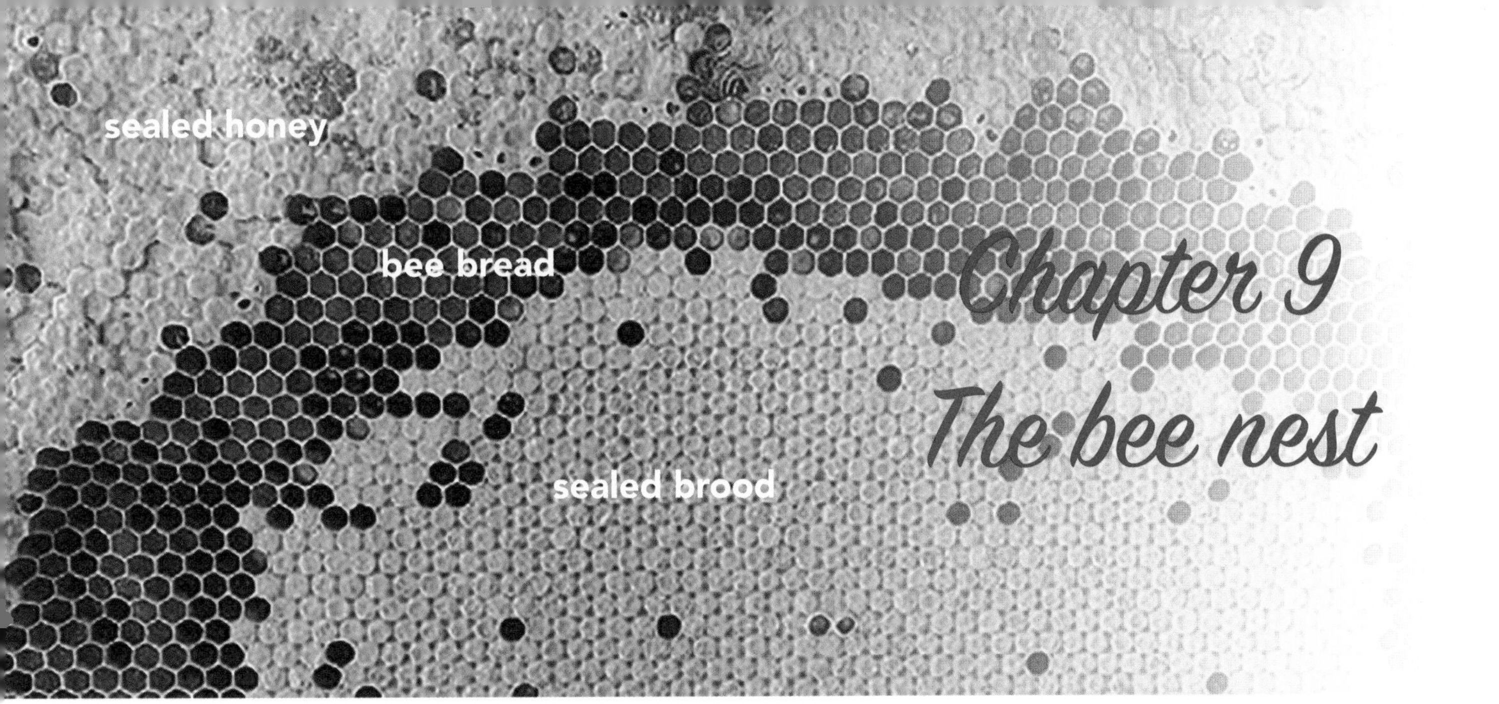

Figure 9-1
The beeswax comb is the key structure inside the bee nest, holding honey, pollen and brood. A. Connor

Concepts

Colony dwelling

Beeswax comb

How bees measure cells

Human-made beehives

Empty comb stimulates foraging

Observation beehives

Colony dwelling

The honey bee evolved as a forest animal but it is adaptable to virtually any habitat. Humans have modified many types of containers for a beehive. To be useful a beehive must utilize the features bees employ when they build a wild or feral nest. Five characteristics recognized in the feral nest are:

- sheltered, darkened enclosure
- small, defensible entrance
- size of adequate volume
- parallel comb constructed with bee space
- separation of brood and food in the comb

Although bees may construct their nest in open, exposed locations (Figure 9-5), a sheltered, darkened cavity is preferred. A tree cavity is a common natural nest site in the temperate area (Figure 9-2). Maple, oak and ash trees are commonly available but bees will select from 20 or more tree species if a suitable cavity is present.

Dr. Tom Seeley examined a series of nests in a forested area adjacent to the Cornell University campus. He found most nest entrances consisted of a single knothole or crack with a total opening of just 10 to 30 square centimeters (2 to 5 square inches). Typically, openings were located near the floor of an elongated, narrow tall cavity, on the south side of the tree. Although they can be close to ground level, bees actually have a strong preference for nesting cavities with entrances located high above the ground.

Most tree nests are in live tree cavities attributed to fungal action on the inner wood. Seeley's measurements revealed the average nest cavity was only about 20 centimeters (8 inches) in diameter and 150 centimeters (60 inches) tall; hence, it had a volume of a standard Langstroth bee box.

Since beeswax comb is fragile, shelter is important for successful survival of a bee colony. When the bees build comb in exposed locations, they are within darkened sites with heavy vegetation or under a sturdy limb (Figure 9-5) or the overhang of a building (as in Figure 9-6). Rain, sun and heat all contribute to the breakdown of wax comb when bees build in an exposed location. A darkened enclosure promotes efficient wax secretion from worker wax glands. Bees in a darkened enclosure secrete more wax and build more comb than bees exposed to light.

Honey bees can adapt to various types of cavities to build their nest. They find entrances to wall voids in buildings (Figure 9-7) where they are usually considered a pest, requiring removal when too close to human activity.

Bees will also select empty containers like large bird houses, grills, water meters (Figure 9-15), scrap water tanks, barrels (Figure 9-18), empty boxes, discarded plastic containers, etc., if they are of suitable volume. Bees also nest in caves and rock wall crevices. Tropical bees even nest in empty animal burrows on occasion or in empty termite nests.

Bees that swarm usually do not move a great distance from their parent hive location to establish the new nest, though there are differences among bee races in this respect. Italian and Carniolan bees search and nest close to their original home site. Colder-climate adapted German bees move farther away while the African bee will move great distances and actually migrate during unfavorable conditions.

Honey bees consider other factors in selection of a suitable cavity in addition to distance from parent nest. In temperate climates, bee swarms selecting new home sites use the following nest selection characteristics:

  • volume—bees prefer 40 liters (range 20 to 100 liters); tropical bees prefer smaller cavities, and will nest in the open

  • height from ground—bees seem to prefer sites higher than ground level but will select suitable cavities close to the ground; usually three meters (ten feet) is ideal but they will occupy cavities higher in forested areas

  • exposure—shady sites in the open. Locations exposed to wind or full sun are less preferred

  • entrance size & position—bees definitely prefer smaller entrance holes, those at the bottom of the cavity and southward facing

  • cavity quality—bees select dry, unoccupied, ant-free sites and prefer the smell of previous bee occupancy

Once a suitable nest site is selected and occupied, worker bees smooth the interior walls to remove loose and decaying

Figure 9-2
Large tree with a bee nest inside, often called a bee tree. T. Seeley

wood. The entrance area is also extensively worked; both entrance and interior walls are smoothed and covered with a thin layer of **propolis** (Figure 9-3). This gives the bees a firm surface to anchor comb and walk, helps prevent further decay of the cavity and increases nest hygiene. Propolis has extensive anti-microbial activity.

Bees may use propolis to reduce the size of the entrance area of their nest. Some races such as Caucasians use extensive amounts of propolis, almost sealing the entrance area. Most nests have a single entrance. The nest entrance is the contact the colony has with the rest of the environment so the entrance is a place that must be guarded. Bees selecting a new home site pay close attention to entrance suitability. As the selection by scout bees illustrates in Chapter 8, Figure 8-19, a smaller entrance is preferred over a larger one and as explained in the previous chapter nest volume is critically important for survival.

When scout bees search for a new home site, they enter potential cavities and walk the inside to measure dimensions. Because most cavities are in trees, the usual feral nest is a tall cylinder (Figure 9-2).

Eventually four or more parallel combs, perhaps four to five feet (1.5 meters) in length, will be built to fit within the cavity.

When human-made cavities (Figure 9-4) used for beekeeping were compared to natural cavities on a volume basis, it was observed that most fall within the same range as the size of the nest cavities selected by bees. Some of these volumes (in liters) are:

Human-made cavities	Volume (liters)
Egyptian pipe mud hive	20
Crete sloping cylindrical clay hive	20-40
Ancient Roman cylindrical hive	44
Top bar log hive	40-130
British skep	15-30
Ten-frame Langstroth brood box	40

It is interesting to note that the smallest hive of this group, the pipe hive of Egypt, is used for the Egyptian race which prefers a natural cavity of smaller size compared to the Italian bee. The Africanized bees of America also prefer a smaller nest site.

There are several situations where bees build comb in exposed areas and not in a cavity. In temperate regions, swarms may have difficulty moving to a new nest location when dark, rainy weather stimulates wax building in their temporary bivouac location. It appears that once comb construction has started, the bees tend not to leave the location. In tropical areas, bees will build combs in exposed locations (Figure 9-5).

Beeswax comb

After the bees move into a suitable nest cavity, they manufacture their only necessary construction material—beeswax. The beeswax is molded into several parallel beeswax combs (Figures 9-5, 9-6, 9-7). Most of the comb consists of worker cells. The cells are six-sided

Figure 9-3
Entrance bark smoothed by bees and covered with propolis.

Figure 9-4
Type of hives: Straw skep, clay pot and log gum. D. Heskes

Figure 9-5
Exposed beeswax comb nest on tree branch. Common in tropical races and when northern swarms are unable to move to an enclosed space, usually due to rainy weather.

Figure 9-6
Exposed comb built in a protected corner. B.K. Councell

Figure 9-7
Colony inside a column. Note the brood comb on the left is darker in color, while the honey comb on the right is thicker and lighter. P. Vincent

reinforced with a thin coating of propolis, at the top of the cell walls for ease in walking and to strengthen the fragile wax (Figure 9-9).

In the natural nest, comb is attached at the tops and intermittently at the sides but not along the lower margin. There is often a space from the lowest comb to the bottom of the cavity where debris can drop and be degraded by scavengers and moisture. Along the sides, the bees leave intermittent passageways, often called **communication holes**. These holes permit crossing from one face to the other—otherwise each comb would be a continuous curtain of beeswax cells.

Comb consists of two basic cell sizes. **Worker cells** (Figure 9-9, 9-14) are used to rear worker bees and for storage of honey and pollen. The worker cells average

(hexagonal) and have a three-part pyramidal shape base. Cells face both directions from a central midrib that provides important comb strength.

Bees build the beeswax combs progressively downward, sloping the cell walls slightly upward. They plane cell walls to desired thickness, leaving a rim of extra wax,

Figure 9-8
Newer beeswax comb starts to darken with the pigments from honey and pollen. Uncapped fresh nectar has been stored in the center of this comb.

Figure 9-9
Bees have added propolis (from popular tree resin and beeswax) to the cell ends and inner layers of the brood cells. This strengthens the comb and provides anti-microbial protection. L. Connor

Figure 9-10
Medium Langstroth frame of freshly stored honey. L. Connor

Figure 9-11
Older beeswax comb darkens due to the addition of pupal cocoons, larval defecation, and pigments from pollen and nectar. This dissected comb shows packed pollen pellets. D. Morgan

about five cells per linear inch (2 per cm). Bees also construct some drone cells in their comb. **Drone cells** (Figure 9-14) are larger than worker cells but are still six-sided and otherwise similar to worker cells. Drone cells are used to raise drones and are used for honey storage. Drone cells average about four per linear inch (1.6/cm). When in a feral nest, bees build about 15 to 20% drone-size cells. In managed hives, beekeepers often minimize the amount of drone comb.

The worker and drone cells may be empty, filled with brood or filled with honey or pollen. Ripening nectar ('green' or **unripe honey**) is a liquid and may completely or only partially fill the cell. When a cell is filled and the nectar fully ripened into honey, the cell is covered over with a **beeswax cap** (capped cell) (Figure 9-8).

Newly-secreted wax is used to cover cells of **honey** and the cell capping is light in color (Figure 9-10). Cappings may become watery-looking with age. Although **brood cells** quickly darken with use, honey cells remain light in color. **Honey cells** may be somewhat deeper and more upward sloping when built naturally in a feral nest such as a bee tree (Figure 9-2) or a building cavity (Figure 9-7).

Bees also store **pollen** in the worker cells, only filling the cells about three-quarters full (Figure 9-11, 9-14). Pollen varies in color depending on floral source. The pollen undergoes a lactose fermentation to form **bee bread**, which better suits the nutritional needs of nurse bees. A glaze of honey is usually placed over the pollen but the pollen is usually clearly visible. Pollen cells are not covered with a capping.

Box 18

HOW BEES MEASURE CELLS

Queens and workers can tell the difference between the larger drone-size cells and the smaller worker cells. Both castes can also differentiate between the vertically-oriented queen cups/cells (Figure 9-12, 9-13) and the horizontal worker/drone cells (Figure 9-14). Bees use both physical size and orientation as well as smell to tell the differences.

Before laying an egg in a cell, the queen measures the diameter with her forelegs. Her legs function almost as calipers. If the opening is the larger 1/4" (4 mm) size of a drone cell, she lays unfertilized eggs. Fertilized eggs go into the smaller worker cells. Queens mark eggs they lay with a pheromone. If we artificially construct cells between these two sizes, the queen either does not lay eggs or her pattern becomes random.

Workers, too, can tell the difference but we do not know how. They do not use their front legs like a queen does so odor may be the way they tell the difference. Laying workers—workers that lay eggs when a queen is not present—prefer drone cells over worker cells for their eggs. Pollen foragers select worker cells to deposit the pollen from their pollen baskets. Hive bees select worker cells over drone cells to use for nectar storage. Varroa mites can tell the difference (and prefer drone brood over worker brood) but they are using clues from the brood since they do not enter empty cells.

Beeswax comb is constantly recycled. When constructed, it consists of newly-secreted beeswax. With use, especially for brood or storage of pollen, it becomes darker and absorbs odors like queen trail pheromones and queen substance. Each larva leaves behind a thin cocoon and feces that are smoothed and covered over by varnish-like saliva when the cell is cleaned by adult worker bees. Experiments have shown that survival of eggs and larvae is higher in cells that have been previously used compared to survival in new comb.

Figure 9-13
Natural queen cells hangs downward into the bee space.

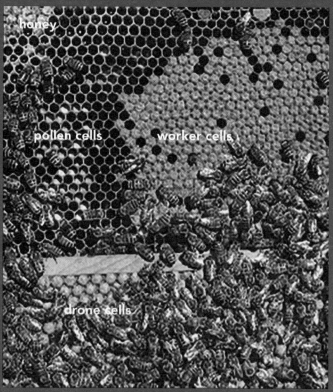

Figure 9-14
Worker cells above and drone cells below. Note the band of pollen and honey around the worker brood. L. Connor

Figure 9-12
Queen cups.

One final cell type seen in a bee colony is the **queen cell**. Queen cells hang vertically; worker and drone cells are horizontal (Figure 9-14). Queen cells, when completed, are peanut shaped (Figure 9-13). Queen cells developed during colony queen replacement behaviors start as a queen cup. Queen cups are cup-like, as the name suggests, and they usually are found at the lower margin of the comb (Figure 9-12); they may also extend from the comb face or are constructed at breaks in comb such as passageways from one face to the other. They are oriented with the open portion hanging vertically downward. More cups are present in the spring and during population buildup than in fall or winter colonies.

Bees place extra pieces of comb between the parallel combs of beeswax and extend comb from top and bottom bars of the frames. Such comb is termed **burr and brace comb**. Such comb serves as ladders from one box to another and serve to strengthen comb and prevent it from moving about. The bees often use such comb to rear drone brood or to store honey since it usually still has the distinct six-sided cell structure. Some beekeepers continuously remove this extra comb but the bees usually quickly rebuild it. Such removal results in colonies being open for a longer time and the scraping/removal can irritate the bees and drop the brood nest temperature.

There are often unusual sized and shaped **transition cells** in beeswax comb. Sometimes the unusual shapes are completely filled in with wax. Unusual-sized cells are seldom utilized for brood or honey storage. Such cells

may occur near the top of a comb where it is attached to the top bar of the frame, at passage holes from one side to the other or in a transition area between worker and drone sized cells.

Although beekeepers seek to maintain parallel combs within a frame outline (as illustrated in Figure 9-10), bees in nature may not construct perfectly parallel combs. The comb may twist and turn, with adjacent combs constructed following the same pattern. Bees apparently orient the combs relative to magnetic fields that they detect in concentration of magnetic sensitive metals in fat-body tissue in their abdomens.

In the natural nest bees build multiple parallel combs at same time rather than sequentially (Figure 9-15). As the colony expands, more combs may eventually be added or, as in most natural nests, existing combs may be expanded by constructing additional cells at the bottom of the combs.

When building their comb, bees adhere to a basic principle in spacing; they leave approximately 3/8ths of an inch (1.0 cm), the height of two bees, between combs. We call this the **bee space**. Each of the parallel free-hanging combs constructed has bee space between the combs and around the sides and bottom. The comb is suspended from the top of the nesting cavity.

In beekeeper hives, spacing of the frames holding the comb is important. Spaces less than 3/8 inch are filled with propolis. If the space is larger than 3/8 inch, the

Figure 9-15
Comb built by a swarm occupying a utility box. Note the combs are parallel, with multiple parallel combs built at the same time. C. Levy

Figure 9-16
Parallel combs in box where the bees ignored the starter strips the beekeeper expected them to follow. The beekeeper and the bees clearly have different ideas about comb design.

Figure 9-17
Two bee skeps flanked
by gum hives cut
from tree sections.

bees will attempt to fill the space with another parallel comb. Sometimes the depth of the cells will be increased slightly, especially in the **honey storage area**, to help fill space between combs as well. Some beekeepers use one less framed comb in supers to promote deeper honey cell construction to facilitate uncapping the combs.

Discovery of the principle of bee space and the importance of proper comb spacing led to rapid development of beekeeping. Many hives have been patented over the years following the basic principle. While spacing between combs has been a key development, the size of the combs may or may not be important to the bees. Over time beekeepers have standardized a limited number of sizes of framed combs in manufactured hives.

Exactly what might be the best size is open to debate. Standard Langstroth equipment uses eight or ten parallel frames holding comb. Africanized bees will often build 11 parallel combs in the same space compared to ten for European bees.

Queens seem reluctant to move from one comb to the next and one box to the higher (or lower) one. Thus some advocate the use of a larger comb frame for the brood while using smaller sized boxes (supers) for honey storage, due, in large part, to the need to remove heavily weighted honey-filled boxes for harvest.

Beekeeping in non-Langstroth hives has become popular. The Warré hive, top bar hive or a system labeled perma-apiculture emphasize the typical natural nest of deeper combs and also less hive manipulations to reduce bee stress. In top bar hives, frames of comb may initially be removable but eventually if the brood area is left unmanaged then only honey-filled combs on the edge of the brood nest are used for harvest.

In addition to attachment at the top, bees may secure the outermost combs to the sides of the cavity. By

Figure 9-18
Bee colony in a barrel. Both bees and beekeepers use a wide array of cavities for colony housing.

Figure 9-19
Langstroth hive on left and box hive on right. Box hives were very common in the Americas because of the abundance of wood.

constructing top bar hives with sloping walls, this attachment can be minimized (Figures 9-27, 9-28, 9-29). In frameless hives, beekeepers often provide a leading edge to the top bar,, coated with beeswax, to encourage the building of parallel combs in line with the bar itself (Figure 9-24, 9-25). However bees may ignore the intentions/plans of the beekeeper and build comb perpendicular or at some angle (cross-comb) to the intended orientation.

Nest organization

In a sheltered, darkened cavity, the beeswax comb, with its bee space, is organized into a **nest**. The bees separate the area where they store their food from the area where they rear their brood (eggs, larvae and pupae). The brood is reared in the lower portion of the beeswax comb in a compact, spherical-shaped section because the growing larvae need a temperature of 90-95° F (32-35° C) for optimal development.

Honey reserves are placed above and to the sides of this central brood rearing area. Pollen, used to feed the larvae, is stored in empty cells in the brood area and immediately to the outside of the active brood-rearing area.

This pattern is shown in the comb of worker cells shown in Figures 9-1 and 9-14. This central sphere of brood expands or contracts depending on the time of the season but the basic principle of separation of brood and food is maintained except in a nest with insufficient total room.

Human-made hives

Today the bee nest, termed a **hive**, incorporates many of the characteristics of feral nests. This was not the case

150 years ago. As humans moved from being honey robbers of bee nests to keepers of bees, one of the earliest containers for the bees was a portion of the original tree the swarm selected (**log gum**). Eventually any small, movable container was substituted as humans began to capture their own swarms. Containers were of wood (crates), ceramic jugs or woven plant parts (skeps or rolled bark cylinders). See discussion in Chapter 1. Rustic hives of suitably sized containers, still in use in the world today, are frequently made of these natural materials (Figure 9-19).

In the small containers—the gums, skeps, jugs, boxes— the beeswax comb was attached by the bees to the top and eventually to the sides of the container. Some of the containers were robbed of their honey and beeswax and

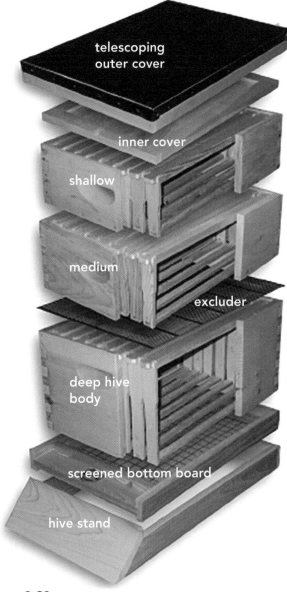

Figure 9-20
Basic Langstroth hive. Brushy Mountain Bee Farm

some left to overwinter. The containers were kept small so the bee colony would expand, fill the container and swarm.

The modern Langstroth beehive

Today, manufactured hives are usually much more spacious than natural nest cavities. Such hives allow bees to store more honey and provide room for expansion so they swarm less compared to bees living in nature.

The typical Langstroth hive is shown in Figure 9-20. A hive consists of one deep (or standard box) for brood, a bottom board (screened or solid), a hive stand, a queen excluder to separate brood from honey storage, and two types of supers (medium and shallow) beneath inner and telescoping outer covers at top.

Some of the important features of the Langstroth hive that incorporate feral nest requirements with ease of manipulation are:

• bee protection from the elements

• small entrance at bottom of boxes

• convenient method of supering (often using a box of reduced height dimension for honey harvesting)

• vertical boxes suitable for brood/honey storage areas

• different size supers for beekeeper convenience.

Management of the Langstroth hive consists of keeping a portion of the hive for the bees (the brood area) and adding boxes at the top (the supers) for potential surplus honey harvest. Beekeepers can use boxes and frames of all one size but many prefer to use smaller depth boxes for supers (as shown in Figure 9-20). The advantage is that honey-filled frames of shorter depth boxes are not as heavy to lift.

Many other beehives have been developed, and we describe several types throughout this chapter. The U.S. patent office has many hive patents. Following

Langstroth, many of the patent designs also incorporated bee space some only changing width or hight dimensions. In some countries, several hives of different dimensions, including Langstroth dimensions, are in common use.

Plastic Langstroth hive

The original Langstroth hive is made of wood with pure beeswax foundation placed in the wooden frames. Various innovative plastic hives and frames are on the market that essentially duplicate the wooden Langstroth hive. Instead of pure beeswax foundation, plastic frames have plastic foundation (coated with beeswax) or are molded plastic.

Beekeepers can mix and match using wooden boxes with plastic frames or plastic boxes with wooden frames. Instead of sheets of pure beeswax foundation, plastic foundation sheets can be used in wooden frames. The types of plastics used vary: polystyrene hives are sturdy and insulate well. Insulated plastic hives provide better temperature stability than wood.

The garden hive (Eight frame Langstroth hive)

The standard Langstroth hive has ten parallel frames. There is an eight-frame model that is 20% lighter. It is popular for those wanting a smaller, lighter hive. By

Figure 9-21
Long Langstroth hive holding 20 frames. S. Repasky

Figure 9-22
Examining long hive.

Figure 9-23
Connecticut beekeeper Becky Jones transferring frames from five frame nuc (cardboard box right) to standard 10 frame Langstroth hive (left). She will add the two foundation frames (near her right knee) to far side of box following placement of the five nuc frames in middle of 10-frame box. L. Connor

Figure 9-25
Warré style frame, but using a wood dowel as the starter. Tuckabee

adding a copper peaked roof it provides an attractive **garden hive**. See illustration Chapter 12, Figure 12-29.

Long Langstroth hive (20-31 frames)

Various horizontal hive designs (long hive, Valkyrie) have addressed the lifting and ergonomics of the size and layout of the typical vertical Langstroth hive of stacked brood boxes and several honey supers (Figure 9-21, 9-22).

In the horizontal hive, frames are arranged horizontally and boxes may be placed on top as supers for honey

Figure 9-24
Hive frame using only a top bar. Steller

Figure 9-26
View of the Warré colony.

Figure 9-27
Kenyan top-bar hive. By keeping the hive horizontal to the ground, well-formed combs will be built.

harvest. Simple plans suggest material costs of only $50 and two hours to build. Thick walls and sturdy elevated hive stands reduce problems with mice and other predators and position them at a more convenient height to manipulate. Frames may be of traditional Langstroth design or simple top bars with starter strips.

Critics cite the bee's instinct to move up, not horizontally, and a greater likelihood of the winter cluster starving during the winter with honey just inches away. This may be a matter of providing adequate top insulation and repositioning of honey stores for winter cluster movement.

Figure 9-28
A straight sided Layens top bar is a horizontal hive holding 20 large frames, 13 in long and 16 in deep. T. Liptak

Five frame Langstroth hive (nuc, split or nucleus hive)

Five frame boxes are used to house a nucleus colony or a mating colony. Such boxes usually hold deep frames as they provide more area for bees to build and store brood and food than medium bodies. See also Chapter 19. Many beekeepers keep single or double nucleus **support hives** as backup for queenless or failing colonies that occur throughout the season and to sell to make new colonies (as shown in Figure 9-23).

Warré hive (the people's hive)

Modified top-bar hives have been promoted as requiring less inspection and intervention. One is the Warré hive (Figure 9-26) which has become popular. Developed by

French beekeeper Emile Warré to use less lumber and to follow the natural comb-building bees use in hollow cavities.

The frames are started with top bars only (Figures 9-24, 9-25), and additional boxes for expansion are placed under the first box(es), termed **nadiring**. It looks somewhat like a Langstroth hive, but is sometimes called a **vertical top bar hive**. Manipulation is very limited as frames are not readily removable and boxes need be removed to add more space (although some owners modify to super above as in Langstroth hives).

Top bar hives—Kenyan, Tanzanian and Layens

Developed in Kenya in the 1970s, the Kenyan top bar hive (Figure 9-27) offers a low-cost, simple horizontal rhomboid design; the Tanzanian version has straight side walls. As name implies a top bar hive uses only top bars (no side or bottom bars) (Figure 9-29) that form a solid barrier to enclose the top of the hive (covers are added for weather protection). The bees build natural combs that hang free in a saddle-bag shape (Figure 9-29).

Top bars are wooden, usually 1 3/8" (35mm) wide and anything from about 15" to as much as 24" long, although the average is 17" to 19". A guide is usually provided to encourage bees to build straight combs—a big help to the beekeeper, but not necessarily the first choice of the bees. This can be a simple groove cut in the underside of the bar and filled with wax, or a thin strip of wood fixed to the bar.

One feature of a top bar hive is that only one frame needs to be exposed at a time. Colony growth is extended horizontally (no adding boxes) with a follower board to define number of frames for expansion. Designs include sturdy legs or hive stand to hold frames at beekeeper convenient height.

The hive commonly referred to as the Kenyan top-bar hive was developed by Dr. Maurice V. Smith and Dr. Gordon Townsend from the University of Guelph in Canada, sponsored by the Canadian International Development Agency (CIDA) under an initial four-year overseas project which began in Kenya in 1971.

Although the hive's management differs strongly from the tub shaped Greek hive, early publications about the Kenyan hive often mention the Greek hive (Figure 1-12) as an inspiration for the hive design.

The original Kenyan hive was designed to hang from trees or poles. Hanging the hive some distance from the ground protects it from both wild and domestic animals, as well as from ants and beetles. It has recently been adopted to serve as a living fence to keep elephants away from crops or homes (Figure 9-30).

The Tanzanian hive was designed in 1972 by G. Ntenga as a transitional hive based on the plank hive that uses movable top-bars. This hive is sometimes called the

Figure 9-29
Kenyan top-bar hive frame. Requires more care to handle, but provides an easy way to harvest bulk comb honey. The sloping sides reduce comb attachment. Stell Apiaries

Figure 9-30
Hanging from posts, these hives keep elephants away from human crops in Africa.

Tanzanian Transitional Hive in literature, and was the original **Tanzanian top-bar hive**. Ntenga's hive had very precise measurements. It used top-bars with either a center groove, a V-shaped bevel, or flat surface. The top-bars had lugs that were narrower than the bar itself. The hive could take 28 combs. The hive was covered with two lids, each covering half the hive.

The Layens horizontal top bar hive was developed by French beekeeper George de Layens. It uses 20 large frames 13 in long and 16 in deep. Sides may be sloping like the Kenyan hive, or with wood with parallel sides (Figure 9-28).

Flow hive

The Flow hive (Figure 9-32) involves use of modified Langstroth-style frames made of two pieces of molded plastic designed to allow the beekeeper to harvest honey from special supers without opening the hive. The Flow frame consists of partly formed honeycomb cells. The bees complete the comb with their wax then fill the cells with honey, before capping the cells. To harvest the honey, the cells are split to flow into channels for the honey to drain into honey jars. The bees remain undisturbed on the surface of the comb.

Flow hive are criticized because of the use of plastic comb, the lack of contact between bees and beekeepers and the high cost ($600-800 per hive). The brood nest boxes below the special honey frames are standard Langstroth equipment; colonies must be managed to maximize strength as bees are sometimes reluctant to enter the super and fill the plastic frames.

AZ (Slovenian hive)

The Slovenian AZ beehive originates from the European country of Slovenia where it was designed by beekeeper Anton Zniderŝic. The hive allows for inspection from the back of the hive without lifting supers or brood boxes. Frames slide backwards. AZ hives are designed to be kept inside a "**bee house**" (Figure 9-33) and may be worked independent of the weather. Only a small amount of smoke is needed at the rear door during the inspection. Some enterprising beekeepers rent their bee house for an overnight 'bee experience' and odor therapy.

Observation Hives

There are many observation hive designs, typically using Langstroth frames with a glass or plastic viewing area for bee observation. They may have one, 1½, 2 or more frames of standard or shallower Langstroth frame size or a mixture of frame sizes. Some even arrange more than one frame horizontally between glass side walls (Figure 9-34).

Many such as the Ulster observation hive are finished to furniture quality. (Figure 9-35). They can be managed year-round but smaller versions may be assembled for seasonal use only. **The five-frame nucleus** (Ulster) observation hive provides portability for temporary use. The bottom base portion is a standard five-frame nucleus colony. The top portion holds a single frame between glass surfaces. When required, a frame of the nuc below is elevated with the queen to viewing in the upper portion. Following use, the frame is restored below. The design keeps bee populations strong and healthy during use.

Figure 9-31
Flow hive at the Univ. California apiary. L. Connor

Figure 9-32
AZ hives in building. Slovenia. W. Blomstedt

OBSERVATION HIVES

An observation beehive is a small colony of honey bees behind clear plastic or glass walls (Figures 9-34, 9-35). An observation hive allows you to see nearly all the activities that happen inside the normally dark beehive with minimal disturbance to the bees. Observation hives can provide hours of entertainment and educational fun and make good exhibits for schools, fairs, parks and public places or events. They also can be a highly effective honey promotion device that attracts a crowd.

A large number of observations and experiments are possible with an observation hive. Bees make excellent study animals. Bees can be used to examine many basic biological concepts. Bees can be models for comparisons with other animals when studying social behavior, communication, vision and odor perception, nesting behavior, preparations for winter, hunting for food and many other subjects.

Observation hives will enable you to see, record and experiment with bee dances. Bees can be marked in the field and their dance observed back in the observation hive. They even become research tools, some with panels that allow removal of bees or placement of items into the interior.

Observation beehives can be established in virtually any geographical area and maintained in any sort of building provided the bees have access to the outside. An observation hive is a small version of a regular beehive. Instead of parallel combs of beeswax we confine a single beeswax comb, normally inside a wooden or plastic frame, between two panes of plastic or shatter-resistant glass to prevent accidental breakage.

You can buy an observation beehive or build your own. At times it is useful to have a portable observational unit with bees confined, without an exit, to take to fairs, schools or markets. Since the bees are confined, it's not really a functional hive. It is possible to keep this unit closed up only for two or three days. You can make up a temporary unit just before it is needed from an existing colony and then return the surviving bees to their original colony upon conclusion of the display.

For information on establishing an observation hive, instructions on how to build your own and activities and experiments you can do with an observation hive consult the book by Caron and Webster, *Observation Hives* (Root Publications).

Figure 9-33
Children are fascinated by the observation hive and the beekeeper's engaging stories about what they see.
B.K. Councell

Figure 9-34
Five-frame nucleus or Ulster observation hive.

key terms

Africanized bees	comb pheromone	horizontal (long) hive	queen excluder
AZ hive	communication holes	Layens hive	queen pheromones
bee bread	drone cells	long Langstroth hive	rabbet
bee space	feral nest	medium (Illinois/western) super	Rose hive
bee gum	flow hive (super)	nest cavity	skep
box (rustic) hive	hexagonal cell	observation hive	shallow super
brace/burr comb	hive	parallel beeswax comb	top bar hive (Kenyan/ Tanzanian)
brood	hive stand	pipe hive	transition cells
capping (brood/honey) cell	gum	propolis	Ulster hive
comb honey super	Hoffman frame	queen cup	Warré hive

discussion questions

Name the basic features of the natural nest and how they are incorporated into our modern hive. A colony organizes its nest, no matter where it is living. Describe this basic organization.

How has examination of the natural (feral) bee nest helped humans in designing beehives? Is one of the reasons for so little success of many hive designs due to the fact that little was known about the natural nest before most movable frame hives were patented? Use your search engine to look up the Langstroth patent (or another hive design available to you) and determine what the designer did and did not know about bee biology.

The Langstroth hive has been widely adopted. Why? Can you see what might be special advantages to a top bar hive (including Warré)? Or to a Long hive? Or keeping hives in buildings vs outdoors? Can you find, other than rustic hives mentioned here and Chapter 1, that might be useful designs?

exercises

Where legal, and with the owner's permission, find a natural bee tree, cut it down and determine its features. Look for suitable how-to references on the Internet. Alternately, create an artificial swarm and hive it in a dark box with a small hole for an entry/exit area. Monitor comb building of the bees in this box over the initial three weeks and then drive the bees out (into a hive) and make comb measurements. Count the number of cells of different brood stages, cells of pollen, honey-filled cells, number of drone cells, etc. Repeat this process (or have several others do the same) and compare your counts. Is there a clear picture of early hive development?

Assemble a Langstroth hive and determine what are the major features (see also Chapter 12) of its various parts. Why has it become the standard 'go-to' hive? How is plastic changing the standard from wood and beeswax only components?

Ask beekeepers in your area who have both a standard Langstroth hive and one or more other types of hives for their opinion on usefulness of different hives. Visit such hives if possible to see first hand what might be pros and cons of each.

Investigate the possibility of establishing an observation hive. If feasible start one. See the Caron and Webster reference for details and what you then might do with such a hive. Assemble a modern Langstroth hive including frames. Compare prices of the standard pieces of equipment from two or more bee suppliers.

references

Blackistan, H. 2020. Beekeeping for Dummies. 6th Ed.

Blackiston, H. 2019. Building Beehives for Dummies

Caron, D.M. and T. Webster 1999. Observation Hives: How to Set up, Maintain and Use a Window to World of Honey Bees. A.I. Root

Edwards, J. Long hive beekeeping: A practical guide. Bee Outside. Hive & Garden, West Linn, OR

Kritsky, G. 2015. The Tears of Re: Beekeeping in Ancient Egypt. Oxford Univ Press

de Layens, G. and G. Bonnier. 2017. Keeping Bees in Horizontal Hives: A Complete Guide to Apiculture, Deep Snow Press, Ithaca, NY

Mangum, W. 2012. Top-Bar Hive Beekeeping: Wisdom & Pleasure Combined. Stinging Drone Publications

Pisano, T. 2013. Build Your Own Beekeeping Equipment. Storey Publishing

Seeley, T.J. 2019. The Lives of Bees: The Untold Story of the Honey Bee in the Wild. Princeton Univ Press

Simon, E. 2011. Bee Equipment Essentials. Wicwas Press, Kalamazoo MI

Figure 10-1
Queen cells at the bottom of a brood frame. C. Hubbard

One queen, usually

The bee colony normally has one single reproductive female—the queen. She is specialized for the functions of egg laying and chemical production, especially queen substance pheromone (Chapter 7). She does not perform the duties of the workers; longterm she cannot survive without a minimum of 200 workers to care for her.

Twenty-four hours a day, the queen alternates between egg laying and periods of feeding, grooming and resting. During the winter months, there is considerably less egg-laying activity. During the busy spring months, the queen alternates 10-15 minute periods of resting behavior followed by 5-10 minutes of egg-laying behavior. It has been estimated that a queen lays over 200,000 eggs in a year, and many queens will produce half a million eggs in her two- to three-year life-span, although most queens live a year or less.

During resting, a retinue of 12 or more worker bees attend to the queen (Figure 10-2). They feed her, groom her, remove her wastes and receive her pheromones. The pheromones are shared with other workers in food transmission (**trophallaxis**) behavior. Newly emerged queens are termed **virgin queens** (Figure 10-3). They receive less worker attention than older mated queens. Virgin queens are smaller in size since her ovaries in the abdomen remain undeveloped until after mating.

The first activity of a newly emerged virgin queen is to eliminate any potential rival virgin queens and queen cells (Figure 10-7). Then, she prepares for mating, beginning orientation flights two to three days following emergence. The queen is ready to mate within a week. Mating flights will last one or more days, during which time the queen will mate with 15 to 20 or more drones. If a queen does not mate within the first three weeks of emergence, her chance

Figure 10-2
Queen resting, surrounded by a retinue of attendant worker bees. Tuckabee

Figure 10-3
Virgin queen with her head down and searching for sisters to kill. L. Connor

of successfully mating decreases. Once mated, she will not mate again in her lifetime.

Following mating, the queen, now called a **mated queen**, quickly gains weight with rapid ovary development. She can begin to lay eggs within two to three days. Her capability to lay eggs increases to the point that a healthy queen in a populous colony can produce 1,500-2,000 eggs in a single day under favorable circumstances.

Queens that do not mate or those that use up their stored sperm can only produce unfertilized (drone) eggs (Figure

10-4). Such queens are termed **drone layers**. Colonies with drone layers are doomed since workers are needed in the colony, and fertilized eggs are necessary to raise a replacement queen. A special, rare case of reproduction is **thelytoky**—the production of female workers or queens from unfertilized eggs. Thelytoky occurs with some frequency in the Cape bee *Apis mellifera capensis* which produce a new queen from laying worker eggs; it occurs in other bee races at very low frequency.

Queen replacement (supersedure)

With just one female reproductive in a bee colony, there is a special procedure to replace the mated queen when it becomes necessary (Chapter 9, Figure 9-13; 10-7). Queens are reared in special vertical-oriented cells (Figures 9-12, 10-1, 10-7). Replacement of a queen by another queen is a process termed **supersedure**. Replacement of the queen with colony division and creation of another colony is a behavior called **swarming**. A third means of replacing a queen, **emergency queen rearing**, is necessary if the queen dies suddenly, is removed by a beekeeper or is somehow injured or lost from her colony (Figure 10-23). Emergency conditions are generally used by beekeepers to rear replacement queens but supplemented by a high bee population (crowding) and colony conditions of food abundance found in swarming behavior.

Queen failure may lead to reduced egg laying, but queen inadequacy is apparently measured through chemical pheromone production. Worker bees become restless in

Figure 10-4
Failing queen with mixed worker and drone cells, apparently running out of viable sperm. W. Madden

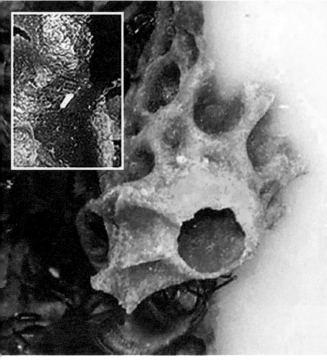

Figure 10-5
Queen cups are empty and found at comb edges all year long. L. Connor
Figure 10-6 (inset)
Egg in queen cup (with wax moved). The queen deposits the eggs in the cups. D. Morgan

Figure 10-7
Queen replacement cells on the face of comb, on the edge of sealed worker cells. L. Connor

as little as one hour after the removal of their queen. Replacement behaviors are seen within four hours as bees sense they are queenless or that their queen is failing by the queen's reduced release of queen substance or the absence of queen pheromone.

Here is how this apparently works: each worker bee needs to receive a certain level of **queen substance**. This pheromone is distributed through **food transmission**. When a queen is taken away the level of this pheromone drops rapidly. In the case of a failing queen, the queen produces insufficient amounts of queen substance, and therefore is fed back less of the pheromone by the bees of her retinue. This feedback system of queen pheromone distribution is vital for communication (Chapter 7).

The first behavior change observable in **queen replacement** is the laying of a fertilized egg in a queen cup (Figure 10-6). Queen cups are special cup-like precursors of queen cells (Figure 10-5). They are always present in a bee colony, though their numbers are greatest in the spring months. They are built at the lower margin of beeswax comb (lower margins of frames in a beekeeper's hive, Figure 10-1) and in spaces where the comb is damaged or left open as a walkway to the opposite side of the comb. Sometimes they are built on a piece of burr comb extended outward from the comb face.

Queen cups are round and cup-shaped, oriented with the cell opening downward—in contrast to the horizontal six-sided worker and drone cells. The vertical orientation of a queen cell stimulates the bees to feed **royal jelly** to the larva. The larva has no danger of falling out as the surface tension of the royal jelly holds it in place. Queens can, in fact, develop normally in a horizontal orientation (or workers in a vertical position) if experimentally reared outside a colony.

The queen herself places the fertilized egg into a queen cup. Once the queen cup is occupied, it is called a **queen cell.** Workers can remove and may eat eggs from queen cells or regular cells, but they are not known to transfer them from one worker cell to another or to a queen cup.

By chewing a hole on the side of the cell, and perhaps stinging the occupant of the cell, the queen causes the workers to remove the larva or pupa inside (Figure 10-9). Queen cells are repeatedly aborted in a bee colony. Many more cells are started than are successfully completed. Why bees start and then stop raising queens and the extent of such behavior is not known.

Frequency of supersedure

Queen replacement via supersedure occurs more frequently than most beekeepers appreciate. There is a somewhat constant level of unsuccessful queen

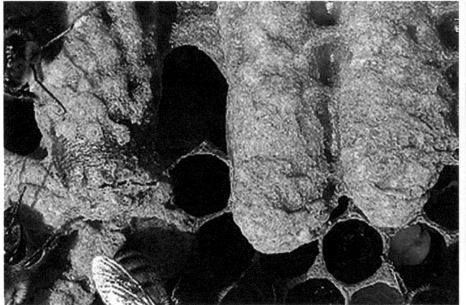

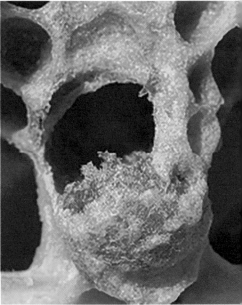

Figure 10-8
Mature and emerging queen cells (see cutting of cap by queen seeking to emerge from cell at left). Wax removal by bees on left cell. L. Connor

Figure 10-9
Queen cell destroyed by a rival sister quee[n]
L. Connor

replacement that occurs under normal circumstances. As a general rule, queen supersedure occurs during the summer or early fall months and involves the rearing of only a few queen cells.

During supersedure, replacement queen cells are more frequently positioned on the face of the beeswax comb rather than its lower margin. These circumstances are not always the rule and predicting the eventual outcome when a colony is observed rearing queen cells is difficult.

Cause of supersedure

Since queen supersedure results when the bees and queen herself perceive a failing queen, when a colony raising replacement queens is reduced in size such as by dividing, the smaller colony often discontinues attempts to raise new queens. Since the bees and the queen determine whether the queen is healthy or failing by the level of production of queen pheromone, queens may produce enough queen substance to satisfy the population of a smaller colony, at least until the colony gets bigger again. However, removing eggs alone does not lead to queen replacement behaviors.

When a queen receives too little queen substance from her attendant workers, she responds by laying fertilized eggs in a few queen cups (Figures 10-5, 10-6). She does this over several days. Workers in no way force her to do this. The queen herself must initiate the behavior. If conditions change in the colony (fewer bees, better distribution of the chemicals, etc.), queen rearing may be aborted; if conditions do not change, replacement queen rearing continues.

Efficient versus inefficient queen supersedure

If the failing queen dies relatively early in the supersedur[e] process — before the new virgin queen emerges — we label it **inefficient supersedure**. If she survives until the new queen emerges — sometimes leading to the two queens coexisting as a mother-daughter queen colony (Figure 10-10) — then it is labeled **efficient queen supersedure**. The

Figure 10-10
Mother (red) and daughter (white) queens laying eggs on th[e] same comb, each with a retinue of workers. A. Abrahams

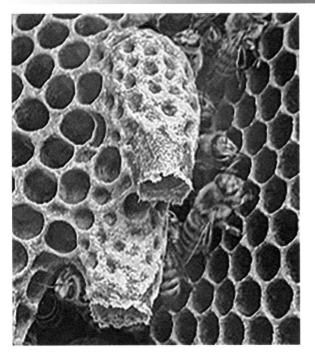

Figure 10-11
Emerged from queen cells. Wax was removed at tips prior to queen emergence. L. Connor

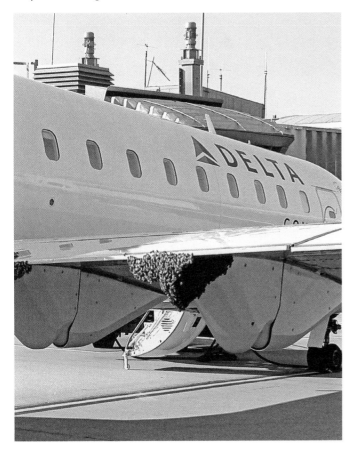

Figure 10-12
A swarm landed on this Delta flight waiting to leave Pittsburgh, PA. S. Repasky

Box 20

BEE SOUNDS

There are many sounds we can hear in a beehive—do bees hear them too? Bees lack ears, but they do hear! Bees communicate with sounds both in queen rearing and in dance language communication.

In swarming and supersedure, 'piping' is a high-pitched sound produced by queen muscle contractions while the wings remain unfolded. The thorax vibrates faster with wings folded than when unfolded, so the sound is not the usual bee 'buzz' but a high-pitched 'piping' sound.

A queen pipes by pressing her thorax against the beeswax comb. Adult queens pipe on or close to the developing queen cells. Worker bees pick up the sound, probably via vibrations perceived by their leg sensors, and have been observed to stop or freeze their movements in the vicinity of the queen's piping. The adult queen pipes for a two-second pulse followed by a series of quarter-second toots. If there are virgin queens within queen cells, they respond with a series of ten short pulses.

Piping is more frequently heard in swarming than in supersedure behavior and is more commonly heard after the primary swarm leaves. It is also heard when a group of caged queens are kept together. We do not know what precise role it plays, but it is believed piping may help time swarm departure, particularly for afterswarms. Also, piping may help the virgin queen locate her potential rivals so she can eliminate them.

The ordinary buzzing sound made by bees when flying may or may not be perceived by bees. If we hold a worker bee in our fingers, she too will make a high pitched sound somewhat similar to queen piping. Worker bees will also emit this sound in the hive—perhaps as a warning or alarm sound?

Sound production is vital in dance language communication behavior. Worker bees must precisely time the length of waggling sound since it encodes the distance to food source. The unique noise of the 'breaking' dance, signaling swarm departure, may also be a sound the bees can hear.

The perception of substrate 'noise' may be via touch receptors rather than airborne sound wave perception. Beekeepers know that jolts and vibrations to the hive serve to alert a bee colony and may result in more stings during colony inspections. The ordinary background hum of bees may likewise be a touch stimulus transmitted through the beeswax comb.

SWARM FLOW CHART

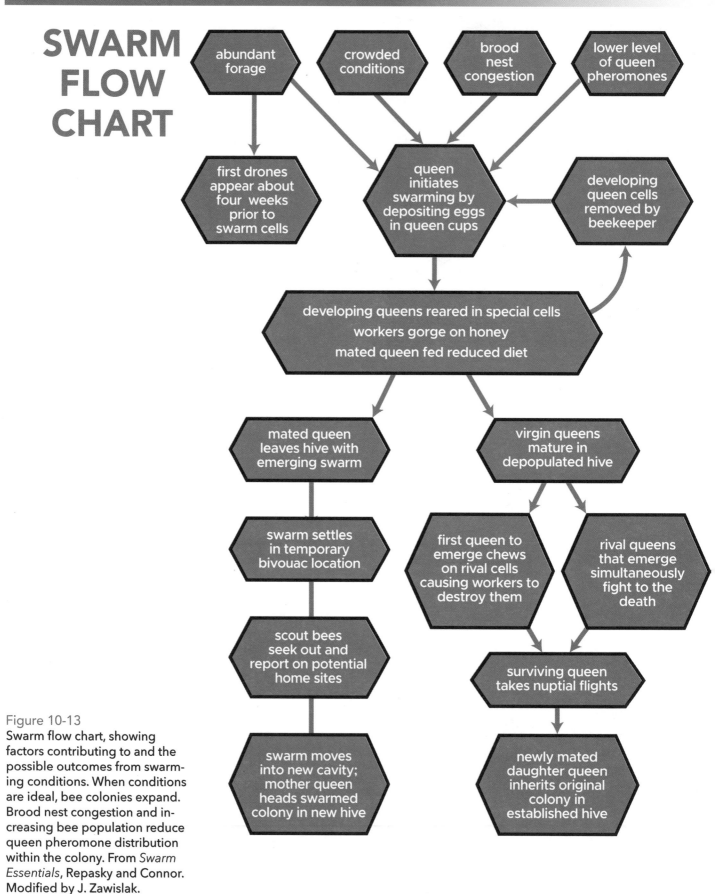

abundant forage

crowded conditions

brood nest congestion

lower level of queen pheromones

first drones appear about four weeks prior to swarm cells

queen initiates swarming by depositing eggs in queen cups

developing queen cells removed by beekeeper

**developing queens reared in special cells
workers gorge on honey
mated queen fed reduced diet**

mated queen leaves hive with emerging swarm

virgin queens mature in depopulated hive

swarm settles in temporary bivouac location

first queen to emerge chews on rival cells causing workers to destroy them

rival queens that emerge simultaneously fight to the death

scout bees seek out and report on potential home sites

surviving queen takes nuptial flights

swarm moves into new cavity; mother queen heads swarmed colony in new hive

newly mated daughter queen inherits original colony in established hive

Figure 10-13
Swarm flow chart, showing factors contributing to and the possible outcomes from swarming conditions. When conditions are ideal, bee colonies expand. Brood nest congestion and increasing bee population reduce queen pheromone distribution within the colony. From *Swarm Essentials*, Repasky and Connor. Modified by J. Zawislak.

longer the old queen survives, the greater the efficiency because there is less of an interruption in the brood cycle.

At some point in supersedure, worker bees apparently kill the old (failing) queen. They do this in a behavior called **balling**. A large number of workers crowd the queen, forming a ball around her. The queen is killed by a combination of suffocation from an elevated level of carbon dioxide and hypothermia due to heat produced by the balling bees. The signal or signals for this behavior are not known.

Since a supersedure colony rears more than one queen, there may be instances when two or more virgin queens emerge at about the same time. In such circumstances, the virgin queens will fight, and one eventually becomes the sole survivor. Some beekeepers believe killing of the old mated queen in efficient supersedure may also be via fighting between mother and daughter queens. More likely, the workers ball the old mated queen as the colony reduces in size and the new daughter queen becomes the sole colony queen.

The process of queen fighting is not well studied, though it is often depicted in films and videos that feature honey bee biology. Worker bees sometimes confine virgin queens in their cells for a day or more, but it is not clear this is intended to protect them. The queens are fed inside their cells when this is done. Confinement often leads to production of the curious piping sound (Box 12). The more queen cells a colony has, the more likely piping will occur since queens often respond to the piping of another queen.

Swarming

Swarming is natural colony reproduction. The behavior of swarming is complex. It is a basic biological instinct of bees since division of the colony unit is essential for the society's continuation. Biologists lack full understanding of the several interrelated factors that are responsible for successful swarming in a bee colony.

Swarming means different things to different people. While L.L. Langstroth, the inventor of the hive with that name, called swarming a 'most beautiful sight,' the general public often finds a swarm a terrifying sight. For

Figure 10-14
Worker vibrating a queen. T. Seeley

Figure 10-15
Newly clustered swarm on a low branch. L. Connor

beekeepers, swarms represent potential new colonies; at one time they were a welcome sight. Today most beekeepers practice swarm prevention and control, but swarms still emerge from bee trees and beekeeper hives.

The appearance of a swarm has been expressed in history as both a portent of good or bad news. Bees that swarm excessively, such as the Africanized bees in South America, represent a potential stinging hazard to be avoided by the general public. Such swarms are a valuable resource for rural subsistence farmers who establish the hive and will return to rob the honey later in the season.

Bee swarms have halted airplane departures (Figure 10-12), auto traffic, delayed sporting events (such as a nationally telecast baseball game in Ohio) and terrorized the US in the book and movie *The Swarm* (1978). Although misunderstood, swarms are only temporary, usually gentle and not a threat if simply left alone, even in the defensive Africanized bee.

Figure 10-16
Swarm leaving a hive. L. Connor

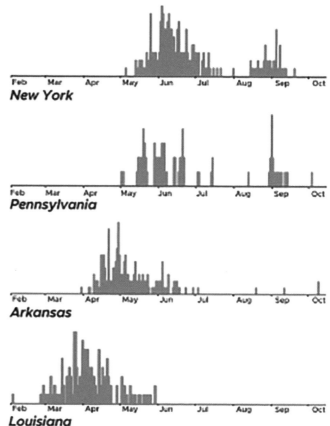

Figure 10-17
Seasonality of swarming at different regions of the USA. Note the fall swarm season in New York and Pennsylvania but less so in Arkansas and none in Louisiana.

Swarm basics

Swarming begins with too little queen substance. Bees prepare to leave and scouts look for a new home. The clustered group (Figures 10-12, 10-15) is called the **swarm,** and the behavior and departure is termed **swarming** (Figure 10-16)

The parent colony may then yield **after-swarms** containing one or more virgin queens and a further division of the remaining adult worker population. Eventually the parent colony stops swarming; one virgin queen becomes the monarch and, after she mates, the original colony returns to a normal existence. The single colony is now two or more colonies.

A swarm issuing from a hive contains 41-80% of the adult workers of the original hive (average 66%). The first swarm to leave (**primary swarm**) usually contains only the old mated queen, but it may also contain virgin queens if weather conditions have delayed swarm departure. After-swarms often contain several virgin queens (up to 20 in one instance) with fewer bees. Virgins coexist in afterswarms without fighting until they reach their new home, when they almost immediately fight.

Swarms as small as 2,400 bees to as large as 41,000 individuals have been reported. Mean populations were 11,800 bees in one study and calculated at 14,000 bees in another.

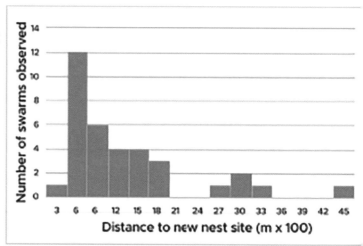

Figure 10-18
Distance (in meters) of swarm movement to new nest sites. D. Caron data

Events leading to swarming

Swarming is not a random happenstance. It is difficult but possible to observe and measure some of the events before the bees depart their colony (Figure 10-12).

Swarming preparations begin when the queen lays fertilized eggs in the vertically-oriented queen cups. Queen cups (Figures 10-5, 10-6) are constructed, often in great numbers, by the bees as colonies expand in the spring. If queen cups are experimentally removed, bees replace them more quickly during the spring than at other times of the year.

Construction of queen cups, expansion of worker and drone brood rearing and raising of queens by colonies are seasonal responses to **increasing photoperiod** and **abundant resources**. The first outward sign of swarming behavior the beekeeper usually observes is the development of queen cells.

Usually, the queen lays eggs in queen cups over more than one day. She commonly selects queen cups at the bottom margin of the comb rather than cups extending from the comb face, although she can use a cup at any location. As in supersedure, the same egg laying queen can return later to these developing queen cells to halt queen rearing. Worker bees do not 'force' the queen to lay eggs in cups nor do they later protect them from her destruction.

As queen cells develop, it is possible to observe several additional events in preparation for swarming. The queen begins to lose weight. Workers begin to treat the queen more roughly, including the behavior of **vibrating the queen** (Figure 10-14). A queen will lose about one-third of her body weight before departing in the swarm. Since a queen is normally very heavy with eggs, most of the weight loss occurs in the ovaries. The queen continues egg-laying behavior but at a reduced rate during weight loss.

Worker bees meanwhile are gaining weight because they tend to gorge with honey when preparing to swarm. This behavior starts up to ten days before the swarm issues. **Engorgement** helps ensure a food reserve for the swarm in transit to a new home since there is little foraging by the bees from the cluster location. As swarming day comes closer, scout bees begin to leave the parent colony to scout for a new nest site (Chapter 8).

Swarm emergence

There is a definite spring seasonality to swarming based on the local environment. The swarming season occurs when colonies are growing before colony peak population occurs. The vast majority of colonies swarm within a six-week period in mid-spring (Figure 10-16). Swarms usually emerge in the middle of the day (10 a.m. to 2 p.m.) on days suitable for flight.

Figure 10-19
Shaking the bees in the swarm into an empty brood box where several frames have been removed. L. Connor

Figure 10-20
Frames returned and before putting the cover on the hive, the beekeeper gently brushes and smokes the bees into the hive chamber. L. Connor

There may be waves of emergence periods when uncertain spring weather holds swarms from leaving with the result that the next nice day a number of colonies swarm. Swarms may leave as soon as developing queen cells are capped, but usually the primary swarm leaves a day or so ahead of virgin queen emergence.

The process of leaving the original hive is rapid, lasting only 10-15 minutes from emergence to clustering at a **temporary bivouac site**. Prior to emergence, bees become quiet in the hive and foraging is reduced. The signal to leave is the **buzz run or breaking dance**. The queen, who by this time has lost considerable weight, may be pushed toward the entrance by her worker bees.

There is no apparent determination of which bees will exit with a swarm or those that will stay. Bees of all ages join a swarm, but the majority are younger, 4 to 23 day-old bees. Anywhere from one-half to two-thirds of the parent hive population will leave in the primary swarm (first swarm with the mated queen). The leaving bees pile out the entrance and join in a circular flight motion (Figure 10-16).

The majority of swarm clusters are formed within three meters (ten feet) of the ground (Figures 10-15, 10-19); a few cluster on the ground itself while others may form at higher locations. Those that select lower cluster sites

Figure 10-22

A caged queen is tied around the chin of this person's bee beard. (Victoria, British Columbia Parliament building)

are easier for beekeepers to capture (Figures 10-19, 10-20). Swarms are known to cluster at the same bivouac sites year after year in apiaries, apparently due to trace amounts of pheromone left by the previous swarm.

Drones join the swarm (average 50 per swarm) but, unlike the workers, do not gorge on food reserves before emergence. During swarm issuance, bees from other colonies may join the swarm, particularly bees from queenless hives.

Although many bees gorge in the parent hive in preparation to swarm, all do not leave. By re-hiving the bees that swarm (after marking a proportion of the population) and permitting them to swarm again, it was revealed that the same bee may or may not go again, suggesting a random division of the adult population at the time of swarm emergence.

Cause of swarming

While the causes of swarming are not completely known, we know that strong, healthy colonies swarm. Timing of swarming is influenced by weather, time of year (Figure 10-17), photoperiod, floral productivity, genetics, age of the queen, her pheromones (and their distribution), physical crowding and additional factors (Figure 10-13).

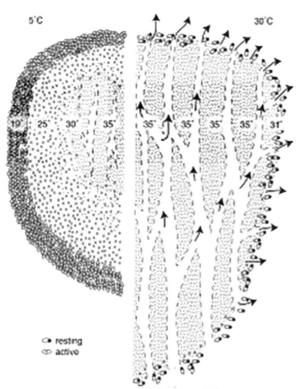

Figure 10-21

The cluster is organized as a sphere with an outer shell of older bees two to three bees thick while inside there are chains of younger bees. The expanded right half shows how airflow is channeled within the cluster core. Seeley modified from Heinrich

Figure 10-23
Emergency cells under construction next to sealed and open worker brood. This occurs when the queen is killed or removed from the hive.

As is the case with queen supersedure, swarming is strongly influenced by insufficient queen substance. Colonies with young queens are much less likely to swarm than colonies headed by queens more than 12 months old. The ability of a queen to produce queen substance varies with age as well as genetic factors and the conditions under which she was reared. A combination of congestion and queen pheromone insufficiency seems to explain the causal factors of swarming.

Queen substance deficiency induces swarming in large colonies which are congested with young bees. The queen may not be deficient but rather high colony congestion means **less efficient distribution of the queen pheromone**. Thus, in the feedback mechanism of queen substance, the queen receives an insufficient amount. She then initiates queen rearing by laying eggs in queen cups. Full-sized colonies in which a queen produces an adequate level of queen substance do not swarm. Their level of congestion is such that the distribution of the pheromone is not inhibited.

Post-emergence behavior of swarms

Exiting swarms move en masse to a temporary site near the parent colony before eventually moving to the eventual new home site. The mass of bees in flight may extend 15 to 30 m (50 to 100 feet) in diameter and 2 to 6 m (6 to 20 feet) high. The queen pheromone (9 ODA) interacts with worker scent glands to maintain the cohesiveness of the flying mass of bees. Individual bees fly in a circular pattern within the swarm. The queen does not lead a swarm, but there must be a queen present for the swarm cluster to remain at the bivouac site.

In the temporary bivouac site, the only bees that leave the swarm cluster are the **scout bees** who search for a suitable nesting cavity. When the scouts return to the cluster, they indicate the location of their find by dancing on the surface of the clustered swarm (Chapter 7).

The temporary swarm cluster is organized as a sphere with an **outer shell** of older bees two to three bees thick while inside there are **chains of younger bees** (Figure 10-21). The inside temperature remains at an optimum brood rearing range of 93° F (around 34° C) while the outside temperature fluctuates with that of the environment. The size of the swarm expands and compacts as outside temperatures rise and fall.

The swarm cluster may remain at the temporary site a few hours or a few days. The swarm moves when all (or nearly all) scout bees are indicating, via dance language, the same site which generally is not too distant (Figure 10-18).

In rare instances, the bees may be unable to find a suitable cavity or the scout bees are unable to agree on one single location. The bees stay as a swarm cluster for a longer time period and may consume much of the food reserves in their honey stomachs. These swarms can be defensive if disturbed and might not behave like the typical gentle swarm.

Defense of its nest site may be related to a reduction in food reserves, but it is more likely that the bees begin to identify with the location and defend the temporary cluster site as they would their hive. Swarms that remain for more than a day begin wax secretion and comb construction at the temporary cluster spot. Exposed colonies often do not overwinter in temperate areas but may persist in warmer climates (Chapter 9, Figure 9-5).

After settling in a new home site, beeswax comb is quickly constructed. The queen rapidly regains her body weight and begins egg laying once comb cells are constructed. The real challenge is that additional comb must be constructed, brood must be raised and sufficient food must be stored to survive the winter.

Survival of such nests established for swarms is less than 25% in the wild, but if a colony survives the first winter season, it has a life expectancy of more than five years. Beekeeper-hived swarms, especially captured on drawn comb and fed sugar, expand more rapidly and exhibit higher winter survival.

What is a swarm worth?

Swarming may occur in any active flight month, but the vast majority of swarming occurs during a six-week window during spring colony development.

Practical wisdom about swarms is contained in the 17th century three-line rhyme:

A swarm in May is worth a load of hay,

A swarm in June a silver spoon,

A swarm in July ain't worth a fly.

By researching the value of these three items, we found that a load of hay is worth $100 per ton. Along the 35-45° north latitudes, swarming often peaks in May and early June. Although May sometimes has rainy weather, May swarms are well-timed for the main June clover flow familiar to our 17th century poet.

Conditions are also good for hiving June swarms, if the bees are able to build their nest fast enough and store adequate food. Silver-plated spoons are worth only a few dollars, but a solid silver spoon might fetch $30—even more if unique. June is also a great month for queen mating with reduced rains.

Come July, swarms are valued as worthless as a fly. The main nectar flow may have been missed, and the chance of survival is significantly reduced. Mating is often still good in July, but sometimes the drone population drops when the nectar flow ends, especially during drought.

What does a swarm cost the beekeeper?

One of the authors has written a book about making increase colonies and recommends the production of a new nucleus or increase colony during the spring swarming season. The goal benefit is two-fold: the colony does not produce a swarm and beekeepers end up with new colonies to augment their hive assets. Both authors have written and spoken about the use of nucleus colonies as **support hives**, providing brood, bees, food and queens to support production hives.

If a colony swarms, what is the financial value of the honey not produced by that hive? In some areas, when a colony swarms, the amount of lost honey might be low, maybe just ten to 20 pounds. But in good forage regions, the honey lost because a colony swarmed may be between 50 and 75 or more pounds. By doing the math, using the average value of the honey you sold during the season, the cost of swarming could add up to hundreds of dollars.

Trapping and capturing swarms are excellent beekeeper activities, but traps cost money to build and set out. Swarms must be driven to, captured and fed. Swarm capture and use are certainly not free of expenses.

Artificial swarms

Swarms can be created by caging a queen and forcing workers to cluster around her. This is routinely used to create a swarm in teaching situations to demonstrate swarm capture. It is also the technique to create a swarm for the demonstration of a **bee beard** (Figure 10-22). To make a bee beard, a queen cage with a living queen is tied beneath the chin; bees confined previously with the caged queen will cluster around their queen in her cage.

It is necessary that the worker bees around the queen cage be well gorged with ample sugar syrup before the demonstration is performed to reduce chances of being stung and to reduce flight activity. Holding the workers overnight with the caged queen helps develop queen fidelity. The sensation of living bees crawling and settling on the body is unique, and only people extremely comfortable around bees should attempt this activity.

The use of artificial swarms has increased our knowledge of bee communication by pheromones, swarm stabilization behavior, bee recognition of their own individual queen and other secrets of bee biology. It is an interesting experience to remove the queen cage from a clustered swarm and hold it as the bees move from the former location to cluster around their queen. Many interesting bee behaviors can be studied with artificial swarms.

Absconding

Under some circumstances, a bee colony may **abscond**. In absconding, all or most of the adult population leaves or abandons the nest site. The bees cluster like a swarm, and scout bees seek a new home site. European race honey bees seem to abscond infrequently whereas the African races (including the Africanized bee in South and North America) abscond more readily. Absconding may be a relic of migratory movement which is more common in Africa and maintained by the alternating wet and dry seasons.

Absconding in the fall has also been termed 'hunger swarming', though it may not always be related to lack of food. In abandonment, a large proportion of the bees may depart the parent colony, leaving it unable to continue to function normally. Absconding is seen in colonies that have no brood or developing queen cells, are very small in population, have an unsatisfactory nest site, are disturbed with continued smoking or dripping water, or may occur after exposure to certain noxious chemicals. There undoubtedly are other factors that may cause a colony to abscond.

Emergency queen rearing

A queen may be lost or killed in various ways. She may sometimes be injured or killed by actions of the beekeeper. Beekeepers may on occasion intentionally remove a queen from a colony to replace the existing queen. Worker bees quickly detect the sudden absence of a queen and promptly begin preparations for emergency queen cells (Figure 10-23). No worker can change into a queen—the bees must raise a new queen.

Emergency queen cells are made by the workers (Figure 10-23). They enlarge a few cells containing one- and two-day old worker larvae within four hours of the disappearance of the old queen. The number of new queen cells the bees will start building is highly variable and depends upon many factors. The workers always begin to rear several new queens rather than a single one.

While workers start more queen cells than they eventually complete to the adult stage, the criteria used to maintain or eliminate specific queen cells are unknown.

Emergency queen cells are distinguished from the queen cells of swarming because they originate from a worker cell (Figure 10-23). The horizontal orientation of the worker cell is quickly changed to the vertical by enlarging the base of the cell and drawing the opening outward and downward. This usually means destroying the cell walls and removing the occupant of three to four cells adjacent to the modified cell.

The newly-modified cell is expanded downward enlarging in development like a regular queen cell. The bees feed **royal jelly** to the developing larvae exactly as when they rear a queen in supersedure or swarming. Capped emergency cells often seem smaller than capped queen cells started from queen cups.

Upon emergence of virgin queens, surplus queens are eliminated. The end result is one single virgin queen after about a 24-hour period of fighting, elimination of queens and balling. The virgin queen then prepares to mate and begin her new life as the mated queen of the colony. The entire process of rearing an emergency virgin queen takes less than two weeks since the bees start from a larva. This is a week shorter than for a swarm or supersedure queen, which starts from an egg laid by the old queen.

If the emergency rearing of a replacement queen is not successful, the workers are left hopelessly queenless. They now lack fertilized eggs or larvae less than two days of age for a second attempt of emergency queen rearing. The workers age and the colony will perish unless a beekeeper intervenes and supplies a frame of worker brood from another colony with at least some eggs and young larvae.

Figure 10-24

Comparison of worker bee at the 11-o'clock position, with a full-sized drone at the lower right and a worker-sized drone on the lower left. The smaller drone was produced in a worker cell from an egg produced by a queen laying unfertilized eggs. Another drone is emerging from a cell. Note the capping flap. L. Connor

Figure 10-25

Tethered queen in a Drone Congregation Area attracting two drones. Copulation only takes a few seconds, then another drone mounts the queen and repeats the process. From *Mating Biology of the Honey Bee*, Koeniger et al.

Figure 10-26
The tethered queen is copulating with one drone while another is ready to take his turn. From *Mating Biology of the Honey Bee,* Koeniger et al.

Queenless colonies

A percentage of colonies become queenless each year when the queen fails to mate or dies. Queenless colonies have no eggs or young worker larvae and remain hopelessly queenless unless a beekeeper intervenes. Otherwise, they dwindle in population and die. During the active season, queenless colonies may result from unsuccessful queen replacement. Perhaps, in fighting, all the queens are killed. Also mating, which occurs first in the life of the virgin queen, is not without its hazards; queens can die, get lost, get eaten or return to the wrong hive after mating flights.

Colonies that are hopelessly queenless develop **laying workers**, hive bees that lay eggs. Without a queen and her pheromones plus the absence of inhibition from worker brood pheromone, worker ovaries begin to develop. After three to four weeks of queenlessness, 10% or so of the workers are capable of producing eggs in four to eight ovarioles that develop in their ovaries. These workers cannot mate, so all the eggs they produce are unfertilized and hence develop into males. Laying-worker colonies, like colonies headed by drone-layer queens, have no future. As the workers age and die, there are no replacements.

The beekeeper can distinguish between laying workers or a drone layer by examining the cells containing eggs. Drone-layer colonies have queens, so the usual situation of one egg neatly arranged in the bottom of the cell will be evident (Figure 10-29). Cells with eggs of laying workers are not so regular. The workers often put several eggs, even up to a dozen, in one cell, and the eggs are often at

Figure 10-27
Drones captured using queen pheromone hanging from a weather balloon within a Drone Congregation Area. From *Mating Biology of the Honey Bee,* Koeniger et al.

Figure 10-28
Drones feeding on a honey and pollen frame in a colony and preparing to return to the DCA to mate. At the end of the season, queenless colonies and colonies undergoing queen replacement attract drones. D. Morgan

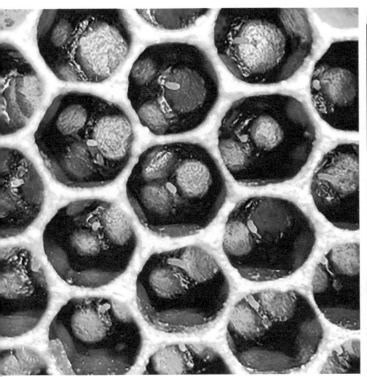

Figure 10-29
Eggs at the bottom of worker cells. They are placed on the bottom and often centered. Tuckabee

Figure 10-30
Worker cells filled with multiple eggs and egg and larva from laying workers. L. Connor

odd angles and locations, depending on cell depth (Figure 10-30).

Larvae from unfertilized eggs appear normal in worker cells, but drone pupae will be identifiably different. Drones reared in worker cells are often smaller-bodied but produce viable sperm.

Mating of queens

When honey bees were first studied, biologists thought that the queen was a king. It was not until the early 1600s that beekeepers came to understand that the largest bodied individual in the colony was a queen. In 1845, Polish apiarist Johann Dzierzon proposed his parthenogenesis hypothesis. He was the first to realize that the male bees of the colony, the drones, develop from unfertilized eggs whereas queen and workers were both females and developed from fertilized eggs.

Knowledge of queens mating with drones is relatively recent. In 1814 the blind Swiss biologist Francois Huber (using the eyes of his servant) observed queens leaving his specially designed observation hive, which he opened like the pages of a book. He also saw her returning to the hive with the mating sign, the drone reproductive organ. Previously, it was assumed that mating occurred inside the hive or that the drones inseminated the eggs in their cells.

The mystery of the mating process is due in part to the fact that it occurs outside the hive high in the air. Early mating biology observations were primarily confined to watching the entrance of beehives for the flight behavior of virgin queens. Dr. Norman Gary of Cornell University was able to study mating by suspending tethered virgin queens in appropriate areas where mating occurs. The technique was expanded to study drone response to artificial substitutes for queens. Mating behavior was recorded over and over to learn the actual details of the mating process.

Queens are known to fly as early as the third day of their adult life, but most early flights are for orientation. Mating occurs primarily on the seventh and eighth day of queen adult life within a normal range of 6 to 13 days.

Orientation flights may be very short initially but can last up to 30 minutes. Mating flights are short, averaging 18 minutes. Since a queen can and often does mate with more than one drone on a mating flight, there are usually one to a few flights by a queen for mating purposes. Mating occurs in the afternoon hours. By two to five days after mating, most queens can produce fertilized eggs.

Drone attraction to queens

Virgin queens and drones pay no attention to each other in the hive (Figure 10-28), in contrast to the workers who regularly attend to their queen. Outside a hive, worker bees are attracted to queen substance at low heights while

Box 21

MASSACRE OF THE MALES

Count Maurice Maeterlinck's *The Massacre of the Males* is a well-known description of the behavior of worker bees expelling the drones from colonies in the fall. His passage, as fantasized in his book *Life of the Bee*, is a mellifluous description, with considerable anthropomorphism (giving honey bees human characteristics, emotions, reasoning, etc.) was perhaps an apt prelude to other writings for which he was awarded the 1911 Nobel Prize in Literature. In his words:

But the patience of the bees is not equal to that of men. One morning the long-expected word of command goes through the hive; and the peaceful workers turn into judges and executioners. Whence this word issues, we know not; it would seem to emanate suddenly from the cold, deliberate indignation of the workers; . . . in lieu of the friendly perfume of honey, the acrid odour of poison prevails; thousands of tiny drops glisten at the end of the stings, and diffuse rancour and hatred. Before the bewildered parasites are able to realize that the happy laws of the city have crumbled . . . each one is assailed by three or four envoys of justice.

. . The wings of the wretched creatures are torn, their antennae bitten, the segments of their legs wrenched off; and their magnificent eyes . . . now, softened by suffering, reflect only the anguish and distress of their end. Some succumb to their wounds, and are at once borne away to distant cemeteries by two or three of their executioners. Others, whose injuries are less, succeed in sheltering themselves in some corner, where they lie, all huddled

Figure 10-31
Drone found dead on the landing board of a colony, soon to be carried away by a worker bee. It was October in Michigan. L. Connor

together, surrounded by an inexorable guard, until they perish of want. Many will reach the door, and escape into space dragging their adversaries with them; but, towards evening, impelled by hunger and cold, they return in crowds to the entrance of the hive to beg for shelter. But there they encounter another pitiless guard. The next morning, before setting forth on their journey, the workers will clear the threshold, strewn with the corpses of the useless giants; and all recollection of the idle race disappear till the following spring.

drones are attracted only above four meters (13 feet) (Figure 10-28). Workers and the drone and queen have their own flight zones. Vegetation level, not ground level, seems to be the base level.

At appropriate locations, called **Drone Congregation Areas or DCAs** (See Chapter 18) drones orient to the odor of 9-oxodec-2-enoic acid (9 ODA), queen substance. This pheromone is a **sex attractant**. It is extremely attractive — only a few molecules are needed to attract a drone. Drones can perceive queen substance up to 60 m (200 feet) away.

Beekeepers have been able to determine the location of DCAs by placing cotton that is scented with queen pheromone into a cage, dangled from helium-filled balloons, and walking these floating devices around the

countryside. When a DCA is entered, drones are sighted visually or captured with traps such as seen in Figure 10-27. The drones may be marked and recaptured at respective hives.

After perceiving the sex attractant, drones attempt to visually orient, perhaps involving UV perception to the lowest point of a queen in flight. V-shaped drone comets of 100 or more drones form downwind, twisting and turning to follow the queen in her flight, compensating for wind shifts. Visual orientation is strictly short range — perhaps one to two meters (three to six feet). Drones also may orient on each other (Figure 10-25).

For mating to occur, drones need another pheromone. Those drones at the front of the comet fly close to the queen and examine her with antennae and forelegs. On perception of the proper chemical signal—thought to be an aphrodisiac from the queen's tergite glands plus the open vagina of a queen—drones attempt to mount the flying queen.

Drones approach the lowest portion of the queen. The flying drone grasps the receptive queen from above with his six legs around her abdomen, making use of the special hairs on his basitarsus to secure his grasp. He deflects his abdomen downward and inserts his copulatory apparatus into the open vagina of the queen. Almost immediately, the drone releases the queen (Figure 10-26), flips backward, apparently paralyzed, as his semen is explosively released into the oviduct of the queen. Part of the drone's endophallus remains in the queen (the mating sign), but the drone breaks off and falls to the ground where he soon dies.

The queen may quickly mate again with a new drone, or she may fly back to her hive with the drone's genitalia still protruding from the end of her abdomen. On occasion, both drone and queen fall to the ground before the queen is able to free herself from the drone.

At some signal, thought to be the number of times the queen opens her sting chamber to receive a drone, the queen ceases mating. She may have mated with fifteen or more drones. DNA tests have revealed that some queens mate with as many as 60 drones. When back in the hive, she quickly gains body weight and starts laying eggs in two to five days. She will not mate again in her lifetime, even if she runs out of sperm.

Drone nutrition for proper maturation

At emergence, like all newly-emerged adults, drone bees beg for food. Nutrition is important for essential sperm migration from the testes to the seminal vesicles. After a few days, the drones begin to feed themselves pollen from the pollen cells (Figure 18-23). It takes about 12 days for all of the drone's sperm to migrate, and this is about the age drones start to fly. Some drones do not start flying until 18 days of age (post emergence).

On days suitable for mating, the drone will make up to six, roughly 30-minute, flights to the DCA. Drones tend to stay local, joining DCAs near their hive, while queens fly about a mile. This allows the drone to spend most of his time patrolling for a queen in a nearby DCA rather than spending valuable time and honey by flying to a distant DCA.

Thirty minutes seems to be the maximum time for a drone flight. Afterwards, he returns to the hive to be fed (if there is a nectar flow underway) or to feed himself, consuming honey to provide energy for the next flight.

Individual drones might fly for a couple of weeks to a month. If they are successful and mate, they die in the process.

While the colony is building bee population in the spring and early summer, drones are produced as the colony allows. During food shortages caused by poor weather, developing drone brood may be removed or trimmed.

In the fall, drones do not become fat to overwinter but instead are kicked out of the hive (Box 21, Figure 10-31).

key terms

absconding	exposed nest	photoperiod	scout bee
after-swarm	flyway	piping	sex attractant
artificial swarm	food transmission behavior	primary swarm	stop signals
balling	head butt	queen cell	supersedure
bee beard	laying workers	queen cup	swarming
chains of younger bees	mated queen	queen failure	temporary bivouac
chilling queens	mating flights	queen fighting	thelytoky
drone congregation areas (DCA)	mating sign	queen pheromone	trimming of drones
drone layer	mother-daughter queens	queen replacement	trophyllaxis
efficient/inefficient supersedure	multiple eggs	queen substance	vibrating the queen
egg laying	multiple mating	queenless colonies	virgin queen
emergency queen rearing	orientation flights	resource abundance	whirring (breaking) dance
engorgement	over-heating queens	retinue	
excessive swarming	parthenogenesis	royal jelly	

discussion questions

If swarming and supersedure begin the same way how do they differ so the worker bees can know to begin their preparations to swa Why is the biofeedback mechanism so important in the beginning of swarming and supersedure behaviors?

Queens begin the process by which they will be replaced, by swarming or supersedure, yet they also have the ability to stop queen development. They cause worker bees to tear down developing queen cells by marking the cells with pheromone and chewing on developing queen cell. What causes queen rearing behavior in bee colonies? What are the conditions under which developing qu cells may lead to successful queen rearing versus conditions where the bees might abort the process?

What are the differences at initiation of queen rearing that might help distinguish between swarming, supersedure and emergency qu rearing? What conditions might be distinguishable after the queen cells have been capped? Describe swarming or supersedure beha from initiation to successful termination. What is the difference between primary versus after-swarms and efficient versus ineffic supersedure?

How can you tell a bee colony is without a queen? Explain if they have an emergency situation, a drone-laying queen, or laying work How can the beekeeper tell if his/her colony has a virgin queen? How could the beekeeper tell if a colony has recently swarmed superseded?

exercises

Prepare a box that has *bee* smell and then capture a swarm. If hesitant, plan to go initially with a local beekeeper as he/she capture swarm. Alternatively, produce an artificial swarm (see the next item below).

Create an artificial swarm. To do this, prepare a package of bees from an established colony or order a package of bees from a supp Feed the bees a dilute sugar solution for at least a day. Remove the queen cage and position it close to a location where you can t shake the worker bees out of the package. The workers will find their queen and through scenting, inform their sisters of her loca and cluster around her. You can then study behaviors such as scouting for a new home site, swarm clustering behavior, and moven of swarms (by removing the caged queen to another close-by location). Only confirmed bee-ophilics (those who love bees) should fas the queen cage below their chin, thereby creating a bee beard of workers clustered on the face and neck around their queen.

De-queen a colony and follow the behavior of emergency queen rearing.

Locate and map drone congregation areas (DCAs) in your area. You will need a helium-filled balloon, virgin honey bee queens and a of patience. You locate DCAs by elevating tethered (or wire mesh caged) virgin queens or queen pheromone from fishing line suspen 5+ meters high from the balloon and walk about looking to spot a V-shaped comet downwind of the tethered queen. Once you loc such an area you can map the DCA area (width, height and shape). Seek or locate additional DCAs with further searching (the seco third, etc. will be easier to find).

references

Collison, C.H. 2018. A Closer Look: Piping, Tooting, Quacking. Bee Culture

Connor, L.J. 2008. Bee Sex Essentials. Wicwas Press

Connor, L.J 2015. Queen Rearing Essentials, Second Edition. Wicwas Press

Heinrich, B. 1981. The mechanisms and energetics of honeybee swarm temperature regulation. Jour Exp Biol 91:25-35 (also Heinrich 1993. The Hot blooded insects. Harvard Univ Press

Gary, N.E. 1962. Chemical mating attractants in the queen honey bee. Science 136(3518):773-774.

Gary, N.E. 1963. Observations of mating behavior in the honeybee. J. Apic. Res. 2(1):3-13

Koeniger, G., et al. 2015. Mating Biology of Honey Bees (Apis mellifera). Wicwas Press

Laidlaw, H. and R. Page 1997. Queen Rearing and Bee Breeding. Wicwas Press

McAfee, A. et. al. Pettis 2020. Nature Sustainability vol. 3, pp. 367–376

Morse, R. 1994. Rearing Queen Honey Bees, Second Edition. Wicwas Press

Repasky, S.J. and L.J. Connor. 2013. Swarm Essentials: Ecology, Management, Sustainability. Wicwas Press

Seeley, T.J. 2010. Honey Bee Democracy. Princeton Univ Press

Chapter 11
Bee botany

Figure 11-1
Black locust (*Robinia pseudoacacia*) is an excellent spring nectar source for bees. L. Connor

Concepts

- **Foraging and bee botany**
- **Nectar secretion**
- **Pollen collection**
- **Optimum foraging strategy**
- **Robbing behavior**
- **Spring**
- **Summer**
- **Fall**

FORAGING

The mating of queen and drone is not the only extra-hive activity of bees—foraging is worker behavior outside the hive. A worker bee, three weeks or older, having completed a sequence of duties inside her colony, is likely to become a **field bee**. She will forage for food, water or plant resin (to become propolis) for the remainder of her life, approximately another three weeks.

Honey bee eyes are less capable of seeing a flower until close to it, so they use a combination of color, form and scent to discover a foraging site. **Scent** is the most important of these signals. Bees readily learn to effectively forage a particular kind of flower by its color and odor. Once conditioned to a particular flower, field bees tend not to visit flowers that are different.

Bees seek nectar and pollen rewards when visiting flowers. Many flowers signal these food rewards with **vivid colors** and **patterns** as well as strong attractive odors. Some flowers offer only nectar, others only pollen, but most offer both, though not necessarily at the same time.

Having adequate honey stores are critical to colony survival, so there are usually more nectar collectors than pollen or water collectors; in normal hives 58% of the foragers are **nectar collectors**, 25% exclusively **harvest pollen**, while the rest collect **water, resin** or a combination of nectar and pollen. While nectar collection takes priority, foraging behavior is flexible, and bees can quickly shift their foraging if pollen or water are in short supply within the colony. Bees do not need a stimulus to collect nectar, which makes beekeeping profitable for the beekeeper.

Types of foragers
We recognize four general groups of foraging bees in colonies based on their activity level and 'attachment' to

Figure 11-2
The floral design of this sunflower attracts bees.

flowers. These are as follows:

• crop-attached bees, good source — foragers actively going back and forth to a known foraging area

• crop-attached bees, poor source — foragers going back and forth to a failing or unattractive forage site who may also wander and search for new sources

• scout bees — bees actively looking for new sources of forage

• unemployed foragers — bees not active in flight or active for only part of the day on a limited source

How bees discover flowers

Bees may fly incredible distances to find food and water, or it may be close to the hive. They correctly navigate to the food source and back. Once they return to the hive, they communicate accurate navigational information to recruit other bees to share the find.

Flowering plants utilize both colors and patterns to attract visitors. Many flowers have **nectar guides** giving the flower a 'bull's-eye' pattern of different colored and/or textured lines that lead to the center of the flower. Some nectar guides are only visible to the ultraviolet-sensitive eyes of honey bees.

Bees recognize flowers by their general form and by their degree of **petal striation** or **brokenness** (Figures 11-2, 20-3). Color pattern and movement in the wind create a recognizable and attractive visual pattern to bees.

Scent is a powerful attractant. Honey bees can find conspicuously scented objects and scented colored ones both real or artificial. Ethologist and Nobel laureate Karl von Frisch concluded that **visual clues** were most responsible for long range detection while **scent** was more critical for short range orientation to flowers. In

memory experiments, bees retain scent information for at least five days but quickly forget visual clues.

In a series of experiments, one of von Frisch's students, Elizabeth Opfinger, investigated how bees fix information in their memories. She supplied sugar syrup and measured the foragers' responses by the number of returns to the correct feeding station (a bioassay experiment). She trained bees and changed the color, form or scent as the bee arrived and departed. **Color** was important on the bee's arrival but not at departure. **Form, scent and short distance landmarks** (20 to 35 cm, 8 to 14 inches) were behaviorally fixed during arrival, which takes only three seconds.

At departure, bees usually circle the feeding site, taking a longer time (mean 10.5 seconds) to depart than arrive. Although the departure flight was not important for fixing information about the immediate site, it was vital for **fixing the location** of the feeding place relative to more distant landmarks.

Although bees fed an average of 73 seconds, Opfinger found this time was not important in fixing information about the feeding site — it was used for syrup intake alone.

Scout bees

When she begins to forage for nectar, an individual honey bee will likely find flowers in one of two ways: by scouting or by bee dance recruitment.

Figure 11-3
Bees returning to hive loaded with pollen pellets on their hind legs. Two different pollen colors are evident.

Box 22

FLOWER CONSTANCY

Figure 11-4
A bee on hawthorn flowers. The pollen load is one color, reflecting a single source of pollen (flower constancy).
R. Williamson

A well-established characteristic of honey bees is their flower constancy. On any single foraging trip, there is a strong tendency for individual bees to forage on only a single flower species (Figure 11-4). Charles Darwin, for one, noted this behavior which is important in cross-pollination of flowers.

Flower constancy has been determined by microscopically examining the pollen loads of bees as they return from a foraging trip. Of 3,000 honey bee pollen loads examined in one study, 6.8% were a mixture of 2 or more pollens. A later study reported 3% mixed loads with an additional 15% having a few grains of pollen of another species. In a third study, 62% of the pollen loads were from a single source. This increased to 80% non-mixed loads during apple bloom. This study classified a load as mixed if even a single different pollen grain was found in the pollen sample.

As with other factors relating to foraging, the proportion of different pollens in a bee's pollen basket load is greatly influenced by environmental conditions. Bees are more flower constant where there are large areas of attractive flowers and more favorable forage conditions with less variation. All bees, including the honey bee, are more constant where there are large expanses of an attractive flowering species.

Honey bees tend to remain attached to a particular flower on subsequent trips and foraging days, as long as the food resource remains attractive (Figure 11-4). If a flower is unavailable, bees tend not to forage (become unemployed foragers). For example, in corn—which offers pollen only in the morning hours—the morning pollen foragers may be unemployed foragers in the afternoon. Although some foraging areas are small, bees tend to move from plant to plant within the area rather than attempting to collect from each and every flower on a single plant.

Marked bees remained on the same pollen source an average of eight days. Only 2 of 10 marked bees stayed on a single source collecting both nectar and pollen for 21 days. If you mark bees, 70 to 90% can be expected to be seen foraging on the same flowers the next day; 40 to 60% will still be there a week later. Bees tend to forage from the same nectar sources longer than pollen sources.

When a bee colony is moved from one site to another, the bees tend to forage the same plants. If a change occurs, it may be due to a difference in relative abundance of one plant over the other at the second site. When bees were moved to an area where one flowering plant predominated, most bees that had not previously foraged on that plant changed their fidelity and began foraging on it. These experiments show individual bees and a bee colony capable of some flexibility and an ability to abandon unprofitable forage conditions to adopt better ones.

Bees that spend time looking for new food sources are termed **scout bees**. Scout bees are critical to colony survival. Anywhere from 5 to 35% of all foraging bees may function as scouts at any one time. Scout bees are more numerous in the early morning hours and when foraging conditions are marginal. Scouts are always present and actively searching, even during the most favorable nectar flow.

With the information from a dancing scout, a new recruit can correctly fly toward the source using scent and other cues received from the dancing bee (Chapter 8). Recruits are also using general visual clues of color, form and movement. Perception of smell, followed by orientation toward color and form, quickly draw bees to flowers. If the correct smell is perceived on her approach, she lands and begins to forage. She fixes information on her

Figure 11-5
Diverse planting for bees.

foraging choice on arrival and uses the departure to fix landmarks for a return to the flowers. Scout bees may be either inexperienced or conditioned foragers and are flexible in their behavior. Scout bees must reconfigure their searching behavior to find a new nest site. To locate a new nest location, experienced foragers use a combination of color and smell, along with previously learned behaviors. They closely investigate cavities with attractive scents for housekeeping, cavity size, previous bee occupancy and entrance location.

Foraging area

Individual bees forage in a limited area of a field, on a particular clump of trees, or sections of bushes, often within a single tree or bush (Figure 11-5). Bees remain flexible, comparing present forage conditions with those in the past (from their memory). Bees will return to an abandoned foraging source after they switch to another as if to 'inspect' the original source.

Forage areas are more narrowly defined under better forage conditions when flowers are providing abundant nectar and pollen content, the landscape has good landmarks and there is little competition from other flower visitors. When foraging sources are poor, bees may become part-time foragers/part-time scouts.

Large monocultures of single-flowering sources lack orientation landmarks making it difficult for foragers to

confine foraging to a small area of the field. Dr. Norman Gary (Entomologist, University of California-Davis) captured foragers on flowering onion heads, glued tiny metal markers to their thorax and set up rows of magnets that removed the tags at the hive entrance. He found that most bees still foraged in a limited area of the field, though the area in flower was quite extensive. Fewer bees foraged throughout the whole field.

Inexperienced foraging bees stay close to the hive initially because they need to take repeated flights to learn landmarks for orientation. When there are sufficient forage sources nearby, most bees forage 200 to 500 m (219 to 547 yards) from the hive. As they age, workers fly farther distances using landmarks they have memorized.

Distribution of bees also depends on the attractiveness of the bloom. Since honey bees do not establish territories, they forage over a wider area and visit more flowers during a forage trip when there is intense competition from other bees. More foragers are found close to the hive, their numbers decreasing as distance from the hive increases.

Foraging bees exhibit a species diversity preference. They may fly a greater distance to a preferred source, flying past other flowering plants to reach foraging sites. They may fly considerable distances (more than 6.5 km or over 4 miles) to seek a favorable source in a situation where the field is a patchwork of different crops (Figure 11-5).

Figure 11-6
Nectar forager with proboscis in flowers of Japanese knotweed (*Fallopia japonica*). L. Connor

Figure 11-7
Blueberry (*Vaccinium* spp.). L. Connor

Perhaps such flowers are more stimulating for the bees than the sources they bypass.

Thus, the flight range of foragers from a hive varies over the season depending on flower distribution, attractiveness and rewards, as well as competition and other factors.

Generally, most bees forage close to their hive if flowers are present nearby. Growers and beekeepers utilize this behavior in planning pollination of crops, particularly those hard to pollinate. In blueberries, for example (Figure 11-7), the beekeeper may move colonies every few days to reestablish the pattern of foraging close to the hive before the majority of foragers learn to fly greater distances using memorized landmarks.

Bees in the field have to make choices in their behavior. When a scout discovers a patch of flowers, she must decide between further searching or foraging on the flowers she has discovered and, upon her return to the hive, whether to dance and inform others or merely continue to forage. She decides how long to forage,

whether and how long to dance or whether to continue foraging or scout further. It turns out the choices faced by scout bees and foragers are resolved really quite simply. We call these choices part of **optimal foraging strategy**.

Foraging statistics

The minimum temperature for active foraging is 46 to 50° F (8 to 10° C). The limiting factor is the temperature of the bee's thorax. Bees must be able to keep the thorax above 86°F (30° C) for flight. Even though they are **ectothermic** (cold-blooded), bees are able to elevate their body temperature by contracting their wing muscles to produce heat.

At high temperatures, the bees have the opposite problem: ridding the body of the excess heat generated by their flight muscles. They shed excess heat by air circulation through the trachea of the thorax and by shunting warm blood to the abdomen where it can cool faster. The ideal external temperature for flight is 66 to 86° F (19 to 30° C).

Average flight speeds of foraging worker bees were calculated at 12.5 mph (20 kph) outward and 14.9 mph

(24 kph) on the return trip. An upper limit has been measured at 25 mph (40 kph), presumably for only a short distance.

Bees have been observed to carry from one-third to one-fifth of their body weight (the average bee weighs 80 mg or 3/1000 oz) in pollen on a single trip. Wing beats of 200/sec don't change with a heavier load, but the wing stroke becomes longer when the bee is fully loaded. Energy for flight comes from glycogen stored in fat bodies. It appears that the size of the pollen load is more dependent upon a bee's ability to pack pollen in her corbiculae rather than flight ability.

Speed and direction of flight are regulated by **mechano-receptor sense organs** located on the wings and **air-speed sensors** at the base of the antennae. Wing sensors are living cells of the membrane-like cuticle served by nerves and supplied with hemolymph flowing through the veins.

In flight, honey bees need to see the ground and, thus, do not fly after dark. Orientation to the polarized light pattern of the sun uses facets at the top of their compound eyes. Bees can fly in light rain and on heavily overcast days using landmarks, scent and memory cues. Dr. James Gould of Princeton University describes bees as having a 'local map' of their foraging areas, though they cannot communicate this map to recruits. The local mental map theory has been challenged by other researchers.

The rate at which bees visit flowers depends on a number of variables. During single foraging flights, nectar-collecting bees may visit between one tulip poplar blossom and over 1,000 sweet clover flowers. When visiting larger numbers of flowers, the foraging time may last one to two hours. Nectar foraging trips averaged 27 minutes to 2 hours in different studies. For sweet clover, the mean number of daily foraging flights was 13.5 (maximum 24) one year but only 7 (maximum 17) the next year, under less ideal weather conditions. The average bee flies fifteen to twenty flights per day, about 500 flight miles in her lifetime.

Pollen foragers take less time to gather pollen loads. Pollen loads vary in size, and both nectar and pollen loads tend to be larger under more favorable conditions. Pollen collection time averages 8.5 to 18 minutes; most pollen foraging trips are completed within 30 minutes.

Nectar collection

Nectar is the stimulus (reward) plants have evolved to attract pollinating insects. Plants secrete nectar from many parts of the flower and even from non-flower parts called **extra-floral nectaries**. Nectar secretion is an active metabolic process and not merely the plant's attempt to excrete excess sugars. Since flowering is the last phase of a plant's existence, soil type, environmental conditions, or other factors that impact the plant during its growth

Figure 11-8
Honey bee probing for nectar with her proboscis.

and development can potentially influence nectar secretion as well.

Nectar secretion by a flower is usually more pronounced the first day or two and then stops, or it may continue over several days. More nectar is secreted on a sunny day compared to a cloudy one because nectar sugars are products of photosynthesis. Once successfully pollinated, many flowers often stop nectar production.

The concentration of sugar in nectar varies widely depending upon plant species. Pear flower nectar may contain only 10% sugar, while sweet clover nectar may be over 40% sugar. Sugar concentration in nectar is strongly influenced by soil moisture, atmospheric conditions, flower size, flower position and many other factors. Shallow, open nectaries are more subject to fluctuation when compared to more closed, tubular flowers. Wind, rain and shifts in weather conditions negatively affect nectar abundance and sugar concentration.

Some flowering plants exhibit a daily nectar-secretion rhythm. Bees have a sense of time and can adjust their foraging behavior accordingly. Nectar collection is best from mid-morning to mid-afternoon from some, but not all, plant species. If a flower was previously visited by a nectar collector, both nectar quantity and quality may be reduced, although, for some plants, total nectar collection increases if the flower is repeatedly visited.

Bees collect nectar using their proboscis, a tube formed from the maxilla and labium of the mouthparts (Figures 5-3, 5-6, 5-9, 5-10, 11-6, 11-8). A bee may collect up to 70 mg, almost her own body weight, of an attractive nectar, but normal loads are 40 mg. Bees are attracted to sucrose over other sugars followed by glucose, maltose and fructose respectively. Mixtures with sucrose as the major nectar sugar secreted are highly attractive. Different flower species have characteristic sugar signatures but it is not known how this might influence foraging behavior.

Nectar collectors generally show less variability in behavior compared to pollen or water foragers. A nectar collector alights on part of the flower (usually a petal) and brushes or laps with the proboscis until the tip encounters nectar. In some flowers, bees can apparently sense the nectar before landing and extend their proboscis.

Like scout bees, foraging bees have to make decisions regarding dancing and how soon to return to the field as they forage. They may monitor other dancing bees before returning to the field. Dr. Mark Winston, a researcher working in British Columbia, found that foraging bees were conservative in changing their foraging behavior. If a forager was presented the alternative of a dancing bee indicating a source three times as good as her current forage situation, the forager returned to her flowers. If the alternative was five times as good, the forager switched to the new source.

Each of the different flowers presents a challenge to the foraging bee. Bees learn to become more efficient foragers with practice. They must also learn how to forage to get the flower rewards. Here are two examples of the types of variation that constitute learned behaviors:

Foraging behavior on bean flowers

In England, researcher Dr. John Free closely examined honey bees foraging on field bean. Three distinct foraging types were observed:

- foragers visiting extra-floral nectaries located underneath the stipules of the field bean flower

- foragers robbing nectar from the flowers using holes bitten in the base of the flower by carpenter and bumble bees

- bees foraging the flower for pollen

The three foraging types spent different times foraging, ranging from 4.7 seconds/extra-floral nectary, 8.0 seconds for robbing and 11.9 seconds for pollen collectors. During a single trip, 86% of the bees observed were constant to one type of behavior, but there was some interchange between nectar-robbing and extra-floral nectary foragers. Extra-floral nectary visitors were most numerous at mid-day whereas pollen foragers were more common between 2 and 4 PM. Extra-floral nectary foragers revisited beans for a longer period in the season. Nectar is available for a longer time from the flower compared to pollen.

Figure 11-9
Apple blossom with a side-working nectar gathering honey bee (left) and pollen gathering native bee (right).
L. Connor

It has been noted that colonies vary greatly in the sources they may forage. In different studies on beans in full bloom, the mean amounts of bean pollen collected daily by colonies has been reported as 63%, 81%, 1%, 70%, 3% and 87% in different years and 35% and 4% for colonies located alongside different fields in the same year. Beans benefit slightly from bee cross-pollination.

Foraging behavior on apple flowers

While conducting research in New York State, Dr. Will Robinson found different groups of bees foraging on apple varieties (cultivars) and that the bees had distinct behaviors with little interchange of foraging types. Some bees forage on the flower of all apple varieties whereas other bees tend to stay on a single variety.

Some side working bees learn to place their proboscis between gaps at the base of the anthers and extract nectar without touching the flower (Figure 11-9). These bees forage only on the Red Delicious cultivar since it was the only one of those studied that had gaps large enough to permit this behavior.

These two studies have implications for flower pollination. In beans, those bees robbing or visiting extra-

NECTAR SECRETION

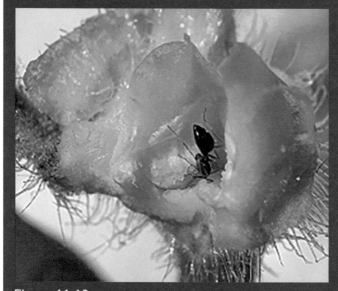

Figure 11-10
Ants and other sugar-feeding animals are attracted to the nectar produced in this squash flower, corolla removed. L. Connor

Nectar contains mostly sugar and water (Figure 11-10). Plants with high sugar content secrete mostly phloem sap (food-conducting tissue). Plants that secrete nectar from the xylem tissue (water-transporting tissue) often secrete more nectar but it contains less sugar.

The major nectar sugars are sucrose, glucose and fructose; minor sugars are maltose, raffinose, melibiose, trehalose and melezitose. Sugar content ranges from 5 to 80% (most range from 20 to 50%); ratios of the different sugars are constant for a species. Small amounts of organic acids, mineral salts, volatile oils, polysaccharides, proteins, enzymes, pigments and alkaloids are also present. They give distinct aromas and tastes to the nectar.

Beekeepers refer to the period of heaviest nectar secretion as a honey flow (or, more properly, a nectar flow). Most areas are characterized by having one or more plants that are predictable nectar-producers one season to the next. Even the best sources vary widely in nectar secretion from one area to another and one year to the next.

Generally, spring-flowering species have a richer sugar content since there are many competitors. Fall-blooming species have lower sugar but often larger amounts of nectar. Agricultural crops that flower are dependent upon grower care. Generally, plants supplied with their normal growth needs, planted on the best soils and supplied with adequate water exhibit a better, more consistent nectar secretion.

There are a few nectars that are poisonous to bees and humans, sometimes only before fully ripening. Nectar is usually diluted, and toxic compounds are minor components. The best known toxic nectars are from rhododendron and azalea (Chapter 1). Though these plants are extremely common in both the United States and Europe, the incidents of poisoning are extremely rare. Some basswood (lime) tree nectar may poison bees but not the common *Tilia* species, American and little-leaved basswood.

floral nectaries do not provide the pollination function nor do the side working bees of Red Delicious apples.

Sub-populations of the total foraging population that may be foraging a plant, as is the case with lima beans and apple, are considered normal variations. Beekeepers and growers may have to take such groups into consideration when they estimate the size of the population that may be needed for optimal crop pollination.

Pollen foraging

Unlike nectar, honey bees need a stimulus to collect pollen. Brood apparently serves as that stimulus since pollen collection increases with brood amount. Declining day length, as in the fall, may likewise be a stimulus. Foragers will go longer distances to collect an attractive pollen compared to nectar foragers.

The hairy body of the bee is ideally suited to collect pollen from flowers. The behavior of rapidly gathering pollen from the anthers is termed **scrabbling**. Bees may use mandibles to dislodge pollen and can be seen actively moving about on the anthers to entrap it in their body hairs.

Bees may also incidentally collect pollen from flowers. In flowers with the petals fused or closed, the anthers are usually positioned such that, as a bee pushes into the flower, she brushes along or against the anthers, and pollen is dislodged onto her body hairs.

There is a daily rhythm in a hive's pollen collection because flowers do not make pollen continuously available. Before pollen can be collected, the anthers must release mature pollen grains. There are usually many early morning pollen plants, then a lull near mid-day, followed by an increase late in the day. Nectar secretion and pollen availability are inversely related. Nectar is often secreted poorly early in the day but increases by mid-day.

Bees recognize pollen as a food because of its odor. It is possible to extract such odors from pollen and watch the bees gather a worthless material such as cellulose. One

Box 24

POLLEN COLLECTION

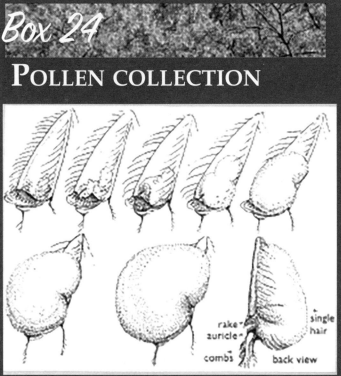

Figure 11-11
The process of adding pollen to the pollen basket of the worker bee. From D. Hodges, *Pollen Loads of the Honey Bee*, 1984

Honey bees have bodies covered with plumose hairs to facilitate the collection of pollen. As she flies, the bee's body becomes slightly positive in electrical charge which causes the pollen grains at the flower to 'jump' toward her body.

Once pollen is on the body of the bee, she uses her legs to comb through body hairs so that the pollen ends up on the hind metatarsus. To help collect the pollen, the bee moistens her front legs with saliva/nectar from the honey stomach, a behavior not unlike a cat grooming. She has great difficulty grooming behind the head, the top of the first part of the thorax and the uppermost portion of her first two segments of the gaster.

While in flight or holding on to a plant with front legs, the bee's hind legs are rubbed against each other, and the rake at the top of the metatarsus collects the pollen from the combs of the opposite leg. This pollen is pressed between the rake and the auricle, a flattened piece at the top of the metatarsus (the pollen press) and squeezed onto the outer tibial surface of the leg—the pollen basket or corbicula.

The pollen basket fills from the lower side. Accumulated pollen is held by the fringe of long, in-curved hairs at the margin of the tibia. A single hair in the middle of the pollen basket helps hold the pollen load (Figure 11-11).

Long, in-curved hairs on the margin of the basket help hold the gathering pollen. The middle legs may pat the pollen in place, but this is not necessary. Bees tend to pack each pollen basket so they are similar in weight in order to maintain balance.

Average pollen pellets (pollen load) are one-sixth to as much as one fourth the weight of the bee herself. Some pollens are difficult to pack. It is not unusual to see bees in the field grooming their body and then discarding the pollen.

Despite combing the body hairs while foraging and grooming behaviors in the hive, both nectar and pollen gathering bees have residual pollen on their bodies that is capable of accomplishing plant germination. Pollen collectors have more pollen on their thorax, where most residual pollen is found, than nectar gatherers, though both have similar amounts on their heads.

Some of the pollen may be of a different species or variety than the type of flower the bee is foraging, indicating there is some transfer of pollen between bees—such transfer occurs in the hive as bees brush against one another.

attractant chemical identified is octadeca-trans-2- cis-9- cis-12 trienoic acid, $C_{16}H_{30}O_2$.

There is no evidence to suggest that bees are able to determine the nutritional value of different pollens. They collect pollen due to its attractive chemicals and the stimulus of brood in their hive. Although individual bees collect mainly from a single pollen source, the cells in the hive are packed with different pollens.

During any one season, the foragers of a bee colony may visit many different floral species. Two colonies under similar circumstances may collect different amounts of pollen or nectar from the same forage area.

Such colony differences arise from chance discovery by scouts and conditioning to different pollens. This preference for different food sources can be exploited to improve crop pollination. Dr. Bill Nye, USDA, bred two divergent lines of alfalfa-pollen-collecting bees in as few as three generations by initial separation of colonies that exhibited high and low pollen collection. After six generations, 86% of the foragers visited alfalfa from the high pollen line versus 8% in the low pollen line.

Water and plant resin collection

Bees do not store water or resin, so some quantity of each material is needed during most of the active foraging season. Water is needed to dilute honey for feeding to larvae, to cool the hive if temperatures get too high and to increase humidity. Plant resins are converted to propolis and used as a cement and to retard deterioration of the interior of the outer wall and help bees sanitize their hive.

Among the foraging population, there are water specialists and some bees that are resin collectors (Figure 11-12). For both resin and water foragers, the feed-back mechanism of hive bees relieving the collector of her honey stomach's water contents or pollen baskets' resin provides the information the forager needs to make decisions. If her load is promptly taken by a house bee she will quickly return to the field. If, at some point, she is so rapidly unloaded she may begin to dance to inform others of her source.

Bees prefer water sources that have an odor over pure water. However, since most sources lack a distinct, identifying odor, foragers also scent at the water collection site to recruit other foragers. Water foragers do not usually go long distances to collect water, and they fill their honey stomach quickly at the source. They can make more trips per day compared to nectar or pollen foragers. If they are not quickly unloaded, they remain in the hive serving as a water reservoir.

Resin collectors use their mandibles to bite the glue-like resin that is secreted by some plants. The bee works it something like taffy and uses her front legs to position the sticky, resinous material onto her pollen baskets.

Within the hive, she goes to the location where the resin is needed to solicit the assistance of a hive bee to remove the material from her hind legs. She remains to help position it where it is needed. The percentage of resin collectors is low, but when an individual locates a source she is likely to continue foraging on it.

Optimum foraging strategy

The basic rules of foraging are conservative. Bees tend to forage at the nearest, most profitable location of each plant source. Individuals prefer a single plant species which they learn to forage and thus become more efficient and effective as they age. Experience with a flower reduces both search time and time spent working it.

In the field, worker behavior flexibility helps them adjust to ensure that they collect a reasonable load. When forage conditions are good, the forager flies a short distance from one flower to another, changing directions frequently. This helps ensure that she does not fly out of the area where the profitable foraging conditions exist. If forage conditions are poor, she more often flies in the same direction she arrived. In row crops, she will fly to a flower in the same row over 80% of departures.

Perhaps one measure of how good a flower is to the bee is the amount of time she spends on an individual flower. When bees spend longer time periods on flowers, they tend to fly a short distance and return more often. Moving in a straight line might take the bee away from

Figure 11-12
Propolis on the corbicula of a returning forager. L. Connor

the good forage situation. On the other hand, straighter, longer flights might move the individual away from an unrewarding area into another that might be better.

A bee colony is much more than just the sum of its individuals. Through a relatively simple feedback mechanism and stimuli, foragers make choices of where to go and what to collect that are based on colony needs. As needs change, the relative proportion of pollen foragers or water collectors can be modified.

Even the decision to dance is regulated this way. If a bee has something better than other dancers, she can dance and stimulate unemployed foragers to follow and will be successful in recruiting more foragers to a good source. The colony will benefit and store more reserves.

During poor forage conditions, the number of scouts increases thereby increasing the possibility of the colony finding a new resource. If a scout discovers something, her dance quickly informs others of the find, and the colony can exploit the resource. Colonies tend to concentrate on the best available resources.

Cornell University's Dr. Thomas Seeley, working in a natural foraging area of forest with meadow patches, has mapped locations of where a colony forages. Maps may vary each day (Figure 11-13). Dr. Seeley calls this information center 'foraging strategy'. He has

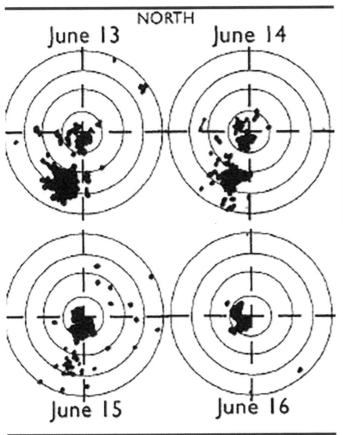

Figure 11-13
Variations in foraging by worker honey bees on June 13-16, 1980. Adapted from T. Seeley, 1980

Figure 11-14
Robbing behavior initiated following inspection of the hives. A. Heck

documented that foraging patterns may change daily based on information scouts bring back. By comparing information available in the dances, recruited foragers concentrate on the highest quality and closest forage opportunities. Experienced foragers can reassess and reevaluate their behavior, though they are conservative and reluctant to change, doing so only if the new source is much better than the one they are working.

To get from hive to flower and back again, bees build an **integrated metric map** of their area. *Integrated* means the bees use a variety of information such as landmarks, food sources and features in the landscape, and *metric* because they are capable of adjusting their image with directional features and distance. This is exactly how you most likely navigate in familiar territory.

Vision plays a major role in bee navigation. The big compound eyes of bees provide a panoramic vision pattern while color supplies subtleties of depth and detail. Polarized light patterns give bees a constant bearing, and an internal clock assists as the sun moves from east to west. Detecting earth's magnetic fields may play a role somehow.

Robbing behavior

Robbing can be considered a special type of foraging — the 'fast track' to filling a honey stomach. Honey bees are generalists and tend to concentrate their foraging on the richest, most readily available sources. Honey stored by another bee colony that is not properly protected has all the appropriate odor attractions and will be richer than anything available at flowers.

The first robbers discovering honey that bees are not adequately defending, such as in a hive opened by a beekeeper, a hive exposed due to vandalism, attack of a bear, etc., can quickly recruit sisters. Robbing starts more quickly in a nectar dearth when the pool of unemployed foragers is greatest.

During robbing, some robbing foragers and challenging guards in the colony being robbed are stung and killed. Robbing stops when the colony under assault can defend itself; weak colonies or those too exposed may be completely cleaned out with subsequent death of brood and queen.

In urban settings robbing may lead to defensive bees and the chance of neighbors being stung. Beekeepers need to reduce colony entrances with robber screens. The best protection is to prevent robbing before it begins.

Figure 11-15
Male (left) and female (right) maple flowers, *Acer* spp.

The season through a bee's eye

A season through a bee's eye is varied and diverse. Bees from one colony may visit over 250 species of plants in a single season. That smorgasbord is important for the bee diet. Here is a glimpse of the season in temperate North America — you should determine the major nectar and pollen bee plants for your geographical area.

Early season pollen/nectar sources

Early sources of pollen and good flight weather enable bees to collect abundant and extremely important pollen to build their colony population. Stored honey initially supplies the energy for foraging but soon nectar collection competes with obtaining pollen. Chapter 16 discusses the conditions that enable honey bees to exploit food resources.

One of the earliest sources of pollen in the season is skunk cabbage (*Symplocarpus foetidus*) whose flowers grow in very wet ground such as marshes or alongside streams. Water temperature is often warmer than air temperature, so plants with their roots in water are some of the earliest bloomers.

Alder (*Alnus* spp.), a wind-pollinated shrub, is an example of a widespread source of early spring pollen. Since the flowers are nectarless, colonies need ample honey stores to take advantage of such pollen.

Red and silver maples, *Acer rubrum* and *A. saccharinum* respectively (Figure 11-15), are widely distributed, pollen-producing plants. They bloom early, often as early as February. Bees readily collect the green-yellowish pollen to feed an expanding brood population. Later-blooming sugar maples may even provide a small amount of nectar for brood rearing. In the Pacific Northwest, the bigleaf maple (*Acer macrophyllum*) may yield surplus honey.

Figure 11-16
Crocus flowers with honey bee forager packing pollen.
L. Connor

If the temperature is warm enough to permit flight, trees such as elm (*Ulmus* spp.), poplars (*Populus* spp., especially cottonwoods) and ashes (*Fraxinus* spp.) are good early pollen sources. In urban and suburban areas, crocuses (Figure 11-16) are an important early pollen source. Crocus blooms early in sunny, sheltered locations, and its brilliant orange-yellowish pollen is readily collected by foragers.

Crocus and other early flowering plants, such as *Scilla* with its unusual blue pollen (Figure 4-5) that grow close to the ground, offer an advantage to foragers on windy days when flight in tree blossoms may be difficult.

Winter honeysuckle (*Lonicera fragrantissima*) grows four to seven feet tall and has many yellow-whitish flowers. Japanese honeysuckle (*Lonicera japonica*) a close relative, is a serious plant pest. It, and many common bush honeysuckles that flower later in the year, have flower corollas that are too deep for honey bees to reach the nectar and pollen.

Figure 11-17
Deadnettle with red pollen mark on the head of the bee.

Figure 11-18
Bees actively collecting pollen and nectar from black willow. M. Connor

Figure 11-20
Flower on a *Citrus* lemon tree. L. Connor

The early-blooming ornamental shrub, laurel cherry (*Prunus caroliniana*), is an evergreen used for color variety in plantings along buildings. The whitish flowers are readily visited. *Forsythia* spp., another early spring bloomer, has no value to bees as it lacks both nectar and pollen.

Early, widespread weeds with tiny, pollen-producing flowers are henbit or henbit dead nettle (*Lamium amplexicaule*) or purple deadnettle (*Lamium purpureum*). The small, purple-flowered plants grow close to the ground in good abundance in lawns, fields and wastelands. The pollen is orange-whitish and, as bees forage, their head and thorax appears to have a white, red or orange streak (Figure 11-17).

Chickweed, *Stellaria media*, is another abundant spring weed. It has a small white flower and grows in areas similar to *Lamium*. Chickweed will also bloom at other times of the year, but it is especially valuable in the spring when it supplies pollen.

Spring beauty, *Claytonia virginica*, with its tiny, blue or white flowers and speedwell (*Veronica* spp.) are other early-blooming ground plants that bees visit on a limited basis for pollen. Wild strawberry (*Fragaria* spp.) is an early season favorite; growers of cultivated strawberry (*Fragaria × ananassa*) rent bee colonies, depending upon variety and field size, to ensure profitable yields.

A widespread blooming tree in early spring is willow. The long flowers (catkins) are highly attractive to honey bees and an excellent pollen source. Perhaps the best known willows are black willow (*Salix nigra*) (Figure 11-18) and pussy willow (*S. discolor*) (Figure 11-19).

Shadbush (serviceberry, *Amelanchier canadensis*) blooms about the same time as willow. The white flowers on shadbush yield pollen.

Figure 11-19
Honey bee collecting pollen from a pussy willow. (*Salix discolor*).

Figure 11-21
The familiar dandelion (*Taraxacum officinale*) is an important nectar source for bees. L. Connor

Figure 11-22
Many mustards are extremely valuable spring yellow flower sources for bees.

Gallberry (*Ilex* spp.), which grows well in acidic soils as an understory shrub, is a major early honey source. Redbud (*Cercis canadensis*), a good pollen source, blooms later.

Citrus trees (Figure 11-20) are a major source of honey in southern states, but acreage has been decreasing. A bacterial disease, Citrus Greening (Huanglongbing or yellow dragon disease), is spread by psyllid insects and has required additional pesticide sprays that put bee colonies at risk.

In addition to citrus, southern states feature several widespread plants not available to more northern beekeepers. Sources such as Brazilian pepper (*Schinus terebinthifolius*), saw palmetto (*Serenoa repens*), trees such as *Eucalyptus* spp., tupelo (*Nyssa* spp.), and broad-leaved paperbark (*Melaleuca quinquenervia*), a serious everglades plant pest,

are good sources. Mesquite (*Prosopis* spp.) is a well-know honey plant, a good source for fall maintenance and early spring foraging important to build colonies.

Inside the early spring bee colony, great changes take place. The low point in adult population is reached in January to March. Brood rearing rapidly expands with warmer temperatures, and, once foragers bring in pollen, the queen increases her egg laying and nurse bees busily provision brood cells.

Mid to late spring

Two common yellow-flowered weeds are major pollen and nectar producers in mid-spring. The familiar dandelion (*Taraxacum officinale*) (Figure 11-21), yields abundant bright yellow pollen. Honey bees are unable to rear larvae on a diet consisting only of dandelion pollen since it lacks tryptophane and phenylalanine, essential amino acid building blocks used to produce proteins. In nature, additional sources of pollen are usually mixed, making dandelion an otherwise excellent source of protein.

Other early common yellow spring flowers include various members of the mustard family (Brassicaceae), such as yellow rocket (*Barbarea vulgaris*), field mustard, (*Brassica rapa*, Figure 11-22) and the cresses (*Barbarea verna*). Edible mustard species, such as cabbage (*Brassica oleracea*) and turnip (*Brassica rapa*) need bees for pollination to produce seed.

Another mustard, oilseed rape (*Brassica napus*), is a major honey plant of the Midwestern U.S. and the prairie provinces of Canada where it is called canola. The spring mustards bloom during or just after fruit bloom and are a major source of both pollen and nectar (Figure

Figure 11-23
Canola or oilseed rape (*Brassica napus*) is a major pollen and nectar source.

Figure 11-24
The White House Beehive shortly after first established by Charlie Brandt in Spring 2009. This photo was taken by Clint Thayer of Focal Flame Photography, who won a prize for this photo in 2010. With permission of C. Thayer

11-23). It is thought that selection and planting of very early flowering mustards (*Sinapis* spp.) might further help boost colonies for early pollination of almonds in California.

Bee colonies expand rapidly with the spring 'yellows.' Colonies that are weak or those responding slowly by the time of dandelion and mustard bloom need beekeeper attention. Colonies with small spring adult populations cannot take advantage of early pollen sources since a greater percentage of the adult bees must participate in rearing brood and help to keep them warm. It is important for the beekeeper to identify slowly developing colonies and boost them with supplemental protein by stimulative sugar-water feeding, hive body reversal, or uniting weak units to form stronger ones.

Fruit bloom

By the time of fruit bloom during the spring months, bee colonies should be at the steepest population rise. Fruit blooms provide a continuation of pollen, supply a fair amount of nectar and, in the very occasional year, surplus honey. In most seasons, bees use this early nectar source to raise more bees. Many ornamental fruit varieties are a good urban/suburban bee source.

Of all the fruit crops, almonds (*Prunus dulcis*) are the most important to large-scale beekeepers. They provide a pollination rental paycheck in February; early season colony buildup provides income from nuc and queen sales and an opportunity to replace overwinter losses. A relative of peach, almonds require pollination assistance of more than two-thirds the managed colonies of honey bees in the US during bloom in February and March (Figure 11-25, also Chapter 20).

Figure 11-25
Forager visiting almond bloom (*Prunus dulcis*). L. Connor

Pear (*Pyrus* spp.) and plum (*Prunus domestica*) are the earliest blooming of the fruit species following almond pollination. Beekeepers move colonies to pear orchards for pollination as most pear varieties require cross-pollination (Chapter 20). Some communities plant pear, cherry and crab apple trees to provide an attractive effect of medium height trees with abundant white bloom early in the spring.

Peach bloom (*Prunus persica*) follows plum and pear flowering. Peach trees have a great number of pink-whitish, sweet-smelling flowers that are attractive to honey bees for both pollen and nectar. Peach growers generally do not rent honey bees; only a small number of peach varieties require cross-pollination.

Most cherry species (*Prunus* spp.) produce abundant bloom, supplying large amounts of nectar and pollen. Wild cherries, such as hardy black (*P. serotina*) and choke cherry (*P. virginiana*), are widely common in the eastern US. Where there are concentrations of these trees, bee colonies may collect a partial super of honey, particularly in years with good bee foraging weather conditions.

Cherries (Figures 11-24, 11-26) are planted as ornamental flowering trees around the Tidal Basin in Washington, D.C. They are an excellent example of a massive number of cherry trees in an attractive setting. Ironically, honey bee colonies were not permitted in Washington D.C., so only foragers from bee trees could legally visit these blooms until a bee colony was established in the White House garden. The White House grounds (Figue 11-24), being federal property, were exempt from district regulations.

Beginning in 2009 during the Obama administration, a bee colony was maintained on the south lawn of the White House; beekeeper Charlie Brandt became one of the most famous beekeepers. Beginning in 2016, Karen

Figure 11-26
Bee colony in a planting of Rainier sweet cherry variety.

Pence, wife of Vice President Mike Pence, established a bee colony at the V.P.'s residence (Naval Observatory) in D.C. In 2021, Vice President Kamala Harris continued to keep the bees. Bee colonies are now legal in the District of Columbia.

The Japanese quince (*Chaenomeles japonica*) is another widely used ornamental shrub; bees readily visit its blossoms. Crabapples, (*Malus* spp.), as mentioned, are commonly planted ornamentals. Their bloom is attractive to honey bees. Some commercial apple growers use crabapple as a pollen source for cross-pollination of their apple varieties.

In most years, bees use apple (*Malus domestica*) blossom nectar to raise honey bees rather than store surplus honey (Figure 11-9), but in years of favorable foraging weather, they may store some surplus honey. Because most varieties of apple require cross pollination, orchards of two or more acres may include several varieties, often including crabapples, for their compatible pollen. Honey bees and increasingly Blue Orchard bees (*Osmia lignaria*) must be rented for pollination.

Apple bloom marks the time of full expansion of brood rearing by a bee colony and the arrival of the first swarms of the season. At this time, colonies should completely

Figure 11-27
Black locust *(Robinia pseudoacacia)*. R. Burns

occupy all of the brood rearing area of their hive (usually two boxes), so beekeepers must be actively inspecting for queen cells and, when found, perform swarm control or risk colony swarming.

Fruit growers, like other farmers, have a large investment in their crop and must rely on herbicides to combat weeds on the orchard floor, fungicides to reduce disease pressure and insecticides to control insect pests of the apples. Such sprays may contaminate water sources being used by the bees or may be applied directly onto the beehives located within the orchard. Bees are killed if the chemical product contacts weeds such as mustards or dandelions, contaminates standing water or is on the fruit bloom itself.

When two or more compounds are combined together, **synergistic effects** have been documented, meaning that there is a greater threat to bees than if the chemicals were applied separately. Beekeepers must avoid sprays hazardous to their bees and move colonies out of harm's way when the danger is high.

By the end of fruit bloom, spring weather becomes more reliable for foraging, and there generally is a wider variety of blooming plants for both nectar and pollen. Depending on early season weather, there may be some of the yellow flowers still in bloom, fruit bloom, ornamental shrubs and perhaps tree bloom in more heavily forested areas. Numerous wildflowers bloom on the forest floor before the canopy completely leafs out, along streams, in and adjacent to cultivated fields and along roadsides. Collectively, this bloom provides food used to raise more bees for seasons to follow.

Early honey plants for surplus honey

Eucalpytus trees, which were introduced to North America to replace native evergreen trees used by early California settlers, provide a major source of nectar and

Figure 11-28
Tulip tree or tulip poplar *(Liriodendron tulipifera)* with nectar overflowing onto the sepal. M. Connor

has become an important early surplus source in the southern states and California. Bloom starts as early as November with some Eucalyptus species.

Another early plant with abundant nectar for honey bees is black locust *(Robinia pseudoacacia)*. Mature trees have large clusters of small white flowers (Figure 11-1, 11-27). Honey from locust is water-white with excellent flavor and aroma. An annual honey crop from locust is not reliable as it has a short bloom period, and weather conditions greatly affect nectar availability—light rain and wind knock large numbers of blossoms from trees. Beekeepers produce up to a full super of honey from locust only about one in every three years if colonies are strong and supers are in place. Note that honey locust *(Gleditsia triacanthos)* blooms at the same time but—in spite of its name—it is not a good nectar source.

Another early nectar source for honey bees is the tulip tree or tulip poplar *(Liriodendron tulipifera)*. The tulip poplar bloom is a large, yellow-greenish flower with orange markings (Figure 11-28). It secretes an abundant amount of nectar, and the ripened honey is dark with a reddish tint. It has a mild flavor. Tulip poplar is listed as

Figure 11-29
Blackberry flowers *(Rubus* spp.). S. Williams

the best or second best honey plant in states from New Jersey to Alabama, where it occurs in great abundance. Surpluses of one or two supers are usually possible if there are older trees in an area.

In order for the bees to store a surplus honey crop, the beekeeper has to **super** bee colonies prior to or at the beginning of bloom. Supers, as the name implies, are added above the brood chamber of a hive. Many beekeepers use shallow or medium depth supers for ease in manipulation. Supers may be added above a queen excluder, especially where a colony is expanding its brood rearing and the nectar source is from an early blooming species such as locust or tulip poplar.

Once bees store some ripening nectar, the food stores become an effective barrier to queen movement. Generally, for locust and tulip poplar, two or more supers are needed for expanding colonies; large populous colonies may need three or four supers.

A widely spread source of surplus honey is blackberry *(Rubus* spp.). There are several species of erect or trailing blackberries. The white flowers produce a white to amber honey of excellent taste (Figure 11-29). Good blackberry locations do not persist from one year to another as these plant invaders are quickly overgrown by other plant species.

Commercial plantings of blackberry may need honey bee pollination if the area exceeds two to three acres. Raspberry *(Rubus* spp.) is a better honey plant in northern states while dewberry *(Rubus caesius)* and other species are a better source in more southerly areas. Salmonberries *(Rubus spectabilis)* grow in the west coast of North America, especially in Alaska. In general, the brambles, when not being sprayed with insecticides, are great sources of pollen and nectar for bees.

Figure 11-30
Thistle *(Cirsium* spp.).

Other late spring plants

Blueberries and cranberries, *(Vaccinium* spp.), two native North American plants, bloom a little later in the season. Where these berries are grown commercially, bees are rented to provide cross-pollination (Figure 11-7). Blueberry provides a surplus flow most seasons, but cranberry is less reliable. Blueberry secretes nectar both from the flower and from the leaf (extra-floral nectary). Elderberry or American elder *(Sambucus canadensis)* is useful mainly for pollen as bees collect little nectar from elderberry blossoms.

Suburban and urban locations have several flowering shrubs that bloom in late spring that bees visit for nectar. Three generally good nectar secretors are *Pyracantha*, *Cotoneaster* and *Viburnum*. There are seldom enough plants available of these (or other ornamentals) to provide surplus honey, and not all varieties are beneficial to bees. Another ornamental, hawthorn *(Crataegus* spp.), provides pollen but not nectar (Figure 10-3).

In some areas, there is a dearth of nectar sources following fruit bloom and prior to the availability of clovers or other summer honey plants. Beekeepers need be aware of this possibility and be prepared to feed sugar syrup to colonies that lack adequate stores. The problem is especially pronounced in seasons where spring is early, followed by the weather turning rainy and cool.

Honey plants of June & July

In high lime soil areas, June-blooming thistles are extremely valuable for nectar surpluses. Canada, bull and musk thistle *(Cirsium* spp., Figure 11-30) are undesirable weeds as they interfere with land use, mainly because of their sharp spines. The purple flowers, however, are highly attractive to honey bees and other pollinators

Figure 11-31
Sumac (*Rhus* spp.)

Figure 11-32
Basswood (*Tilia* spp.). L. Connor

and produce a water-white honey. Researchers are using biological control methods of thistle-attacking beetles to slow the rate of spread of several thistle species, which are serious pasture pests that spread very rapidly.

Blueweed or vipers bugloss (*Echium vulgare*) is not a pest. It thrives on high lime soils and produces a very light honey of excellent quality. One or two supers of surplus are usually possible each season. Clover flowers thrive on similar soils and a vipers bugloss flow may phase into a sweet clover flow, resulting in abundant light-colored honey surpluses.

Depending on the area, other locally abundant June blooming plants may provide a nectar flow. Along coastal areas, lower river and marsh areas, native hollies (*Ilex* spp.) can be a good nectar source. Holly is also a widely planted ornamental, but there are usually too few plants to yield a crop and drier soils may adversely affect nectar yield.

Gallberry (*Ilex glabra*) consistently provides a super or more of surplus honey along the Atlantic and Gulf of Mexico coastal plain areas. The honey is light amber with a very pleasant aftertaste. The beekeepers of the southeast like gallberry as a chunk honey source because it is very slow to crystallize.

Several sumacs (*Rhus* spp., Figure 11-30), are good nectar sources, although, like holly, the honey may not be very pleasant-tasting. Staghorn and smooth-barked sumac seem to be the best for nectar secretion. Sumac may overgrow briars like blackberry in cut-over fields being abandoned to forests but result in localized areas of good nectar flows for several years.

The last of the early summer nectar sources is basswood or linden tree (*Tilia americana*). The cream-colored linden flowers extend from beneath leaves (Figure 11-32), and bees forage upside down to obtain the abundant nectar. Basswood yields a very light-flavored honey. Many people describe the taste as minty; for a light honey, it is quite distinctive even after storage. Basswood trees bloom in late June and early July. Even weak spring colonies have time to expand and can usually store basswood honey if there is a concentration of trees in an area. The little-leaf linden, *T. cordata*, is being utilized as an ornamental tree in suburban and urban plantings. It also is a good source for bees if soil conditions are not too dry.

Another tree species common in the southern Allegheny forests, especially above 2,500 feet, is sourwood, *Oxydendrum arboreum*. The white blossoms are freely visited by foragers in June and July when other bees are foraging basswood at lower elevations. Beekeepers do not secure a surplus crop every season from sourwood for unknown reasons. The honey is one of the finest available US honeys—it contains a delicate balance of sweet and sour. Sourwood honey may range from water white to darker amber in color. It is often sold as chunk

Figure 11-33
Dutch white (Ladino) clover (*Trifolium repens*). L. Connor

Figure 11-34
Crimson clover (*Trifolium incarnatum*). L. Connor

Figure 11-35
Yellow sweet clover (*Melilotus officinalis*). C. Burkhead

Figure 11-36
White sweet clover (*Melilotus alba*). L. Connor

Figure 11-37
Alfalfa (*Medicago sativa*) is a preferred soil-building hay/pasture crop. L. Connor

Figure 11-38
Burdock (*Arctium minus*) is a rich source of pollen. L. Connor

honey. Two supers of surplus honey per colony are common in a normal season.

Clovers, vetch & alfalfa

The earliest of the clovers is white clover or Dutch white clover (*Trifolium repens*) (Figure 11-33). It is common on lawns, roadsides and as a waste area plant on drier soils. Provided there is sufficient soil moisture, white clover is capable of secreting a tremendous amount of nectar; yields in excess of a hundred pounds have been recorded. White clover honey is light and delicate. It makes beautiful section or cut-comb honey. Ladino clover, a larger-flowered variety of white clover, does well for grower and beekeeper in irrigated agricultural areas of the west.

On some soils, alsike clover (*T. hybridum*) is a better nectar secretor. Alsike tolerates wet clay soils better than other clovers. The flower size is intermediate between white and red clover heads; it has a pinkish tinge of color. Growers in northern states and the eastern Canadian provinces planted large acreages of alsike as hay or pasture cover crop a few years ago, but less is planted today. Crimson clover (*T. incarnatum*; Figure 10-34) is popular in southern states.

Overlapping with Dutch white clover is yellow sweet clover (*Melilotus officinalis*) (Figure 11-35). Yellow sweet clover blooms 10 days to two weeks before white sweet clover (*M. alba*) (Figure 11-36). Combined, the sweet clovers are the best honey plants in the U.S., particularly in the mid-western states. Sweet clover grows on a variety of soil conditions and does especially well on

alkaline soils and in a dry climate. Both are excellent plants to help recover worn out soils with vigorous growth and weed suppression.

Sweet clover honey is one of the finest honeys available, but some consumers may not appreciate the peppery after-taste. It granulates quickly, necessitating the need to process with heat and filtering in an effort to slow granulation of the shelf pack. Unfortunately, sweet clover is no longer widely planted, having been replaced by alfalfa in many areas.

There has been some selection of sweet clovers, and there are good bee varieties, such as Hubam clover, available for commercial planting. It is interesting to note that beekeepers once scattered sweet clover seed wherever they went. Now, there is a government-funded effort to eliminate this 'dangerous and invasive weed.' Beekeepers were blamed for its spread whether they helped or not.

Red clover (*T. pratense*) is an exception among the clovers in that the honey bee proboscis is often not able to reach the nectar in the deep flower corollas. Bees forage on red clover for pollen, and in late summer, when other nectar sources are not available, foragers do collect some nectar.

Although hairy vetch (*Vicia villosa*) and purple vetch (*Vicia americana*) are not as widespread as they once were, they are excellent nectar sources for bees. They grow in poor soils and are useful to help hold banks and slopes where other plants grow poorly. Vetch honey is water white with an excellent taste. One vetch that is not useful to bees is crown vetch (*Coronilla varia*). Crown vetch flowers are nectarless, and bees rarely visit them for pollen.

Figure 11-39
Sweet pepperbush or white alder (*Clethra alnifolia*).

Figure 11-40
Vitex (*Vitex* spp.).

Crown vetch is widely planted along roadsides in the mid-Atlantic states for erosion control and to reduce mowing. Farther north, bird's-foot trefoil (*Lotus corniculatus*), another legume, is the preferred roadside plant. Trefoil has abundant yellow bloom from June to August and yields the typical light-colored legume honey.

The last legume to consider, alfalfa (*Medicago sativa*; Figure 11- 37), is the preferred cultivated hay or pasture legume crop for soil building. It has replaced large acreages formerly planted to clover. Animal nutritionists recommend that alfalfa be cut just before bloom for highest protein content, so most alfalfa fields do not bloom until the last cutting when farmers allow some bloom to reseed the fields.

Beekeepers need to add supers to colonies to obtain surplus clover honey for harvest. Some attempt to super just at the beginning of the bloom of clover while others add supers as colonies expand in late spring. Beekeepers in tulip poplar or thistle areas must super earlier, of course. Once colonies start storing nectar in supers, beekeepers must ensure there is enough empty super space for bees to store nectar. Few beekeepers continue brood examination of supered colonies since there is a great deal of work involved in removing and re-stacking supers above brood.

When there is a great amount of nectar available to the bees, fully expanded colonies should be oversupered. The bees need the room because nectar is spread out to aid evaporation. As the nectar ripens, hive bees consolidate the stores. As the major bloom passes, undersupering forces bees to consolidate their stores.

Summer

In the summer, honey bee foragers have a wide range of plants to visit. Some provide surplus honey but, outside of the clovers and vetches, most merely help maintain the large colony populations. Late spring and early summer blooming forage trees include catalpa (*Catalpa speciosa*), chestnut (*Castanea dentata*), persimmon (*Diospyros virginiana*), blackgum or tupelo (*Nyssa sylvatica*), *Mimosa* spp. and tree-of-heaven (*Ailanthus altissima*). The latter two have escaped cultivation and are abundant in some locations. Both drop seeds and are considered messy. Tree-of heaven yields a bitter tasting honey.

Some common summer weeds that bees visit are wild carrot (Queen Anne's lace; *Daucus carota*), black-eyed Susan, various species of the daisy, *Chrysanthemum* spp., wild parsnip (*Pastinaca sativa*) and Devil's paint brush (hawkweed; *Hieracium* spp.) — the latter is a serious weed species in some areas. If clovers and cultivated crops attractive to bees are absent, foraging bees may heavily visit these plants. Surplus honey is unusual from them.

If widespread, bees may store a surplus from species such as Hercules club (Devil's walkingstick; *Aralia spinosa*), a shrub or small tree with white flowers or dogbane (Indian hemp; *Apocynum cannabinum*), an herb supposedly toxic to dogs, that resembles milkweed with white flowers blooming from June to August. Two additional 'sticky' plants are milkweed (*Asclepias* spp.) that does well in wet locations and burdock (*Arctium minus*; Figure 11-38) in drier sites. Seed heads stick to clothing and pet hair for transport to new germination sites — they are credited in the invention of Velcro®.

Figure 11-41
Cucumber (*Cucumus* spp.). L. Connor

Figure 11-42
Bee collecting fallen corn pollen (*Zea mays*).

Bees may be seen carrying the sticky, flag-like pollinia of milkweed on their legs and bodies as they visit the purplish milkweed blooms from June through August (Figure 11-44). Purple loosestrife (*Lythrum salicaria*) is easily recognized in wet and marshy areas with its bright purple flowers opening up along a stalk. Buttonbush (*Cephalanthus occidentalis*) grows in the same habitat and is readily recognized with its round clusters of white tubular flowers that look like cotton balls stuck on a spreading shrub. Both produce pleasant tasting honey. Purple loosestrife is considered a serious plant weed, crowding out native species in wetlands; it is popular as an ornamental.

Another plant that grows in moist areas that can provide a localized honey crop is coastal sweet pepperbush (*Clethra* spp.; Figure 11-39). It grows in areas along the Atlantic coast and has white flowers in midsummer. It is fragrant when in bloom and is increasingly being used in ornamental plantings and in parks, but it is not common enough as an ornamental to be a reliable honey source.

There are several home and park landscape ornamentals that can be considered as good sources of nectar for honey bees. Most of these are not sufficiently widespread to be of major significance. Good examples are the various Viburnums such as arrowwood, cranberry bush or nannyberry. Their bloom is attractive to honey bees, and the viburnums are excellent for the attraction of birds and other wildlife to gardens and parks.

Several Euonymous species are also good ornamental plants. Euonymous is used as a shrub to screen or border — their small flowers are readily visited by bees. Common and Japanese barberry (*Berberis* spp.) are also

popular ornamental plants which bees utilize — the Japanese species is considered an invasive species.

Two widely planted ornamental shrubs are the various privet and boxwood species. Privet (*Ligustrum* spp.) is a white flowering shrub that produces a dark and bitter honey. Since this bitter taste may persist when mixed with other sources of honey, privet can 'spoil' white clover honey because they overlap in bloom. Boxwoods (*Buxus sempervirens*) used in more formal plantings have a very small and inconspicuous bloom which bees will visit when other sources are not readily available.

Another common ornamental that blooms a bit later is English ivy (*Hedera helix*); its despised relative, poison ivy (*Toxicodendron radicans*), also has blooms attractive to honey bees. Ivy honey may not taste very good — but it is not dangerous for allergic individuals to eat.

Three additional summer-blooming ornamentals of special interest to beekeepers are the bee-bee tree (*Tetradium daniellii*), the goldenrain tree (*Koelreuteria paniculata*), and Vitex (Figure 11-40). The bee-bee tree has numerous small white blossoms that are highly attractive to honey bees. The tree is sold as a good source of summer nectar by seed and garden outlets that specialize in nectar and pollen plants. Goldenrain tree is a medium-height tree that blooms in early summer, and the yellow fragrant blossoms are highly attractive to bees. Vitex is a shrub that is being increasingly utilized as an ornamental. It has a long bloom period which usually extends from midsummer until fall. Certain varieties produce a nice-flavored honey and, like bee-bee and goldenrain tree, are extensively visited when in bloom. Globe thistle (*Echinops ritro*) also blooms in August.

Figure 11-43
Wild and cultivated sunflower are important nectar sources for honey bees and other pollinators (*Helianthus* spp.).

Some common summer-blooming plants are of very limited use to honey bees. Honeysuckle and red clover have flowers that are usually too deep to permit bees to gather nectar except when flowers are stunted by drought. Rhododendron and the various laurels are beautiful early summer-blooming plants in woodlands or as ornamental plantings but produce very little for honey bees. Bumble bees prefer these flowers. Ornamentals like forsythia, lilacs, roses, certain flowering plants and shrubs selected specifically for showy flowers are often of little value to bees.

Cultivated crops

In home gardens and in cultivated fields, various cucurbits such as cucumber (Figure 11-41), pumpkin, squash or melon require pollination for fruit set. The cucurbits do not have a high flower density so beekeepers seldom secure surplus honey from plantings. Where cultivated fields are two or more acres in size, one or more honey bee colonies per acre are necessary to supplement natural pollination. A few cucurbit plants in a backyard will be pollinated by wild bees, honey bees from beehives in the area, or native non-*Apis* pollinators, providing plenty of zucchinis and/or gourds.

Corn (*Zea mays*; Figure 11-42) is widespread throughout the U.S. Corn does not secrete nectar but it is a source of considerable pollen. Bees fly among the corn tassels and readily pick up the light, wind-blown pollen but do not assist in plant pollination.

Soybean (*Glycine max*) and cotton (*Gossypium*) may yield a surplus honey crop when there is a combination of variety, good soil and favorable environmental conditions.

Figure 11-44
Honey bee on common milkweed; pollinia on hind legs. (*Asclepias* spp.) C. Burkhead

Cotton is a better known honey source than soybean. It has extrafloral nectaries that provide the sugar source. Pesticides used on corn, soybean and cotton pose considerable risks to the beehive.

Such crops are being increasingly examined for methods of using biological control for serious insect pests. In some areas, it is necessary to spray plants that are in bloom to protect and secure a commercial crop. This practice results in large losses to foraging honey bees foraging on the same bloom. In addition, large-scale herbicide use means there are fewer weed plants to forage.

Sunflower (*Helianthus* spp.; Figure 11-43), both wild and cultivated, is another source of nectar for honey bees. Bees readily visit the blooms and although the honey is not the most flavorful, sunflower honey blends well with other honeys. Different varieties vary in their usefulness to honey bees.

Two other cultivated plants of use to bees are lima bean (*Phaseolus lunatus*) and buckwheat (*Fagopyrun esculentum*). Buckwheat was introduced to the U.S. by the early colonists and, for a time, was a staple flour in America. The acreage of buckwheat is now confined to the Appalachian area of the US where it is mainly planted in small fields and in the west. Land managers welcome buckwheat to suppress weed growth on bare soil. It germinates quickly, approximately in ten days.

The honey from buckwheat is very dark and strong-flavored, but it demands a premium price—buckwheat honey remains a favorite in the preparation of the bread and pastries used to celebrate the Jewish holidays. Lima bean honey is the opposite—very light and mild-flavored. It is a good honey to blend with darker honey to obtain the light amber color preferred by consumers.

Around the home

Many ornamental shrubs, plants and ground covers supply bees with abundant pollen or nectar. Over two dozen species, from crocus of early spring to privet and ivy, have already been discussed. Other areas around the home, such as herb, flower and vegetable gardens, may be planted to supplement a bee colony. Numerous herbs are among the most attractive plants to foraging honey bees.

Examples of those most attractive are anise, basil, bee balm, borage, chicory, chives, horehound, lavender, marjoram, oregano and many of the mints such as catnip, spearmint, sage and thyme. The last mint, thyme (*Thymus pulegioides*), occurs wild in New York and New England and is a honey flow plant. Most of the others are never numerous enough to provide surplus. Some yield strong-flavored honeys.

September blooming seven sons flower (*Heptacodium miconioides*) is a Chinese import used in ornamental planting worldwide. Attractive to honey bees and other bee species, it also provides food for migrating monarch butterflies in some areas (Figure 11-49).

Perennials are more attractive to honey bees and other bee species than annuals. It is recommended that gardeners start small and expand as space and interest dictate. There are a growing number of lists to consult to determine what plants might be attractive to bees and pollinators. Visit The Xerces Society (xerces.org) and Horticultural Research Institute (hriresearch.org) to find "plants bees like best."

The vegetable and flower garden can be a source of flowering variety for honey bee colonies. In the garden, asparagus, beans (especially lima beans), broccoli, all of the cucurbits (melon, squash, cucumber and pumpkin), okra, peppers and virtually all of the fruits or berries will be visited by honey bees. Garden flowers bees will visit for food storage include bachelor button, bellflower,

Figure 11-46
Japanese knotweed (*Fallopia japonica*).

Figure 11-47
Goldenrod is a widely distributed fall source of great benefit for bee This bee is collecting nectar. C. Burkhead

Figure 11-45
Smartweed. (*Polygonum pensylvanicum*). **L. Connor**

Figure 11-48
New England aster. L. Connor

Figure 11-49
Seven sons (*Heptacodium miconioides*). C. Burkhead

crocus, dahlia, forget-me-not, hollyhock (single-flowered varieties), marigold, phacelia, portulaca, salvia, spider plant and globe thistle.

Fall

In some locations, a fair number of late summer blooming plants yield nectar that provide stores for the overwintering bee colony. Boneset (*Eupatorium* spp.) is a widespread herb and one species, Joe Pye weed, (*Eutrochium purpureum*) is a source of surplus honey in some northern states. Smartweed (*Polygonum* spp.; Figure 11-45) has a number of common names such as smartweed, knotweed and ladysthumb. Several species are reliable producers of honey from midsummer to frost, especially where they are locally abundant. Smartweed supposedly does not yield a very flavorful nectar. Japanese bamboo is a knotweed and buckwheat relative that has a very attractive bloom to honey bees and may produce a surplus of honey (Figure 11-46).

Goldenrod (Figure 11-47) is a widely distributed fall source of great benefit for bees. There are some 80 species of this widely distributed native plant, but not all are of use to honey bees. Generally, the 'flat-topped' species are

the better nectar secretors compared to the plume-shaped flower types. Cool nights followed by warm days favor good nectar secretion. Goldenrod honey is deep golden in color and has a heavy 'flower' taste. It represents the only seasonal surplus honey for some beekeepers in certain parts of the northern U.S. Goldenrod is extremely important to cap-off the winter stores of colonies where it carpets the countryside.

Nearly 200 *Bidens* spp. are found widespread and visited by bees. Spanish needle, beggar ticks, sticktights and bur marigolds are common late summer and fall flowers, especially on low swampy land. Tickseed sunflower (*B. trichosperma*) blooms from mid-August until late September along the coastal plain and in wet areas. Spanish needle blooms in early spring in southern locations but is an important fall source in both the North and the South.

Ironweed (*Vernonia* spp.) has purple flowers that are moderately attractive to honey bees. It begins blooming in August and is of value before goldenrod and aster if no *Bidens* are available to the bees.

The last of the major widespread plants in bloom that honey bees utilize are the asters (Figure 11-48). Over 100 species of aster exist in North America, and some produce abundant nectar. Like the goldenrods, a combination of cool nights and warm days is the best nectar secreting weather. Because it crystallizes fairly quickly in the comb, beekeepers do not always harvest aster honey. It may not be the best food source for overwintering bees. In some locations, a super or more of aster honey may be harvested if the first fall frosts are not too early and the daytime temperature is warm enough to permit adequate bee flight.

Bees reduce brood rearing as the last of the goldenrod, *Bidens* spp. and aster flowers end their blooming cycles or are killed due to frost. As bees prepare for winter, weaker colonies are less able to fight off robber bees, when foragers from stronger colonies enter smaller hives to rob honey (Chapter 4). Various wasp species will also attempt to rob honey from weaker hives. This leads to defensive fighting. It is a difficult time of the season; once the flowers have finished blooming, colonies must live off the stored food reserves of the past season and pass the winter inside the hive.

Honeydew

In some areas and certain seasons, honey bees store a surplus of honeydew. Honeydew is not nectar but the exudations of plant-sucking insects. The main source of honeydew are insects such as aphids, scale insects and leafhoppers. These insects sink their mouthparts into plants and excrete a concentrated waste of high sugar content. Bees gather the honeydew and bring it back to the hive to ripen it as they would nectar or sugar water.

Honeydew comes from insects on evergreens, such as pine or hemlock, and from insects on deciduous trees, such as oak, beech and hickory. Honeydew honey (called forest honey in some parts of the world where it is common) has a loyal following of enthusiasts. Turkish pine honey is the honeydew from the excrement of a scale insect feeding on *Pinus brutia*. It frequently has a high mineral content, crystallizes very rapidly and is difficult to extract. Beekeepers whose bees utilize honeydew for overwintering report that the colonies do not winter well on this source. The amount of honeydew stored in one season is highly variable. Bees will forage

Figure 11-50
Dutch white clover in a lawn. A-M. Fauvel

for nectar from flowers, if they are available, rather than collect honeydew.

Notes

Honey bees may visit more than 200 plant species in an average season. Every beekeeper should develop plant lists (a bee botany season) that includes local blooms of importance. Such lists will include some plants that provide early season pollen. Continuation of spring buildup requires more pollen and nectar resources from a larger variety of flowering plants for colonies. Then, as colonies grow large, one or a few plants should reliably provide sufficient nectar for the bees to store surplus. Summer variety means continuing brood production and maintenance allowing harvest of surplus honey by the beekeeper from colonies that developed normally. Finally, the bee plant season should provide fall plant resources of pollen and nectar to ensure successful overwintering.

key terms

auricle	floral designs	patterns	robbing behavior
bee botany	forager	pesticide/insecticide/herbicide/fungicide	scent
blue orchard bees	foraging area	petal striation	scout bees
brokenness	honey (nectar) flow	pollen	scrabbling
bulls-eye effect	honeydew	pollen collection and packing	side working foragers
citrus greening (Huanglongbing or yellow dragon disease)	landmarks	pollen collectors	stimulus (rewards)
constancy	nectar	pollen foraging	super
corbicula(pollen basket)	nectar collectors	pollen pellets	synergistic effects
cultivated crops	nectar guides	propolis	unemployed foragers
ectothermic (cold blooded)	nectar secretion	propolis collectors	visual clues
field bee	nutrition levels of legumes	queen excluder	vivid colors
fixing the location	optimum foraging strategy	rake	water
	over/under supering		water collectors

discussion questions

What materials do bees forage for outside the colony? Why is foraging something a bee does after completing hive duties in her sequence of adult behaviors? How do the bee's anatomy (Chapter 4) and foraging behavior interrelate?

Describe how bees discover a new source of flowers. Distinguish between the types of foragers in a colony. If you see a bee with pollen entering a beehive how could you determine where she gathered her pollen load? How can you recognize water foragers? Propolis foragers?

Potentially, a bee could visit a wide variety of flowering plants. How does a single bee sort out options and decide on the most profitable, richest sources?

What is the bee season in your area? What are important sources for pollen, spring buildup and fall and winter survival in your area? What plants would you include to write the seasonal summary of your apiary? Distinguish between a good floral source and a potential nectar (honey) flow source.

If your bees do not store much surplus how could you increase your harvest? What plants are "missing" in the bee season that might benefit your bees and provide a potential harvest?

The flowering plants are the engine that drive our seasonal management. What are the critical times during the flowering season that beekeepers might need to examine and manage colonies? How can we determine if it is time to add supers? When do we need to harvest?

exercises

Establish an observation hive or use a regular hive to watch foraging behavior at the entrance of the colony. Count the number of bees entering and leaving. To do this, you will need to reduce the entrance size of a regular-sized colony. Have bees exit through a wire screen funnel to count departing bees. Can you see a daily pattern? Sample bees that return by capturing them, dissecting their honey stomach and weighing their pollen loads. To measure honey stomach contents, remove the bee head to cut the digestive tract tube and pull at end of the abdomen with forceps. The entire digestive tract will unfold for content analysis, and you will see the honey stomach as the first portion most distant from the tip of the abdomen. Repeat over several days or over a season to compare samples.

Visit a group of flowers to observe the number and species of insects foraging on them. Select a flowering shrub, small tree or flowers like dandelion, clover, sunflower or squash. Observe how the bees forage and how wide an area they forage in to gather nectar and/or pollen. Can you tell if they detect if a flower has been previously visited? You can observe individual flowers or the flower visitors. Which is easier and most useful in answering basic questions about foraging?

Collect your own honey bee foraging statistics on flight behavior. In a diverse habitat of several flowering plants, mark some foraging honey bees (Chapter 8, Box 13, 'How to mark bees') and observe their foraging. Use a stop watch to quantify how long they visit a flower, how many flowers they visit per 30 sec., and how they move from flower to flower. Develop a foraging map. If possible, compare honey bee foragers with foragers of another bee species.

Examine how bees collect pollen. With some careful, repeated observations you should be able to describe the sequence of how bees fill their pollen basket. Look for differences in pollen collecting on different flower species. Make a seasonal diary of the flowers blooming within a radius of 300 feet (275 m) to two miles (3 km) from your apiary, by scouting and identifying the significant flowering plants on a weekly basis. Include your assessment on the amount of flowers and how long they are available to the bees. Do not include plants honey bees do not visit.

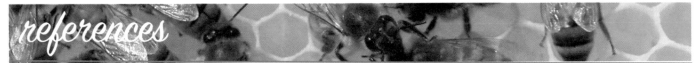

references

Ayres, G.S. and J.R. Harman. 2015. Bee forage of North America and the potential for planting for bees. Chap 13 In: The Hive and Honey Bee. Dadant & Sons

Burnham, T. 2018. Charlie Brandts and the White House bees. Bee Culture Nov 2018

Free, J. 1962. The behaviour of honeybees visiting field beans (*Vicia faba*). Journal of Animal Ecology 31(3):497 DOI: 10.2307/2049

von Frisch, K. 1967. The dance language and orientation of bees. Harvard University Press.

Gary, N.E. et al. 1977. Area fidelity and intra-field distribution of honey bees during the pollination of onions. Environ. Entomol. 6(2):303-310.

Gould, J.L. 1986. The locale map of honey bees: Do insects have cognitive maps? Science 16:232(4752);861-3. DOI: 10.1126/science.232.4752.861

Hodges, D. 1952. Pollen loads of the honey bee. Bee Research Association

Lindtner, P. 2014. Garden plants for honey bees. Wicwas Press

Lovell, J.H. 1918. The flower and the bee: Plant life and pollination. Reprinted by Wicwas Press

Lovell, J.H. 1926. Honey plants of North America. The Root Company

Opfinger, E. 1931. Ueber die Orientierung der Biene au der Futterquelle. Z. vergl. Physiol. 15: 431-87

Pellet, F.C. American honey plants. Reprinted by Dadant Publications

Robinson, W.S. and Fell, R.D. 1981. Effect of honey bee foraging behaviors on Delicious apple set and development. Hortic. Sci.16(3), 326–28

Seeley, T.D. 1985. Honeybee ecology. Princeton University Press

Winston, M. 1991. Biology of the honey bee. Harvard Univ Press

Wray, M.K. et al. 2008. Honeybees do not reject dances for 'implausible' locations: reconsidering the evidence for cognitive maps in insects. Anim. Behav. doi:10.1016/j.anbehav.2008.04.005 (2008).

Use space below to record your seasonal bee botany notes.

Opposite page: Two seasons of beekeeping. C. Burkhead

SECTION 2
BEEKEEPING

THE CRAFT AND SCIENCE
OF KEEPING BEES

Figure 12-1
An apiary with bees located within vegetation behind fencing.

Concepts

Requisites to start

When and how to start

Personal equipment

The hive

Transferring bees

Obtaining bees

Bait hives

The apiary

Starting requisites

All kinds of people become beekeepers. One hundred years ago many farmers kept bees, but fewer do today. There are an estimated 1,000-1,500 **full-time, professional, commercial beekeepers** in the United States. Such persons manage thousands of honey bee colonies, often moving and living with their colonies, following the bloom, and using their colonies in pollination rentals for part of the year. Pollination rental income has replaced honey production as the major income generator for most commercial beekeepers.

Other individuals keep bees as **sideline beekeepers**, managing dozens to hundreds of colonies of bees. Their bees pay for their keep and provide supplemental income for the household. Most generate income from honey sales, via retail, wholesale and on-line sales. Some sideliners also rent bees for pollination purposes.

The vast majority (greater than 95%) of the estimated 80,000 beekeepers in the United States are **small-scale (backyard or hobby) beekeepers**. They maintain less than 50 colonies, but collectively make up an estimated 10% of the total number of colonies in the U.S.

Small-scale beekeepers are suburbanites as well as those living in towns and cities. Most have other jobs—they may be professional people like doctors or lawyers and individuals who own their own businesses or who work in factories or offices. Others are employed in government, education and in countless other occupations. A considerable number are middle-aged to retired. Once mainly a male occupation, small-scale beekeepers are increasingly female and younger.

Many **'newbees'** annually replace individuals who quit beekeeping after one or two seasons. Relatively few small-scale beekeepers sell honey or rent bees for pollination. Whatever their job, number of colonies or wherever they live, the common factor among beekeepers is an interest in learning about managing and improving their honey bee management skills. While the sideline and commercial beekeepers keep bees to make money; recouping investment is less often the motivation for the small-scale beekeeper.

The requisites to starting beekeeping are:

- information and knowledge of bee biology
- a beehive and understanding its components
- bees
- a location (apiary) for hives
- personal protective equipment and tools
- commitment of time and interest
- physical ability to manipulate colonies
- a mentor or experienced beekeeper for help

In nature, bees use a hollow cavity for their nest. They also need flowering plants, temperatures above 65° F (18° C) for sustained flight, and a source of water. They construct beeswax combs and collect resins from plants to make propolis to reduce the cavity entrance size, reduce drafts and to coat the interior of the nest.

Beekeepers usually provide a convenient home, the **beehive**, and locate the new colony in an **apiary**, a convenient location to both beekeeper and the bees. The bees build their **parallel beeswax combs** using frames and a beeswax template foundation so the comb can be removed and inspected. The comb cells are used to rear their young and store honey and bee bread, collected as nectar and pollen respectively. Beekeepers may supplement both foods when necessary.

When and how to start

While a bee colony can be started any time of the year, most beekeepers start their first hive in the spring. This is the best time to start because the bees have the remainder of the season to become established. The new hive will benefit from supporting weather and abundant floral resources. In the warmer southern states where bee colonies are active nearly 12 months of the year, beekeepers have to learn the hive's longer activity period. In northern states and Canada, the active season is shorter, the days are longer, and preparation for winter is critical. Bees do well in most areas if adequate floral resources are present and colonies adapt to varying climatic conditions.

A good question, along with when to start, is how many colonies should be started? If you have the money you could buy an entire beekeeping operation and become a beekeeper tomorrow. This is not recommended. Rather, it is suggested that a beekeeper start small; it will be easy to expand. Beginning more than one colony will allow comparison between colonies and permit management practices like exchange of brood or honey. Two or three colonies allow for good learning opportunities and ensure there is desire to continue with bees before making the additional time and financial investments in larger numbers of colonies.

Learning basic bee biology takes time and preparation (Figure 12-2). Some new beekeepers pick up beekeeping equipment at a local farm store and start beekeeping without preparation. The smarter individual takes time

"Would you mind sending the equipment by overnight express—I'm in a bit of a hurry!"

Figure 12-2
The tardy beekeeper. D. Heskes

Figure 12-3
Beekeeper Tom Chester faced many decisions to determine the type and size of the bee equipment used in his apiary, but found great satisfaction as a result of his efforts.

to read, take classes, visit beekeepers, and maybe even attend a local beekeeping club meeting or field day. They start with the necessary bee biology knowledge and take time to understand basic hive equipment and starting with bees (Figure 12-1).

The new beekeeper should order bees, equipment and personal protective gear in advance and have an apiary site prepared for the new hive(s). Remember the advice of Chapter 1 — Anticipation not reaction.

What to expect

Honey bees are living organisms with complex social lives. Good beekeepers need to understand a considerable amount of bee biology but not everything. Beekeeping is both a science, the biology of the bee, and an art, the skillful application of bee biology knowledge with proper timing and understanding. Experience is also a good teacher. Bees provide a continuous learning experience. Just when beekeepers think they have seen or experienced it all, the bees do something different.

Skillful and perceptive individuals make better beekeepers. A willingness to try something new, to experiment helps, as does understanding and assimilating what others say about bees and bee management. As with most other things in life, some individuals have a better temperament that allows them to keep bees while others are challenged by the process.

It is a joy to watch skillful beekeepers. Their every movement is fluid; they quickly assess the colony condition and are ready to perform the proper management without hesitation. All beginning beekeepers should initially have and use a mentor-instructor to help understand the bees and also to work alongside during hive inspections. Use this person's skill set as you observe, learn, and enjoy working bees.

As a beekeeper, knowledge and inspection skills will help in managing the population of the intricate social life of the bee and beehive. With experience and patience, beekeepers can expect, in addition to the pleasure of keeping bees, to recoup their financial investment or maybe even make extra income. The level of commitment alone will provide ample rewards — whether it is a few hours with two hives or eventually includes more extensive colony numbers, time and resources (Figures 12-1, 12-3). The bees will store some surplus honey and pollinate plants in the vicinity of their hive regardless of beekeeper skill. Most new beekeepers experience great joy and satisfaction while working their bees.

Personal equipment

Learn to dress properly to work bees. When you are dressed to reduce stings it will allow you to concentrate on the bees. You need to feel comfortable and protected. Some may wear just a veil, while others wear a full bee suit, veil and gloves (Figures 12-4 and 12-5).

A veil is considered the minimum level of protection needed when working beehives. Veils protect the face, including sensitive eyes, ears and throat from stings. Such stings, in addition to being more irritating, can cause permanent damage.

Veils can be simple affairs, like used army-surplus mosquito net veils, or more elaborate, sturdy beekeeping veils with special helmets designed so they are held away from the skin but permit easy movement, vision and airflow. They need be bee tight around the edges so will feature long tie-down strings, elastic bands or zippers. Veils with black wire mesh allow for ease in seeing the bees but may attract bees towards the face. Beekeepers should spend what they feel is appropriate — expect to pay more for the best quality.

A word of caution: if a bee manages to get inside the veil or protective equipment, either smash the bee or exit the apiary before opening the veil to allow the bee to escape. Panicking and attempting to remove the veil while still in the apiary will mean more bees and increase the potential for multiple stings in the face.

Figure 12-4
Well-protected beekeeper with a frame covered with bees. The baseball cap holds the veil off the face and keeps bees from stinging through the top of the veil.

Gloves, coveralls and boots or sturdy shoes are also recommended. Clothing with elastic closures around the ankles or wrists or Velcro® straps are handy. The ideal beekeeper's outfit needs to exclude bees (bee-tight) but not be tightly fitting. Openings or floppy shirt sleeves or clothing that interfere with inspections should be avoided. For individuals with more extensive resources, acquire a pair of specialty coveralls that includes a veil with sturdy zippers or Velcro® closure, allowing secure attachment and removal of the veil (Figure 12-5).

More economical, light-colored work-type coveralls and gloves, appropriate for chores around the house or farm, may be adequate and cooler. Coveralls made from cotton or fabric blends are cooler; nylon coveralls may be hot but both will repel stings. Once you are willing to accept a few stings to the hands, you can work gloveless with greater ease and still reduce the possibility of stings.

A good **smoker** is indispensable (Figures 12-6, also see Chapter 13). Unless you plan on working a large number of hives, buy a medium to large-sized smoker. Avoid smokers that are too small, as they need to be refilled with the fuel source too often. Extra-large smokers are used by commercial beekeepers and those working with Africanized bees. For fuel, beekeepers use whatever is available such as dry, rotted wood, pine needles, wood shavings, dry grass/hay, leaves, bark, and/or weathered bailing twine or burlap. You can purchase smoker fuel from bee suppliers. No one smoker fuel is "best" so choose one based on availability and cost. Keep smoker fuel in a container with a tight lid so it stays dry.

Some beekeepers feel the need to "add something" to the smoker to calm the bees. Don't harm the bees. Be careful, as such additives may be detrimental to the bees or your own lungs. Obviously do not use a fuel that might trigger an allergic reaction or are overly irritating.

The **hive tool** is a second item essential to examining a bee colony. It is used to separate boxes and frames during colony inspections as well as various prying and scraping tasks. Several sizes and types are available (Figure 12-7). As with the smoker it takes practice to become efficient in their use. It is worth trying out a few different

Figure 12-5
Full bee suit with A. veil, B. ventilated suit, C. gloves and D. hive tool. From *BeeCabulary Essentials*, A. Connor

Figure 12-6
A typical smoker, showing bellows, firebox, burn protection guard and hook to fasten to hive while inspecting the colony. L. Connor

Figure 12-7
Various types of hive tools, left to right: Typical hive tool. J-Hook, Scraper with J-Hook, Wood-handled J-hook. From *BeeCabulary Essentials*, A. Connor

types of hive tools to find one that is of a style and size comfortable in your own hand. An alternative is a frame lifter (See one being used in Figure 13-5) — one popular design includes a pry-bar extension so it functions both as a hive tool and to aid in lifting frames. It is handy for individuals who do not want to touch bees.

Together, a sturdy hive tool and quality smoker are the beekeeper's best friends, so consider their purchase carefully. The price range and quality of smokers and hive tools varies considerably. Expect to pay $35 or more for the two. A veil, coveralls and gloves will cost from a few dollars to a hundred or more dollars.

Protective gear, a smoker, hive tool and the beehive itself, can all be purchased from local and national dealers, or online. Free catalogs are available by mail or Internet ordering. Many beekeepers support their local bee supply dealer. Consult a recent issue of the journals, *Bee Culture* magazine (A.I. Root Co., 623 West Liberty St., Medina, OH 44256) or *American Bee Journal* (Dadant & Sons, Inc., 51 S. 2nd St., Hamilton, IL 62341) to view bee supply and bee related ads; or conduct an Internet search for bee supply dealers. They offer a wide range of supplies and prices.

The hive

The home for honey bees is termed the hive. The term **hive** refers to the wood/plastic structure that bees live in while **colony** specifically means the living organism, although beekeepers often use the terms colony and hive interchangeably. The standard construction material is wood, but plastic hive components are increasingly being used. A hive consists of a series of boxes, called hive bodies or brood boxes, each of which holds suspended frames. A bottom board, which includes the beehive entrance, and inner and outer covers complete the basic hive (Figure 12-8 and review Chapter 9). You can add other items, concentrating on the basics, as experience and knowledge expand.

Figure 12-8
A complete Langstroth hive. Dadant & Sons. Inc.

You can purchase a complete beginner's kit or buy hive items individually. Beehive or personal equipment need not be purchased from a single source. Width and length dimensions of hive bodies are standardized in the U.S. with only minor variations from one manufacturer to the next.

The major difference shows up in how bee space is built into the suspending of the frames from the rabbet (sometimes termed rebate), a recessed cut into the ends of the hive boxes. Because of variations in the rabbet cut by different manufacturers as well as variations in the width of top bars, it is recommended to always get boxes and frames from the same manufacturer. Space variations result in the bees building excessive burr and brace comb.

Alternative hive styles that just use top bar frames (without side or bottom bars) have been developed. Two top bar hives, the Kenya top bar hive (KTBH) (Figure 12-10, left) with sloping side walls, and Tanzanian (TANZ) with straight side walls, are utilized in parts of Africa and by urban beekeepers who do not wish to practice highly interventional inspections. Keeping the parallel combs within the top bar alignment will allow some inspection and management.

Another hive design, the Warré hive (Figure 12-10 right) is also a top bar design. Boxes are smaller and manipulation is not facilitated if bees do not remain within the frame outline. One disadvantage of alternative hives is their incompatibility with the standard Langstroth design if the beekeeper wishes to switch. With top bar hives, feeding and disease and varroa mite inspections are not as easy to accomplish as with movable frame hives unless initial

Figure 12-10
Four different hive types. L to R: Kenyan Top Bar Hive, Long hive with 20 Langstroth frames, Langstroth hive in two deep, ten-frame bodies and Warré Hive. S. Repasky

establishment is closely monitored to ensure a series of straight and unconnected combs.

Standard removable frame Langstroth hives usually includes ten parallel frames. A popular alternative is an eight frame version. Also, some individuals prefer "coffin" or long horizontal hives which might have 20 or 30 parallel frames (middle hives in Figure 12-10).

Beehive equipment is usually purchased new. Precut wood pieces are shipped unassembled and must be assembled (Figure 12-9). It is recommended that beginners buy new equipment and assemble it themselves to better understand hive basics. Assembly directions are included with new equipment. Others purchase pre-assembled and painted hive equipment at a higher price.

It is often possible to buy used bee equipment from beekeepers with extra equipment, or from individuals going out of business. It is very risky for beginners to buy used equipment. You need skills to determine if it is a good value at the asking price. The equipment should be standard size, in good enough shape, and disease free. **New beekeepers should avoid buying used equipment.**

Due to the possibility of disease transmission, State laws may prohibit the movement of used bee equipment across state lines without an apiary inspection certificate.

Individuals familiar with basic carpentry tools will find some hive parts relatively easy to make. With a clear set of instructions (see Simon, *Bee Equipment Essentials*), some hive parts are relatively easy to cut and assemble. But most beginners should plan to assemble and use the standard eight- or ten-frame Langstroth hive, purchased from a major manufacturer, before trying to build one. Frames are complicated and time consuming to manufacture and even skilled woodworkers typically avoid making frames.

Figure 12-9
Using a jig to hold numerous end bars. Use of good wood glue and cross nailing or stapling will ensure that frames will last for years. L Connor

The basic hive or brood box (the part where brood rearing occurs), consists of one or more hive bodies, two being standard. Each hive body requires eight or ten frames

Figure 12-11
Starter strip in a medium frame for honey production.

Figure 12-12
Full frame of capped honey.

Figure 12-13
Frame of honey with pieces cut out for packaging.
L. Connor

Figure 12-14
Cut-comb honey in plastic containers. L. Connor

with beeswax or plastic foundation. Hive bodies and their corresponding frames come in several depths as shown in Figure 12-8.

Beekeepers in northern locations often use two standard-size deep hive bodies to allow colonies to rear their brood and store adequate pollen and honey to feed the brood (as shown in Figure 12-8). Modification to one standard and one medium (also known as Illinois or western) hive body is a common alternative — sometimes three medium depths are used instead of two standard depth bodies.

Beekeepers in southern locations or using special management systems are more likely to have a single deep box brood chamber (or two medium-depth boxes). Some beekeepers feel that colonies develop larger brood areas in larger boxes with deeper frames. However, this adds considerable weight; the boxes and frames of the standard depth can be difficult to handle when filled with honey.

Many beekeepers use one size box with one size frame for both brood boxes and honey supers. There are advantages and disadvantages in doing this. Using a single depth frame facilitates frame interchange between boxes. The heavier weight of deep frames stresses the beekeeper's body, especially during the honey harvest.

Frames of a single size simplifies their use in making increase colonies (when splitting hives), as explained in Chapter 19. Talk to local beekeepers to learn their experiences, and work alongside them while they are making new colonies. You can always change your system in a subsequent season.

Other beekeepers use one sized hive box for brood rearing and shallower boxes for honey collection.

Hive equipment is expected to last many seasons, so it is important to prepare it properly for outdoor exposure. Assemble it carefully. Pre-drill nail holes and use a good wood glue on all joints, in addition to nailing or screwing them (Figure 12-9). Use a top quality paint or wood stain on the bottom board, the outside and rims of hive bodies and the outside of the top cover. Paint or wood stain helps the hive look good, equipment last longer, and assists the bees inside with temperature regulation. Painting the outer cover (sometimes with a reflective paint) has been shown to reduce the inside temperature by up to five percent.

While hives are often painted white, the use of different colors increases colony orientation and reduces drifting. Avoid black or dark colors in hotter environments or when hives are placed in direct sunlight. So let your imagination go wild (Figure 12-3). A good quality paint is recommended. Paint bought at garage sales or mis-mixed paints from paint stores can be obtained at lower cost. Hive bodies may be of different colors or with painted designs incorporated into the color patterns. Stains and natural wood preservatives are preferred by some beekeepers, especially for hive stands in contact with soil.

Figure 12-15
Two hive stands holding two colonies each. The four-inch boards have been placed on concrete blocks to provide ease in working the hives. Beekeeper can drive a truck behind the colonies. L. Connor

Some beekeepers individualize their beehives by adding peaked covers instead of flat ones, (Figures 12-10, 12-29). European beekeepers have a tradition of distinctive hive fronts, often elaborately carved or painted (as illustrated in Figure 9-23).

Beekeepers often take great pride in their bees. The hives themselves may be beautifully hand-crafted and carefully maintained. Beekeepers with individualized hives must still master the basics.

Types of honey

Every new beekeeper needs to consider the type of honey they plan to produce—comb or liquid. Many presume the objective is to produce honey—but not all beekeepers want to do so. Liquid or extracted honey usually requires the use of a honey extractor and other equipment (see discussion of honey extraction in Chapter 16). Comb honey can be harvested with nothing more complicated than a knife/specialized comb cutter and draining equipment.

Extracted honey is perhaps the easiest to produce and sell, but extracting equipment must be obtained to spin the honey from the beeswax combs, and use of uncapping knives and settling/bottling equipment in addition to the extractor adds to investment costs. Liquid honey must be allowed to settle in a bucket or tank and may be stored before bottling in metal, food-grade plastic, or glass containers.

Producing honey in the comb is traditional and links us to the honey hunters and gatherers who robbed honey from bee trees and later bee gums and skeps. Honey harvested directly in the comb (Figure 12-13) does not require complex equipment necessary for extraction, but for the production and sale of quality product, the bees must produce more wax, meaning there is less honey to harvest. Comb pests and crystallization of honey in the

comb cells leads to a shorter storage period and the need to sell/use it quickly. Advantages include less processing equipment expense (knife and drain pan) and inexpensive packaging. The production and sale of quality product (Figure 12-14) results in a product that usually sells at a premium price.

There is also a combination product of liquid and comb, called **chunk honey** where a piece of comb honey is surrounded by liquid in a wide-mouth jar. Some distinctive honey varietals, such as orange blossom and sourwood are frequently marketed as chunk honey.

The type of honey to produce is not a decision that needs to be made the first year. Most of the honey the bees store the first year is required for their own survival during their first winter.

The type of honey impacts the type and depth of supers and foundation to purchase. Some beekeepers prefer not to use the standard-size deep hive body size for a honey super as it becomes very heavy when full and the frames are harder to uncap and extract (Figure 12-12 shows a medium depth frame full of honey). Supers for honey are therefore frequently shorter in height and lighter in weight. The advantage of a shorter box is that it will be easier to lift and handle when full of honey. The disadvantage is that more boxes may be needed.

Beekeepers who produce honey in top-bar hives (Kenyan and Tanzanian) as well as beekeepers who use starter strips to produce natural comb (Figure 12-11), will have the options of producing cut-comb, chunk or liquid honey. Comb may be cut out of a frame (Langstroth or top-bar) (Figure 12-13) to fit into plastic boxes (Figure 12-14), wrapped in plastic or suspended in liquid (chunk honey).

Cut-comb honey is produced in shallow boxes, sometimes using thinner top bars. Extracted (liquid) honey or chunk

Figure 12-16
Beekeeper dumping worker bees from a package onto the queen positioned between empty frames. L Connor

Box 25

TRANSFERRING BEES

It is sometimes necessary to transfer bees from one piece of equipment to another, or to remove bee colonies from house voids, tree hollows or other natural dwellings. Colonies that inhabit box hives, log gums, skeps or other rustic hive equipment (in which the combs are crosswise, or not within frames) should be transferred to movable-frame hives. It is recommended to transfer bees during the spring. Colony populations will be smaller and the bees will have less honey stores and brood comb than later in the year. Transferring a colony early in the active season will allow the bees time to build up their colony population and time to collect sufficient stores for successful wintering.

To transfer bees into standard movable-comb equipment, place a standard hive body with drawn comb, or foundation if comb is not available, on top of the container with the bees you wish to transfer. Close all entrances except through the standard hive body. Eventually the original colony will expand into the standard hive.

When the queen has vacated the old nest, place a queen excluder between the original and standard hive body to prevent the queen from reentering the original nest. Remove the nonstandard box in three weeks, after all brood has emerged.

Bees may be drummed out of nonstandard hives. To do this place a new hive with drawn comb or foundation on top of the container containing the bees you wish to transfer. Figure 12-17 illustrates transfer from a skep. Beat vigorously with a rubber mallet, stick or hammer on the side of the old hive continuously for eight or ten minutes. The regular drumming causes the bees and queen to move upward. Smoking the colony also stimulates movement.

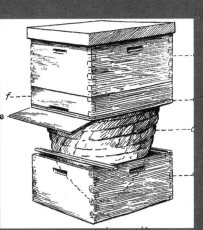

Figure 12-17
Transfer of rustic skep hive into standard hive body. An empty hive body is used for support.

Figure 12-18
A cardboard box is tied to a concrete pole requiring bees to exit through the box. The box is filled with comb to collect the returning foragers.

When most of the bees have moved up into the new hive, place a queen excluder between the new and old equipment. Close all entrances except for a single one through the standard hive. After several days, the new hive can be checked for evidence of the queen.

If the queen is not above, the queen excluder must be removed and the drumming process repeated. Three weeks later, all the brood will have emerged below so the old hive may be removed and discarded.

Removing bees from a building or hollow tree/cavity (Figure 12-18) should be attempted by every beekeeper at least once. If the beeswax combs cannot be exposed and the bees and comb transferred directly into a hive, the adult bees may be trapped into an empty hive.

To trap a colony, close all entrances except one. Fashion a screen cone over the single remaining entrance permitting exit but not return of the bees to their old home (Figure 12-18). This cone can be made of wire screening and should extend 12 to 18 inches (30±5 cm) outward, narrowing from between 8 and 12 inches (20 and 30 cm) to an outer opening of 3/8ths inch (1 cm). Place an empty hive supplied with foundation, or preferably one or more drawn combs, adjacent to the screen cone opening and fix it temporarily in place. The adult population minus the queen will exit and adopt the new hive. Supply a queen or a frame of young brood so the adult bees transferring to the empty hive can rear a new emergency queen. Eventually, the colony inside will weaken. It can be later exposed for comb removal.

honey can be produced in any size super, though supers are often shallow or medium depths. Honey produced for direct consumption (cut-comb, section or chunk honey) all require use of a special thin pure beeswax foundation, or a starter strip (Figure 12-11).

Supers may be added to colonies above a queen excluder (Figure 12-8) or without use of the queen excluder. Adding supers as colonies require storage space for incoming nectar helps ensure separation of honey storage and brood rearing areas in the hive. If supers are added prior to a nectar flow or without queen excluders, the queen may expand the brood nest into the supers. The decision to use a queen excluder or not is a matter of beekeeper preference.

Hive stands

While bee colonies are generally kept as separate and distinct hives, they may be grouped together on **hive stands**. This keeps the hives off the ground, rather in direct contact with the soil. Hive stands can be made of any material or commercially purchased. Hive stands of stone, metal, treated wood or plastic are especially useful in damp locations or areas where termites and ants are common.

Some beekeepers prefer individual hive stands (Figures 12-3, 12-8) while others place two or more colonies on a hive stand (Figures 12-15, 12-20). Commercial beekeepers often arrange several colonies on wooden pallets to facilitate colony loading and unloading during periods of migration (Figure 12-33). Others permanently fix colonies on trailer body frames for ease in movement and hauling.

In parts of Europe, and occasionally in the U.S., bees are kept in hives placed in a building or '**bee house**.' The bees exit their colony through the side of the building using brightly painted and patterned entry/exit holes (Chapter 9, Figure 9-33). Inside, each hive is distinct and separate. The beekeeper saves in painting and upkeep of equipment with the bee house but manipulation of the colonies is more difficult.

Obtaining bees

There are several means to acquire bees to start a beekeeping adventure. Whatever is best for you is your best way to start. You can always add to or make changes in subsequent years after you 'test drive' your bees and equipment. Think about basics needs of the bees.

Transferring bees

Transferring bees from a natural site can be an adventure that becomes a nightmare for the inexperienced beekeeper. Moving bees from a tree hollow, the side of a building or from a cement pole into a hive (Figure 12-18), is not the easiest or most convenient method to obtain bees. Under ideal conditions, transferring a colony of bees into a hive may be a source of free bees (Box 14) but it can also be a lot of work with uncertain results. Feral colonies

Figure 12-19
Beekeeper showing how gentle a new swarm can be, before shaking the swarm into a box. R. Weiske

often prove difficult to transfer and manage afterwards.

Transfer of bees can be a good learning experience. Bee clubs may do this as an educational program and/or community service project. Experienced carpenters can generate income offering bee removal services, commonly referred to as **cut-outs**. Some prefer to use vacuum suction to remove adult bees for minimal structural damage. Bees can be coaxed to simply expand from natural/artificial tree or wall voids into standard equipment under some situations (Figure 12-17). In general, it is far wiser for a novice to leave wild (feral) colonies alone, and either purchase a package of bees or capture a bee swarm.

Package bees

Beginning beekeepers often start by purchasing package bees. Package bees, consisting of queen and two or three pounds of bees in a wood and wire cage, are ordered in advance (Figures 12-16, 12-32). Packages are reasonably priced, the bees are gentle, and bees and queen can be conveniently installed into the beehive. Since the arrival date is estimated, bee equipment can be purchased, hives assembled and everything readied in advance of the arrival of the bees.

Package bees were once routinely shipped by U.S. mail or package delivery service directly to the beekeeper or a central pickup point. Now, more commonly individuals go to suppliers for customer pick up. Many bee clubs make a group purchase or have a local individual who sells package bees. Package bees are usually installed in the early spring.

Directions on how to transfer the package bees into the hive are included with the package or in *Package Essentials* (Wicwas Press). There are several options. One recommendation is that the bees be shaken from the shipping package (Figure 12-16) leaving the queen in her separate cage with the cork removed from the candy

Figure 12-20
Five-frame nucleus increase colonies are a good invest-
ment for starting two to four hives with good results.
L. Connor

Figure 12-21
Senior author in apiary 'behind the barn' with wind protection. L. Connor

end. Another option is to allow the bees to vacate the
package after the queen, still in her cage, is removed and
positioned between frames.

The disadvantage of this second option is that on occasion
the bees are reluctant to leave the shipping package where
they begin constructing parallel combs creating a mess
that must be corrected. Leaving the queen caged (indirect
release) is preferred over direct release of the queen
during installation.

The package colony, as do all small colonies, needs to be
fed a dilute sugar syrup. Usually the package is installed
into a single box and then a second brood box added five
to six weeks later to allow for expansion.

Novice beekeepers can grow in experience and confidence
as a package colony expands the first season — a real plus!
Package bee colonies seldom produce a honey surplus
the first season. They need to consume a large amount of
honey to produce the beeswax combs.

Capture a swarm

One of the easiest and cheapest methods of starting a
bee colony is by capturing a swarm (Chapter 9). Swarms
newly arrived at their bivouac are usually gentle (Figure
12-19). Most swarms, depending on the cluster site,
will be relatively easy to capture and place into a hive,
especially if they are at a convenient height from the
ground and relocated close to your home or work site.

The basic technique is to maneuver a collection box
beneath the clustered swarm and shake or scrape the
majority of the bees into the collector hive/box. Using a
hive body with bee smell is advantageous since the bees
are likely to stay when shaken or dropped into such a
container. If the queen stays in the box, the rest of the bees
will join her, scenting to guide the others into the box.

Once it is evident that the queen is in the box and bees
are settling in, it can be beneficial to give some time to
allow the remaining bees to find their way into the new
dwelling. If the situation allows, leaving the box until
dusk and returning to collect it will result in a minimal
number of bees being left behind.

Attract a swarm with a bait hive

Bait hives use our knowledge of the bees' preference
for nesting cavities to attract bee swarms seeking a new
nest cavity (Box 15). In one experiment, 96 baited hives
attracted 43 swarms in a seven-week period. Bait hives
(Figure 12-22), such as the paper carton cone planter
commonly used in Africanized honey bee trapping
programs, can be purchased or a bait box constructed
from scrap wood (Figure 12-23). Most beekeepers simply
use an empty hive body (or nucleus box) as a bait hive,
taking advantage of the attraction of bees to bee smell
(Figures 12-17, 12-18). Other attractants include bee
balm or lemon grass brushed inside the bait box, a piece
of beeswax comb or synthetic Nasonov scent gland
pheromone, available from bee supply dealers.

Place bait hives about ten feet (three meters) high
and visible with the small entrance facing a southern
exposure. Place outside the apiary for best trapping
success. Beekeepers frequently have empty boxes (with
or without frames) in storage around apiaries which may
inadvertently trap a swarm.

Buy an established colony

Yet another source of bees is to buy an established colony.
In this case both bees and hive equipment are purchased.
Prices are usually reasonable, maybe even a real bargain.
Purchasing used equipment, without the bees, is also an
option for the beginner. The greatest advantage of starting
with an established colony is the possibility of securing a
surplus honey crop the first season.

When buying someone else's hive, your first task will be
to move the colony to the apiary location. This is done at
night after closing the bees inside and securing the hive
bodies, bottom board and cover with duct tape, straps,
staples or with other suitable materials.

Box 26

BAIT HIVE BASICS

Bait hives have been used by beekeepers for centuries. In East Africa today, baiting migratory swarms of the African bee is the principle way of obtaining bees. To avoid problems, Africanized honey bee swarms are baited in the southern United States (and eliminated). As a means of increasing colonies (or trapping AHB swarms), modified 15-inch, wood pulp, cone style 'flower pots' make inexpensive bait hives (Figure 12-22). They are available from several bee supply sources.

Alternately it is possible to use unoccupied hive bodies, empty nucleus boxes or to make a bait box yourself. A good bait hive is a box slightly smaller than a standard hive body with a small (1.25 inch or 3 cm) entrance near the bottom of the box. Figure 12-23 illustrates a suggested design developed from research at Cornell University.

Empty boxes will attract some swarms but baiting greatly increases the yield. Eastern African beekeepers brush their bait hives with attractive flowers and reuse their hives to enhance the residual bee smell. You can add a piece of beeswax comb or use wood from recycled bee boxes to make bait hives. Pheromone (swarm) lures are available from bee supply dealers.

One lure will last a month or more. Bait hives are best used during the swarm season. For best results place bait boxes ten feet (3 m) or more above the ground and visible to the bees. Full sun sites will be less attractive to bee swarms than those partially in the shade. Beekeeper experience indicates that painting of bait hives so they blend in better helps reduce vandalism. Bait hives are not illegal but maintaining a captured swarm in one would be since it would not be a movable comb hive. Thus bait hives should be checked at least weekly during swarm season and periodically after that if left in place longer.

Captured swarms should be promptly transferred to standard bee equipment. If occupied for several days or longer, the colony will construct parallel beeswax comb and begin to fill the comb with honey and brood. Such comb can be cut and pieced into standard frames when transferring to a standard hive. Worker brood comb would be the priority; such comb should

Figure 12-22
A garden container is used as a bait hive. It is attached to a tree, about ten feet off the ground, facing southeast.

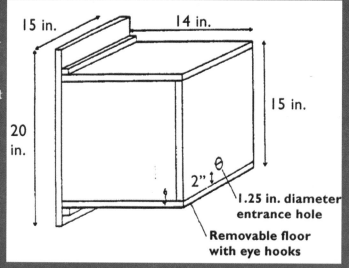

Figure 12-23
Bait box dimensions from Cornell University Bulletin 187, 'Bait Hives.'

be held securely within the frame via string or rubber bands until the bees secure it to the frame itself. Provide additional frames with foundation at time of transfer.

Two disadvantages for the novice in purchase of an established colony are that the colony might be too strong for their experience level, or the beginner might be buying someone else's problem such as foulbrood disease.

When hearing of bee colonies or bee equipment for sale ask some basic questions. Why is the colony/equipment for sale? Are the bees gentle? Is the equipment standard? Will the seller help the beginner with any problems?

A big challenge faced by the beginner is in accurately evaluating a colony and determining if the price is reasonable. Used hives are sometimes offered in classified ads on the Internet and in farm and bee journals.

Buy a nucleus colony

An increasingly popular alternative to buying a package or an established colony is to buy a nucleus colony (Figure 12-20). These nucs are smaller in size (usually three to five frames), should have a young queen, and be sold with newer drawn combs. Nucs have the potential to gain strength and supply honey during the same season if established early enough in the year. They also offer a better chance of winter survival compared to package bees or a captured swarm because nucs initially include all stages of brood and bees. Locally produced nuclei may also be preferable since local beekeepers make them for sale within their community, although queens may be purchased elsewhere, especially early in the season.

The apiary

Honey bees are adaptable to a wide variety of weather conditions, whether one to several colonies bees are kept in the **apiary**. Traditionally bees were kept 'out behind the barn' (Figure 12-21), within or alongside wooded areas of rural farm sites (Figure 12-24, 12-29), behind fences in suburban backyards or on a rooftop, as in New York City (Figure 12-31). While convenience of access for the beekeeper is an important criterion, it would be negligent of the beekeeper to place colonies where human or domestic animal traffic is expected.

Locations for 25 or more bee colonies, where a commercial honey crop might be produced, are more limited. Full-time and sideliner beekeepers, in contrast to the hobbyists, usually seek to obtain the best possible honey crop. This frequently involves the physical movement of colonies to a better nectar location where bee colonies consistently store a large crop. Larger beekeepers may have 25 or more colonies at one location (Figure 12-24).

For the small-scale (backyard) beekeeper, one to a dozen bee colonies (Figures 12-21, 12-29) can be successfully maintained with at least some surplus honey production in virtually any location, although some communities may restrict colony number.

Temporary apiary sites are established at pollination rental situations. Such locations may have an excessive number of colonies and often are used when natural

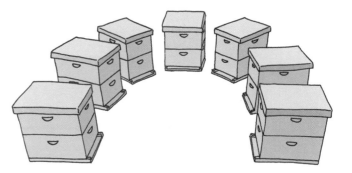

Figure 12-25
Inward U: Smaller space where the base of the U faces south with the sides facing east and west. All colonies face inward for focused bee flight. Suitable for tighter locations. J. Zawislak

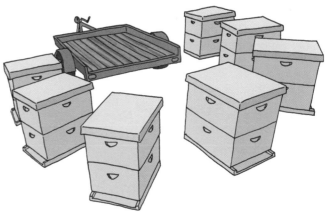

Figure 12-26
Outward U: Larger space allows the beekeeper to back up a truck or trailer and reduce walking. Face the base of the U toward the south with the sides facing east and west. All colonies face outward so bees are less likely to cross another colony's flight path. J. Zawislak

Figure 12-24
This apiary is in a piney woods in Texas. It has partial shade with a solid road access, allowing the beekeepers to spread the bees out over a wide distance. L. Connor

Figure 12-27
Palletized colonies may be angled out a minimum of 15-45° difference from the neighboring colony. Colonies may be repositioned for transport. J. Zawislak

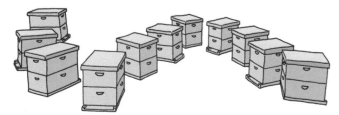

Figure 12-28
Serpentine pattern of hives is ideal for permanent yards, nucleus colonies and mating nucs. Alternate entrances. Set up so small colonies may be moved after an adjoining strip of land has been mowed. J. Zawislak

flower resources are scarce so colonies must be heavily fed at such sites. Good nectar-flow apiary sites are scarce and already occupied by other beekeepers.

Bees in cities and suburbs

In cities and towns, bees may be kept on roofs (Figure 12-31), porches, elevated on structures or behind fencing and vegetation. Suburban and city bee locations might lead to neighbor problems so the most important consideration may be neighbors rather than beekeeper convenience.

Locating colonies out of sight behind the barn or garage (Figure 12-21) is good common sense. Even better, growing a shrub barrier or vegetative corral that partially conceals the apiary is recommended for the suburban/urban beekeeper. Such obstructions require bees to fly upward and over the heads of pedestrians and traffic. Be sure to leave enough room within the corral to comfortably manage the colonies.

Some city or suburban areas may have local laws or zoning ordinances which prohibit or limit beekeeping. Often regulations, especially zoning ordinances, are open to interpretation. One community may permit beekeeping, with bees interpreted as common household

pets while another may interpret beekeeping as an agricultural pursuit with the very same or similar zoning ordinance language. The major restrictions, when there are specific restrictions, concern minimum lot size, especially when the apiary has more than two or three colonies, and colony location relative to neighboring residences and property lines.

A beekeeper can be ruled in violation of general nuisance statutes which exist in virtually all communities. Unless specifically forbidden by law, the beekeeper has appeal and hearing rights in enforcement of zoning or nuisance regulations. Penalties are not usually assessed unless the beekeeper fails to comply with rulings after receiving notification of specific violations. If you are told 'beekeeping is not permitted,' ask for a copy of the specific statute.

Renting an apiary location

It is possible to rent bee colony locations. When more space is needed or additional colonies maintained, beekeepers establish out-apiaries. Owners of vacant waste land or farmers with wooded areas or pieces of non-cultivated land often permit beekeepers to locate on their property.

Rental fees are usually paid in the form of honey rather than cash. When renting, the beekeeper should locate hives where theft or vandalism will not be a problem. It is also possible to place bees on state or federal properties. You should obtain permission before you do so, of course. There may be an assessment or fee to locate an apiary on government properties. Colonies should be properly labeled/marked so that the owner can be readily contacted if there are problems.

Figure 12-29
Identical, pretty white beehives arranged in a row may be attractive to the human, but cause excessive drifting to the outside hives. Different colored paint will reduce drift.

Drifting of bees

It has often been the practice of beekeepers to paint beehives white and to locate them in apiaries in nice even rows (Figures 12-15, 12-29). Unfortunately, such arrangements make it difficult for individual bees to learn their hive location and successfully return to their own hive. Some bee races, such as Italian bees, are notorious for their drifting behavior.

It is important that bees return to their own individual hive because each colony has a distinctive hive odor. Bees attempting to enter another hive may be intercepted and killed. Bees accidentally entering other colonies may lead to an imbalance in colony strength in the apiary. Colonies at the end of rows often benefit from drifting bees while those in the middle lose many valuable foragers.

Using several color combinations when painting equipment and providing landmarks for bees to find home is good bee management. Uneven placement rather than straight rows is better for colonies. Adding 'natural or artificial structures' also aids bees. A row of 20 white bee colonies positioned along the edge of a field or in an open area might result in considerable drifting.

Figures 12-25 to 28 shows four hive arrangement schemes that are alternatives to straight rows. Configurations shaped as a U or V are favored as they allow closer vehicle access by backing into the work area. There may be instances when movement of bees from a parental colony to another is not a problem. Under good resource conditions and during periods of rapid growth of populations, there is greater acceptance of drifting bees.

Figure 12-31
Colony on a roof in New York City. The color was selected to 'blend in', and the location is wind protected.

Commercial beekeepers, by frequent movement of colonies and equalizing of colony strengths with movement of frames between colonies, are often less concerned with drifting. Strong colonies may be interchanged in apiary position for weaker ones to boost the weaker units. Generally, it is wise to help the bees with individual hive orientation.

Considerations in apiary locations

In selecting a location for beehives, several factors can be considered.

Bee considerations

- secluded location, away from traffic, human or animal disturbance

- full sunlight or locations shaded in the afternoon

- good air circulation and no stagnant air pockets

- good water drainage in area above flood level

- source of fresh water within immediate vicinity

- no large bodies of water that may flood

- close proximity to early/plentiful pollen-plants

- protection from direct winter wind

- southern or eastern exposure for morning sun

- free from pesticide application to the bee colonies or their forage

- abundant flowering plants of multiple nectar sources

Figure 12-30
Normally a dry apiary location, this beekeeper experienced a '100-year flood' and was forced to move hives out of rapidly rising water. A large hand truck and moving straps help prevent one disaster turning into another.
B. Jones

Beekeeper considerations

- colonies close to beekeeper's home or a friend's location
- firm, dry ground year-round and not prone to flooding (Figure 12-30)
- vehicle accessible during all seasons with few obstacles or gates
- sufficient manipulation and expansion space for new hives
- building space for storage of tools/bee equipment
- colonies reasonably close to extracting and equipment storage area
- secluded area where bees will not be disturbed or vandalized
- colonies screened from view
- colony flight away from or above humans, animals or traffic
- reasonable or free location rental fee
- easy access to pollination or honey crop sites

What is the best apiary?

Beekeepers with a few colonies usually find and use a location based upon convenience. Beekeepers planning to make money seek locations near good nectar sources.

While the best apiary locations have often been claimed by another beekeeper, or limited due to changes in agriculture or development, good sites remain available. Once-good sites may become less suitable. In suburban Maryland, a backyard beekeeper near a small wooded area of older locust and tulip poplar trees (the major nectar flow source for his area) was producing a good honey surplus each year. When the trees were cut down for a shopping center the honey yields dropped.

Figure 12-32
New beekeepers buying package bees. Most obtain and install them in April or May.

Box 27

Ten tips

1. Consider neighbors first and ensure they have no reason to complain or fear your bees.

2. Keep gentle bees that exhibit a minimum of flight about the head. If colonies are defensive, requeen them.

3. Know bee biology and manage bees so the neighbors are not even aware the colony is nearby.

4. Halt swarming since neighbors will not know that swarm bees are gentle—a swarm can be frightening to non-beekeepers.

5. Keep an attractive water source nearby so your bees do not visit neighborhood pools, bird baths or yards to obtain water.

6. Conceal or camouflage hives behind shrubbery, a fence or other convenient structure. Remember 'out of sight, out of mind.'

7. Inspect colonies only under optimum conditions and work quickly and efficiently so manipulations are not prolonged.

8. Do not permit robbing to start when inspecting colonies. Halt inspection quickly if it starts and reduce entrances to allow the guard bees to restore order.

9. Add supers to colonies as needed; remove and extract honey supers in such a way that few bees are left flying about. Avoid situations where bees are trying to get into structures where you handle honey or store equipment.

10. Join your local and regional bee associations to learn how to become a better beekeeper.

Changes in agriculture have a profound impact on those beekeepers trying to make some money with their bee colonies. The decline of the family farm and development of larger and more efficient farming methods have greatly impacted beekeeping. Reduced acreage of such crops as buckwheat and clover has negatively impacted beekeepers, as has harvest of alfalfa prior to bloom. Increases in sunflower and canola (oilseed rape) have been positive changes. Beekeepers need to keep up and know what is happening within the agricultural industry and may need to become involved in policy decisions that protect bees and beekeeping.

Within the apiary, the beekeeper may modify a location so it is better suited to the bees by planting bushes or erecting fences to provide a wind shelter, create a barrier to protect from humans or livestock and to direct bees into flight lanes, making it more suitable as an apiary site.

More information

New beekeepers (Figure 12-32) need information to become successful. There are many good books, on-line programs and YouTube videos on bees and beekeeping. Many states have free or low-cost extension publications on various aspects of beekeeping; beginners are encouraged to subscribe to a bee journal. Some chat-rooms and blogs are a great source of free information, but not all of it necessarily useful or completely accurate.

Many individuals become a beekeeper solely on what they have read. Other individuals learn best through experience working with established beekeepers. Get to know a beekeeper in your area who is willing to take time to explain bee culture and demonstrate how to keep bees.

Join local and state beekeeping associations and attend their meetings where expert beekeepers share how they keep bees. Some groups have meetings devoted to 'newbees' and have local experts to answer questions.

Some groups actively promote local mentoring of new beekeepers. Some programs are very informal—experienced beekeepers showing new beekeepers a few procedures in the apiary. In a few clubs, the mentoring program lasts all season. A few states/organizations have a Master Beekeeper training program that feature courses and mentoring. New beekeepers should seek out and attend a beekeeping short course convenient to home—be sure to ask lots of questions. Beekeeping is not all cut and dry—there are multiple answers to many questions.

The key to success will be how well the beekeeper understands bee biology. Humans have not domesticated the honey bee. Beekeepers adapt to the honey bee rather

Figure 12-33
A commercial beekeeper with a pallet holding two strong colonies and two replacement hives. The new hives were made from frames of brood and bees from the strong colonies and are being fed sugar syrup. L. Connor

than change it to their ways. One can do almost anything with the bees—they are flexible and forgiving. Good beekeeping involves experimenting and trying something new with the bees to see what might happen. Beekeepers should look, learn, observe, experiment, ask questions and most of all ENJOY. Honey bees provide hours of pleasure and enjoyment and even some rewards.

key terms

active season	bottom board	inner cover	queen excluder
Africanized honey bees	brood boxes	Kenyan top bar hive	rabbet
American Bee Journal	buying a hive	Langstroth equipment	reducing stings
anticipation	chunk honey	liquid honey	renting apiary location
apiary	city bees	locating hives	semi-professional/sideliner
art and science of beekeeping	commercial beekeeper	medium deep	skillful beekeeping
attracting a swarm	coveralls	mentor	small-scale beekeeper
backyard	cut-comb honey	minimum protective gear	smoker
bait hive	drifting	neighbors	smoker fuel
basic hive	gloves	newbees	staining hives
Bee Culture	hive	nucleus hive	supers
beehive	hive bodies	outer cover	swarm capture
bees in veil	hive stands	package bees	Tanzanian top bar hive
behind the barn	hive tool	painting hives	transferring bees
best apiary	hobby	personal protection	used bee equipment
boots	individualize hives	professional beekeeper	veil

discussion questions

Imagine for one crazy moment that you want to start a bee colony. What information do you need? What would you need to purchase? Where would you get what you need? Where would you establish your apiary? How would you go about getting the bees?

Discuss the pros and cons of the several ways of obtaining bees to start a beekeeping hobby. What would be the advantages and disadvantages of starting with used bee equipment versus starting with everything new?

If you find equipment that was put into storage many years ago, what should you do before using it to start a new bee colony in your back yard?

Explain the difference in hive box sizes. List the advantages and disadvantages of all standard-size boxes versus the use of medium (or shallow) supers. What size brood and super boxes would you purchase to begin beekeeping?

What would be the advantage and disadvantage of customizing some of the requisite pieces of equipment? What would you do to personalize your beehives?

Select a backyard you know, a location on some government property and a rural property each large enough for an apiary of 3-10 colonies (pick real sites). Describe the best features of each site for an apiary. What might you do to overcome the two most negative aspects of each of the three sites you picked?

Discuss how you might establish an apiary of two or three colonies in a city or suburban location. What considerations of neighbors might take precedence over beekeeper point of view?

exercises

Get a bee equipment catalogue and compute the costs of starting a beehive. List the items you need for protective equipment, hive manipulation equipment and the various pieces of the hive itself for this comparison. Don't forget about protection from bears, if present.

Buy bee equipment, assemble it and then install a package of bees in the assembled hive when the weather permits.

Prepare a list of the advantages/disadvantages of various frame/hive body sizes. Establish a hive by capturing a swarm. Investigate the possibility of transferring a colony from a nonstandard site. Transfer only if you are comfortable and feel prepared to do so.

Visit local apiaries (or view photos/Internet images of apiaries) to compare good and less desirable location features. Focus on how beekeepers have modified their sites to accommodate bee colonies.

Interview two or more beekeepers about how they started with bees and what they recommend as the best way to start beekeeping. Prepare an essay on how to start beekeeping.

references

Caron, D.M. 2020. The Complete Bee Handbook. Rockridge Press, Emeryville, CA

Connor, A.L. 2018. Bee-Cabulary Essentials. Wicwas Press, Kalamazoo, MI

Connor, L.J. 2012. Bee-Essentials: A Field Guide. Wicwas Press, Kalamazoo, MI

Connor, L.J. 2020. Package Essentials. Wicwas Press, Kalamazoo, MI

Delaplane, K.S. 2007. First Lessons in Beekeeping. Dadant and Sons, Inc., Hamilton, IL

Gary, N. 2018. Honey Bee Hobbyist: The Care and Keeping of Bees. Companion House Books, Joy, PA

Repasky, S. and L.J. Connor. 2013. Swarming Essentials. Wicwas Press, Kalamazoo, MI

Sammataro, D. and A. Avitabile. 2021. The Beekeeper's Handbook 5th edition. Cornell Univ Press, Ithaca, NY

Seeley, T.D. and R.A. Morse. 1982. Bait Hives for Honey Bee. Cornell Extension Bulletin 107

Simon, E. 2011. Bee Equipment Essentials. Wicwas Press, Kalamazoo, MI

Figure 13-1
Frame of nearly solid worker brood, sealed.
C. Hubbard

Concepts

Basics of management

Wear a veil & protective gear

When to manipulate bees

Bee stings

Queen spotting

Smoker lighting

Hive inspection—Reading frames

Robbing

Basics of management

New beekeepers often find colony inspections difficult because they are very fearful of the bees. To them, honey bees and stings are synonymous, since honey bees sting intruders to protect themselves, protect their food reserves and guard their queen.

With experience, new beekeepers learn that bee stings should not be a serious deterrent to keeping bees. Once they learn when and how to inspect a colony, beekeepers reduce the chances of being stung, learning that bees are remarkably tolerant of beekeeper manipulations.

The what, when, where, how and why keys to successful hive management/inspections are:

- what to wear
- when to inspect
- how to inspect and manipulate the opened colony
- where to keep the colonies so inspections are easier
- why colonies become more defensive and ways to handle them

Wear a veil—use protective equipment
Bees concentrate stinging activity where features contrast, such as the face, where sleeves end at the wrist and around the ankles. By always wearing a **veil**, most individuals feel more relaxed when bees buzz around the face and neck.

Without a veil, bees may become entangled in hair and buzz loudly while trying to get to the scalp to sting. A veil prevents permanent injury to the ear or eye if stung at these sites. Face and throat swelling are serious issues.

There are many bee veil designs with a wide price range. Veils that have wide hat brims so the veil fabric itself does not come in contact with the skin are best as bees can sting through most veil material. If you use a folding type veil, use a hat to keep the veil off the face and scalp (Figure 12-4). Veils should conveniently fasten and remain bee tight with the beekeeper's movements. Veils that zipper onto coveralls provide the most secure facial covering. Shirt collars should go inside (Figure 12-4). Veil security should be checked before opening the colony.

NOTE: If a bee does manage to get inside the veil, walk away from the colony first and then remove the bee or pinch it in the fabric. Caution is advised as this will release an alarm odor. Do not remove the veil around the open colony or in the apiary if many bees are flying about. Avoid swatting or flailing at bees.

Use protective clothing. There are many options in bee apparel. Select and wear white or light-colored coveralls over regular clothing. Bee supply manufacturers sell a special bee suit or bee jacket with a securely fitting veil (Figure 13-2, 13-3). A cheaper option is to use a windbreaker jacket with long sleeves. Avoid dark or rough-textured clothing since bees react more defensively to dark objects. Bees can grasp rough textures more easily than smooth surfaces. This a a place to splurge. Purchase secure body covering that remains bee tight (Figures 13-2, 13-3). You can spend a little or a lot.

Use elastic, Velcro® ties or tape to keep veil, pant legs and shirt sleeves bee-tight. Use boots and fasten pants or coveralls inside or over boots. If a bee gets under clothing, crush her quickly or walk away from the apiary and open clothing to allow her to escape. If bees continue to gain access, walk away and determine what needs to be adjusted to keep bees out!

NOTE: Find your comfort level in bee attire. Concentrate on your inspection activity and not about stings or bees getting inside your veil or clothing.

Gloves are handy, especially during unfavorable weather or when moving colonies (Chapter 12, Figure 12-5). Heavy, bulky gloves accumulate bee stings, and frames cannot be manipulated with a fine touch while wearing gloves.

Beekeepers keeping Africanized bees or other defensive bees use gloves more extensively since defensive bees, such as the Africanized population, sting more readily. Heavy, dark fabrics such as wool, suede or leather gloves that retain stings are best avoided as bees respond to the alarm odor left with each sting. Figure 13-10 shows bee gloves with many embedded stings, each one emitting the alarm pheromone odor.

Figure 13-2
A beekeeper wearing a protective bee jacket is smoking the colony entrance prior to beginning inspection.

Figure 13-3
Beekeeper is wearing bee jacket with secure wide-brimmed veil. Note: the hive tool is in his right palm. He is not using gloves, holding the frame over the open hive after removing the first frame with honey—no brood.

Figure 13-4
This beekeeper is wearing a jacket with a veil. Note he has a smoker placed at arm's reach of where he is working and has his hive tool in his right hand.

Some beekeepers use disposable gloves to reduce disease spread and keep propolis off their hands. Plastic or close-fitting latex/vinyl gloves, like those used by medical/dental personnel (beekeeper in Chapter 12, Figure 12-4, is wearing this glove type) or the type of gloves used to wash dishes/do household chores, are good alternatives. Bees can readily sting through such gloves, but they tend not to, and the gloves keep sticky honey and propolis off the fingers.

It will take practice and confidence to get used to the veil and protective clothing. Learn to not always wear gloves to do hive inspections. Leave them in your pocket as you gain experience manipulating colonies (Figures 13-2 to 13-4).

What tools to use

Beekeepers need to have a functioning smoker handy, ready to dispense a cool smoke after a couple of pumps on the bellows. The hive tool should be held in the palm of the hand or in a handy holster so it is always accessible (Figures 13-3, 13-4). Excessive movement or stretching over the open hive to pick up/

put down these two basic tools will extend the length of hive inspection, thereby further increasing the chances for stings.

Use the smoker. The smoker is an indispensable tool as it:

- tends to disperse bees, driving them away from the hands or areas of the hive that the beekeeper wishes to manipulate

- causes some of the bees to take flight but stimulates others to gorge on honey, thus they are no longer guarding

- masks odors, which helps counter the alarm pheromone chemical

The smoker is not a torch. Use a fuel that burns slowly while generating a good volume of smoke, with an acceptable odor and is readily available. Do not use anything that might generate toxic smoke. Before opening a colony, ensure that the smoker is properly functioning and capable of generating a suitable volume of 'cool' smoke. A smoker should generate smoke after a couple of pumps on the bellows even after it has been sitting for a few minutes.

It takes practice learning how to light the smoker — the secret is starting with a readily combustible fuel and adding additional fuel on top of the fire, continuously pumping the bellows to engage the additional fuel without burning it up. You want smoke, not fire! Initially, it may take longer to get the smoker functioning properly than it does to do the hive manipulation. You want the smoker to stay lit long enough to do a proper inspection (See Figures 13-15 to 13-20 on proper lighting of smoker).

Individual beekeepers have their favorite smoker fuel; dry grass/hay, dry pine needles, weathered burlap/bailing twine or dry wood chips are common choices. Some fuels light easier than others. Some require an initial kindling that fires easily, such as paper, to get the main fuel smoking properly. Fuel that is damp or dense will be harder to start. Find a fuel that is agreeable, readily available and reliable. Larger volume smokers are easier to light and continue to function for a longer period.

If the smoker goes out and you have not finished your inspection and reassembled the hive, you need to relight it. Merely putting fuel on the top is rarely adequate. Restart by getting the starter fuel burning on the bottom and then repacking with the smoke-generating fuel. You may need to remove your gloves and exit to the side of the apiary away from the bees to rearm the smoker.

One approach to having a long lasting and effective smoker is by packing the smoke cylinder tightly but only after getting the starter fuel and the cylinder heated up. Smokers burn too hot when they have consumed the majority of the fuel. Consider packing with a cooler fuel (green grass) on top to slow the burn.

Hot smokers may start fires in dry grass/brush. Keep smokers off the ground by hanging them from the hive being inspected (Chapter 12, Figure 12-6), placing them on the top bars (Figure 13-4) or placing them in a metal pail. Extinguish smokers completely when

Figure 13-5
A frame grip is a useful tool to remove a single frame, taking care not to roll bees and the queen in the removal process. Avoid rapid movements with this device. Note the hive cover with supers, set crisscross, atop it during inspection.

done with inspections by corking the nozzle or putting the smoker in an airtight canister (used military ammunition carriers are handy). When not needed for further inspections, empty the smoker's contents into a burn barrel.

Use other handy devices. It is possible to carry too much to the apiary, but other tools that beekeepers might find handy are:

- **Frame lifter**—an alternative tool to lift frames out of the hive so hands do not come into contact with bees (Figure 13-5). Some models include a scraping extension so it functions as both hive tool and frame lifter.

- **Manipulating cloth**—a dry, heavy cloth that is placed over portions of the open hive body not being inspected. One model has a metal-framed opening to give access to frames for inspection while reducing robbing of opened hives. The cloth may be wet or damp towels substituted during hot, dry, windy weather. A heavy cloth (not plastic) that can be rolled back as the inspection proceeds also works as a substitute.

- **Tool box/stool**—a homemade device (some bee supply companies sell a commercial version) to keep tools close by and something to sit/lean on to help make the inspection more comfortable. Some individuals use a five gallon honey bucket with a tool apron to organize and hold a variety of items. These include queen cages, markers (queen and hive), a first aid kit, duct tape, extra dry matches (or lighter), an extra hive tool and other tools and basics.

- **Hive tool holster/smoker hook/frame holder**—are other handy devices; the latter two to hang the smoker and removed frames from side of the hive.

- Don't forget your **cell phone**, especially if you are planning to work alone. Keep it in an outside pocket so you do not need to remove the bee suit.

When to manipulate bees

If you are able, open and examine bee colonies on warm, dry, windless, sunny days between 10:00 a.m. and 4:00 p.m. Avoid cold, windy or showery days. More bees may be in the hive on cloudy days than on sunny or partly sunny days, and bees may quickly return before an approaching electrical storm or weather front, so avoid working in these conditions. It is easier to examine bees during a nectar flow. Even a gentle colony may be challenging to handle during a nectar shortage (dearth) when there are few flowers available as forage. Feeding colonies sugar syrup during dearth periods may aid manipulations, but only feed if robbing is avoided. Work the hive quickly.

Because colonies are easier to examine when they have a smaller population, it is easier to open hives in the spring or late fall (compared to summer or early fall) and when colonies are actively foraging. Once colonies are supered for the nectar flow (beginning in late spring), beekeepers usually only inspect/manipulate the honey supers, and do not enter the brood chamber until the honey supers are removed.

Usually there is little need to look at brood during the summer, but new colonies and weaker colonies without honey supers are the exception. Check the queen's status, brood-rearing activity and general hive welfare during such periods.

Bees may fly out and land on your body. They are not likely to sting unless squeezed or pinched between body parts and clothing. These bees should be of no concern. It may take some getting used to having bees walk on gloveless hands as the frames are manipulated (Figure 13-6). Learn to handle the frames with bare fingers without crushing the bees. Puff smoke on your hands and fingers to mask odors. If you are constantly smoking to chase bees off your hands, put on your plastic or cloth gloves.

Some colonies defend by flying directly into the intruder—a veil properly keeps them away and out of your face and hair. Manipulations that require that you keep the hive open for a longer time period, such as searching for queens or queen cells, may lead to lots of flying and crawling bees (see 'Handling difficult colonies' in this chapter). Secure, bee tight veil/clothing and a functioning smoker are your major defenses against stings in such circumstances. Flying into and bouncing off of intruders is a major means of bees defending their home short of stinging intruders.

How long to keep a hive open

Bees are usually quite tolerant to moderate beekeeper manipulations of five to ten minutes under nice weather conditions. Brood chamber examinations should never be prolonged. Avoid keeping colonies open where there is danger of chilling brood such as when temperatures are below 75° F (23° C) or when a strong wind is present. Keep frames out of full sun exposure if possible during hotter inspection weather to prevent overheating of the brood.

Studies have demonstrated that colonies opened and manipulated gain 20 to 30% less weight the day of inspection compared to colonies not opened. Frequent visits may elevate stress levels and increase the incidence of nosema disease (Chapter 22). In all examinations, keep the colony open only as long as necessary. Novice beekeepers learn to become more proficient. It is not necessary to inspect every frame to evaluate the hive.

During hive inspection, it is customary to remove a frame from the side of the hive box to provide room for further frame manipulations. This will help speed up your inspection as it creates space to slide the remaining frames apart. Be cautious when removing frames. You can lean this frame against the hive away from your feet or place it in an extra hive body. Some beekeepers use a frame holder that fits on the side of the opened box and conveniently holds removed frames. Others use an empty nucleus box for this purpose.

If a colony becomes noisy, shows excessive flight activity or bees are bouncing off your veil or seriously attempting to find entry into your veil or clothing, finish your inspection and close the hive.

Figure 13-6
Continue smoking the hive as inspection continues to make frame removal easier.

Removed supers and hive bodies can be set aside for a few minutes under normal conditions. Cover them with extra covers or a manipulation cloth if manipulations run longer. Inspections that disorganize the nest are not advised. If the brood chamber has more than one box, as is the recommended case for all but weak colonies, begin your inspection in the lowest box first. Once manipulations/inspections are complete, replace the upper box, then continue your activity there. The beekeeper in Figure 13-7 is shown doing brood inspection in the lowest box after removing the top brood box and placing it on the upturned cover to one side.

Combs containing honey quickly attract robbing bees when there is no nectar flow. In the possibility of robbing, cover hive bodies and supers not being examined. If robbing starts, stop examinations for the day. To minimize the impact of robbing, reduce hive entrances and/or install robbing screens. Avoid robbing as it is a difficult behavior to stop once started (see 'Robbing' in this chapter).

Is it okay to inspect?

Colony inspection disturbs the colony and reduces its productivity. Keep inspections short. Only open a colony to inspect/manipulate when the apiary site is warm, usually during the middle of the day when the sun is out and the wind is not strong. Every time you open and inspect a hive, you will probably kill some bees, chill or overheat some brood and interfere with normal hive behaviors like guarding, nectar ripening and queen egg laying.

Figure 13-7
Inspection of the lowest brood box after removal of second box, now on top of the outer cover to the left on hive stand.

As a rule of thumb, if you do not feel warm in light clothing, you shouldn't be in your bee colony. Select apiary sites with a southern exposure that gathers heat and a windbreak that allows late winter and later fall inspections. But even during the cold of winter, it is better to open the top of a hive to provide colonies with food stores than to let them starve.

During cold and windy days, hive inspections should not be prolonged. You do not need to see the queen on every inspection. If the day is overcast and the apiary shaded, it will be difficult to see her eggs. If you remove boxes with bees and brood, cover them with the inner cover or a manipulation cloth. This will help the bees preserve precious heat and disrupt internal hive activities to a lesser degree.

Pull frames with brood only partially out of the box, look at them quickly but carefully, and then replace them, keeping the same sequence and orientation of frames, especially during early and late season. Do not leave frames with brood outside the hive during inspection if it is too cold. Do not spread out or interrupt the brood sphere, carefully arranged by the bees, at any time, especially during the late winter or in the fall after bees have spent time organizing a compact brood sphere.

You should have the colony open five minutes or less under cool temperature conditions. It may take you longer to get the smoker going than the amount of time needed to inspect a colony under extreme conditions.

Bee stings

The **sting** (Figure 13-8) is a defensive tool used by honey bees to defend themselves and protect their nest. A honey bee without a sting is defenseless. For the beekeeper, bee stings are a fact of life. Stings hurt and are unpleasant. Most beekeepers seek to minimize opportunities for bees to release defensive behavior, minimizing the number of stings.

Bee stings are not bites. Anatomically, the sting is an ovipositor, a highly modified part of the female reproductive organs (Chapter 5). In most female insects, the ovipositor is used by the female to deposit eggs in or on food sources. In honey bees the ovipositor has evolved into a defensive sting for the hive's survival. The honey bee queen does not use the ovipositor to lay eggs, reserving it to use only as a sting on a rival queen. Workers, members of the other female caste, do not normally lay eggs.

It has been estimated that 100,000 individuals are stung annually in the United States. The actual health risk of serious damage or death is similar to dying in a cataclysmic storm, four times less than death in hot weather and five times less than death from alcohol poisoning.

Figure 13-8
Worker bee stinging a person. The barbs of the sting structure alternate as they drill into the flesh. Venom is pumped by a set of muscles. K. Garvey

Avoiding stings

When examining a hive, bees may land on or crawl upon hands or clothing. Do not attempt to brush such bees away; leave them as they are not likely to sting. Avoid the natural reaction to flinch or wave (windmill) at bees flying about the head (Figure 13-14). Using the smoker to move bees away from frames being removed for inspection can help avoid crushing bees when manipulating bees without gloves.

When hive inspections are completed, move away from the colonies before removing the veil. Many beekeepers (or their apiary visitors) receive stings when they remove the veil too soon after finishing colony inspections. Brush bees from your bee suit and remove it only if you do not have bees flying about you when entering a vehicle. If bees follow you into a vehicle, crack open a window and allow them to escape on their own. Picking up or swatting such trapped bees may lead to a sting.

Avoid strong odors. Bees sometimes react defensively to strong odors. If bees are always around the face, try changing cologne, perfume, hair spray or other personal cosmetics, even your shampoo. Strong body odors, artificial or natural, may lead to more stings.

NOTE: When a honey bee stings skin or clothing, it loses the stinger and, in so doing, deposits the alarm pheromone (which smells like banana oil). When stung, promptly scrape or pull the sting from the skin. Remove stings from clothing (such as gloves) when practical. If clothing or gloves receive many stings, move away from

the apiary for a few minutes to allow the alarm odor to diminish. Wash bee clothing regularly to remove residual odors and dried venom.

Types of reactions following stings

Neighbors of beekeepers ask about stings and often blame 'your' bees for stings, whether by a honey bee or another stinging insect. Beekeepers are not qualified to provide medical advice (unless trained to do so), but it is useful for them to know some general information and educate others about bee stings to allay normal fears and concerns.

Reactions to bee stings, as well as stings by wasps, hornets, or ants, are grouped into three general categories: normal, allergic, or toxic. During a sting, various toxins and proteins produced by glands associated with the sting are injected beneath the skin and directly into the body. If there is to be a serious reaction, it usually appears very quickly after a person is stung.

Normal sting reaction

In the normal sting reaction there are five features:

- pain
- inflammation of a wheal (raised mark)
- redness developing around the wheal
- swelling
- itching

The amount of pain an individual experiences after being stung varies a great deal. Stings around the face or neck, wrists or ankles or those beneath the fingernails hurt more than other body locations. Some people have a higher tolerance for pain than others. A sting is an open wound, and material from a sting gland is injected that causes pain. Pain lasting a few minutes is normal.

An elevated white round wheal usually begins forming within the first few minutes after a sting is received. Redness will radiate from the wheal, depending on the sting site. A puncture mark is usually visible at the center of the wheal. The wheal will feel hard and may persist for a matter of hours.

The amount of swelling and the discomfort from a sting varies a great deal in a normal reaction. The extent of swelling may be nothing more than a bump or it may be a large amount of swelling (Figure 13-9). Repeated sting events may vary in the amount of pain and/or swelling without an apparent pattern. Generally, if the swelling is confined to the site of the sting, it can be characterized as a normal reaction. If the swelling moves to other parts of the body or is widespread, it is an indication of something more than a normal reaction.

Many persons consider itching the most objectionable part of being stung. Itching will likely intensify as

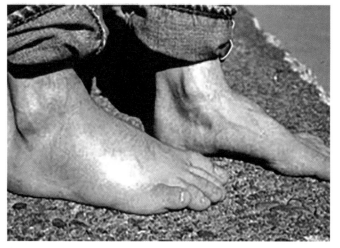

Figure 13-9
Local swelling on the right foot.

swelling begins to subside and may persist for several days. The extent to which the sting site is scratched may affect the amount of swelling and itching. Swelling and itching both may extend for two or more days with overall normal reaction lasting up to a week. For some individuals, the itching sensation is a burning type of reaction. Since there is an open wound, scratching a sting may cause a secondary infection. It is possible to have a delayed reaction to a sting. Swelling and itching are more pronounced in a large local reaction.

Normal reaction treatment

Treatment for a normal reaction is to help the individual forget about the initial pain and then provide comfort from swelling and itching. Something cool covering the sting site helps alleviate the pain. Application of an ice pack, a chilled beverage container, cool water, toothpaste, honey, mud, vinegar, baking soda, meat tenderizer compress or an over-the counter lotion/aerosol such as a sting remedy may be used. A cold compress can reduce the amount of swelling when applied quickly and used off and on for the first couple of hours after the sting. The psychology of doing something, even if not physiologically significant, is of value. The person that is stung should receive plenty of sympathy.

Applying an over-the-counter commercial itch relief remedy may lessen the itching reaction, usually the greatest discomfort in a normal reaction. An ointment or lotion such as a first aid cream or an antihistamine ointment can be applied to provide relief. If there is an open wound, use a topical antibiotic to avoid an infection at the sting site. Products containing Benadryl® provide relief and some beekeepers like to take a low dosage of a liquid formulation before they visit the bees, then take more if they have received one or more stings after completing their colony inspection. Preference and personal experience form an individual's choice of remedy.

Allergic reaction

An allergic reaction is usually widespread over the body, including generalized itching and hives throughout the body, especially on parts of the body other than the sting site. Generalized reactions, swelling in the neck or face, and difficulty in breathing indicate an allergic reaction.

Allergic reactions are not subtle in expression. Individuals may make a wheezing sound, like they are gagging. They may experience hoarseness in speech. Dizziness or sudden drop of blood pressure resulting in shock may also occur.

Allergic reactions following a sting can be grouped into two types of responses: a systemic allergic reaction or a large local reaction. The most severe allergic response, the systemic reaction, occurs within minutes of receiving the sting and usually includes loss of consciousness.

Such a reaction can be expected to occur in less than 1% of the human population. Some allergic sting reactions are fatal. The large local reaction form of allergic reaction is less life threatening, though complications like excessive swelling in the throat can restrict breathing. Symptoms may occur quickly following a sting or may be delayed for a day or more in their expression.

Figure 13-10
Work gloves covered with stings from Africanized bees.

Queen Spotting

Do you need to see the queen?

It is not necessary to see the queen in a hive every time you are inspecting, but most beekeepers like the reassurance of seeing her. Queen finding is an art; it can be frustrating but also satisfying. Why do you need to see the queen? Looking at a queen may enable you to say she is fat, big, little, thinner, lighter in color, etc., but so what? You really do not learn anything useful when you see her except for the peace of mind that she is present!

If you like to see the queen, buy and introduce a marked queen into your colony since marked queens are easier to spot (Figures 13-11, 13-12), or mark her yourself.

Develop the habit of looking for evidence of the queen's presence every time you inspect the brood chamber. What do you need to see? Confirm that there is normal egg laying in the colony. If you see eggs, one to a cell and situated at the cell bottom, you know your hive had a queen within the last three days. Beekeeping is not rocket science. Since we know eggs will develop into larvae in three days, this is enough to say 'YES, THE COLONY HAS THEIR QUEEN!'

In addition to looking for eggs, get into the habit of examining the brood pattern—it, too, tells us what we need to know about the queen. A compact brood nest with cells containing brood of similar age and free of many cells of nectar or pollen are signs of a good queen in early spring and late fall. The amount and health of brood, as well as the expansion or contraction of the brood sphere, are what we evaluate in later spring or earlier fall inspections.

Instead of spending time looking for the queen, evaluate the brood and nest. Colonies should be gentle when handled, not prone to rear replacement queens, have low swarming tendencies, exhibit good disease and mite resistance and, of course, store plenty of honey. These are the qualities we expect of a colony with a good queen.

When do you need to find the queen? We need to find her to requeen and to show her to visitors. To increase the probability of finding a queen, use as little smoke as possible. Look quickly but carefully in the brood area, concentrating on frames of open (not capped) brood where you are more likely to find her. Hold the frame at a 45 degree angle so the queen stands out in profile.

Figure 13-11
A new wax frame, bees, and a new queen. Can you spot her? Still can't see her? Look for her longer and thicker body. Compare the enlarged image—her banding patterns and size are different from those of workers.
L. Connor

Figure 13-12
Queen with green dot surrounded by attendant bees with antennae extended. L. Connor

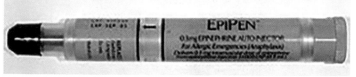

Figure 13-13
An epinephrine injection is useful for people with severe allergies to venom, foods and environmental contaminants.

Treatment of sting allergy

The treatment for a sting allergy depends on the severity of the allergic reaction. It is not to be dismissed or taken lightly. For the large local reaction, Benadryl® or Chlor-Trimeton® (chlorphenamine) are usually of value. These materials may make the patient sleepy but will reduce the severity of reaction.

The absorption of the venom may be slowed by the application of ice to the sting site. In the systemic allergic reaction, the prescribed medication is an injection of adrenaline (epinephrine). A physician can prescribe a portable emergency sting kit or epinephrine injection (Figure 13-13).

When seeking medical advice, it is important that the medical specialist have experience treating bee sting reactions. In any exaggerated, severe and/or sudden reaction, the individual showing symptoms should be transported to a medical facility as rapidly as possible for treatment by trained professionals. You do not need to collect the stinging insect; just indicate to medical personnel what you have observed.

Persons who suspect serious allergic reactions can undergo testing for sensitivity and then be desensitized. If an individual has had a serious reaction, the chance of another, if stung again in a reasonable amount of time, is about 60%. After desensitization, the chance is less than

Figure 13-14
Beekeeper with Africanized bees flying around the veil. Although the beekeeper is protected, the bees will attempt to find a gap in protective gear.

5%. Desensitization studies are currently underway. The value of desensitization for the large local reaction is not known. All treatments should be done with an extract of pure bee venom (bv). Older treatments consisted of whole body extracts (wbe) but studies have shown that wbe treatment is not as effective when compared to bv injections. Once desensitization shots are taken, they must be continued periodically as the immunization is not permanent.

Toxic reaction

While a person or animal should be able to tolerate a certain level of a foreign material introduced into the body, it is possible to receive too many bee, wasp or ant stings in too short a period of time for normal body systems to handle. If too much venom is introduced over too short a period of time, such as may happen with multiple stings, a toxic reaction may occur. This is apparently the situation with human and animal deaths attributed to the highly defensive Africanized bee of the Americas (Figures 13-10, 13-14).

Healthy individuals can tolerate several hundred bee stings without a life-threatening toxic reaction. One individual received over 2,200 bee stings and survived without any side effects. Factors such as a person's health, body weight and age are interrelated as to how many stings might be tolerated. Certainly, it is best to not incur a large number of stings at one time. Beekeepers receiving numerous stings during hive manipulations sometimes report a dull headache or dizziness.

Beekeeper sting acceptance

Beekeepers often become complacent about bee stings; they are a normal occurrence of keeping bee colonies. With an increase in the number of stings, beekeepers may become less reactive to the stings. They are a fact of life, something to tolerate as a beekeeper. It is important to recognize the normal fear and hesitation other people have around bees and normal apprehension to being stung. Bee venom is a dangerous substance and beekeepers must guard against complacency.

It is a normal reaction to wave arms about and to try to brush bees away, though such behaviors often result in the undesired opposite effect—a sting. Staying still, allowing a bee to investigate and then be on her way is the best defense.

Individuals know they are a 'real' beekeeper when they can stay still, not jerk the hand away, not be preoccupied about being stung or not notice bees crawling on their clothing or hands. Beekeepers who purposely handle bees in a rough manner, thus inviting stings, are another matter.

All beekeepers should be prepared to respond if someone appears to be having an allergic or toxic reaction to bee or wasp stings. Have an emergency plan. Proper procedure is to take the person to a trained medical person as quickly as possible after being certain that no further stings will occur. Keep the person as quiet and calm as possible.

Some beekeepers keep an emergency sting kit, conveniently available in the form of an epinephrine auto injector, like EpiPens and their generic equivalents, which can be used even by untrained individuals to administer a dose of epinephrine. Epinephrine injectors are only available through a doctor's prescription so consult your local physician about the advisability of obtaining one and if it should be used on anyone other than yourself.

Keep in mind that there is a liability risk involved in giving another person a shot of something as powerful as epinephrine, so be sure you understand what you are doing and how and when to use an epinephrine injection if you elect to keep one handy and have to use it in an emergency.

What to do when stung

When a honey bee stings, the stinger stays behind due to tiny barbs (like a fishhook) on the sting shafts themselves. As the bee attempts to walk or fly away, the end of her abdomen is ripped open (Figure 13-8). She will soon die. The sting structure contains glands which secrete chemicals that include an alarm odor. Scrape or scratch the stinger from the sting site using the edge of the hive tool or finger nail, side of hive box or some convenient surface. Do this in a smooth motion as soon as possible to remove the alarm odor and reduce the amount of material injected into your body.

If other bees quickly sting the same area or buzz about the area, puff smoke on the site with the smoker. Withdraw from the open colony and rub or wash the site with water to remove the chemical odor.

The sting site will hurt for a while. Apply an over-the-counter sting relief remedy or a cool compress, ice, mud, or meat tenderizer to provide some relief. The rare instance of an allergic reaction will require that you seek medical attention promptly. Because this excessive reaction may occur at any time, taking a functioning cell phone to the apiary (especially when working alone) and having an emergency plan, just in case something happens, is good common sense.

If you receive multiple stings

Multiple stings may create more discomfort than a single sting. The amount of swelling will not necessarily be more extensive with multiple stings but the itching may be more intense. Some individuals complain of a dull headache-like or dizzy feeling following multiple stings.

Allergic reactions are not a result of the number of stings or volume of venom in the system, but a negative physiological response to the molecules in the venom. People who are not allergic receive stings without this reaction. As discussed earlier, excessive stings may result in a severe toxic reaction to the venom compounds.

Defensive bees (sometimes incorrectly referred to as aggressive) may be indicated when a beekeeper receives multiple stings. Perform manipulations and close the hive as quickly as possible without further examination under such circumstances. After the bees have had time to calm down, they may become manageable once more. If they do not, then requeening is the next best option (see 'Handling defensive colonies' in this chapter).

Colony manipulations

When opening a colony, begin with a lit smoker that readily dispenses a good volume of cool smoke. Avoid smoke with sparks or thin, hot smoke (Figures 13-15 to 13-20). Smoke should be puffed in the hive entrance to repel guard (responder) bees before lifting the cover (Figure 13-24). Continue with two or three additional puffs while proceeding into the colony at a leisurely pace (Figures 13-26, 13-27). Give the bees a minute or more to respond to the smoke.

Continue using the smoker while examining the hive. If bees are lined up between the top bars ('looking at you'), disperse them with a few light puffs of smoke. If they are gathered where you need to grasp the frames, one or two puffs directed there moves them out of your way. Avoid the nervous 'smoke, smoke, smoke' syndrome. You seek to change the behavior of bees, not conquer them.

Make all movements around bees smooth and deliberate. Avoid jarring, bumping, or scraping hive parts against one another when approaching and inspecting colonies since bees are very sensitive to vibrations. Pry hive covers off gently after freeing them of their propolis seal (Figure 13-21). Continue using the hive tool to free propolis-sealed boxes and frames before attempting removal. Keep the smoker, hive tool and other equipment within easy, close reach; avoid reaching over the open hive to retrieve these tools.

Manipulate the bees standing at the back (Figure 13-23) or the side of the hive (Figure 13-21). Stay out of the bee flight path at the front of the colonies as much as possible when walking near or examining colonies. Hold removed frames over the open hive during inspection and keep removed frames away from feet where they might be stepped upon (Figures 13-22, 13-29). Hive spacing in the apiary can help make hive manipulations more efficient and effective and reduce stings and time of hive inspections.

It is important to be relaxed and comfortable during hive inspections. Elevate the colony on a hive stand (Figure 13-29) so there is less bending. Or construct a combination tool box/seat to make inspections as convenient as possible. Leaning over while inspecting colonies quickly tires the back, and bending, lifting and then twisting with the frame/hive weight is a recipe for future back troubles. Gently smoke the bees as your return hive bodies to their original position to minimize crushing.

Box 29

SMOKER LIGHTING

Figure 13-15
Lighting pine straw that has been made into the shape of a small bird's nest.

Figure 13-16
Gently tamping down the pine straw, making sure you do not put out the fire.

Figure 13-17
Adding more straw.

Figure 13-18
Use the bellows to build the flame and smoke.

Figure 13-19
Smoker should generate smoke without use of the bellows before closing.

Figure 13-20
At rest, a smoker should issue a soft stream of cool smoke. All L. Connor photos

Hive inspection and frame handling

Hive inspections (Figures 13-22 to 13-29) are performed for different reasons depending upon the season and the needs of the colony. It is seldom necessary to inspect all the hive bodies or all the frames to evaluate or 'read' a colony. Comprehensive frame-by-frame brood inspections necessarily take longer—they are primarily done in spring and fall when colonies are smaller. Late spring/summer inspections usually only involve looking in the supers. Colonies that lose their queen, have disease or pest issues or remain weak/become too strong may involve longer inspections or more extensive manipulations.

When all boxes (or supers) are to be examined, start with the lowest one. After removing covers, pry up the top

Figure 13-22
Two people help the inspection go faster. Note the first frame is outside the box, facilitating inspection of the other frames.

box to break the propolis seal and puff smoke between the boxes. Remove the top box and place it on the upside down hive cover or an extra hive body in close proximity but outside your immediate working space (Figure 13-7). Proceed to remove all boxes until the lowest one can be examined. Cover the boxes removed with the inner cover, an extra cover, or a manipulation cloth. Examine these boxes after replacing them on lower ones, working upward.

In each hive body, start your inspection by removing a frame near the outside; the second frame adjacent to the outermost frame is often a good first frame to remove (Figure 13-26) since the outer frame is often glued tightly to the side of box, and it often tells very little about the colony (Figure 13-3).

Some beekeepers maintain nine frames in a ten-frame box which facilitates easier removal of the first frame during inspection. If robbing is not a problem (nectar is available and bees are busily working on flowers), lean the first frame you have removed against the outside of the hive, away from your feet and working area (Figures 13-22, 13-29) or use a frame holder.

If robbing occurs, temporarily place the frame in an empty box and cover it with a manipulating cloth or

Figure 13-21
Lifting the inner cover after smoking the colony and removing the telescoping cover. Note that the beekeeper is standing to the side of the colony and not blocking the returning foragers.

a damp towel. The space provided by not replacing this initial frame back into its proper space leaves extra room in the box being examined to work the remaining frames with ease and greater speed. Do not leave frames, especially those with brood, exposed to direct sunlight or cold, windy weather conditions.

To remove a frame, pry it loose on both sides from adjacent frames with the hive tool. Do not pry against the thin upper section above the rabbet of the hive body as this may break this portion of the box. Use the hive tool to pry against adjacent frames and slip the hive tool beneath the top bar of the frame and lever it upwards. Grasp the loosened frame firmly with both hands or a frame lifter and pull it gently upward, being careful not to scrape or crush bees against adjacent frames.

After the initial frame is removed and placed outside the box, pry frames into the vacated space and remove them to inspect. These additional frames can be put back into the hive body after examination. When inspecting brood, you should get a good colony 'read' and see eggs after looking at two to three frames (Box 28).

Frames should be held securely at all times so they do not slip or fall. Examination frames over the top of the opened colony. Grasp the frame top bar at the shoulders and turn the frame 180 degrees to view the opposite side.

Handle frames with both hands (Figures 13-27, 13-30). Avoid changing hand position or contorting the hands or body into awkward positions.

To see eggs, position yourself so that sunlight passes over your shoulder and illuminates the bottom of the cells (Figure 13-30). If the mantel of covering bees limits your ability to view the cells, give the frame one sharp 'air' shake so the majority of the bees fall back into the open box. If you need to closely examine a brood cell (for possibility of disease), free one hand by leaning one end of the frame over the open hive body and use a toothpick or stick to uncap a suspect cell.

Be comfortable and relaxed and the bees will be too. If pieces of burr or brace comb interfere with frame removal scrape them off and place then into a can or container. Do not leave bits of comb or wax lying about the apiary where it may attract pest animals; save this valuable wax for rendering and use in candles, cosmetics or other uses.

Scraping burr and brace comb can be an irritation to the bees as it is a jarring movement. If done, it should be left as the last task before closing and exiting the hive.

Why inspect colonies?

Have a reason for a colony inspection. Beginners need to learn about bees and gain experience manipulating colonies under different conditions. They tend to inspect more and keep colonies open longer than experienced beekeepers. On the other extreme, good bee stewardship means not avoiding colony inspection or manipulations when attention is warranted.

Reading the frames

If a beekeeper-provided hive is the bees' house, the frames are their furniture. Well drawn frames of wax cells are the most valuable asset of the bees and for the beekeeper. When you open the hive you should learn to look and read the frames. What should you be looking for?

Sealed brood — The capped stage (pupa) of the worker (Figure 13-1). The cells are distinctly six-sided and the capping should be uniform and slightly convex (domed). The capped cell region should be compact and spherical or semi-circular in pattern. Look for an amount of capped cells and completeness of the capped cell pattern as appropriate for the season.

Healthy brood — There should be no sign of brood disease which will show as unhealthy looking larvae, capped cells that are sunken, greasy looking or with irregular perforations (Chapter 22). Most cells should contain an egg or a developing bee. The brood in hygienic bee stock colonies may look irregular if mite numbers are high.

Capped honey cells — Cell cappings of honey are not distinct like brood cell cappings and are found along the top or top corners of the frame (Figure 13-31). Some frames may have little or no capped honey cells if brood occupies most of the cells (Figure 13-1). Uniform frames with mostly capped honey have little information and may be set aside to concentrate on frames of brood in your inspection.

Eggs — Cells containing eggs will look empty until you get the frame positioned so light penetrates to the bottom of the cell. Then the tiny white egg can be seen. Concentrate on cells along the outer margins of the frame or center if capped brood has hatched recently. There should be one egg per cell, more or less centered, standing on end at the bottom of the cell (Chapter 10, Figure 10-29).

Queen cups/cells — You will likely see queen cups at the lower margin of the frame. They are normal, even numerous at times. Occupied queen cells means the colony is preparing to replace its queen. You need to differentiate between emergency queen cells (started from a worker cell base) versus a swarming or supersedure cell started from a queen cup (Figure 13-29).

Condition of the cells — Are there high numbers of the larger, drone-sized cells or is the frame mainly worker cells? Poor frames with high numbers of drone cells need to be moved from the center to the sides of the brood boxes. Excess drone brood may be removed from the colony after all brood has emerged (Figure 13-29).

Condition of frame — Is the frame a good one that you should keep or one with old dark comb that needs to be replaced with new foundation? Are the 'ears' okay and the frame sturdy and intact? If repairs are needed, work the frame to the outside edge of the hive and mark for future attention.

Box 30

HIVE INSPECTION

Figure 13-23
Put a gentle puff of cool smoke into each hive you will work in the next few minutes.

Figure 13-24
As the cover is removed, use a circle of smoke over the top of the frames to maximize the smoke's effect.

Figure 13-25
Add more straw as you work more colonies.

Figure 13-26
Removing frame from #2 position.

Figure 13-27
Holding frame securely, rotate finger position to view opposite side, viewing from an angle to locate the queen.

Figure 13-28
Once the hive is inspected, carefully return the inner and outer covers. Minimize crushing bees. Photos L. Connor

Figure 13-29
Queen cups and drone cells on an uneven frame.

Change from last time — Is the colony stronger or weaker than the last visit? Is it growing in accord with the season or properly contracting with poorer forage conditions and the approaching winter season? This will take practice to read; reading should be done relative to other colonies for that particular season and location.

Hive maintenance — Do the hive bodies, covers, or bottom board need attention? Are feeders full of dead bees? Are there frames in need of repair? Is there need to remove burr/brace comb interfering with your frame manipulation or blocking hive ventilation?

Each colony should have a thorough spring and fall inspection (Chapters 14 and 15 for further details on fall and spring inspections). Colonies are smaller at this time and inspections can be made more quickly and efficiently. Examine brood combs for disease symptoms, poorly drawn combs, or broken frames. Remove and replace damaged bottom boards, lids, feeders or hive boxes,

In the fall, make sure every colony has adequate winter stores and the cluster is positioned correctly for the winter. Provision for venting of excess moisture should be made and any medications or pest control should be completed prior to the onset of clustering temperatures. Spring colonies should be checked to be sure that colony expansion is proceeding, that queen cells are not being reared in preparation for swarming and, as the colony becomes larger, supers are added in anticipation of the nectar flow. Other than the initial inspection, each of these monitoring inspections do not require an extensive examination of the brood nest.

If you remove a frame of brood, it should be checked for queen presence, the brood pattern and absence of disease. Check for swarm cells by checking the bottom of the frames. If the colony needs supers, add them rapidly and without extensive manipulation. Once supers are in place,

Figure 13-30
Reading the frame. Rotate so the sun shines into the cells. Note the outside frame propped against the hive.

further brood inspections are not usually performed until the honey is removed.

Manipulations require more time when you encounter specific issues. Colonies may need to be fed, medicated, broken frames removed or repaired, additional supers added, full honey supers removed or any number of actions performed. Some of this is seasonal, related to colony conditions and philosophy of the beekeeper. Colonies do not take constant care but attention to detail improves both personal enjoyment and potential rewards.

Different management approaches yield different results. Some beekeepers manage fewer colonies but inspect them more often. Others keep more colonies but look after them less frequently, letting the bees 'do their own thing.'

Beginner beekeepers spend more time making hive inspections so they can learn and understand colony manipulations. It takes time, experience and patience to become more proficient.

In some seasons, bees swarm several times and beekeepers will need to focus on swarm control. Beekeepers experiencing heavy winter losses may need to provide more fall attention than a neighboring beekeeper that has average losses. Greater attention is needed to maximize bee populations for pollination and for honey production.

The good news is that bee colonies do not require daily or weekly care. There are even whole months when no attention is needed. However, if there is an interest in doing more, colony stewardship is likely to be rewarded with more, purposeful manipulation. There is no 'one size fits all' when it comes to beekeeping or in bee colony care.

Handling challenging colonies

The second season with bees is the most difficult for many beekeepers because more may happen. Colonies may not survive the first winter and the beekeeper has to start all over. Determining why they died is often difficult and the cost of more bees was not anticipated. Other colonies survive and become larger quickly the second spring and may be harder to manage due to the beekeeper's inexperience. They grow large quickly, rear queens and then swarm. The bees may sting a lot more. It won't always be this difficult—perseverance is essential.

Some bees are more defensive (Figure 13-32), and there are conditions when colony examinations and manipulations are more difficult. Certain weather conditions or seasonal forage conditions may add to the defensive behavior of the bees.

Other challenges include queenlessness, a sudden halt to a honey flow and the lack of foraging resources, a rapid change in the weather, or a large population of adults requiring food. Robbing may occur when comb is left exposed (Figure 13-34), or when vandals tip colonies from their stands (Figure 13-33).

Figure 13-31
Frame of brood, sealed, with a few bee bread (pollen) cells at left. Honey filled cells are at top corners. Comb cells hanging from bottom bar are mainly drone cells with one queen cup, center left.

Box 31

INSPECTION TIPS

Open and examine bee colonies on warm, dry, windless, sunny days between 10 a.m. and 4 p.m. Avoid cold, windy, rainy days when foragers are likely to be in the hive.

Examine bees during nectar flow or feed to simulate flow if you need to inspect during poor forage conditions.

Colonies are easier to examine when they have a smaller population. Inspect colonies more thoroughly in spring or fall. Manipulate only as necessary during the summer and winter seasons.

Always wear a bee veil. Use bee-tight, smooth-textured, protective clothing or coveralls, and learn to use gloves sparingly.

If a bee gets inside, crush her quickly. Exit the apiary before removing your veil or clothing to release bees that get inside. NEVER REMOVE YOUR VEIL WITHIN THE APIARY.

Always have a lit smoker ready to dispense cool smoke. Use smoke before opening a colony and continue use during inspection of the hive. Keep your smoker and hive tool conveniently close and avoid unnecessary movements around an open colony.

Keep a colony open only as long as necessary. Bees are usually tolerant of moderate beekeeper manipulations of five to ten minutes. Avoid re-entering colonies for a few days after an inspection.

Make all body and hand movements smooth and deliberate. Avoid jerky or rapid moves. Avoid bumping or jarring the hive. Work from the side or back of hives, out of the path of bee flight.

Start inspection by careful removal of the frame near the side (not middle), being careful not to roll or crush bees as the frame is removed from the box. Leave initial frame outside for remainder of inspection to permit easier removal of additional frames.

Hold frames securely over the top of the open hive, rotating 180° with a minimum amount of hand position changes to view the opposite side. Work from lowest hive bodies upward. Be comfortable in back and body positions.

Combs with exposed honey may incite robbing and brood frames left exposed may result in chilled brood. Cover hive bodies and supers not being examined. Work efficiently, but not hastily.

Figure 13-32
An Africanized bee colony may be difficult to manage.

Vandals may throw stones or disturb colonies in other ways, leading to more defensive colonies.

If a normally gentle colony becomes noisy, overly excited or it persists in stinging, close it as quickly as possible. Do not examine other colonies in the apiary. Try examining the colony in a few days. If it remains defensive, consider replacing the queen.

When a beekeeper must manipulate defensive colonies, such as to replace its queen, try moving the hive boxes temporarily to a new location several yards in front of the old location. Place an empty hive or move a weak hive to the vacated location. As the foragers leave the defensive colony to forage, they will return to the old location. Wait one to two hours or a day before you attempt to inspect the colony. Inspect quickly, having all the tools and a spare queen ready before you open the hive. Smoke the hive before opening the hive and wait a minute or more before opening. This allows the smoke to stimulate worker engorgement of honey.

Some beekeepers manipulate gentle colonies more than defensive ones, and colonies left alone may out-produce manipulated ones. Good colony stewardship means

Figure 13-33
Vandalized apiary. Exposed or overturned colonies are often defensive.

assisting all colonies where needed but also leaving colonies alone to 'do their own thing.' Colonies that are more defensive, that constantly raise queen cells, are consistently weak or otherwise require more beekeeper management time can be a real challenge and a valuable learning experience.

Robbing

Robbing is a specialized form of foraging where the adult bees visit another colony and steal honey from it—a 'fast track' to securing honey reserves. Robbing usually occurs during poor foraging conditions since bees prefer to visit flowers. Beekeepers unknowingly promote robbing by opening and inspecting colonies when forage conditions are poor or by leaving unattended comb in the apiary. Smoke use during inspection disrupts normal guarding behavior and inspection creates additional openings into the honey reserves of a colony. Robbing may stimulate colonies to become very defensive and hard to manage. Robbing has also been shown to increase the spread of disease (Figure 13-34).

Robbing behavior is not always easy to diagnose in its initial stages. Bees flying in a zigzag pattern and hovering about the entry area, bees seeking to find openings into the colony between boxes, under the covers, at holes or cracks and an excess of flight without landing at the colony are some clues to help detect robbing. Robbing is sometimes confused with orientation flights of new foragers learning their hive location, or with heavy drone mating flight.

Unchecked, robbers can remove all the honey stores and the colony under attack dies of heat stress due to elevated temperatures created within the colony being robbed.

Figure 13-34
Robbing after working hives. A. Heck

There are several options to handle robbing—the most successful are those measures that prevent robbing from starting. Since it is believed that the beekeeper facilitates robbing by opening colonies and breaking down their guarding defense, the beekeeper should seek to avoid opening colonies or removing honey when robbing is most likely to occur. That may not always be obvious but we believe robbing is most common in later summer and into the fall when foraging resources are inadequate.

To protect against robbing, keep equipment in good condition, free from holes in the hive bodies, and tops and bottom boards properly positioned and in good repair. For small colonies, such as nuclei, reduce the colony entrance. If still warm and entrance reducers produce congestion, consider use of a robbing screen (Figure 13-35).

A robbing screen can be made at home. The screen is placed before the entry area, extending upward several inches. The opening at the top should be an inch or two deep between the screen and the hive. Resident bees crawl up and out to fly over the screen. Such simple devices work because robbing honey bees hover in front of a hive under attack, attracted to expelling hive odors, and then seek to dart inside quickly. They get isolated outside the screen while bees exiting from inside come out their entrance and walk or fly upward over the top of the screen and then reenter the same way. Small colonies benefit most from entrance modifications.

Figure 13-35
A robbing screen placed at the colony's entrance. Exiting bees walk up to exit at top of screen; robbing bees unsuccessfully seek to fly directly to the entrance.

If you install the screen in the morning, the resident bees learn within hours to crawl up over the screen to get out and back in. House-cleaning bees have no difficulty carrying bodies of dead bees and other debris over the screen. The screens can be nailed to the hive front with two-headed nails to permit easy removal or held in place with hook and eye latches.

Another possible robbing deterrent is construction of a larger robbing barrier. Make an open-top four-sided screen cage large enough to enclose the colony (4' x 4' x 6' or larger), leaving enough space to enclose yourself and room to permit colony inspection. Conduct colony manipulations inside the screen enclosure. Bees from the opened colony will readily exit through the open top but not learn how to reenter. Returning foragers and robber bees will remain outside the cage. Before removing the screen cage, reduce the colony entrance after finishing the colony examination. This will help the guard bees re-establish order at the hive entrance.

Feeding bees

Colonies need adequate food reserves all year long. In winter, they need enough stored honey (or sugar) or they may starve. They need enough food to get through spring dwindling, a late spring, or an early fall dearth. Bees also need food reserves to rear brood for spring expansion and to rear fall bees for overwintering.

During much of the active season, bees can locate some forage. Ten to 15 pounds (five to seven kg), two to three deep frames, usually provides sufficient food to last them a few days until they can find additional forage. Colonies in areas with extreme weather (high winds, storms or cold weather) require larger emergency food reserves.

Figure 13-36
Colony with homemade in-hive feeder— bees need a ladder or rough internal surface to crawl into the lower part of the feeder without drowning.

When forage is limited, colonies may be more defensive because there are more older-aged guard bees at the entrance. Feeding colonies makes inspections easier at such locations and/or under such circumstances. Supplemental feeding increases food reserves for the winter and helps colonies during a dearth period. Besides avoiding starvation, other reasons to feed bee colonies include:

- stimulating brood-rearing
- feeding medication
- obtaining a higher ratio of pollen foragers
- providing food for a newly captured swarm or divide
- feeding newly installed package or nucleus colony
- making queen rearing easier and obtain better virgins
- stimulating a colony to rear more drones for mating
- improved drawing of foundation frames into worker comb

Not all beekeepers feed their colonies. Yet feeding is not a negative, a failure of the beekeeper or the bees. Leaving

Figure 13-37
Commercial in-hive feeder features two mesh cylinders that the bees use to reach the syrup, reducing bee loss.

abundant food reserves is good stewardship and it can make the difference between colony survival or death. Not all colonies need to be fed nor is feeding necessary every season. Because feeding is labor intensive and tedious, find and use methods that allow you to replenish the supplemental feed without actually going into the colony for minimal disturbance and fewer stings.

There are a number of ways to feed a colony of bees. Usually bees are fed sugar syrup (Figures 13-36 to 13-38) but honey can be fed if available from a disease free colony. Protein too may be fed in the form of a pollen substitute or supplement. Supplements can be "peppered" with natural pollen but that comes with the potential of disease. Some beekeepers add stimulants, vitamin mixtures, amino acids or other additions.

Feeding sugar

Bees utilize virtually any sugar fed to them, but sucrose is the preferred type. They perceive a wide range of sugars as sweet. In their search for cheap bee feed, beekeepers may obtain and feed sugars containing additives and contaminants that may or may not be acceptable. Sugars from dairy products, like lactose and galactose, are toxic to bees. Sugars containing starch (powdered sugar for example) may compact in the bees digestive tract and disrupt digestion.

Beekeepers feed cane or beet sugar. Some beekeepers avoid beet sugar since much of it comes from genetically modified sugar beets. Feeding the simple sugars fructose and glucose offer no advantage to bee digestion even

Figure 13-38
Drops of sugar syrup from inverting the can feeders over the frames stimulates feeding by bees.

though they are already reduced chemically. Bees do not benefit from low calorie sugar substitutes which do not taste sweet to them. Never feed brown sugar, maple syrup, molasses or sorghum.

During confinement periods and overwintering, use `pure' sugar without contaminants. Some beekeepers use high fructose corn syrup (HFCS) but there is danger of honey adulteration with HFCS if bees store it rather than use it directly. Also, HFCS that is improperly stored or over-heated may contain HMF (Hydroxymethylfurfural), a toxic break-down product of fructose. (HMF levels are used as a guide to the length of storage and the amount of heating of processed honey; some countries set an HMF limit for imported honey.)

Sugar may be fed granulated, as a solid cake (Figure 13-39) or as a syrup mixed with water (Figure 13-38). Except for bees confined during winter, beekeepers normally mix water with granulated/dry sugar to form a sugar syrup or purchase a liquid syrup such as HFCS. Feeding dry sugar, except during winter confinement, is not recommended as much of it is wasted by the bees. Both granulated sugar and a solid candy cake require that the bees have water to utilize the sugar—both may serve as emergency feed in late winter and are common methods of feeding bees in wet tropics and the Pacific Northwest. Feeding a liquid during winter or rainy season confinement may add too much additional moisture into the bee colony.

Sugar syrup may be fed thick (concentrated) or dilute. A more concentrated 2:1 syrup (2 parts sugar to 1 part water, or 3:2) is fed in the fall so the bees quickly store it for winter stores. A more dilute 1:1 syrup (equal parts sugar to water either by volume or weight) or very dilute 1:2 syrup are fed to stimulate the bees to rear more brood.

Figure 13-39
A candy board is a special piece of equipment that allows the beekeeper to pour sugar fondant into the device so it hardens. Then it is inverted and put over the colony. This photo was taken in early November, and the bees had already consumed about half the sugar. L. Connor

Some suggest addition of cream of tartar (to assist sugar conversion), a teaspoon of vinegar (to avoid mold) or feeding stimulant such as Honey-B Healthy®. All are of questionable value. Cream of tartar promotes HMF and salt may produce a toxic syrup.

There are an extensive array of feeder types available to assist in feeding sugar syrup. Beekeepers may use a metal can with a removable lid (empty coffee can), a glass jar (empty peanut butter or mason jar or larger empty condiment jar from a restaurant), a plastic pail or an airtight plastic bag. The feeder is prepared by punching the point of a six-penny nail through the lid of the container, filling with sugar syrup and then inverting the feeder over the top bars or inner cover of the colony (Figures 13-38, 14-4). Bees access the syrup by sticking their proboscis into the holes and withdrawing the liquid.

There are many syrup feeders: wood or plastic hive-top (Miller) feeders, wooden/plastic in-hive (division board) feeders (Figures 13-36, 13-37) that replace frames within the boxes, or jar entrance feeders designed to sit outside the colony entrance. The latter are often sold in introductory kits. All have their adherents. Outside top pail/jar feeders are used by commercial beekeepers (Chapter 14, Figure 14-5).

A can, jar or plastic bag can be placed directly on the top bars of frames and enclosed in an empty hive body. Keep the syrup close to the bees, so it can be easily replenished without going into the colony itself. Be careful not to spill syrup or leave containers open. Check syrup feeders to be sure they are not leaking. When not in use feeders need be cleaned and stored.

A colony must be secure at the top and level during syrup feeding. Feeders can be positioned directly on top bars, provided bees can access the holes in the lid. When adding a new feeder, invert the syrup container directly over the top of the colony. The initial drips (Figure 13-38), until the vacuum forms, stimulate the bees to take syrup from the feeder. Plastic bags ooze syrup from slits made after placement on top of the frames in the colony.

Open, feed-lot style feeding of sugar syrup in large open containers is not recommended, as it leads to robbing and spreads disease. Open feeding may be used with dry protein feeds (Figure 13-42, 13-43). Water is commonly provided in dry Western states in open containers.

During winter, feed dry sugar or a solid sugar candy using a candy board (Figure 13-39) or a rim feeder. To make a sugar cake, dissolve 15 pounds of sugar into 3 pounds of glucose (white sugar syrup or light corn syrup) and 4 cups of water (small scale: 4 lb. sugar, 1 cup water, 1 cup light corn syrup) by stirring and boiling the mixture until the temperature of the syrup is at 242° F. Let it cool to 180° F and beat thick. Pour into a candy board mold or aluminum pie plates and allow to harden. Place in a rim board directly on top of the upper brood box (or use an empty super) to accommodate the solid sugar cake. Drivert® or fondant sugar may be substituted as a sugar source; the latter is used to make queen cage candy.

Feeding honey

Beekeepers often transfer frames of disease-free honey from stronger to weaker hives as their preferred method of feeding. Honey in the comb is readily accepted by a colony that did not produce it. Single frames or entire supers may be fed as needed. The honey may be placed in existing boxes or added as a super.

In the fall, feed surplus honey frames by slashing the cappings of honey-filled frames and placing them below the brood. Since this requires heavy lifting most beekeepers place the frames above the inner cover with a hole open. The bees clean the 'mess' and organize the honey for their fall nest. Remove the emptied frames before winter.

Store 'extra' capped frames of honey in a freezer for use as emergency food. If lacking such space, store honey-filled frames in a bee- and pest-tight manner. Wax moth, ants, cockroaches, small hive beetles, mice or other scavengers may invade stored honey-filled frames when stored improperly.

DO NOT feed honey if there is any danger of spreading American foulbrood and other diseases. Do not buy honey to feed to your bees, but sometimes beekeepers have non-salable or honey crystallized in the comb that is

Figure 13-40
Bees feeding on supplemental protein patty placed on top bars of upper brood box. L.Connor

Figure 13-41
Late winter feeding of protein patty (top) and sugar candy (white at bottom) of five-frame overwintered nucleus colony.

best utilized as bee feed. Beekeepers may let their bees rob honey from older combs and burr and brace comb, risking the spread of disease.

Feeding protein

Beekeepers feed **pollen supplement** with bee-collected pollen added to a protein mix. A **pollen substitute**, derived from soybeans and other protein sources, is fed without added pollen. A generous amount of sugar must be added to the mix for bees to feed on the material.

Figure 13-42
Feeding dry protein (in large bowls) under a shelter. L. Connor

Tested, commercial, ready-to-use protein products are available to feed bees (Figures 13-40, 13-41). Try it on an experimental basis. Some may contain modified plant materials in their ingredients.

If feeding a pollen supplement, the source of the pollen should be known. To avoid disease, do not purchase pollen unless irradiated. Beekeepers should instead buy a pollen trap (Figure 13-44) and collect pollen directly from their own disease-free colonies to feed their bees. Trapped pollen is easily preserved in a freezer or air-dried and mixed with sugar until needed.

As with feeding sugar (or honey), feeding protein has been demonstrated to be beneficial to colonies. Feeding protein with sugar (Figure 13-41) may not necessarily be economical. Such feeding is time consuming and labor intensive. Protein feeding can assist colonies rearing queens or to stimulate rearing of drones for mating purposes. Protein feeding stimulates colonies early in the season before natural pollens become reliably available.

Figure 13-43
PVC dry protein feeders; Protein mix needs to remain dry. Foraging bees pack the dry protein like pollen.

Figure 13-44
Pollen trap placed at front of hive. Betterbee

key terms

alarm pheromone	brood nest	frame holder	hydroxymethylfurfural (HMF)
allergic reaction	candy board (sugar candy)	feeding/feeders	large local reaction
anaphylaxis	defensive bees	fondant	manipulation cloth
bee gloves	desensitization	high fructose corn syrup (HFCS)	marked queen
bee veil	division board feeder	hive tool	Miller feeder
Benadryl	Drivert sugar	Honey-B-Healthy	nectar flow
Boardman feeder	Epipen		normal sting reaction

pollen substitute/supplement	'reading' a colony	sealed (capped) brood	spring dwindling
pollen trap	robbing	smoker	toxic reaction
queen excluder	robbing screen	soldier (responder) bees	wheal

discussion questions

Describe the appearance of the average beekeeper properly prepared to open and inspect a bee colony. What do you feel comfortable wearing when you inspect a bee colony? What are the functions of standard veil, smoker, hive tool (or frame lifter)? Describe how these standard tools are used in colony inspections.

What are the best conditions for colony inspections? How do you inspect a colony? How long should it take?

Describe how a beekeeper whose philosophy is intensive management differs from another with a more 'leave them alone' attitude as regards the number of inspections and reasons for manipulations.

What are the basic minimum number of inspections that should be performed and when are they best conducted? Why would more inspection and manipulation necessarily be better or worse for the bees? For the beekeeper?

How would you determine you have an overly defensive colony? What would you do about it? What are some additional conditions that might make inspections difficult?

What should you as a beekeeper know about bee stings? Describe how you might differentiate between a normal or allergic (or toxic) sting reaction? What is your emergency plan for dealing with an allergic sting reaction?

Describe how a basic manipulation like feeding can be accomplished with less chance of being stung. What should be fed? How can bees be fed carbohydrate, protein or water if they are not adequate in the environment?

When and under what conditions would you supplement colony stores by feeding of sugar? Or feeding of protein? What is your 'best' method of feeding?

How can robbing be avoided when feeding bees? Are defensive bee colonies likely to be robbed?

exercises

Determine the costs of outfitting the beekeeper to inspect a colony and avoid stings. Equip one with the best quality, top-of-the-line personal protective equipment and tools. Equip a second as cheaply as possible. List your sources of equipment and prices. At the next beekeepers meeting in an apiary, evaluate the equipment you see and categorize the costs.

Demonstrate to an interested family member, friend, fellow student, or another beekeeper how to do a standard colony inspection that includes brood/food assessment. If weather does not permit actual working with live colonies, do your demonstration with empty equipment.

Investigate feeding of bees. Buy or make several different feeders and compare how effective and efficient they are related to their cost/time to make and use and measure how rapidly the bees use the sugar. Plan to stimulate and add fall food to a colony. Try feeding a pollen supplement or substitute. Under what conditions would feeding be worth your time and expense? Survey beekeepers at a future bee meeting how they feed their bees, handle robbing or deal with defensive colonies. Divide colonies into two groups feeding one group the material and the other an equivalent amount of sugar without the protein to confirm that it provides the difference sought. Caution is advised in areas where small hive beetles are present.

Develop your own top 10 list such as '10 tips to avoid being stung,' or '10 tips to fame and fortune as a beekeeper.'

references

Blackiston, H. 2020. Beekeeping for Dummies, 5th Edition. For Dummies, Hoboken, NJ

Caron, D.M. 2001. Africanized Honey Bees in the Americas. A. I. Root Co, Medina, OH

Connor, L.J. 2012. Bee-sentials: A Field Guide. Wicwas Press, Kalamazoo, MI

Delaplane, K. 2007. First Lessons in Beekeeping. Dadant and Sons, Inc. Hamilton, IL

Flottum, K. 2020. The Backyard Beekeeper, 4th Edition. Quarry Books, Beverly, MA

Kearney, H. 2019. Queen Spotting: Meet the Remarkable Queen Bee. Storey Publishing, North Adams, MA

https://www.mayoclinic.org/diseases-conditions/bee-stings/symptoms-causes/syc-20353869

https://www.webmd.com/allergies/insect-stings

https://www.healthline.com/health/allergies/bee-sting-anaphylaxis#1

Chapter 14
Fall & winter

Figure 14-1
Bees in cluster in December. L. Connor

In the beehive

Taking care of bee colonies in the fall ensures successful overwintering and strong, productive bee colonies next spring. The colonies' new year begins in middle summer while the beekeeper is ending one season and beginning the next. Fall usually is a shutting down as resources become scare but for some, fall can mean surplus honey production and a second swarm season.

Climate change, warmer fall seasons, and periods without flowering plants present a challenge of a longer brood rearing and reduced winter preparation time. Highly fluctuating winter temperatures are hazardous for successful overwintering.

Timing is critical for successful beekeeping. Keeping accurate records of each season helps time beekeeping activities properly, sharpen your observations and assist in recognizing the needs of your colonies. One season or year can differ considerably from the next, so you need to be prepared—no two seasons are ever alike. Monitor temperature patterns and moisture levels, plant growth and hive populations. By monitoring, beekeepers better anticipate what will or could happen, not merely reacting after the fact.

Fall
August—September—October

Most beekeepers rely on fall nectar sources to provide honey stores to overwinter colonies. In areas where late-summer and fall-blooming plants like goldenrod produce surplus nectar, beekeepers often extract such honey. This may start in August and end after the last flowers finish blooming or are killed by freezing nighttime temperatures. Because it is critical that enough fall honey be left for the bees to overwinter, beekeepers harvesting the fall crop either need to move their colonies to a milder climate or heavily feed sugar syrup to supplement colonies and ensure colony winter survival.

Goldenrod yields a heavy, strongly-flavored honey which may crystallize rapidly. It is usually mixed with aster honey, which blooms after most goldenrods finish flowering. It may be highly odorous when ripening and some beekeepers worry they have a spoilage problem, but this odor quickly fades. Goldenrod honey is not considered ideal for bees during long confinement, because of possible dysentery problems. Other fall sources for potential late harvest include *Bidens* spp. (Spanish needle), fireweed and cultivated crops like cotton and lima beans.

Fall management

For beekeepers, fall management traditionally begins around Labor Day (first Monday of September) and finishes by Halloween. Mite sampling, control and requeening activities may start in mid-August. Requeening is most successful when done during a nectar flow or immediately following a honey harvest.

The **major fall beekeeping objective** is to ensure that colonies have **adequate overwintering food stores**, a **vigorous queen** and are **healthy**. To meet these objectives, major activities of fall management include:

- preparing colonies to overwinter
- sampling varroa mite level and treating if too high
- making sure colonies have young, productive queens
- checking for diseases and treating if needed
- ensuring colonies are large enough to overwinter
- providing protection from winter weather
- protecting colonies from pests like mice
- ensuring venting of moisture from colonies

Fall inspection

Fall management begins once surplus honey is harvested. September is the 'normal' month to perform fall management in northern U.S. states. Late nectar flows or a delay in harvesting surplus honey leaves less time to properly prepare colonies for winter.

Figure 14-2

Inspecting a colony in the fall can help confirm a central, compact brood pattern located primarily in the lower brood box with pollen and honey stores to the side and above the brood sphere. The top box should be filled primarily with capped honey stores.

Winter preparation is delayed in more southern areas until October or even December in the far south. There, winter preparations are less critical to colony survival because colonies will not be confined as long and isolated from fresh floral resources.

Plan to give each colony **two standard inspections**. In northern states, the first inspection (Labor Day) checks for and corrects problems. A second, early-October inspection should confirm that colonies are fully prepared for winter and mites remain under control. Hive inspection should check for:

- amount and position of honey stores
- extent and pattern of brood area
- size of adult population
- brood and adult bee health
- condition of the beeswax combs
- condition of hive equipment

Bee colonies instinctively prepare for winter by moving honey above and to the sides of the brood sphere (Figures 14-2, 14-16). In the early September

inspection, the beekeeper may correct problems with inadequate honey stores by adding frames of honey. In seasons with a poor nectar yield because the fall bloom was not adequate, colonies need to be fed sugar syrup to supplement their honey stores.

Pay attention to colonies with a low adult population — perhaps a recently captured swarm or a divide made late in the season. Also monitor those colonies with large adult populations still continuing to raise large amounts of brood (certain genetic strains). Add bees and brood to weaker units, centralize the brood area in the lowest brood box, and feed thick 2:1 sugar syrup to help compact and reduce the size of the brood-rearing sphere to improve overwintering success, as detailed below.

The ideal brood and food arrangement for individual frames should resemble Figure 14-2, and the colony Figure 14-16. The brood pattern should be a shrinking sphere positioned primarily in the lower box — honey stores should be to the sides and above this sphere. Do not disrupt or modify this arrangement, other than

Figure 14-3
As drone and worker brood emerges, this colony is filling brood cells with pollen and/or honey. This frame was in the upper hive body, and this behavior, called backfilling, reflects the fall instinct to move the brood nest to the lower box. L. Connor

moving it downward into the lower box during the fall inspection, especially late in the season.

During the fall inspection, remove frames with extensive areas of drone cells to the edge of the brood sphere, and remove poorly drawn or incompletely drawn frames, as well as any frames in need of repair. Your objective is to allow the bees to expand in the spring on the best drawn comb containing worker cells. Move poor frames containing brood toward the outer walls of the lower hive body to cull (remove) next spring.

At the first inspection, colonies may not be progressing toward the ideal configuration (Figure 14-16, left). Colonies started during the season (swarm captures, cutout hives, divides and packages) often require careful attention. When late spring development, summer drought or excessively rainy conditions have impacted colony growth, the colony may require more fall management. While the bees do the actual work, beekeepers must assist the bees by improving overwintering conditions.

Fall food stores and feeding

A reliable and accurate way to estimate honey stores is to inspect the colony in the fall and estimate the amount of honey on each frame. Weigh a few representative frames to establish an average weight per frame, then count the number of honey frames and do the math. This will give you an estimate of total available stores.

Experienced beekeepers estimate the amount of honey stores by lifting the back of the hive. Tests have shown that individuals tend to overestimate static weight, but colonies with too few stores should be obvious. Counting full and nearly full frames of honey is fast and often more accurate. Practice will help improve your honey store assessment abilities.

Colonies low on honey stores need to be fed in the fall. **Fall feeding** is also useful to compact the brood sphere in the lowest hive body. There are many methods available to feed sugar and many types of feeding equipment to do the job (Review 'Feeding bees' in Chapter 13).

The key to having bees store syrup in the fall is to mix a heavy syrup (two parts sugar to one part water by volume or weight) and to put it in feeders over the brood area where the bees will quickly locate it and fill food storage combs. Generally, placing the syrup feeder directly on top of the brood chamber—within inches of the brood—results in the fastest uptake and storage (Figure 14-4).

It is not necessary to buy expensive feeders to feed sugar syrup to bees. Adopt materials you have at hand—jars or cans with removable lids work well. Most beekeepers feed sugar syrup in a removable-lid can/pail, such as a new empty paint can, used coffee can, or a large glass jar.

Punch a dozen or so holes in the lid using the point of a common six-penny nail. Invert these containers directly on top of the frames of the brood area so the holes are accessible to the bees (Figures 14-4, 14-5). A vacuum is created when the container is inverted, allowing the bees to put their proboscis into the holes to suck out the syrup.

Some beekeepers prefer to feed syrup in a container that fits on top of the hive through the hive cover (Figure 14-5). This is popular with migratory beekeepers who frequently use a single top cover, without an inner cover. It is relatively easy to remove an empty syrup container and replace it with a full one. When not feeding, the feeding cap is left in the cover. Other commercial beekeepers prefer to use an in-hive feeder (see examples Chapter 13, Figures 13-36, 13-37) that replaces one or two frames at the edge of the standard hive body. The disadvantage of this method of feeding is that the colony must be opened to refill the feeder, usually from a large syrup tank housed on the beekeeper's vehicle.

Once started, continue fall syrup feeding as long as the bees take it—it is difficult to feed bees too much syrup. Some beekeepers believe combs of stored sugar syrup are better overwintering stores than honey from fall flower sources such as goldenrod or aster. One advantage to feeding bees and having them store sugar syrup in the fall is that they backfill cells from which brood emerged, helping compact the brood area (Figure 14-3). Thus the stores go into the best position to serve as a winter food source— immediately to the sides and above the active brood area.

Feed honey only if the source colony is free of American foulbrood (AFB) disease. Following extraction, feed bees wet frames or frames with crystallized honey. Open capped cells with a hive tool or cappings scratcher and place the frames in a hive body below the brood area—this stimulates the bees to move the honey above and beside the brood nest.

Alternately, slashed frames can be placed in a box on top of the colony, over the inner cover with the oval opening unrestricted. Bees will clean up the honey, rearranging it above and to the sides of the brood cluster where it will be needed during the winter. If some colonies have more honey stores than they need for winter, remove frames (or entire supers) from the honey-strong colonies, and add the frames directly to those weaker colonies after brushing frames free of clinging adult bees.

Liquid honey from disease-free bees can be made into a syrup and fed to a bee colony. Dilute it 1:1 with hot water and feed it like you would a sugar syrup. Open feeding of honey from barrels or drums is not recommended.

Northern bee colonies have a longer period of cold weather and require more winter honey reserves than colonies farther south. Colonies in the Gulf Coast states may survive with 30 or fewer lbs (14 kg) of honey reserves, and can be fed more easily during the nonproductive months. Colonies in more northerly areas need up to 90 lbs (40 kg) of honey reserves. Intermediate area colonies will survive, generally, with 60 lbs (27 kg). Honey reserves need to be positioned above the brood sphere so they remain accessible to the bee cluster over the entire winter period.

Decrease winter losses by managing the amount of honey stores bees have available for winter. Colonies

Figure 14-4
Three feed cans of thick syrup are placed directly on the hive body. Strong colonies take down the syrup and store it. Feeding dilute syrup may stimulate brood rearing and defeat the purpose of fall feeding–survival!

that die from insufficient honey stores do so as a result of a failure of adequate fall beekeeper stewardship. Failure to estimate how much stored food each colony has and failure to provide adequate stores can result in needlessly dead colonies. Evaluate and feed early enough so the bees can organize their nest correctly.

Generally it is not advisable to feed protein to bees in the fall unless done early. Feeding protein may lead to more brood at the expense of stored honey. Since fat fall bees with greater fat body content are a key to successful overwintering, colonies where pollen sources are not available in July or August (in the north), or September-October (in the south) might benefit from additional protein feeding. A more common alternative is to heavily feed supplemental protein in the spring to rear new bees to replace the aging winter population.

No one system is best to supplement colonies low on winter stores—beekeepers should use one that is convenient for their situation and budget.

Fall brood & adult population

Guessing the size of the colony population is a skill that requires practice and refinement. How many bees are needed to overwinter successfully? Studies demonstrate that colonies with 30,000 bees (roughly 10 lbs or 4.5 kg) are average-sized in the fall. In the spring, a colony may have half that population, and even fewer if the colony is mite-infested or diseased.

If a colony is deficient in adult bees or brood in late summer or early fall, boosting the hive population is good management. Stimulating the queen to lay more eggs is one option. The brood pattern of the colony will reflect the queen's performance. Stimulating fall colonies is not always successful as colonies have their own 'plan' of brood area compaction and honey storage.

In a second fall inspection, check to see if the brood pattern is compact and spherically shaped in the lower portion of the hive (Figure 14-16, left). The area with brood should have few open cells and queen egg laying should be within a reduced area, especially by October or November. As the bees reduce their brood area, the colony may initially have a spotty brood pattern as the bees may backfill empty cells in the brood area with pollen and/or nectar (Figure 14-3). Remember, bees selected for hygienic behavior also may have spotty brood patterns, especially in the fall when mite numbers are elevated and more cells are being uncapped to remove mite-infested pupae.

If uncertain about the size or compactness of the brood pattern, mark the colony and examine it a week or two later to see if it is more regular. If the bees are fed a heavy sugar syrup between inspections, empty cells may contain ripening syrup so the cells of capped brood will continue to appear irregular. Generally, there should be few occupied drone brood cells in the fall.

In a large colony, beekeepers may wish to force bees to reduce their brood pattern by using a queen excluder to confine the queen to the lower hive body. It is labor-intensive management. Place empty frames and those with open brood below the queen excluder with the queen. Capped brood can be left above the excluder in the center of the hive body. As the cells empty, the bees should store honey and bee bread in these upper combs. Extensive manipulations such as this should only be performed early in the fall.

Remove the queen excluder before winter, otherwise workers moving the winter cluster upward might isolate their queen below the excluder. Isolated queens quickly freeze.

Feeding a bee colony a heavy sugar syrup forces the bees to compact their brood area. It is easier fall management than manipulating the colony with a queen excluder. New colonies, those started from packages or colonies of Italian stock will more likely

Figure 14-5
Plastic jugs containing sugar syrup are easily put on, checked and replaced. Many commercial beekeepers feed one or more gallons of sugar syrup in the fall, the amount depending upon colony need.

have larger, less compact fall brood patterns, especially during the initial fall inspection.

Regulating bee population

It is challenging to accurately estimate the adequacy of the adult population. A desirable fall colony should form the initial cluster on five to six of the frames of a hive body. This would be approximately 25,000 to 30,000 bees, a reasonable size to expect for successful overwintering.

There are few options other than feeding or combining to bolster weak colonies in the fall. Beekeepers should keep records and decide after a season or two of experience how many bees (and how much brood) are needed to successfully overwinter in a location.

Some believe that good management means taking potential winter losses in the fall. If there is a poor queen or a colony has a small population, eliminate winter loss by **combining** the weak colony with a stronger one. To combine two colonies, first reduce each to one box of brood comb and their adult population. Then place one on top of the other with a sheet of newspaper between the two boxes (Figure 14-6). Allow the bees to chew the newspaper and mix the two units at their discretion.

The use of a combination board allows beekeepers to combine different sized hives together. For example, Figure 14-7 shows a nucleus being combined with three medium boxes. Once the bees in the nucleus have joined the new, strong hive, brood and food frames in the nucleus box should be combined with the colony, and the combined hive fed for winter.

Another option is to transfer frames of capped brood (without clinging adults) from strong colonies, judged to be still too actively involved in brood rearing, to weaker colonies. The newspaper method is not necessary if bees are first shaken from the frames you transfer. Caution is advised as extensive manipulations in the fall may demoralize colonies leaving them vulnerable to stress.

Manipulations must be done early in the fall to allow enough time to check on the colony to be sure strengthening has been accomplished and the bees have time to organize the nest for winter. When frames are moved from one colony and put into another, you might spread disease — movement of frames is best done only under disease-free colony conditions.

Plan to feed a heavy sugar syrup to the combined unit or plan to leave another box (super) of honey on top of newly united/strengthened colonies to ensure they have enough food reserves for the winter.

Figure 14-6
Newspaper combining method.

Fall requeening

It is not uncommon for a certain percentage of bee colonies to be queenless during the first fall inspection. These colonies may have produced honey and may have appeared fine the last time they were checked. You may not know precisely why such colonies become queenless but it probably had to do with unsuccessful queen replacement after swarming or supersedure. Many colonies replace their old queen during the nectar flow, a time when many beekeepers are less likely to check the brood nest.

Young queens help ensure overwintering success with fewer swarming problems next spring. Requeening with a young, mated queen is possible in early fall but beekeepers should not wait too late to requeen since the colony needs to establish a compact brood area and stock up with sufficient honey stores above the brood sphere for winter survival.

If there is a good adult population in a queenless colony in the fall, you might attempt to requeen it. However, when colonies have been without a queen

Figure 14-7
Combining a nucleus to a three medium box hive using a combining board (piece of plywood with a hole cut to nucleus size). After merger, the top nucleus box is re-moved and brood rearranged to lower two boxes. From *Bee Equipment Essentials* by E. Simon.

for awhile, laying workers are probably present. Small colonies, especially those with laying workers, are not worth fall management time. Simply shake the bees in front of another hive and store the equipment for restocking next spring. Populous yet queenless hives can be united with a stronger colony that will benefit from the extra bees.

Introduction of queens into colonies deemed worthy of requeening is done the same way in the fall as in other seasons. You can use the newspaper uniting method (Figure 14-6) to requeen a fall colony after killing the weaker/less desirable queen. You can requeen with a newly purchased queen, a locally raised and mated queen or a queen from a captured swarm.

If there is a nectar flow on, and there are abundant drones in the area, a queen cell may be used. This colony must be rechecked to confirm that the queen

Figure 14-8
Checking brood health during fall inspection. Look for evidence of brood disease and varroa mites by removing larger larvae and pupa and examining them with a hand lens or taking a close-up photo with your cell phone.

successfully mated. Otherwise unite a queenless unit to one with a queen. For best results, requeen by combining a queenless colony with a nucleus colony headed by a desirable queen as shown in Figure 14-7, (with the lower three-box colony queenless or recently dequeened).

Combine colonies early in the fall so the bees have time to reorganize the two boxes into a single brood sphere and store adequate honey in the proper position. Feed a heavy sugar syrup to the combined unit or add a third box with five or more honey-filled frames to ensure enough food reserves for the winter. Uniting a queenless colony with a queenright nucleus or killing the queen of a weak queenright colony and then uniting it with a queenright nucleus or colony accomplishes requeening.

Healthy bees — mite & disease control

Bee colonies must enter the winter months healthy, with low varroa and tracheal mite populations and adults with low nosema spore counts.

Colonies infected with American foulbrood (AFB) may not survive the winter or only survive with a small spring population. Any remaining honey stores in the spring may be robbed by bees from other colonies further spreading the disease to healthy colonies. Colonies with AFB need to be destroyed (Chapter 22, AFB control).

European foulbrood (EFB) and brood diseases chalkbrood and sacbrood will more likely be seen in the early spring than in a fall inspection. Bee colonies with spotty brood patterns and snot (or crud) brood are symptomatic of parasitic mite syndrome (PMS) and/or Colony Collapse Disorder (CCD) and are unlikely to survive the winter. See discussion of both CCD and PMS in Chapter 21.

Nosema, a microsporidian (fungus) disease of adult bees, can spread and prosper during confinement of overwintering bee colonies. At one point, prophylactic feeding of the drug fumagillin (Fumidil-B®) was recommended but potentially injurious levels are not common except in a low percentage of colonies. Additionally, such feeding has been suggested to aggravate the problem. It is possible to take a sample to check levels of nosema but it is expensive and only a few labs offer the service.

If concerned, to personally evaluate the effectiveness of fumagillin feeding, divide the colonies in an apiary into two equal portions. Feed one-half a syrup mixed with fumagillin and the other half just the

Figure 14-9
Yellowjacket trap.

THE WINTER CLUSTER

By the relatively simple behavior of clustering, the social honey bee is able to generate and conserve enough heat to survive whatever most winters have in store. A spherically shaped brood area and clustering behavior assists bees in maintaining a basic body temperature in the 59° F (15° C) range, regardless of outside temperature (Figure 14-10). The process is termed **thermoregulation**.

Bee clusters have a definite structure (Figure 10-21). The outer portion is an insulating shell of tightly clustered bees, varying from one to three inches (2.5 to 7.5 cm) thick. For warmth and to form the shell, the bees fill the spaces between the parallel combs and occupy empty cells in the comb. Bees on the outside are too cold to move but can protrude the sting if disturbed.

Within the center of the cluster, the bees are warmer and less crowded. They move about taking care of the brood and their queen, as well as performing routine comb maintenance. Heat generated by adult bee movement, moving wing muscles and the brood metabolism provide the heat that keeps the bees warm. Considerable metabolic water vapor is released. Since bees use winter stores most efficiently at 57° F (14° C), the amount of honey stores they need to consume to maintain a winter cluster is small. The lowest temperature which a colony can survive depends on food availability and the number of bees. When they are broodless, the temperature in the center of the cluster is around 70° F (21° C) while the manageable temperature range is approximately 54° to 94° F (12° to 34° C). When brood is present, the temperature will be at the upper limit.

During moderate winter temperatures, the bees move honey from storage cells at the exterior closer to the

Figure 14-10
A winter cluster on hive frames. Note the compactness of the bees and the bee-free space around the cluster.

cluster. During colder spells, the cluster becomes more compact from the behavior of individual bees moving inward to exchange position with warmer bees as their body temperature becomes too cold. As winter progresses, the cluster moves upward in the hive, seeking to maintain constant contact with stored honey (Figure 13-16, center and right).

There is a practical limit to which bees can contract their cluster. A portion of the cluster must be in contact with honey stores at all times since this is the fuel needed to run the muscles which generate the heat. Heat loss is proportional to the number of bees in the cluster. Smaller clusters are less likely to survive compared to larger clusters.

sugar syrup alone. Early next spring determine if the colonies receiving the drug have greater survival and are in better shape, showing less evidence of poor buildup and/or dysentery. If the bees have a nosema infestation, there will be a noticeable difference.

Tracheal mites were an important factor to consider in fall management, but infestations are less common than when the mites were first introduced in the 1980s and there is a reduced need of control.

On the other, hand varroa mites are widespread in US colonies. Fall management should include sampling representative colonies in the apiary to determine the varroa mite level (See Chapter 21 for sampling techniques). Ideally, such sampling should be done periodically throughout the growing season.

If there is a high varroa infestation, colonies can be treated with a miticide to better enable overwintering colonies to survive. Treatments can be done before supering or begun after removal of surplus honey as soon as possible in the early fall, especially with use of some of the available products that are temperature sensitive. Reducing varroa mites helps reduce viral disease levels.

Mice, voles, deer mice, skunks and wasps are common fall pests of beehives. To avoid mice moving into beehives, reduce the colony entrance (Figure 14-11) early in the fall before these rodents move inside to establish their winter nest. Many beekeepers wait too long to put mouse guards on colonies; bees winter better if mice are kept out of the colony.

Some beekeepers prefer the wooden cleat entrance reducer shown in Figure 14-11 be turned upward to help ensure that the opening does not become clogged with dead bees. Mesh hardware cloth (1/2 or 1/4 in. mesh) can be substituted for wooden reducers. Plastic entrance reducers are also available.

Reducing the entrance helps bees defend their hive from mice, skunks and yellowjackets. Many beekeepers in the Pacific Northwest, where yellowjacket predation is severe, practice season long trapping of yellowjackets using commercially available attractant traps. Early season trapping with pheromone bait eliminates queens; workers are trapped and removed in sweetener baited traps in the fall (Figure 14-9).

Then there's bears. Adult bears preparing for hibernating are an increasing pest problem (Figure 14-14). The only effective long-term bear protection is to enclose the colonies within a bear fence (Figure 23-30).

In the fall, beekeepers should protect stored beeswax comb from wax moths after the combs are removed to prepare bee colonies for winter. The adult moth may lay eggs on the comb before removal from the hive. Drawn comb that has been used to rear brood is more likely to be attractive to the female wax moth.

Drawn brood comb were traditionally fumigated with paradichlorobenzene (PDB) insecticide; however the compound is readily absorbed into beeswax, leaving a residue toxic to bees. It is best to put drawn brood comb in a freezer and then store comb in plastic bags.

In some locations, especially in the southeastern U.S., beekeepers need to consider small hive beetle control in the fall colony. Strong colonies are the best defense. Adult small hive beetles will overwinter in colonies

Figure 14-12
Rim on top of colony inner cover as extra airspace includes upper entrance hole. Note the bees congregating at the entrance on the left wall. The rim can be filled with an absorbent material placed directly on top of frames without an inner cover.

and become destructive next spring in the weakened colony. There is a selection of small hive beetle traps on the market that will help reduce adult populations (Chapter 23).

Winter protection & insulation

At one time, northern-climate beekeepers routinely protectively wrapped colonies for winter. Today, many beekeepers forgo the time and expense of providing extra protection for their overwintered hives. Colonies not protected survive as well as protected colonies, as long as the bees are protected from winter winds and they have sufficient fall stores.

Double wall hives, tar paper wraps, burying colonies, moving bees into protected environments, using heat

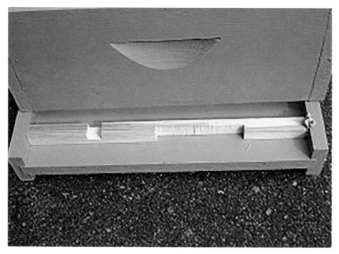

Figure 14-11
Entrance reducer at the entrance of a hive. The reducer must be firmly placed at the bottom of the front of the bottom hive body. Use a piece of paper or fabric to secure a tight fit. From *Bee Equipment Essentials* by E. Simon.

Figure 14-13
Insulation board (reflective foil on both sides) used as a top insulation and is installed during fall inspections. The insulation is between the inner cover (which provides an upper entrance) and the cover. L. Connor

Figure 14-14
Bear damage to hives in Vermont.

Figure 14-15
Wrapped colonies in early December snow in northern Vermont. L. Connor

tape (or a light bulb above a colony) or other such protective measures are generally not necessary for colony survival. Insulation may be detrimental during warming spring temperatures and, because the colony is warmer during the winter, the bees in artificially heated colonies will eat more food stores. For those wishing to insulate there are a number of materials that may be used as hive insulation, to darken the hive exterior to catch weaker winter sun rays, absorb moisture at the hive top and/or provide a dead air space beneath the hive top insulation (Figure 14-13). Each method has its adherents.

Beekeepers in areas where winters are extreme such as in Canada, Northern Europe and across Northern Asia still prefer to provide extra winter hive protection. Some traditions continue simply because that is how it is done. Moving reduced-size colonies into insulated, darkened buildings where it is possible to provide constant air exchange and control the temperature between 38° to 45° F (4° to 7° C) is one option in use today. Another method practiced by northern US large-scale beekeepers is to harvest most of the honey from their colonies, then truck the bees to a warmer climate for the winter to increase winter survival.

Upper hive entrances and using a rim to add moisture-absorbent material at top of the colony are other proactive colony managements (Figure 14-12). Covers should be weighted to protect from being blown off in winter storms. Colonies can be checked to confirm bees are alive by lightly tapping on the side and listening for a gentle buzz (Figure 14-19).

A good honey producing apiary may not be the best overwintering site. Sunny areas out of direct wind (within a windbreak) are best for overwintering bee colonies. If the apiary lacks a natural windbreak, provide a temporary one to help colonies avoid the drying effects of the wind. Vegetation, board fences, hay bales or other suitable materials can be used to break the wind from blowing directly into the apiary. Avoid areas with pockets of low, stagnant air.

If colonies otherwise well prepared for winter do not survive, the beekeeper should look for an alternate wintering site. Sometimes a short move of the apiary site may provide better wintering results. Consider sunny sites with early spring apiary access where it is possible to look after the colonies. One factor which should not be overlooked is a reliable early spring source of pollen.

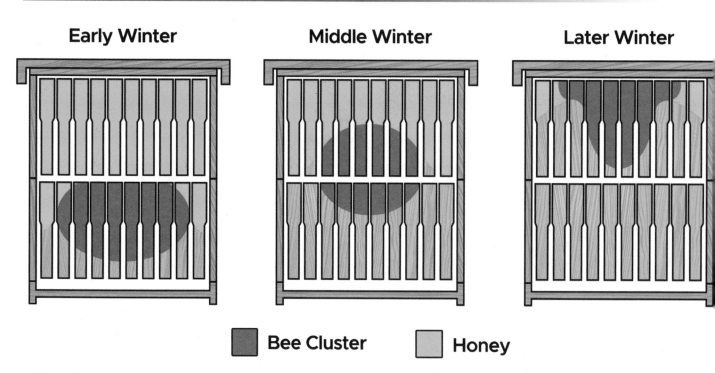

Early Winter   **Middle Winter**   **Later Winter**

■ **Bee Cluster**   □ **Honey**

Figure 14-16
The thermal cluster moves from the lower part of the nest to the upper during the winter months (left). The winter cluster consumes much of the honey and pollen in the lower hive body and moves into the upper hive body (center). By late winter the cluster is at the top of the nest with few food reserves remaining (right). The cluster size changes according to external hive temperatures (Table 14-1). J. Zawislak

Beekeepers should provide upward ventilation in every hive during the winter. Some bees propolize heavily, so removing the covers and scraping the propolis to allow warm, moisture-laden air to escape from the top of each colony is good late-fall management. An alternative is to place a wooden shim, carpet tack or stick in one of the corners at the top of the hive. Some beekeepers prefer to drill holes in hive bodies or use spacers or inner covers designed to allow air ventilation. In any event, gusts of wind should not circulate through the hive—a small entrance vent is all that is needed. If the propolis seal is broken, be sure the covers are weighted down to prevent their blowing off in a storm.

Many beekeepers prefer top insulation and upper ventilation. Top insulation helps the bees retain heat while providing an insulating surface, so moisture from respiration of bee cluster does not drip onto the bees (Figure 14-13). As the bees reach the top of the box, close to the insulation, they are able to move over the tops of frames as the heat spreads. This allows them to reach honey reserves that would not be available if the top of the hive was not insulated.

In summary: Proper preparation for winter is the key to colony survival and successful spring expansion. The ideal fall colony has a compact brood sphere

primarily in the lowest brood box, barely extending into the top brood box. The area above and to the outside of this sphere and the top box should be solid with honey stores as shown in Figure 14-16, right.

Late fall-winter
November to February

By late fall, bee colonies will nearly or entirely cease brood rearing. Colonies headed by older queens and more northern adapted stock like Carniolan and Russian bees will have stopped brood rearing sooner than colonies with younger Italian queens. As the cluster moves upwards it comes in contact with fresh honey stores and repositions itself above its earlier location in the fall. Ideally, colonies should resemble Figure 14-16, left image.

Beekeepers have few options to correct problems late in the fall. If some colonies are still light on food stores, it is possible to continue feeding. It is recommended to switch to dry sugar or a sugar cake, which should be placed directly over the cluster. If cold temperatures persist, the bees may not break from the cluster to take the sugar. It is important that the bees have a connection to honey stores overwinter, especially in the spring when colonies are actively rearing brood. Some bees, termed 'filling station bees,' need to leave the cluster to bring honey back to the nurse-age bees, which have higher body temperatures, for successful wintering of the colony.

It is important to remove the queen excluder if one was used earlier in the year. On the final fall visit, check to confirm top insulation is still adequate. Put a weight on the cover to avoid it being blown off during storms. Colonies should be leaning forward so moisture does not accumulate on the bottom board. Some beekeepers close the open bottom when using screened bottom boards.

Wintering success in beekeeping depends on several factors. Good overwintering colonies start with good queens. The overwintering population needs adequate honey stores which can be accessed during the colder weather. Older bees die over the winter, so pollen reserves and disease-free brood are important to winter survival. Overwintering success also improves with the size of the population, at least to a certain size. Undisturbed bees overwinter best, so pests like mice or over-manipulation by beekeepers should be kept to a minimum.

Wintering in many areas sometimes means fluctuating weather changes. Winter can bring cold spells, often snow or freezing rain, and sometimes bright sunny days when the temperature is warm enough for some flight, particularly in the middle of the day. Wet winters with widely fluctuating temperatures are more stressful on bees than dry seasons with a more consistent temperature.

During mild spells, the bees may be too active and heavily consume stored honey and pollen before fresh pollen and nectar becomes readily available. Wintering bees (fat bees) are physiologically different than summer bees. They have large hypopharyngeal glands and more fat body reserves, a whole body storage of food complementary to colony storage of honey. They live longer as they have little brood to feed and are not as active—the normal aging process is suspended. They also perform clustering behavior, which functions something like hibernation in mammals. Tropical bees are less acclimatized to cold weather and display inefficient clustering behavior.

Whatever the season, honey bees maintain an elliptical or spherical brood nest shape within their parallel beeswax combs for heat conservation and when brood is present to keep the brood at the ideal brood temperature (Figures 14-2, 14-10). As temperatures drop and less nectar and pollen become available, the brood sphere becomes more compact. When the temperature in a beehive drops to 14° C (57° F), bees start to cluster over the brood area. With a further drop in the external temperature, the cluster becomes more compact and better defined as illustrated in Table 14-1.

Table 14-1
Winter cluster size as related to external temperature

External temperature	Cluster diameter
+5° F	14 inches
+2° F	11 inches
-14° F	10 inches
-26° F	4 inches

Why colonies die overwinter
Colonies die during the winter because:

- the bees run out of honey
- there are too few bees to maintain an adequate cluster, often due to high varroa mite numbers
- the bees' digestive tract is compacted with too much waste matter
- they exhibit symptoms of disease or mite damage

Successfully wintered colonies have adequate food reserves, are strong enough to cluster, are free of diseases, have low mite numbers and other pests.

Figure 14-17
A colony in early February taking a cleansing flight.
S. Schwitek

Figure 14-18
Dry sugar feeding, with granulated sugar poured around the entrance of the hole in the inner cover.

An individual bee is sick if it has many uninvited guests in its gut. Such bees do not work as hard nor live as long as a healthy sister. Conditions that lead to accumulation of wastes in the digestive tract should be avoided. Since healthy bees only void wastes outside the hive (Figure 14-17), accumulation of wastes in the digestive tract results in poor overwintering.

Requeening with disease-resistant bees may reduce colony losses, but requeening has to be done in the summer or early fall. Requeening too late may result in a colony lacking sufficient time to complete preparations for overwintering. Such stock is not yet available but improvements are being made.

Managing the overwintering colony

Too often, beekeepers over-manage colonies. Let the bees do the work. The beekeeper's job is to assist bees, consistent with their biology. In most cases, this means staying out of the colony during the winter.

Over-managing colonies in the more northerly areas means too many inspections or providing too heavy a winter insulation. Farther south, colonies can receive more attention, but beekeepers must resist disturbing colonies and especially the brood cluster. Merely removing the covers and looking down between frames is often sufficient to confirm all is okay (Figure 14-10). If hive inspections are made during warm periods, they should be brief so little harm comes to the wintering cluster.

Most winters are not mild enough for continuous sugar feeding—liquid feeding should be completed in the fall and resumed in the early spring if a brief early spring inspection reveals low honey stores. During a mild winter, when more flight occurs, bees eat more honey.

During the winter, dry sugar feeding can be done by pouring granulated sugar around the hole in the inner cover (Figure 14-18) or preparing a candy board. Bees need water to convert dry sugar to a liquid; their proboscis is incapable of using dry sugar or hardened sugar candy. Often, water recovered within the

digestive tract is enough to liquefy the sugar or candy. Occasionally, some colonies laboriously remove the sugar and toss it out front but most hives will use it reasonably well as an emergency feed.

Providing an upper bee entry/exit is recommended in areas of heavy snow cover if the lower entrance is likely to become blocked with snow or ice. Snow provides good insulation and need not be removed, especially since this might disturb the cluster within the hive and the increased bee movement will result in more honey consumption and more warm air escaping the cluster. Upper entrances help vent moisture-laden air and the bees can use upper entrances for mid-winter cleansing flights to void accumulated feces (Figure 14-17).

Weak colonies in the fall will be weaker the next spring. Weaker colonies require more intensive management or they will not thrive. It is a good practice to 'take winter losses in the fall' by uniting two or more weak colonies or combining such units with stronger colonies to improve the chances of survival, thought it is difficult to judge proper colony size. The late winter colony will usually include a small, compact brood sphere and cover four or more frames (Figures 14-16, right).

Some locations are better wintering sites than others because they protect bees from prevailing winds to allow more cleansing flights on cool but sunny days. Close proximity to early spring pollen is a big advantage once temperatures warm, permitting flight. Such areas are often found near a stream or river since plants rooted

Figure 14-19
Tapping on the upper hive body to confirm continuing winter survival.

in water develop more rapidly and often bloom early. Situate the hives so they are not flooded.

Bees kept in or close to suburban locations may find abundant, early flowering plants with pollen and even some nectar. Such sites may later lack good nectar-producing plants, but many small-scale beekeepers do not necessarily seek to maximize honey harvests.

It is possible to overwinter weak colonies and even nucs or sometimes even extra queens. With less investment, losing smaller-sized colonies will have less economic impact. Nucs or special queen stock can be wintered on top of stronger colonies by allowing warmth to rise from the stronger colony below to the weaker colony/nuc above. Use a double screen between the two units. Nucs made from fall bees are meant to be combined in early spring to bolster weaker colonies or those needed for early season pollination duty. It may take some practice to develop a technique that yields consistent overwintering success with nucs and/or small colonies.

Figure 14-20 shows one system for overwintering nucs. They may be positioned above and/or between standard colonies as opposed to the standard single nuc box placed alone in the apiary. This conserves heat and improves overwintering success. Nucs can be used in the spring to bolster weaker colonies or moved into standard-sized boxes to grow into productive hives.

Beekeepers have other wintertime activities to perform. There are stored frames and beehive equipment to repair/repaint/ refurbish. The winter period should also be a time to review the past season and plan for the next one. Some specific additional tasks for the winter beekeeper are:

- order packages or reserve nucs
- review the previous season successes and challenges
- clean, scrape and paint hive bodies, bottom boards and covers
- thoroughly clean and store feeders and other bee equipment

Figure 14-20
Overwintering double nucs (twin deep red boxes) above single deep box hive.

- clean frames and reinstall foundation; assemble new frames
- visit the apiary to ensure colonies are upright and have tops in place
- remove dead-outs and clean and store equipment for restocking
- attend winter bee meetings, social events or bee school
- enroll in and complete a web-based training program
- browse new bee supply catalogs
- check food stores periodically
- catch up on the latest bee journals and bee books

key terms

backfilling	cutout	laying workers	spotty brood pattern
candy board (sugar cake)	fall inspection	newspaper uniting	thermoregulation
cleansing flight	fat bees	*Nosema*	top insulation
cluster	feeding sugar syrup	nuc (nucleus) colony	tracheal mite
combination board	'filling station' bees	queen excluder	varroa mite
combining two colonies	foulbrood (American and European)	requeening	weak colony
compact brood pattern		sacbrood	winter wrapping
cull/culling			

discussion questions

What basic behavior occurs to ensure a bee colony survives the winter? What are the minimum management techniques a beekeeper should attempt to ensure successful overwintering of his/her bee colonies?

Why should requeening and mite monitoring/control be done before Labor Day, the suggested normal start of fall management? Why do we recommend two basic fall inspections and how would they differ?

In what ways would fall and winter management differ for a beekeeper living in Florida versus New York State? Would survival necessarily be better in southern locations versus in more northerly climate conditions? Should northern beekeepers wrap colonies in the fall in black covering compared to southern beekeepers not doing so.

What are the four major reasons bees die overwinter? Give the manipulations a beekeeper should do to reduce the possibility of excessive winter losses for each of these.

Why is it inadvisable to open and inspect bee colonies during the winter? If colonies are opened what could be determined and what management performed? Why is it inadvisable to feed sugar syrup during the winter months?

If bees do not take sugar syrup in the fall, what options are available to ensure colonies have sufficient food reserves to survive the winter?

exercises

At a bee meeting arrange a hive-hefting contest. This activity involves guessing the weight of three 'hives.' These will have no bees but will have bottom boards, two hive bodies, inner and outer covers. Each will be weighted with known weights, using sandbags or gym weights. One will be too light, one good weight and one too heavy. The best guess can win a prize. Chart the guesses. What kind of range did you find? Do you think you will find that beekeepers accurately estimate colony weight?

A similar contest could be done by guessing the number of adult bees on a frame. Remove a frame from a colony and have individuals make written estimates of the number of adults on one side. Then shake the bees into a funnel and count how many bees were actually on the frame—assume equal distribution on both sides. This obviously needs to be done during good weather; alternately you can take photos of two to three frames during the summer season and have individuals guess the adult number after viewing the photos. Chart the variation in guesses—was there much consensus?

Examine a bee colony periodically over the fall and winter months. Determine initial cluster location in the fall. Observe cluster movement upward in the hive over winter. Diagram cluster movement. Use caution as these examinations could result in loss of the colony.

Determine how the recommendations for correctly overwintering a bee colony have changed over the last 100 years by looking in older bee literature and journals. Summarize what authorities and beekeepers recommended at one time to prepare colonies for overwintering. Summarize what beekeepers do today.

Read U.S.D.A. Technical Bulletin 1429 by Owens, Charles D. 1971, The Thermology of Wintering Honey Bee Colonies. 32 pp. Summarize in a written or oral report what this study reported on overwintering biology of bees.

Bee mites have greatly changed the overwintering situation since their discovery in the United States in the 1980s. Document this change. How are beekeepers adjusting to the need to change and be more proactive in fall/winter bee management? Determine what current research is saying about bee mites with an oral or written report on the topic.

Watch bee flight on a good winter day. Capture some bees and pull out the digestive tract by first cutting off the bee head and then pulling from the end of the abdomen. The entire digestive tract will unfold and you should be able to see how full the rectum is of wastes, if the mid-gut is distended and swollen (a sign of a nosema infection) and the amount of nectar in the honey stomach. Measure the water content of larger honey stomachs with a refractometer.

Repeat this on several bees over different days during the winter. Chart and explain the changes observed. How useful are bee dissections in providing information on overwintering?

references

Connor, L.J. 2012. Bee-Essentials: A Field Guide. Wicwas Press, Kalamazoo, MI

Blackiston, H. 2020 Beekeeping for Dummies. For Dummies. Hoboken, NJ

Owens, C.D. 1971. The Thermology of Wintering Honey Bee Colonies. https://naldc.nal.usda.gov/download/CAT72345678/PDF

Sammataro, D. and A. Avitabile. 2020. The Beekeepers Handbook. Cornell Univ. Press, Ithaca, NY

Figure 15-1
Spring forager, gathering critical nectar and pollen resources while pollinating apples in Michigan. L. Connor.

Concepts

Spring management
   early spring
   watching the entrance
   mid-spring
First spring inspection
   feeding sugar and protein
   expansion
Management for spring nectar
Preventing bee swarms
   removal of queen
   removal of brood
   separation of brood
   shook swarming
   Doolittle increase
Late spring

Spring management

Spring is the busiest time of the year for the beekeeper as things happen very quickly in the beehive. It is a natural time for making new bee colonies and the beekeeper often has to make decisions based on relatively little information. It is probably the toughest management season during the year since timing is everything in bee manipulation.

Spring
March — April — May

Arbitrarily, we divide spring into early, mid and late spring periods. Exact timing of these periods depends upon location and, of course, all bee colonies in the apiary are not at the same level of development unless equalized by the beekeeper.

In early spring, we clean up and store equipment from winter losses and ensure that all colonies are healthy and rearing brood. In mid-spring, the management emphasis shifts to keeping colonies intact and colony populations high by using swarm prevention management and eventually swarm control when colonies start queen cells. The last aspect of the busy spring season is supering colonies for the nectar flow, done in concert with swarm control since colonies need a large population to fill the honey supers.

Early spring

At some point in January or February (in southern states) or early March (in the northern states), the winter weather will ameliorate for a brief period. There may still be snow and ice and colder nighttime temperatures but when the temperature at the bee entrance warms to 10° C (50° F) bees will appear at the entrance to take cleaning flights.

There may be a couple of days of such weather before cold temperatures return. During such a spell many bees will leave their hive to void wastes (although some may not make it back to their hive and will be found scattered on the snow or ground). Inside, bees will reorganize their honey stores. These breaks will be earlier in the mid-south, Texas and the West Coast.

A respite from winter is a good time for a midwinter inspection (Figure 15-2). The inspection should be brief, mainly to check for adequate winter stores and confirm that the bees are producing brood. Honey bees monitor increasing day length and instinctively begin rearing more brood in January or February, initially using stores from last fall. Colonies still need at least half their winter stores because they will use greater amounts of honey to rear brood. The more brood, the more honey they need! Do not disrupt the brood cluster or lift brood frames outside the box.

The primary reason for the midwinter inspection is to determine if surviving colonies have adequate stores and to diagnose the reason(s) for any winter-kill (Figure 15-3). To keep the initial spring inspection brief, experienced beekeepers estimate the amount of honey stores by lifting the back of the colony or briefly remove outer frames to count the number of frames containing honey. Again, do not expose brood frames to cold windy weather that might disrupt the brood sphere—by simply removing a brood frame and putting it in backwards might result in chilled brood and bee death.

If you discover that colonies are short of honey stores, you can transfer frames of honey from colonies that have more than they need or use frames of honey stored for just such emergencies.

Some beekeepers feed dry sugar (Chapter 14, Figure 14-18) or sugar candy (Chapter 13, Figure 13-39) to colonies in danger of starvation. It is not recommended to feed liquid sugar syrup in early spring as this will add to the moisture stress of the colony. Colonies generally do not die from low temperatures but cold temperatures combined with a small bee population put colonies at risk (Figure 15-3). Mark those colonies judged to be light on stores as priority colonies for further spring attention.

Closely examine colonies that fail to survive the winter to attempt to determine why they died. Dead hives have tales to tell! Did they starve (Figure 15-3)? Did they have American foulbrood disease (Figure 15-4)? Was the population too small? Look for water staining indicating excessive moisture condensation. Each of these will have a different appearance.

If the honey stores are gone (or too far from the cluster) and the bees died while clustered, the colony probably died from starvation (Figure 15-3), perhaps due to prolonged separation from food at the edge of the comb. Also, the honey stores may have been robbed by

neighboring hives before you looked into the colony. There may still be some adult bees in such colonies and the presence of robbing bees can fool even the veteran beekeeper. A telltale clue of robbing is whether there is evidence of torn wax cappings on former honey frames. If there are honey stores with a small dead cluster, the loss was probably due to too small a population.

Another important reason for checking winter-kill dead-outs is to be sure colonies that died did not have American foulbrood (AFB). If you find a small cluster of bees not covering the brood or entirely off the brood area, check brood remains carefully for AFB symptoms (Figure 15-4; See also Chapter 22). Chilled brood may be confused for diseased brood.

Do not leave equipment from winter-kills exposed to other colonies, especially if there is any suspected disease. Close dead colonies and make them bee tight or, better still, remove the equipment to a bee-proof storage area. Transfer frames that contain honey or pollen only if you are certain there is no disease. Airing frames from dead-outs before reuse is a good idea if disease free. It is usually not necessary to destroy drawn combs if there is no AFB. Drawn combs are a valuable asset.

Figure 15-2
Mid-winter/early spring check of remaining stores and size of the winter cluster. D. Priebe

Figure 15-3
Dead cluster with no food visible. L. Connor

Figure 15-4
AFB diseased colony. Sunken cappings, holes in cappings, and mummies at the bottom of the cells are all visible. All are a concern. The disease spreads if other colonies rob out this hive; the equipment is permanently contaminated.

On a nice early spring day, when bees are actively flying, clean the bottom board/screen of the hive. There will be lots of discarded wax cappings, hive debris and maybe accumulated dead bodies that the bees have not yet removed. White granules may be crystallized honey the bees are discarding. Simply scrape or brush the bottom and replace the boxes. Remove winter wrapping and tip the hive forward so rain water does not run inside. Cleaning the bottom board will save the house-cleaning bees considerable labor.

One other chore to consider is to begin apiary record keeping with this initial inspection. You do not need to keep extensive records—remember KISS (keep it simple, stupid). For starters, record date, what you found (generally or for each colony inspected), and what you did. Keep general apiary records and specific records for colonies that require follow-up. Highlight colonies that will require specific management, such as colonies light on stores or suspected to have a queen problem. Indicate management, such as colonies supered or those for which a sample was taken for disease analysis.

If you desire, colony records can be more extensive. There are manual aids as well as record systems for your cell phone or computer. After a couple of seasons, apiary records, even simple ones, will improve your beekeeping experience by providing an instructive comparison of different seasons.

Watching the entrance

Watching bees at the colony entrance can reveal quite a lot about the colony. Bees in the spring need pollen to raise young so pollen foragers should be evident. The pollen can range from light to dark, with one color sometimes predominating, reflecting one major pollen source.

There should be lots of bees active at the entrance on a warm, sunny day. Some young bees will be performing orientation flights, learning the landmarks. Others will be functioning as guards, inspecting each incoming bee. Foragers will be the most numerous bees seen at the entrance as they fly directly from the entrance and disappear quickly inside when they return with their collected bounty. Some foragers may be water collectors (Box 22, Figure 15-5). Look also at what the bees carry out of the hive, like dead bees, chalkbrood mummies (Chapter 21), drone brood or mouse debris.

The bees will not necessarily use the entrance provided if alternatives are available. Holes in the corners of the boxes, holes drilled for added ventilation or areas not completely filled with propolis between poorly fitting equipment will all serve as alternate flight entrances for foragers. The bees seek an open and unrestricted passageway.

If you placed entrance reducers on the colonies in the fall, leave them in place until the weather becomes warmer

Box 33

WATER FOR BEES

Honey bees do not store water in the hive but need water to dilute honey for use in brood rearing and to cool the hive if it gets too hot. Most water foragers go short distances. In one study bees traveled a mean distance of 300 feet (90 m), although some went over a mile (1.6 km) to collect water. Water foragers take water into their honey stomach rapidly and fly 50 to 100 round trips per day from hive to the gathering site. Some foragers become 'water specialists.'

It is best to supply bees with a clean water source in the vicinity of the apiary if natural water sources are not close to the apiary site. Hot, dry sites can benefit from supplemental water. Apiaries where the bees might use contaminated water, such as in an orchard where pesticides are used, should be supplied supplemental water. Urban and suburban beekeepers must seriously think about providing water for their bees to avoid water foragers using neighborhood bird baths or swimming pools, thus preventing an unnecessary beekeeper-neighbor conflict. Beekeepers can supply water by feeding a dilute sugar syrup or water within the hive.

Water feeders should be of a size adequate for the number of colonies in the apiary. Water containers should be reasonably clean. A shallow source is much better than

Figure 15-5
Water gathering by bees from aquatic plants. L. Connor

a large, open container. A shallow trough or cement pond filled with sand, rocks, used water filters, sponge-type material or water plants for the bees to stand on and take up the water are all adequate (Figure 15-5). The water need not be running continuously but containers need to be replenished before they dry to avoid bees switching to other water sources.

and flight activity is reliable every day. If you discover a mouse nest, dispose of it. Block the entrance to prevent the reentry of mice by using an entrance reducer or wire of sufficiently small mesh to limit mouse passage, while still permitting the bees to freely come and go.

First spring inspection

Make the first spring inspection as soon as conditions permit. During spring inspection, look for the basics of brood, food stores, colony equipment condition and decide what, if any, colony management is needed (Figure 15-6). The key to inspecting a colony is to have fun doing the work and to learn something about the bees that will help make the next management decision easier.

In the spring, a healthy bee colony expands very rapidly from its lowest population level. Small populations are vulnerable early in the year, especially if the weather changes rapidly. Brood spheres will be small so it is relatively easy to look for evidence of brood disease at this first inspection. It is possible to see evidence of brood

chilling so look closely at any dead brood cells, especially at capped cells that should have hatched, to determine why they have not. Some apiary locations experience high levels of EFB disease in the spring; you may elect to treat with Terramycin® if symptoms of this disease are found (Chapter 22). The disease will likely disappear later in the spring. Contact a veterinarian to purchase this antibiotic.

Spring colonies cover fewer frames so the first and subsequent inspections are a good time to move old, defective drawn combs, those with lots of drone cells, older brood combs or frames in poor shape. Many beekeepers subscribe to the idea of systematically replacing old drawn combs with new foundation after a few years.

If you have extra drawn comb, you can substitute good comb for poor but should not yet add frames of foundation—wait until forage conditions are better. Replace poor combs with drawn comb or move to the outside of the boxes until new comb can be provided. Do not remove frames without a replacement as the bees will seek to fill the void.

As spring weather improves, colonies are a delight to inspect. They are small and the workers are fully occupied so they are often gentle. Changes are readily evident from one inspection to the next. In the spring, the beekeeper can positively affect what will happen for the rest of the year.

Stimulating weak colonies

There are three major methods of stimulating colonies to expand brood rearing in the spring: feed a dilute sugar syrup, feed pollen substitute, and open the colony brood area.

Feeding sugar syrup

Feeding a dilute sugar syrup (one part sugar to an equal volume of water) stimulates the queen to lay eggs and increases brood rearing. Feed the sugar syrup directly above or beside the brood sphere, but do not separate the sphere itself (see Chapter 13). An in-hive feeder replaces a frame at the edge of the brood box. Jars, cans, or sealed plastic bags of syrup may be placed on the top of the frames, making sure to place burlap or newspaper around the feeder (or feeders— you can add more than one if you wish) and an empty hive body to enclose the feeder.

Cover this feeding chamber and place a cement block or a couple of bricks on the cover to keep it from blowing off in spring winds. One thing to always avoid when

feeding syrup is robbing behavior. It is best to reduce the entrances on weak colonies before feeding them and avoid excessive spillage of syrup in the apiary. You do not want syrup to pour down on the bee cluster. Containers with numerous holes may leak unless the hive is level. Feeding is always a chore so find a convenient method to feed syrup and use that technique.

Feeding pollen substitute

Beekeepers usually feed protein patties to those colonies they have selected for honey production, pollination rental or queen rearing (Chapter 13, Figure 13-40). Weaker colonies may be fed protein patties, but in smaller amounts, directly over the brood nest. Moving a frame of stored bee bread from a strong colony to a weaker one is another way of stimulating weak colonies.

Because small hive beetles overwinter in winter clusters, you should only feed an amount of protein proportional to the size of the brood area. Provide enough protein for two or three days at a time. Otherwise the beetles may lay eggs, and the beetle larvae will slime out the colony during a warm period.

Opening the brood nest

The easiest way to expand the brood rearing area is to reverse hive bodies (Figure 15-8). Since the brood sphere is likely to be entirely in the upper box, and bees prefer to expand upward, changing the position of the two boxes will stimulate expansion by the colony, provided

Figure 15-6
Early spring inspection.

Figure 15-7
A successfully overwintered nucleus should build up to this strong colony by apple bloom time. M. Palmer

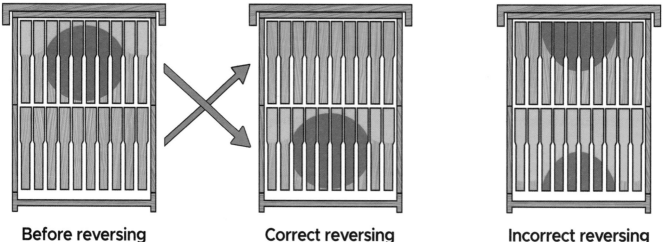

Before reversing   **Correct reversing**   **Incorrect reversing**

Figure 15-8
Correct and incorrect reversing. The middle colony's cluster is entirely below following reversing, and can work upward. The colony on the right has a split brood cluster, which may cause chilled brood, interfering with growth. J. Zawlisak.

sufficient pollen and honey are available. Feeding sugar syrup will help draw the bees to expand upward. Colonies headed by a young queen will quickly respond to reversal and/or feeding by increasing egg output.

Reversing should be done only if the brood sphere is entirely in the top box. Do not reverse when brood is split between two boxes until later in the spring when the temperature is warmer and there is less danger of chilling brood. Larger colonies benefit from reversal in late March or April. The right and wrong results of reversing are shown in Figure 15-8.

Another method of stimulating bee colonies to expand in the spring is by opening (expand) the brood area and adding empty combs. This must be done carefully as spreading of the brood sphere may lead to chilling of brood with lower nighttime temperatures or during a cold spell. If you don't understand the idea of a brood sphere and clustering, don't perform extensive early spring manipulations as you are likely to do more harm than good.

Sometimes the reason the brood sphere is between boxes is because the colony still has heavy honey stores above the brood area (a condition called 'honey bound'). Honey-filled cells can be a barrier and may potentially restrict brood expansion. If this condition is found, remove the middle frames and place open drawn comb in the center of the top box.

Score the honey-filled cells on the two adjacent frames to stimulate the bees to use these stores. Check in a week to confirm this management has opened the top brood box.

Additional spring inspections

After the initial spring inspection, beekeepers should perform periodic colony inspections. Colonies that are being fed will need to be checked to determine if they need additional stores. If a colony is being fed because it was short on honey, do not let the syrup feeder run dry for even a day as the bees may be completely dependent on the syrup and will quickly starve.

Expansion

After one reverse, beekeepers might reverse again to push a colony along. This will usually split a brood area but splitting later in the season, when the weather is warmer, should not cause harm. Alternately, simply move some frames around to enlarge the brood sphere by adding drawn comb into the brood sphere. As with all management, actions should be for a reason. Do not

Figure 15-9
Stronger colonies will add wax and honey to foundation.

Box 34

THE SWARMING INSTINCT

We do not fully understand factors that lead to swarming in colonies. As discussed in Chapter 10, the factors are complex because swarming is fundamentally reproductive behavior. Usually, we recognize that bees have begun swarming preparations only after they are well underway with queen cell production (Figure 15-10). Remedial measures become more limited and less successful as the colony gets further along in the swarming event. Too often, beekeepers are merely trying to catch up with what the bees are doing. We are supposed to be the managers—not have the bees managing us.

There is a swarming season when 75% or more of the swarms of the entire year will occur (Figures 10-17, 15-11). This happens before peak population is reached in the colony. Swarms may be more numerous in years with mild winters or early springs following a mild fall. These are seasons when drones appear early in colonies that have been stimulated with syrup feeding.

Because there is a time window when most swarms appear, the swarm urge or 'impulse' can be managed. As with other aspects of bee biology (such as defensiveness or choices in foraging, etc.) it is easy to think of bees in human terms, of bees behaving in a reasoning, rational way, but bees are not human, nor do they have human traits. Bees preparing to swarm are reacting to signals from other bees, to pheromones, to hormones within their own bodies or for other instinctive reasons. With a behavior as complex as swarming, we resort to terms like urge and/or impulse

Figure 15-10
Three queen cells in a top bar hive the day after its first swarm. A. Connor

because we know too little about the basic biology, much less how to manage it.

reverse because someone writes 'reverse,' 'reverse every two weeks' or worse, 'reverse by April 15.' The cookbook approach rarely works well with honey bees, though checklists help the new beekeeper.

Do not overwork bees. Colonies do not need to be examined every week. You do not need to examine every frame of the brood nest during every inspection. It is not necessary to always find the queen or scrape burr and brace comb from the top bars of frames. If beekeepers wish to perform intensive management, and are learning something every time, then this strategy should be continued.

Bees are extremely tolerant of what we do to them. The goal during the spring buildup period is to expand the brood nest so it occupies the majority of the space in the brood chamber. Figure 15-13 diagrams a colony that has brood on all but the outside frames. A super has been

placed over a queen excluder to capture an early nectar flow. Most northern colonies need two deep brood boxes or three medium boxes for full development.

Management for spring nectar flow

In some regions, the early bloom constitutes the major nectar flow. Standard spring management means colonies use this flow to build their population rather than store it as surplus. Beekeepers in such areas need to build colony populations faster and earlier to take advantage of early nectar sources. Two examples of an early nectar flow are: locust/tulip poplar, which blooms in late April/early May for about three weeks east of the Appalachian mountains in the eastern U.S., and big-leaf maple in the Pacific Northwest.

Probably the best management beekeepers can do to prepare for an early nectar flow is to have young

Figure 15-11
Swarm in an apple tree during bloom.

Figure 15-12
Feeding protein patty directly over brood frames. L. Connor

queens head colonies. Young queens will respond more rapidly to increasing day length and resource availability, resulting in faster colony expansion in the spring. This is important because colonies need to triple their population in a couple of months. Requeening to ensure young queens for spring expansion needs to be done in the previous summer/fall. If spring colonies are expanding poorly, an overwintered nucleus colony, if available, will supply a new queen and new bees for expansion.

Beekeepers wishing to have bees store early nectar flows such as from apple blossoms (Figure 15-11) versus using the source to grow larger should consider stimulating colonies as early as possible. Merely opening and inspecting the colony provides some stimulation. Cleaning bottom boards also is beneficial. The major stimulation the beekeeper can provide is feeding sugar syrup as early as the bees will leave the cluster to take it.

This results in more foragers gathering pollen. The developing brood further stimulates colony expansion. Opening the brood area is good management too, but it must be done skillfully so brood is not chilled; opening or manipulating too early may set the expanding spring colony back.

In large-scale operations, moving colonies to a location where there is an early nectar flow is another management possibility. Beekeepers need to be aware that good honey locations are not always the best location in other seasons. Thus, even moving colonies within an area may be helpful in situations where bees can be moved to overwintering sites with abundant early

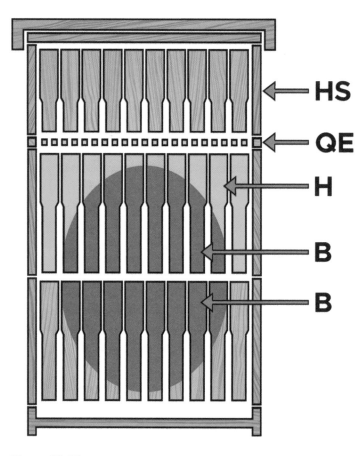

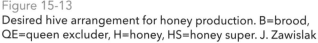

Figure 15-13
Desired hive arrangement for honey production. B=brood, QE=queen excluder, H=honey, HS=honey super. J. Zawislak

Box 35

MANAGE FOR SUCCESS

People keep bee colonies for different reasons. Few hobbyists care if the bees pay their own way. The opportunity to harvest some honey, not the maximum possible, is all that is expected. Hobbyist management is different from management practiced by the sideline or commercial beekeeper where location, intensity and timing are critical factors influencing the bottom line.

Managing for success means keeping the bees alive during the critical early spring and allowing the colony to expand as forage conditions improve. Successful management means keeping colonies from swarming (Figure 15-14) by monitoring for queen cells (Figure 15-10) and taking appropriate measures to control those colonies that begin swarm preparations. Later, you want to super in time and with adequate storage space to allow the bees to store a surplus that can be harvested (Figure 15-13).

Management of bee colonies cannot be successful if not integrated and performed during the entire year. Proper preparation of overwintering colonies in the fall months is essential to producing a strong spring colony.

Surviving winter colonies should have a balance of adult population to brood. Such a balance depends on the colony having adequate winter stores and an adult population of sufficient size to be able to forage new pollen sources in the spring. Spring dwindling might occur if bees and food are not balanced.

Successful colony management is a complex application of art and science that begins with understanding bee biology and skillful use of information to meet beekeeper objectives. Timing is everything.

Figure 15-14
Capturing a swarm by knocking bees into a bucket to transfer to an empty hive. C. Burkhead

pollen and the colonies are sheltered enough to fly and take advantage of the stimulus the fresh pollen provides.

Some beekeepers like the stimulatory effects provided by feeding a pollen substitute or supplement (Figure 15-12). Not all are in agreement that spring feeding is economically worthwhile. Pollen substitutes and supplements work best if supplied to colonies shortly before natural pollen sources bloom and during the initial days when foraging bees may be able to spend only a few short hours foraging outside the colony due to the vagaries of spring weather.

The use of a scale helps the beekeeper observe the changes in colony weight as it grows and produces honey (Figure 15-22). Electronic scales monitor hive changes.

Mid-spring

Colonies normally expand rapidly in spring when natural pollen and nectar become available. Whether the beekeeper stimulates expansion of the brood area or not, healthy colonies expand to hopefully fill the brood boxes (Figure 15-13). Mid-spring is a critical time because some colonies do not have enough honey stores to support rapid expansion. In stronger colonies with adequate reserves, management emphasis eventually changes to ensuring that colonies remain intact. This means swarm prevention and swarm control.

By mid-spring, the brood nest area of colonies should have doubled in size one or more times. First-time beekeepers initially are merely observers of the expansion of colonies. As beekeepers gain experience

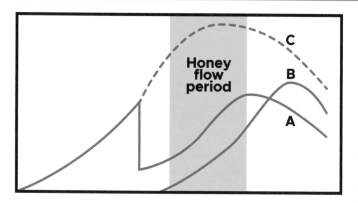

Time

Figure 15-15

Three colonies at different population sizes during the main nectar flow. Colony A is a colony that swarmed. Colony B was a swarm colony, package or nucleus that used the flow to build in strength. Colony C reached peak population during the nectar flow, and produced surplus honey.

with such monitoring, it becomes easier to make judgments about colonies. For example, a normal balance of eggs, larvae and pupae in the brood rearing area would mean that for every cell with an egg, there should be twice as many with larvae and four times as many with capped pupae (remember 3, 6 and 12 development days for worker brood discussed in Chapter 4). It takes practice to see this balance.

As a minimum, spring inspections should reveal:
- an expanding brood nest
- enough adult bees to cover brood cells
- minimum of two to three frames of honey
- pollen stored within and just to the edge of brood
- active bee flight when weather permits
- no disease (or treatment underway)
- whether queen cells are developing

It is apparent that some of these factors are going to be difficult to measure.

How fast should expansion be? How many adult bees are enough? How many brood cells should be examined to say there is no disease? Management decisions will need to be made if one or more colonies are not performing as expected. The value of multiple colonies (and good records from previous years) is the opportunity to compare and contrast between colonies. If fully three-fourths of the colonies are expanding, healthy, and performing up to expectations, colony development is on track and management is simplified.

The strongest colonies will present a different management challenge in mid-spring as such colonies may swarm. Although a natural behavior, swarming is a challenge to beekeepers because swarming divides the population of a colony before the target nectar flow is

reached, effectively negating any management performed to build a colony to a maximum foraging population. Thus colony management is directed toward preventing swarming and keeping the growing colony intact.

Figure 15-15 reflects what happens to the building colony if it swarms (line A). If the beekeeper successfully captures a swarm issuing from a colony and hives it, the swarm needs to use incoming nectar to produce beeswax comb and grow the colony population (line B). Neither the parent colony nor the swarm will equal the potential production of a colony which does not swarm (line C).

What about swarming?

The behavior of swarming is probably one of the most dramatic occurrences in the life of a bee colony. Swarming is the natural method of colony reproduction and a means of beekeeper colony expansion (Figure 15-16). In temperate areas, swarming becomes a greater management challenge the farther north you go. Bee colonies in temperate climates swarm every year or every other year, on average, if left unmanaged.

Three factors that are connected with the behavior of swarming are the brood and adult population relative to the amount of room within the nest and the amount and

Figure 15-16

Preparing to hive a swarm after dark.

Figure 15-17
Queen cup, with no developing larvae inside. Note: Two drone cells to left and one above the cup. L. Connor

Figure 15-18
White painted hives with entrance facing south, providing sufficient brood expansion space (here two standard boxes) and early supering (above queen excluder) represent standard swarm prevention measures.

distribution of available queen substance. The third major factor, the environmental influence, is beyond control of the beekeeper. (See Chapter 10 for swarming discussion).

The hive environment

Once a colony starts rearing replacement queens in the spring, beekeepers must assume that the bees have begun swarm preparations. It is relatively easy to check for developing queen cells by examining the bottom of frames within the brood area. The earlier in the queen rearing cycle it is determined that a bee colony is rearing replacement queens, the greater the chance for halting swarming. When the queen cells are not discovered by the beekeeper until well advanced, more drastic action will be necessary to try to stop the colony from swarming.

Preventing bee swarms

The measures listed below are all aimed at ensuring that bees do not start queen cells, the first step in swarming. In most years, attention to each factor will keep the incidence of swarming at a low, tolerable level:

1. Provision of plenty of room for queen egg laying in the brood nest. Two full-depth hive bodies may not be sufficient room for brood rearing in strong colonies; one hive body is rarely adequate in healthy colonies. All brood nest combs should be in good condition for egg laying, contain a minimum of drone comb and should not possess large amounts of stored honey or pollen after late March (Figure 15-20).

2. Provision of sufficient nectar storage space. Some super space should be available for nectar from late April to mid-August (Figure 15-13). When supers are added, it is sometimes necessary to entice bees into working in them immediately. Bottom supering (adding supers on top of brood area, below other supers) and baiting of new supers (raising a frame or two of ripening honey into supers added or by dripping syrup on the comb face) are recommended (Chapter 16). Full supers of foundation should not be added until the honey flow has begun.

3. Colonies should receive maximum sunlight early in the season. Afternoon-shaded apiary sites are acceptable. Colony entrances facing the morning sun or south are preferable. Painting hives white will help the bees regulate the temperature in the colony (Figure 15-18) but may lead to excessive drifting if not distinctly marked.

4. Sufficient ventilation should be present. Winter entrance blocks (for mice) should be removed by mid-spring. Some apiaries with poor air circulation could benefit if colonies are supplied with a screen bottom board and a top screen in place of inner cover to improve ventilation. Breaking the propolis seal increases upward ventilation within the colony.

5. Young queens heading all colonies. This is the most important thing that can be done to aid in swarm

Figure 15-19
Caging the queen will break the brood cycle.
L. Connor

prevention. All requeening should be done from stock with low swarming tendencies. Queens that have not been through a spring tend to swarm much less than older queens, although most new queens swarm when in congested nests.

Swarm control

It is normal for bee colonies to build queen cups (Figure 15-17), especially during spring expansion. However if there are occupied queen cells (containing eggs, larva, or pupae) you must assume the bees have started swarm preparations. If nothing is done the colony may swarm.

To halt the preparations, two management steps are necessary. First, eliminate all the queen cells, both capped and uncapped, and second, manipulate the brood area so the colony does not resume queen rearing. Once done, colonies should be rechecked every seven to ten days and the control technique repeated if developing queen cells are again observed.

It is critically important to eliminate, by killing or removing, all developing queen cells in the colony. Once all queen cells are destroyed, one of several management variations, as described in the next three pages, should be performed. Select a method that suits your situation.

Swarm control is a lot of work and unless done skillfully and at the right time might not successfully halt swarming. Remember, if nothing is done, a swarm may emerge from the colony once the colony has developing queen cells. When bees swarm, the bees are managing the beekeeper.

Removal of the queen

De-queening a colony rearing queen cells is effective swarm control. A disadvantage is that it often takes considerable time to search for the queen. After finding and killing her or placing the queen in a holding cage (Figure 15-19), the colony is left queenless for seven to ten days. Following this, requeen the colony using the old queen (that you have been holding in a cage) or with a new queen, after first destroying all queen cells present in the colony.

By removing the queen, you create a break in the brood cycle which should weaken the colony enough to halt swarm preparations. The brood developing in their cells will continue to emerge and the adult population will continue to expand for another three weeks. If the target nectar flow begins within this time, there will be a large population of workers available for foraging as there will be less brood to tend. Requeening again seven to ten days later restores an expanding brood nest and creates a 'normal' condition.

Variations of this technique include the destruction of the original queen and introduction of a new queen purchased or reared in another colony, or the addition of a capped queen cell seven to nine days later. Instead of introducing a capped queen cell (produced in another colony), cut out all queen cells except one. There is a small risk the colony may swarm with this single virgin queen when she emerges. This risk increases if you leave more than one capped queen cell. This re-queens the hive and creates a brood cycle break, which can be combined with reducing varroa mite population growth in the colony.

Removal of the brood

Brood removal divides and weakens a strong colony and will usually halt swarm cell production. Brood removal offers the beekeeper the beneficial aspects of swarming at the beekeeper's convenience and without the work of swarm capture or risk of missing or being unable to capture the swarm. This management method is frequently used to produce divides or nucleus colonies, but the removed brood may be used to boost weaker colonies.

Once queen rearing has started, kill all developing queen cells. Remove three to five frames of brood with clinging bees, similar to Figure 15-20. Place these frames in a small hive (nucleus) and add a queen cell or new queen.

Alternately, kill all the queen cells on frames left in the parent but leave intact the queen cells on the frames you move to the nucleus colony. Place the new unit in a new location (within same apiary or move to a different apiary if this is an option) and reduce the entrance to help prevent robbing and aid field bees in orienting to the new location.

Instead of making new colonies, frames of brood removed from colonies requiring swarm control may be added to weaker colonies to strengthen them or to equalize colony strength, provided disease is not present. Continue inspections for queen cells at seven to nine day intervals.

If new queen cells are found, repeat the manipulation. The advantage of this control technique is that it leaves the majority of the main colony intact so it will be a populous colony for the nectar flow.

Figure 15-20
Brood frame with capped brood (drone brood cells along bottom). L. Connor

Separation of brood

A variation of brood removal involves the separation of adult nurse and field bees within the hive (dividing the brood rearing and nectar ripening areas). This technique calls for placement of the queen and one or two frames of unsealed brood in an otherwise empty box of empty drawn comb on the bottom board. A super is usually added on top of this box. A special double screen (Snelgrove double screen; Figure 15-21, see reference) with eight wedge openings (four top and four bottom openings) is then put on top of this box. All remaining brood frames (one or two boxes) are placed on top of the double screen.

Once in place, open the front wedge screen to permit forager entry and exit into the top brood hive body. Leave the entrance to the lower brood chamber open. After seven to nine days close the upper front entrance at which time the lower wedge opening of the same side is opened. Another top opening, either on the side or back of the hive, is then opened to allow normal egress from the top hive body. At the time you change the openings, move filled brood frames from the box below (leaving the queen behind) to the hive box above the screen, exchanging now-emptied brood frames from above the screen after removing all queen cells to brood boxes below for frames full of capped brood.

After this action, field bees foraging from the top brood hive body do not adjust quickly. Most go below to the honey super when they return from their first flight following the closing of the wedge opening into top box, instead of learning the location of the new top entrance. Older foragers will use the lower hive area while younger bees remain above on brood frames. This technique does seem to work but it takes a lot of effort and attention to detail, plus the special double screen.

Separation of queen from the brood

The process of separating a queen from her brood (also called Demaree method after Kentucky beekeeper George Demaree who first described this management in 1892) is a widely used swarm control practice. A large number of variations exist and almost all recent articles on swarming include some variation of the basic principle of queen and brood separation.

The technique involves rearranging the colony which is rearing queen cells in preparation to swarm. The queen is placed with one or two frames of sealed brood in a hive body of otherwise empty comb (or foundation) on the bottom board and then a queen excluder is placed over that single hive body. One or two honey supers with drawn comb are added above the excluder and then the remainder of the frames containing brood are placed on top of the same colony in another hive body.

Figure 15-21
Double-screened divider board for separating brood over a colony. Also called the Snelgrove screen. E. Simon photo from *Beekeeping Equipment Essentials*.

The same procedure of separating most brood from the queen should be repeated seven to nine days later when all queen cells are removed from frames from the top chamber. Alternately, some beekeepers permit a queen to hatch above and then provide a second entrance. This results in a two queen colony with two brood chambers.

The two brood areas are united into one single brood chamber for the nectar flow. To accomplish requeening, kill the old queen and leave the new queen in control of the combined colony.

A modification of this manipulation permits the bees to expand their brood nest through four standard hive bodies in the spring. This is accomplished by reversing the two wintering hive bodies in March or early April, raising one frame of brood to the second body (formerly the lowest), and adding two standard hive bodies or three shallow supers. The brood chamber is allowed to expand upward into the third and even the fourth hive body.

At start of nectar flow, the queen has to be found and placed into the lowest two hive bodies and a queen excluder placed over the newly restricted brood chamber. As the brood in frames above the newly installed excluder hatches, the now emptying brood cells will be used for honey storage.

Virtually all management that involves separation of brood and queen requires the use of additional hive bodies and drawn combs. Supers will go on top of the brood chambers so colonies may be piled high with boxes by summer. Such colonies will need attention in the early fall to be sure the brood sphere is restricted to the lowest box (Chapter 13).

Shook swarming

Another variation closely resembles swarming and is often called **artificial swarming** or the **'shakedown' method**. This technique calls for shaking all bees from the hive onto the ground at the entrance to a colony that is raising queen cells.

All the queen cells are eliminated and then one or two full hive bodies of foundation and the queen are put above the bottom board with a queen excluder placed above them. Honey supers are added on top of the queen excluder. The frames of brood can be put on top or removed to bolster weaker colonies or create nucs.

Shook swarming can result in a surplus honey crop if performed at the right time. Nectar will not be needed for the diminishing amount of developing brood ensuring it will be stored as surplus. This creates an interruption of brood expansion because it will take the bees time to draw the foundation for the queen to lay eggs. Any available nectar will be stored in cells in the supers and in cells emptied as adults emerge from the frames at the top if you put them on top. This manipulation also results in drawing of several new frames which can be used to replace older drawn comb or damaged frames.

Figure 15-22
A scale will let the beekeeper monitor weight changes during the season, improving swarm control and timing of supering for the nectar flow.

Box 36

DOOLITTLE INCREASE

We will discuss G. M. Doolittle in Chapter 18, when we share his role in developing our contemporary queen rearing methods. Less well-known, Doolittle provided beekeepers with a simple method of making new colonies.

His method allows a beekeeper to make a new colony within an apiary without moving it to a new location. It relieves the new or inexperienced beekeeper with the chore of finding the original queen before moving frames into a new hive. If no queen is provided, this is called a Doolittle walk-away split, as the colony will need to raise its own queen.

The Doolittle method relies on the biological attraction of frames of brood to nurse bees. It involves the use of a queen excluder cut to fit a combining or conversion board (Figure 14-7).The combination of brood pheromone and the impulse of nurse bees to feed larvae make this system work.

Select strong colonies for this method, perhaps colonies that have started to prepare swarm cells. Use brood frames from one colony and bees from another if neither colony is as strong as you want.

1. Select three to five frames of brood, ideally mostly capped brood with emerging bees and at least one frame of younger brood containing eggs and larvae. This spreads out the age distribution of the emerging bees.

2. Shake or brush the worker bees off these brood frames and place the frames into a hive body or nucleus box above the queen excluder. The bees may be shaken at the entrance of the hive and the bees allowed to crawl inside. Replace removed frames with frames of drawn comb or foundation. This also reduces swarm pressure.

3. If the queen is not seen, don't be concerned, as she will be shaken or brushed off the frames. In the new colony introduce a mated queen, a virgin, a ripe queen cell, a 48-hour old queen cell or allow the bees to raise their own queen.

4. Fill the box with brood and food frames. Cover the hive to allow the bees to crawl through the excluder and onto the bee-less brood frames.

5. Later that day or the next day, move the increase box containing the brood frames and bees to a hive stand in your apiary.

6. If you have introduced a mated queen or a virgin, remove the cage cap or cork and allow the bees to chew the queen out of the queen candy in the cage.

Figure 15-23

Double deep hive, conversion board, nucleus box with bee-less brood frames, a queen, and lid used to make a Doolittle Increase hive. L. Connor

7. Reduce the size of the entrance as there are few guard bees in the population of bees you have moved.

8. Make sure to have a frame or two containing honey and pollen in the box to provide adequate food. You may want to add a small feed container.

9. Check the hive every seven to ten days for strength and the condition of the queen.

This method reduces the swarming instinct in colonies and produces a new colony. First year beekeepers have success with this two to three months after starting a nucleus hive or a package colony.

Connor, Lawrence. 2014. Increase Essentials, Wicwas Press, Kalamazoo MI
Doolittle, G. M. 1908. A Year's Work in an Out-Apiary. Reprinted 2005, Wicwas Press, Kalamazoo, MI

Making divides and increase nuclei hives

Swarming is the way colonies naturally multiply. However, since only one in five will survive the initial winter, bees do not quickly overpopulate an area. When the beekeeper intervenes and captures the swarm, feeds it sugar syrup and continues managing the colony, its winter survival odds greatly improve. Thus beekeepers capture swarms to increase colony numbers or replace winter losses.

The most common method of obtaining replacement colonies or increasing the number of managed colonies is through dividing existing colonies. Divides (also termed nucs) are a great way to start a bee colony. Spring is an ideal time to divide. When dividing is done properly, the original hive, and even sometimes the divide, will yield surplus honey (See Chapter 19 for more complete discussion of making and using nucs).

Dividing colonies costs little compared to buying package bees or established colonies. An additional benefit to dividing a colony is the reduction of swarming, the eliminating of the work of swarm capture and the potential risk of missing or being unable to capture a swarm.

Late spring

In addition to the need to control swarming, there are additional important managements of spring colonies. Productive colonies need three or more frames of honey, healthy brood and good combs. Poor combs and frames need to be cycled out of the brood nest. Weak colonies may still need stimulation. Colonies that are slow to develop can be fed sugar syrup, given frames of capped brood to bolster small adult populations, reversed or have the brood area opened up, united with stronger colonies, combined with another weak colony or re-queened.

The final activity of spring management will be to super the strongest colonies as the season advances toward the nectar flow. Late spring and summer are periods when bee colonies normally store surplus honey. This is the nectar or honey flow period, the target time when the aim is to

Figure 15-24

If the weather, flowers and bees collaborate, you may be faced with hundreds of pounds of honey to process. E. Simon photo from *Beekeeping Equipment Essentials.*

achieve the largest population in all colonies. Some colonies can store truly impressive amounts of surplus honey when everything goes right (Figure 15-24). Even in average seasons, some colonies will do better than average in their honey production.

The late spring period prior to the honey flow is sometimes labeled the **pre-flow spring management** period, and is the busiest management season for the beekeeper. Getting and keeping strong colonies ready for the main nectar flow remains a focal point in honey bee stewardship.

key terms

adult bee population	chalkbrood mummies	early spring	increase nuclei
American foulbrood	chilled brood	entrance monitoring	making divides
bee coverage of brood	cleaning flights	expanding brood nest	mid-winter inspection
brood population	crystalized honey debris	expansion	opening brood nest
brood separation	dead bees	feeding pollen substitute	overworking bees
brood spheres	Demaree method	feeding syrup	pollen foragers
candy boards	Doolittle increase	flight activity	pollen substitutes
cause of winter death	dry sugar	honey minimum	pre-flow spring management

queen pheromone distribution	separating brood from queen	spring nectar flow	Terramycin®
queen removal	shook swarming	starvation	trimmed drone brood
record keeping	small population	swarm cells	ventilation holes
reversing brood nest	Snelgrove screen board	swarm control	
robbing signs	spring	swarm prevention	

discussion questions

Describe the three major components of spring management. How can you tell if a bee colony needs expansion, swarm control or supering? Why is management potentially so time-consuming during the spring?

Compare and contrast what you should look for and expect to see in the standard spring and fall inspections (Chapter 14) of bee colonies.

How do you know a bee colony is preparing to swarm in the spring? How do you check colonies for swarm preparations? Under what circumstances might it be better to remove the queen vs. divide a colony preparing to swarm? How is separation of brood different from dividing colonies? Define the similarities/differences between the Snelgrove board, a double screen and Demareeing managements.

Distinguish between swarm prevention and swarm control.

Outline the conditions to control swarming in which queen removal is the best option. Do the same with queen and brood separation.

Why is dividing a colony a better option to increase colony numbers for beekeepers already owning colonies compared to buying packages, capturing swarms, or other options?

exercises

Conduct a standard spring inspection. If it is not the appropriate season, do this inspection with empty equipment describing what you should expect to see.

Examine the literature and evaluate management methods given to prevent and/or control swarming. Are the methods time consuming? Are they more practical for a hobbyist or a commercial beekeeper? What might be a reasonable amount of effort for expected results?

Capture a swarm of honey bees (you might need to first create an artificial one; See Chapter 19 for a more complete discussion of making and using nucs).

Make a divide. If conditions and number of colonies permit, use more than one of the techniques described and then compare results for the developing and original colonies.

Make a divide by keeping the bees together in one hive using the Snelgrove double screen. What problems did you encounter?

Prepare a typical calendar that would potentially include all the activities of March, April and May. Do one model for the backyard beekeeper with three colonies and another for a sideliner with 60 colonies at four apiary sites.

references

Connor, L.J. 2012. Bee-sentials, Wicwas Press, Kalamazoo, MI

Connor, L.J. 2014. Increase Essentials, Wicwas Press, Kalamazoo MI

Connor, L.J. 2019. Keeping Bees Alive, Wicwas Press, Kalamazoo MI

Delaplane, K. 2006. Honey Bees and Beekeeping, Third Edition. The Georgia Center for Continuing Education, Athens, GA

Doolittle, G.M. 1908. A Year's Work in an Out-Apiary. Reprinted 2005, Wicwas Press, Kalamazoo, MI

Morse, R.A. 1983. A Year in the Beeyard. Scribner, New York

Simon, E. 2011. Bee Equipment Essentials. Wicwas Press, Kalamazoo, MI

Snelgrove Board use https://www.betterbee.com/instructions-and-resources/stop-that-swarm.asp

Wilson-Rich, N. 2018. The Bee: A Natural History. Princeton University Press, Princeton, NJ

Chapter 16

Honey production

Figure 16-1
Forager hovering over flowers of swamp milkweed.
C. Burkhead

Concepts

Nectar or honey flow
plants
weather
peak population
'morale' of the hive

The work of honey production
pre-flow management
supering
queen excluders
inspections during flow

The honey harvest
drawing foundation
extracting
honey in the comb

The honey harvest

Honey is a sweet viscous liquid produced by honey bees. Bee colonies that grow and expand in the spring are capable of storing a large amount of honey in a short time. Honey bees hoard honey, a concentrated carbohydrate that contains its own preservatives and when consumed requires no further digestion of the principle sugars.

Foraging honey bees do not need a stimulus to leave the hive to forage for **nectar**, the raw ingredient of honey. While bees instinctively find and collect nectar from flowers, not all flowering plants or locations provide the same nectar reward. Flowering plants that produce large amounts of nectar are called **honey plants**.

Most beekeepers maintain their beehives all year. In most areas, nectar collected and processed into honey is used by the bees to feed larvae and adults. It is their dietary carbohydrate. While nectar production occurs from early spring to fall, the surplus honey is produced for only two to three weeks each year. During this time, beekeepers expect payback on their investment, as this is when the bees store more honey than they need to consume. This nectar flow becomes surplus honey to potentially harvest.

Nectar or honey flow

The relationship between honey bees and plants is complex. Although the chief value of honey bees to humans is their pollination of fruit, fiber, nut and seed crops, bee colonies are usually kept by beekeepers to produce honey. A strong honey-producing business has helped ensure adequate colonies of bees for the indispensable pollination of plants. Backyard beekeepers (Figure 16-2), on the other hand, may not wish to produce large amounts of honey while the bees pollinate local fruit and vegetable flowers.

There are four major factors that influence the storage of surplus honey. They are:

- presence of nectar and pollen plants
- weather suitable for nectar secretion and bee foraging
- peak populations of bees at main nectar flows
- physical ability of the bees and colony 'morale'

The presence of nectar-secreting plants

Beekeepers depend upon extensive acreages of both wild and propagated plants in the vicinity of the apiary. A sequence of nectar and pollen sources throughout the season is important for bee colonies. It is generally not considered practical to plant crops specifically for the use of honey bees, although bees may be a consideration in the use of land. There are some situations where land already owned by the beekeeper or other party (i.e. it is a fixed cost) could be planted in bee forage for little or no additional cost.

Beekeepers are usually dependent upon the abundance of weeds and agricultural practices and must search for profitable locations. The best locations have already been found by beekeepers seeking surplus honey crops.

Many of the changes we affect to our environment are negative for our bees. For example, beekeeping is

Figure 16-2
The English garden hive.

negatively impacted by the decision to cut legumes before they bloom in order to produce a higher protein hay crop. More intensive care and use of land for cash crops with fewer uncultivated, set-aside areas is also a negative. Suburban and urban environments may decrease honey yields in spite of the fact that the bees are provided a wider variety of flowering plants.

The number of honey plants can be increased by:

- planting honey plants on roadsides and waste areas, including trees beneficial to bees
- developing nectar and pollen plants useful all season
- adjusting soils for optimal nectar secretion
- breeding plants for high nectar secretion

Land conservation and groups creating conditions more favorable for honey bees and other pollinating insects have undergone a renaissance. Organizations such as the non-profit Xerces Society for the Conservation of Invertebrates and a number of federal agencies have practical solutions that focus on how to improve habitat for beneficial organisms such as pollinators. Many have lists of techniques to improve pollinator conservation including flowering plants of greatest value to pollinators. Within limits, we can potentially improve forage for honey bees.

Weather suitable for nectar secretion and gathering

When enough sunlight reaches leaves, sugar is manufactured through photosynthesis. Temperature and sunlight affect bee flight.

Correlations between weather and honey yields have been inconclusive because of the complexity of the factors involved. Healthy, vigorous plants produce more nectar than unhealthy, stunted plants. Ordinarily, the availability of nutrients strongly influences nectar secretion in plants, while a maximum period of intense sunlight is needed for nectar secretion by the most important honey plants.

Adequate moisture must be available to the plant to promote nectar secretion. The ideal amount of rain varies with the soil type. Sufficient rainfall is critical at certain plant growth stages. Irrigation may both positively and negatively affect foraging honey bees. Interestingly, during periods of intense moisture stress, the lack of rainfall results in greater photosynthesis, and many plants are stimulated to secrete more nectar to attract pollinators and ensure seed production.

Temperature has a marked influence on plant growth and nectar secretion (Box 37). It influences nectar flow at the time of flowering and there is a long-term effect on plant growth throughout the season. Warm days and cool nights favor secretion of nectar, as long as nighttime temperatures do not dip too low. High humidity and rain make for a more dilute nectar but do not affect the amount of sugar produced. Bees must work harder to make honey from dilute nectar.

The amount and concentration of nectar influence the number of bee visits to plants which, in turn, affect both surplus honey production and pollination. For example, bees prefer apple blossoms to pears as apple nectar contains more sugar.

Plants can be bred for characteristics such as nectar quantity, flower color, plant vigor, or other factors that influence their usefulness to bees and beekeepers. Unfortunately, such plant research has a low priority. Although breeders have selected plants with higher nectar secretion, this research has not resulted in commercially available, high nectar-producing plants. Plant breeders tend to concentrate on other plant traits other than flower attractiveness to pollinators.

Peak populations for the nectar flow

Generally, the more bees in a colony during a nectar flow, the bigger the crop (Review Chapter 1, Figure 1-3). Colonies have a seasonal colony population cycle. Successful wintering is limited by the size of the worker bee population. Weak spring populations delays a rapid population buildup with the queen's level of egg production limited.

Nosema disease, mites, brood diseases, poor queens, along with reduced population and slow spring buildup all impact population growth. A dwindling supply of nectar or pollen leads to reduced egg laying and slows buildup. Bees will dispose of drone brood and, later, worker brood if the food supply becomes exhausted.

It is often practical for the beekeeper to divide the strongest colonies early in the spring to make up overwintering losses and increase colony numbers. Keep in mind that two weak colonies do not store as much honey as one strong colony (Figure 16-3). Feeding sugar syrup and supplementing protein in early spring helps strengthen colonies. Effective swarm prevention and swarm control management after swarm queen cells are started are necessary to keep strong colonies intact for the flow.

Physical ability of the bees and the 'morale' of the colony

It is possible to breed bees for characteristics such as tongue length, body size, speed of flight, disease resistance, and aspects of foraging behavior. As a general flower pollinator, the honey bee is well-adapted to forage on a wide variety of plants. Whether a colony discovers and profits from flowers depends of many factors. When colonies fail to do well, colony morale might be invoked, but poor colony performance is usually linked with poor nutrition, pesticide exposure, diseases, parasites and queen issues.

Figure 16-3
A strong colony with three deep, eight-frame hive bodies on a screened bottom board. The two boxes on the bottom contain the queen and brood, and the top box contains surplus honey and extra food reserves. Additional honey boxes or supers will be added as necessary for the nectar flow. L. Connor

Beekeepers do not always diagnose such situations in time to take corrective action. Colony success is influenced by swarm or supersedure preparations, the balance of bees of different ages, space in the hive for nectar ripening/ storage, temperature and air circulation inside the hive as well as other factors. Beekeeper manipulation of the hive can prevent development of queen cells and swarming behavior. While beekeepers speak in terms of maintaining good morale, poor performance relates to a multitude of factors negatively impacting a colony.

Obtaining large, harvestable surplus honey crops is a complex interaction of many biotic and abiotic factors. Successful beekeepers are those who consistently produce honey in most of their bee colonies and an exceptional amount in a few colonies. Most seasons, the majority of colonies exhibit average honey production. Surplus honey production will be outstanding as a rule-of-thumb one in five to one in ten years. Skillful beekeepers are ready and manage their colonies to be prepared for such seasons when plants and weather work together. Experienced beekeepers anticipate, not only react.

GROWING DEGREE DAYS

Growing degree days (GDD), also called growing degree units (GDUs), are a learning tool in phenology (the study of cyclic and seasonal natural phenomena, especially in relation to climate and plant and animal life). GDD are a measure of heat accumulation used by horticulturists, gardeners, beekeepers, and farmers to predict plant and animal development rates such as the date that a flower will bloom, an insect will emerge from dormancy, or a crop will reach maturity.

Indirectly, the timing of certain beekeeper activities, such as swarm prevention and supering, are assisted by our knowledge of the GDD impact on bee flora.

Figure 16-4
Elderberry starts to bloom when the growing degree days reach 330 to 400 GDD. R. Burns

Table 15-1. Growing degree days for common flowers visited by pollinators.

Common name	Latin name	Number of growing degree days baseline 10 °C
Witch-hazel	*Hamamelis* **spp.**	begins flowering at <1 GDD
Red maple	*Acer rubrum*	begins flowering at 1-27 GDD
Sugar maple	*Acer saccharum*	begins flowering at 1-27 GDD
Norway maple	*Acer platanoides*	begins flowering at 30-50 GDD
White ash	*Fraxinus americana*	begins flowering at 30-50 GDD
Crabapple	*Malus* **spp.**	begins flowering at 50-80 GDD
Common broom	*Cytisus scoparius*	begins flowering at 50-80 GDD
Horse chestnut	*Aesculus hippocastanum*	begins flowering at 80-110 GDD
Common lilac	*Syringa vulgaris*	begins flowering at 80-110 GDD
Beach plum	*Prunus maritima*	full bloom at 80-110 GDD
Black locust	*Robinia pseudoacacia*	begins flowering at 140-160 GDD
Catalpa	*Catalpa speciosa*	begins flowering at 250-330 GDD
Privet	*Ligustrum* **spp.**	begins flowering at 330-400 GDD
Elderberry	*Sambucus canadensis*	begins flowering at 330-400 GDD
Purple loosestrife	*Lythrum salicaria*	begins flowering at 400-450 GDD
Sumac	*Rhus typhina*	begins flowering at 450-500 GDD
Butterfly bush	*Buddleia davidii*	begins flowering at 550-650 GDD

https://en.wikipedia.org/wiki/Growing_degree-day#:~:text=Plant%20development%20%20%20Common%20name%20,at%201-27%20GDD%20%2021%20more%20rows%20

| GOOD BEES | + | GOOD WEATHER | + | GOOD LOCATION | = | SURPLUS HONEY |

The work of honey production

Nectar is gathered honey stomach by honey stomach. It has been estimated that bees visit two million flowers to produce a one-pound jar of honey. During a single season, the amount of honey a colony will produce depends on many factors. Collecting, processing and storing 50 pounds of honey is only enough for the colony to get through the season. Beekeepers need double that production to hope to harvest any surplus honey.

Not all beekeepers are interested in maximizing honey production. Beekeepers are often late adding supers and lack sufficient experience to manage the rapid growth spurt of the spring colony. Timing is everything. Understanding the basic seasonal pattern is key to timing management (Figure 16-5). Some areas experience early spring growth followed by a dearth before widespread availability of honey plants, while other areas and different seasons have late spring growth patterns. Potential honey production is just that—potential. It takes experience to maximize colony honey production to consistently produce large surpluses.

Pre-flow management

Beekeepers monitor colony development and need to manipulate (manage) colonies that are not performing as expected. It takes experience to learn the signals of poor colony performance. To produce honey, colonies must have a large adult population at the time of the bloom

Figure 16-5
Irish apiary. Poor weather and only a single nectar source (heather on hillside behind colonies) require skillful beekeepers to obtain harvestable surplus.

providing the nectar, and have enough cell space to store ripening nectar for honey storage.

Colonies that are left alone, such as feral colonies in bee trees or colonies in the wall of a house, will produce some to a lot of surplus honey, provided they have enough storage space and there is a large colony population.

Colony management to produce surplus honey in managed hives is a matter of understanding and utilizing basic bee biology. Full-sized colonies in late-spring (Figure 16-3) should have a super or two on top of the brood chamber, with or without the queen excluder between brood and honey super. Use of a queen excluder is optional. Without use of the excluder, populous colonies may expand their brood chamber into the supers.

After an initial super is added, the beekeeper should continue to check the brood boxes for queen cells until the nectar flow starts. This means removing the super and checking between the brood boxes for queen cells. If developing queen cells are discovered, the beekeeper should seek to control swarming (or not depending upon management philosophy). It is a lot of work. Colonies found with queen cells will require continuous monitoring. Once the nectar flow begins in earnest and additional supers are added, most beekeepers discontinue looking for queen cells because the bees focus on nectar collection and ripening.

When lifting supers, the beekeeper should be conscious of their weight. Look into the super, between the frames, to see how extensively the cells are being used. The bees usually will start in the middle frames so check frames to the sides of the super as well as those in the middle. If in doubt, lift a few frames to see how much nectar is being stored. Cells with ripening honey will not initially be capped with beeswax. Colonies should be over-supered and have a surplus of available empty space prior to the major nectar flow.

The initial super added to the spring colony may be one stored from the previous season. The bees may be reluctant to cross the queen excluder and adopt the initial super offering. When adding a super, it is a good practice to subsequently check to see if the bees are using it.

Nectar flow management

During the actual nectar flow, a period of one to three weeks in some areas, the major beekeeping activity is to monitor storage of the incoming nectar crop and continue to add supers to those colonies needing them. Skillful bee stewards need only to look within the covers or between the super frames to assess how the colony is doing. One important clue, in addition to the numbers of bees present, is the presence of white wax (**whiting**) on the top of the frames (Figure 16-6). Examining a few frames can confirm initial diagnosis (Figure 16-7).

Supering

A super is a box and frames (drawn frames or with foundation) placed above the brood area for honey storage. Supers may be standard deep boxes or may be smaller in depth (but with the same width and length dimensions). Supers have various names such as half-depth, medium-depth, western super or shallow super (Chapter 12, Figure 12-8).

Many beekeepers prefer the shallower boxes for honey since the standard box may weigh nearly 80 pounds (36 kg) when filled with bees and honey. That is a lot to lift using only fingertips and backs—hive structure making it difficult to position the body to properly lift with the legs. Supers are added to a colony with or without a queen excluder (Figures 16-9, 16-10).

Many beekeepers reduce (as illustrated in Figure 16-6) the number of frames in supers to nine or sometimes eight. This enables the bees to extend the cell depth when they fill honey cells. Combs filled beyond the limits of the frame are easier to uncap for extraction of the honey. When reducing frame numbers, beekeepers need to manually space the frames so they are evenly spaced or use a frame-spacing device to ensure uniform frame separations.

Beekeepers who have kept bees for more than one or two seasons, and who protect beeswax comb in storage from wax moth (Chapter 23), will be able to super with drawn comb. The drawn comb provides a stimulus for the bees.

Early in the nectar flow, colonies should be over-supered (more supers added than less). Beekeepers who are new or who lack sufficient drawn comb will need to super

with frames of foundation. To avoid distorted combs, when supering with foundation, use ten frames in ten-frame equipment or eight frames for beekeepers who prefer eight-frame boxes. Rather than supering early, foundation frames should ideally only be added when the flow has actually started and conditions are optimal.

Supers may be added:

- at the top (over the brood box on top of other supers), called **top-supering or over-supering**

- on the bottom (over the brood but beneath other supers), called **bottom-supering**

- by **baiting**, exchanging two or three frames from supers already on the hive with frames from supers about to be added

The advantages of one supering method over another are not large. It is far easier to add supers directly on top of others already on the colony. One disadvantage to **top-supering** is that the bees may not 'discover' and utilize

Figure 16-7
Inspecting a colony to determine if it is ready for its first honey super. L. Connor

Figure 16-6
Whiting, evidence of bee activity in a super.

the empty drawn comb. You can remedy this possibility by checking the supers after adding them to confirm the bees are using them, or by baiting added supers.

Bottom-supering takes more effort since supers in place first need to be removed before adding additional supers to the colony (Figure 16-8). If the colony does not have a queen excluder, the bees may utilize the comb cells of added supers to expand the brood nest upward. Adding supers at the bottom, however, does increase the stimulus empty comb provides to the bees and it is the best location for drawing foundation frames. Additionally bottom-supering means nectar being ripened in cells is moved to the top of the colony where it will have the most favorable micro-climate for passive evaporation.

The third method of adding supers, **baiting**, is a variation of top-supering. Supers are added at the top of existing supers after exchanging a couple of middle frames,

Figure 16-8
Adding a second super under the first (bottom-supering). The first honey super in foreground will be put back on top after the new super is added. NOTE: no queen excluder is being used. L. Connor

on which the bees are already storing nectar, with empty frames taken from the super being added. This management opens up the middle of the super already in place and ensures that the bees 'discover' the additional comb space being provided. On the negative side, this arrangement may encourage 'chimneying,' whereby the bees use only central combs of the supers to store surpluses. Bees can be reluctant to move to outer frames of the supers.

An alternative form of baiting is to **drip sugar syrup** (or honey) on some of the frames of supers to be added. The bees will move onto such frames to clean up the 'mess.' Baiting stimulates new comb building and food storage. Do not do this if there is any danger of robbing.

A few beekeepers selectively remove full frames, and replace them with empty frames. After extracting they may return them if the flow continues. Beekeepers in the south are more likely to use this labor-intensive management where wax moth population pressure makes storage of drawn comb very costly and the nectar flow is more likely to be light and extend over a longer time period. This method does not take advantage of the stimulus empty comb provides to bees and it extends the extracting season for the beekeeper.

Queen excluders

The queen excluder can efficiently maintain the separation of brood and food in the colony (Figure 16-9, 16-10). In nature, separation is maintained by capped cells of honey — the queen searching for empty cells to deposit eggs turns and reverses her direction when she reaches an area where the cells are filled with honey. Beekeepers do not need to use a queen excluder when this condition occurs in their colony (Figure 16-11).

Fully expanded colonies use most of the comb cells in two boxes for brood, except on the outer frames, so there may be few capped honey cells above the brood sphere. When a super is added above the top brood box the bees sometimes expand their brood into the empty cells before the bees have an opportunity to use the cells to store nectar. This happens more frequently when drawn comb supers are used. Therefore, adding that initial super might not accomplish the expected goals of providing room for nectar storage.

Some beekeepers feel that queen excluders can be 'honey excluders' as they impede ventilation and the flow of bees within the nest. This may be compounded when bees fill the excluder space with burr and brace comb.

Providing an upper entrance for foragers directly into the super, or use of the queen excluder only until the first super is being used by the bees for honey storage and nectar ripening, can help alleviate this negative. Once honey is being stored in the initial super, it is okay to remove the queen excluder.

Figure 16-9
Adding a queen excluder over brood nest before adding super.

Figure 16-10
Adding first honey super on top of the queen excluder.

Figure 16-11
Beekeeper using frame grip examines a brood chamber frame. The bees have expanded brood to the outer frames of the second deep box and there is considerable capped honey above the brood, a good indicator that colony is in immediate need of supers. A queen excluder would not likely be necessary, as the honey acts as a barrier for the queen. L. Connor

Excluders are not a tool to prevent swarming. If the old queen is prevented from exiting the hive, the swarm will wait for a new virgin to emerge and she may slip through the excluder and join the swarm. Excluders can interfere with drone movement—if drones are in the hive above the excluder and there is no top entrance their dead bodies may eventually clog the excluder. This can be avoided by keeping all brood comb below the excluder.

The queen excluder is probably the most misunderstood and abused piece of bee equipment in use. Some beekeepers feel they cannot do without them. Others believe the best use of the queen excluder is to throw in front of the colony to keep the grass from blocking the entrance! Despite some potential disadvantages, the queen excluder is a valuable management tool when used to separate brood from honey. Like all tools, it should be used wisely to be of service.

Looking into supered colonies

Once colonies have supers, most bee colony inspections consist of merely looking in the supers to ascertain if additional supers are needed. This requires experience to measure and most beekeepers over-super at the beginning of a honey flow. Under-supering is practiced as the flow proceeds and less equipment becomes available.

DRAWING FOUNDATION

The difference between modern beekeeping and that of our ancestors is the movable comb hive. Obtaining good quality drawn comb from frames of foundation is critical to managing movable comb equipment. You can never have enough good drawn comb.

There is an art to producing good drawn comb. The most appropriate seasonal period for bees to draw out foundation is during the nectar flow period, for this is when there are large bee populations and abundant nectar and pollen resources for forage. This results in high quality drawn comb (Figure 16-12).

Beekeepers without drawn comb must super with foundation. Supering with foundation is different than supering with drawn comb.

Foundation supers should only be placed on strong colonies. Beekeepers should wait until the bees have abundant nectar resources and a large colony population before supering with foundation. Timing is more critical to secure properly drawn comb when supering with foundation.

Foundation frames can be added as an entire super or as replacement of two to four drawn frames. The foundation frames or super of foundation should be placed in the center of or immediately above the brood nest where it will receive maximum attention from the bees. Some beekeepers prefer to stagger foundation and drawn comb frames in the super.

If foundation frames are not drawn immediately by the bees and comb construction completed within a week or so, the chances of obtaining poorly drawn comb increases. If bees initially ignore the foundation, it will not yield first-rate comb when finally drawn by the colony. Bees will chew holes in the foundation, construct drone cells or only partially draw the foundation cells. Frames of foundation should be drawn only in the middle of the brood area/super and only under the best weather and forage conditions possible.

Without foundation, the chance of obtaining well-drawn comb within a frame outline decreases. Figure 16-13 illustrates the exception. Here a natural comb, without foundation, is being drawn within the frame by using a starter strip made of wood. Once firmly fastened to the frame by the bees, it can be used in an extractor if handled carefully by the beekeeper.

To obtain marketable section (comb) honey, cut-comb honey or the honey-filled piece of comb for chunk honey,

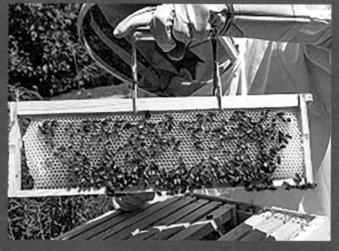

Figure 16-12
Frame of foundation being drawn out by bees on nectar flow.
L. Connor

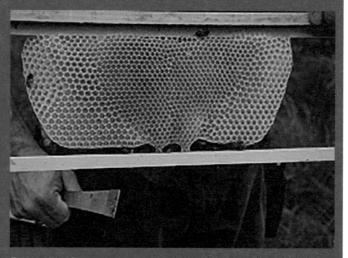

Figure 16-13
Comb being built with a wood starter strip and without foundation. The bees suspend the comb from the top, here in desired alignment with frame. Note the middle comb is built of worker cells, with drone cells on the left and right.
L. Connor

colonies annually need new foundation to be drawn and filled with honey by the bees. To produce salable product, colonies need to be strong to work in the special super used in comb honey production so beekeepers usually crowd the brood nest of the bees as the special supers are added to force the bees to quickly draw and fill the new comb. Special, thin foundation must be used. Foundation frames for cut-comb and chunk honey can be alternated with drawn comb.

Well drawn comb is the most valuable asset of the bees and for the beekeeper.

How can one tell if more supers are needed? Looking in the top of the colony between frames enables experienced beekeepers to determine how full the super may be. It is possible to assess how many bees are present and where they are working. Another clue is to look for whiting, the addition of new, white wax to deepen and repair cells (Figure 16-6). The newly-added wax bees use to cap honey cells will also appear lighter.

Less experienced beekeepers need to remove a few frames to determine if another super might be required (Figure 16-14). The unripened honey will likely run out of the cells so frames should be kept vertical when looking at them. Look on outer frames to see if they are being used. If outer frames are full it usually means the center frames are as well so additional empty comb should be added. Use the 50% rule—if 50% or more of the cells are being used by the bees for nectar ripening or capped honey early in the season, add more empty comb.

Some beekeepers like to move and interchange frames in supers as they are being filled by moving outer, less filled or poorly-drawn foundation frames toward the center and moving the more fully occupied frames to the outside.

Figure 16-14
Looking at honey frame at edge of super. The super has been removed from the colony—normally, there is no need to remove a super to check whether additional supers are needed.

This is labor-intensive work and beekeepers with large numbers of colonies do not feel it worth the effort. Use of this or other labor-intensive techniques depends on a beekeeper's management philosophy and objectives.

Bees need more comb to ripen honey than they will to store it, so over-supering will likely lead to larger surplus harvests. As nectar flows slow, it is advisable to change to under supering and individual frame manipulations. The bees will consolidate the honey stores, reducing the need to handle as many supers and frames when the honey crop is removed. When exactly to switch is difficult to determine—part of the art, not science, of beekeeping.

Experience and knowledge are the best guides.

If you use standard hive bodies for the brood nest and smaller-sized supers, it is a good idea to have the bees store honey in at least one hive body of standard size. Instead of harvesting this box, place it aside (in the freezer if space permits) to be used for emergency feeding in the fall or next spring. If not needed, it will still be possible to extract and use the honey.

One key to producing surplus honey is providing plenty of supers after the colony has fully expanded brood rearing. There are alternative systems to producing larger surpluses. One is the use of two queens to produce, within one stack, two brood areas. At nectar flow, the colony is consolidated and supers are added over the top brood area. If timed correctly, this **two-queen system** can produce a larger surplus harvest (Chapter 15).

Another alternative is to **tower super**. This system utilizes two colonies immediately side-by-side with queen excluders and partial hive covers. Supers are added so both colonies share and store honey in the same stack of supers (Figure 16-15).

The honey harvest

Bees do the work of comb building and honey production. As stewards of colonies, we seek to provide the proper home and conditions for spring colonies to grow populous when the weather cooperates and nectar bearing flowers coincide with peak bee populations. By providing supers, we supply both incentive and space to store surplus. If all goes as planned, the bees fill the supers. We harvest the extra. Sometime before the fall, surplus honey can be removed from the colony.

If for some reason removal is not possible, leave the honey on the bee colony or distribute the surplus honey to colonies that have not produced an adequate amount of stores for winter feed. Considering the varroa problem, recommendations are for removing honey from colonies by July to allow time to apply varroa control treatments.

The steps involved in harvesting honey are:

- removal of honey-filled supers or selected frames from bee colonies

Figure 16-15
A hive where honey supers are placed on two hives at the same time. Boards or special covers protect the exposed comb.

• removal of cappings from combs and extracting of liquid honey, or

• cutting of honey-filled comb into sections for cut-comb/chunk honey

• processing of liquid honey

• processing of cappings wax

• cleaning and storage of extracted frames

• handling bulk honey and/or preparing liquid/comb honey for retail sale

NOTE: If only section or cut-comb honey is produced, removal of the supers (without damaging cells), separation of the individual sections or cutting the comb and packaging of the sections or cut-comb pieces for sale is all that is required (See Box 29).

Honey super removal

Honey is ready for removal when three-fourths or more of the honey-filled cells have been capped. Most beekeepers harvest just once a season. There may be good reasons for removing honey from the colonies more than once, such as:

• lack of sufficient equipment

• desire to harvest honey from different nectar sources

• need for product early in season

• strong nectar flow and supers piled too high

• break between nectar flows

• need to move colonies

• need to treat the colony

Honey should not be removed from the beehive unless it will be extracted or processed within a few days. Otherwise small hive beetles or wax moths may destroy the combs. The bees protect the honey and keep it from fermenting, leaking or being eaten by another animal. Beekeepers cannot store it with any assurance of being able to protect it as well as a strong colony of bees can. Removed honey only when it is ready for extraction!

There are four general methods to remove honey, either entire supers or individual honey filled frames, from bee colonies. Described in Box 39, these include:

• bounce and brush

• bee escape

• fume board

• forced air (bee blower)

When honey-filled supers or frames are removed, beekeepers should work quickly and be watchful to prevent robbing behavior. Cover cleared frames and supers. Do not leave honey-filled frames exposed to robbers within the apiary or on transport vehicles. Harvest only the amount of frames that can be comfortably handled at one time with extracting area capacity. Remember, the honey must be sufficiently ripened so it will not ferment. If some frames are not yet ready for harvest, or if frames contain brood, place them back onto strong colonies.

Extracting

When honey-filled supers are removed from colonies, they should be stored in a warm room at 90° F (32° C) for one to two days to warm the honey. Where small hive beetles are a problem, removed supers should be extracted immediately. Use a dehumidifier to keep the relative humidity below 50% to slow beetle development. Use a small fan to circulate the room air and prevent hot pockets from developing.

Since it is unlikely that frames will be entirely free of bees, the heated room should include a bee escape. If the room is dark, fashioning a cone of wire cloth extending outside from a single exit near the top of the room will allow bees to exit but not reenter to rob the honey. Ideally the warm room is also convenient to the extracting facility.

Once warmed, the frames will be ready to extract. First remove the wax cappings covering the honey-filled cells with a thin, hot, uncapping knife. Beekeepers can purchase such knives, electrically or steam heated, or interchange knives warmed in a pan of hot water. Knives may be serrated or not. One variation is an uncapping plane. Large-scale beekeepers purchase a machine (uncapper) that automatically uncaps the frames (Figure 16-23). Various uncapping tools are used to uncap honey.

The cappings are captured in a tank above a screen. They can contain considerable honey which needs to drain

Box 39

Removing bees from supers

Beekeepers commonly bounce and brush frames from each super by bouncing the top bar on the ground in front of the hive or giving the frame a sharp snap or shake to dislodge the bees back into the super. Use a soft bristle brush (Figure 16-16) or a stiff feather to remove any adult bees remaining. Don't bounce frames on the hive itself. Use care or heavy frames may break.

Bee escapes are an effective low-technology method to remove bees from supers under certain conditions. There are several modified versions, such as the triangle escape board (Figure 16-17), that work efficiently. Such devices replace the standard inner cover.

The Porter-type bee escape is a metal or plastic device that fits in the oval hole of the inner cover (Figure 16-18). The bee escape is placed in the inner cover hole and the inner cover positioned between the top brood box of the brood nest and under the super(s) you wish to remove. When installing, it is important to use as little smoke as possible and to not tear or puncture honey-filled cells, as bees will seek to clean up the honey, delaying their exit from the supers. If supers contain brood or nights remain warm, this simple clearing device does not work as well.

A fume board (Figure 16-19) is essentially a modified cover with an absorbent cloth on one side and a shiny cover on the side that faces the sun. To activate, a small amount of repellent chemical is sprinkled on the cloth and the board placed directly over the super to be removed. The sun's heat volatilizes the chemical and the odor forces the bees to move downward in a few minutes. Bees will crawl outside the hive and create 'beards' while avoiding the chemical.

Approved repellent chemicals are: Bee-Go® (butyric anhydride) and Fischer's Bee-Quick®. These chemicals work well under the proper conditions. Use care not to spill these chemicals in transport vehicles or on clothing; residues could be a contamination issue.

Bee blowers (Figure 16-20) use forced air to forcefully blow the bees out of the honey supers. Supply firms sell electric or gasoline-powered bee blowers. Lawn leaf blowers can be adapted by the smaller operator. Blowers disorient bees and throw them into the air so there is little organized hive defense. It is recommended that the bees be blown toward the entrance of their colony. The beekeeper must take care not to walk on the ground where the bees are blown.

Figure 16-16
Brushing bees off a comb.

Figure 16-17
Triangular bee escape.
Betterbee

Figure 16-18
Porter-style bee escape fits into inner cover.

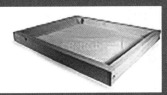

Figure 16-19
Fume board uses a strong odor to repell bees.
Betterbee

Figure 16-20
Modified leaf blower blasts bees out of the super.

Figure 16-21
Inexpensive homemade extractor assembled with a plastic tub, a power drill, and hardware. From *Bee Equipment Essentials*. E. Simon

Figure 16-22
Small extractor in use. One person hand cranks to spin the frames and two others hold the extractor in place.

from the wax cappings. Commercial beekeepers move the cappings into a wax melter to speed the process.

Much of the heating is accomplished with hot water in doubled-jacketed equipment. A solar wax melter can serve the small-scale beekeeper. All honey and capping-handling tanks are preferably of stainless steel, although plastic equipment is increasingly being utilized.

After uncapping both sides of the frames, they are placed in an extractor (Figures 16-21, 16-22, 16-25). Extractors are machines that remove the honey by use of centrifugal force. A suspended basket holds the uncapped frames as they are rotated within a metal or plastic cylinder. Centrifugal motion forcefully throws the liquid honey out of the comb cells against the outer wall. The liberated

honey drains downward (gravitational force) and is removed from the bottom through a honey gate.

Larger extractors hold frames radially (perpendicular to the axis); honey is removed from both sides of the frame at the same time. Electric motors do the work. Frames are positioned tangential in less expensive, smaller models; only one side of the frame is emptied at a time. Most work manually with a hand crank (Figure 16-22). Figure 16-21 shows a hand drill motorization. Frames need to be manually turned 180° in tangential extractors to extract the opposite side.

Extractors are constructed to hold from two to 80 or more frames. Commercial operations use the larger volume extractors and may need more than one machine since it takes up to fifteen minutes to extract honey from frames.

The extractor is a large expense for a small-scale beekeeper. Prices for the smallest hand-operated models start around $200 and for the entire extracting outfit of extractor, tanks, knife, etc. around $500.

Some bee clubs own extractors and rent them to members having a small number of frames to extract. Beekeepers upgrading to larger-volume extractors offer used extractors for sale from time to time. Since extractors are not heavily used, those properly cared for hold much of their original value. A few beekeepers custom extract for other beekeepers.

Destruct harvest

If an extractor is not available, consider a destruct harvest method to separate liquid honey from wax. In destruct harvest, the comb is cut from the frames and placed in a suspended nylon or fine mesh cloth where it is crushed so the honey may drain out. This process works better in a warm area.

Figure 16-23
Automated commercial frame uncapper. The frame drops into a chute, the front and back cappings are sliced off before moving on a chain conveyor belt, to the extractor.

Figure 16-24
Small-scale beekeeper uncapping setup. The frame is positioned on a board over a collecting tray that drains cappings once cut off the frame with an uncapping knife. The uncapped frame is then placed into the extractor. C. Burkhead

Figure 16-25
Extractor with a screen at the honey gate; in back is an uncapping setup. In front right: cart with supers and empty combs, front left: settling/bottling tank with bottling gate. C. Burkhead

Box 40

HONEY IN THE COMB

The alternative to extracting honey is to harvest and sell honey as stored by the bees — in the original beeswax comb. There are three common methods of producing and selling honey in the comb: section, cut-comb or chunk honey. They do not require the purchase of expensive honey extraction equipment. However, colony management is more difficult and colony management more intensive than for extracted honey.

Section (comb) honey is produced by the bees in original containers that are used directly by the consumer (Figure 16-26). Cut-comb are pieces of comb cut from the frame (Figure 16-27) while chunk honey is a piece of comb surrounded by liquid honey (Figure 16-28).

Production of honey in the comb requires use of special supers and thin, pure, edible, beeswax foundation. The bees work in small sections of wood (Figure 16-26) or plastic circles held in specially designed supers. For top quality appearance, the supers are not added until the nectar flow begins. They need to be promptly removed following completion and capping of the honey-filled cells to remain clean of bee feet traffic.

Since bees are sometimes reluctant to work in these smaller spaces, the production colony must be crowded and bees stimulated to draw and fill the sections quickly. Such management is labor-intensive and proper timing is essential for a quality product. The crowded colony must be managed to avoid swarming.

Cut-comb honey does not require special supers. Thin foundation is used. To improve yield, the bees are crowded in the brood area of the production colonies. Once capped, honey-filled frames need to be promptly harvested to prevent staining of the cappings and damage by pests.

The filled frames are placed on screening, comb pieces are cut from the frame and honey allowed to drain from the cut edges for a day or so before being packaged into containers (Figure 16-27).

For chunk honey, cut-comb honey is cut from the frame and placed into a wide-mouthed jar or container. Liquid honey (from an extractor or squeezed and drained from the comb) is poured around the piece of comb to fill the remainder of the container, immersing the piece of honey-filled comb. This is a regional product favored by the producers of orange blossom honey in Florida and sourwood honey in the Carolina mountains (Figure 16-28). Avoid this product if you have fast-crystalizing honey.

Figure 16-26
Comb honey in wooden sections. A specialty product.

Figure 16-27
Cut-comb honey processing: top-cut and drain comb pieces, middle-empty containers, bottom-packaged comb honey.
C. Burkhead

Figure 16-28
Sourwood chunk honey.

Figure 16-29
Liquid honey or crushed honey comb may be strained into a bucket through a long, open-top nylon filter. L. Connor

Another destruct harvest method is to put combs of honey in a double boiler and carefully heat the water to a temperature sufficient to liquefy the wax and free the honey. Use only enough heat to melt the wax, as too much heat impairs the flavor and darkens the honey. The heat should then be turned off and the honey and wax allowed to cool (cooling quickly is advised). The wax will rise to the top and can be lifted off in the form of a cake after it solidifies.

Do not directly heat the wax combs — beeswax has a low flash-point and might catch on fire.

Settling and packaging

Following extraction, liquid honey should be coarsely strained (Figure 16-29) and then allowed to settle so air bubbles, large particles of beeswax and other impurities float to the top. Use a large container, termed a **settling tank**. For smaller quantities, use a food-approved five-gallon bucket with a honey gate. Honey may be coarsely filtered through metal or plastic filters at this stage. Honey from the extractor and honey drained from cappings can be placed together into a single large settling tank. In a warm environment, settling only takes a day or so.

Smaller-scale beekeepers use buckets to transfer liquid honey — commercial beekeepers connect uncappers, extractors and settling tanks with large diameter hoses and use a geared-down honey pump to move the liquids. In either method, care should be taken so as not to incorporate additional air bubbles into the liquid honey.

Honey may be directly bottled from the settling tank (Figure 16-31) or collected into five to fifty gallon (20 to 200 liter) buckets or barrels to wholesale or store for bottling later.

Honey in storage may granulate within the storage containers if not immediately bottled, especially when not heated and strained. Naturally crystallized honey has a gritty or coarse structure, often unpleasant in the

Figure 16-30
Following extraction, tip the tanks to pour out the last of the honey into a five gallon (19 liter) bucket. L. Connor

mouth. Consumers who see naturally crystallizing honey on shelves or in their cabinet often mistakenly consider it spoiled and throw it away.

Granulated honey, whether in bottle or storage container, needs to be reliquified. Such honey should be gently heated in containers so as not to harm its flavor or color by overheating. Reliquifying is often a challenge and most operations that handle honey in bulk containers have adopted a convenient way to accomplish this task. **Double jacketed tanks** that heat water to circulate around the storage container are the best means of reliquifying honey. Care is needed to avoid pockets of excessive heat.

An alternative is to convert the liquid into a granulated form. When done correctly, the honey will have a consistent, smooth, butter-like consistency with long shelf life (see Chapter 17, Box 30 for details on honey granulation).

Liquid honey may be further processed by flash-heating and pumping the liquid through fine filters, mainly to prolong shelf life since this will delay granulation. This process is called **filtering**. Such further processing additionally helps to clarify the final bottled product.

Depending upon the type of filter used (and time/amount of heat), most of the pollen that gets into the liquid honey during the extracting process is removed along with impurities. Such honey may then be difficult to identify as to floral source.

Figure 16-31
Bottling honey from a five gallon plastic container. From *Bee Equipment Essentials*. E. Simon

Figure 16-32
These hexagon jars were just filled with honey and will be capped, labeled and taken to market. L. Connor

Honey processed by local beekeepers for artisan or varietal sales is seldom heated or finely filtered.

Handling beeswax

Wax cappings (removed by the uncapping knife) are the principle harvest of beeswax. One to two pounds (1/2 to 1 kg) of beeswax is the usual harvest per 100 pounds (45 kg) of honey extracted. This beeswax will be light in color and top quality, once cleaned of honey and impurities.

To process, allow the majority of the honey to drain from the beeswax cappings before melting the wax in a double boiler. Pour the liquid beeswax into molds for cooling. Beeswax should never be heated directly due to its low flash point and fire hazard. A beeswax fire is very difficult to extinguish.

Some beekeepers scrape extra wax from top bars and collect pieces of burr and brace comb the bees build in their hive throughout the season. This wax can also be melted (using a solar wax melter or in a double boiler) and placed in molds. It is likely to be darker (due to travel stain) so it should be kept separate from cappings wax.

Cleaning up

After extraction, empty comb can then be returned to the bees for refilling or saved for another season. Extracted (termed 'wet') frames are messy and sticky. They can be stored in this condition but are best returned to a hive so the bees will clean up any residual honey and start to repair the comb.

Wet supers can be returned to the apiary for robbing by bees. It is recommended that the supers be placed above colonies over the inner cover hole so bees from an individual colony can clean the wet combs (controlled robbing). It is not necessary to return the supers or individual frames to the colonies from which they were removed if the apiary is free of bee diseases. Weaker colonies will benefit most from controlled robbing. The wet frames can be used to feed colonies light on honey stores.

Extractors, settling tanks, tanks for cappings etc. need to be thoroughly rinsed of residue and stored dry until subsequent use. Some states inspect and/or license honey extracting facilities (often for beekeepers over a certain volume of honey production, excluding the majority of the small-scale beekeepers). Beekeepers contemplating expansion or sale of their product should determine local regulations—members of local or state beekeeping associations will know those laws and regulations and can help advise on such matters.

There are strict regulations on labeling of bee products for retail sale. Check with local associations or individuals offering honey (or other bee products) for sale regarding these requirements.

Non-flow (summer) management

Non-flow management follows the nectar flow and includes:

- completing the ripening of honey and cleaning of wet supers

- removal (and repair) of poor combs/bee equipment in need of repair

- trapping pollen (Chapter 17)
- transferring colonies into standard equipment (Chapter 12, Box 14)
- rearing queens (Chapter 18)
- making summer/fall nucs (Chapter 19)
- sampling for varroa mites and possibly treating (Chapter 21)
- monitoring colony health (Chapters 22 and 23)

In the summer remove frames in poor condition—old, dark brood frames, comb with unwanted drone cells and those in need of other repair. Replace other equipment as you are able.

key terms

baiting	destruct harvest	growing degree days (GDD)	settling tank
bee blower	double boiler	honey plants	straining liquid honey
bee diseases	drawn comb	natural comb	super
bee escape	drawing foundation	nectar (honey) flow	top supering
bottom supering	extracted (liquid) honey	nectar secretion	tower supering
bounce and brush	extractor (radial & tangential)	nectar sugar concentration	two-queen colony
cappings	filtering honey	*Nosema*	uncapping knife
chunk honey	foundation	pesticide exposure	uncapper (machine)
colony morale	frame grip	queen excluder	wax melter
crystallized (granulated) honey	frame spacer	robbing	wet extracted frames
cut comb honey	fume board	section honey	whiting

discussion questions

Do all nectar-producing plants produce a nectar flow? What are the four conditions that help ensure a good amount of surplus honey? What long-term measures could be done to improve beekeeper harvests?

Describe supering. How does supering with drawn comb differ from supering with foundation? Distinguish between top or bottom supering and why baiting of supers makes sense. What is meant by oversupering or undersupering and when should one vs. the other be done?

What are the four methods of removing honey from bee colonies? Describe the process of getting honey into bottles for sale. What are the advantages and disadvantages of harvesting honey once per nectar flow and once per year?

What should be done if you are not able to extract or process surplus honey promptly? Why do we cease looking in the brood chamber of a colony once we add supers? How do you inspect a super differently from a brood chamber?

Describe the processing of extracted honey from both commercial and small-scale beekeeper perspectives. What are the costs of processing equipment? What are the benefits and drawbacks of producing honey in the comb? Or destruct harvest of honey-filled combs? What is your view of the need of filtration of honey whereby most (all) of the pollen might be removed?

exercises

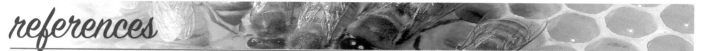

Demonstrate the three variations in supering a bee colony. If colonies are not available, use empty equipment. In your demonstration seek to use full-depth boxes, supers of one or more sizes, comb honey supers, and supers with foundation frames. Evaluate the advantages of one over the other. Discuss supering with supers of full-depth frames versus shallower supers. How does supering with foundation differ from use of drawn-comb supers?

Draw frames of foundation under several conditions as follows: early spring during population increase, in late spring, during the nectar flow and in the fall or a non-flow period. Keep conditions constant by placing two frames of foundation in the middle of the brood area during each time period. Determine differences in the drawn combs and measure the time needed to draw the comb. Prepare an essay or oral presentation on the advantages/disadvantages of drawing foundation under each of these conditions.

Design a honey extraction facility that would be convenient for a sideliner with 50 to 150 colonies. What would be different from the extracting/honey handling of a one- to five-colony beekeeper and that of a commercial beekeeper?

Seek to assist a local beekeeper with removal, extraction and processing of honey. Visit a large commercial honey extracting facility near you or a honey processing plant. Evaluate for efficiency.

Determine the legal requirements (if any) for honey extracting facilities and for sale of honey in your state.

references

Binnie, B. 2018. Processing honey: A closer Look. Bee Culture. March 2018. https://www.beeculture.com/processing-honey-a-closer-look/

Connor, L.J. 2012. Bee-sentials, Wicwas Press, Kalamazoo, MI

Connor, L.J. 2019. Keeping Bees Alive, Wicwas Press, Kalamazoo, MI

Crane, E. 1975. Honey, A Comprehensive Survey. Crane, Russak & Co, New York, NY

Delaplane, K. 2006. Honey Bees and Beekeeping, Third Edition. The Georgia Center for Continuing Education, Athens, GA

Doolittle, G.M. 1908. A Year's Work in an Out-Apiary. Reprinted 2005, Wicwas Press, Kalamazoo, MI

Morse, R.A. 1983. A Year in the Beeyard. Scribner, New York

Scottish beekeepers. 2016. Processing honey. https://www.youtube.com/watch?v=xheqa6h3R9E

Simon, E. 2011. Bee Equipment Essentials. Wicwas Press, Kalamazoo, MI

UGA. Processing honey leaflet. https://bees.caes.uga.edu/bees-beekeeping-pollination/getting-started-topics/getting-started-processing-honey.html#top

Figure 17-1
Food exchange between a forager on the right and a house bee on the left. L. Connor

Concepts

Honey and hive products
   what is honey?
   fine crystallization
   uses of honey
   comb honey
Beeswax
   uses of beeswax
Royal jelly
Bee brood
Propolis
Pollen
Live bees
Bee brood
Other income opportunities

Honey & hive products

Undoubtedly it was honey, one of the oldest sweeteners, that attracted humans to the honey bee. Other than ripe fruits in season, honey was just about the only sweetener in the human diet until sugar was brought from China to the Mediterranean area about 700 AD. Sugar cane juice was first used 4,000 BC and sugar granules harvested about two thousand years ago.

Sugar was initially a very expense spice used medicinally. It was not readily available until sugar cane was carried by Columbus to the New World.

In ancient literature, honey and honey bees are mentioned with much feeling and gratitude for their bounty. The Bible perhaps expresses this best, speaking of a land 'flowing with milk and honey.'

In the early days, honey was gathered from the nests of wild (feral) bees in trees and rock crevices. Later, bees and their hives were part of every monastery, castle and farm garden. As honey was the principal sweetener until the 19th century, many small rural households kept bees. Old English manor account books indicate that meats like hams were originally cured in honey and fruits preserved in honey solutions. The rinsing of the combs was used to make mead, the ancient honey drink that was known to all people of antiquity, from the Druids in Britain to the Persians of the Middle East.

Throughout the world honey is used not only as a sweetener and in cooking/preserving but also for medicinal purposes. Even today, honey is used medicinally to heal wounds and to treat burns, in ceremonies and worship and is considered by some to be the elixir of life.

Some of the statements and medical claims made about the virtues of honey and bee products are questionable. Still, there are many who believe that honey has special virtues, not only as a sweetened specialty diet product and dietary carbohydrate, but also as a cure and preventive for many ailments.

HON-EY (hun'e), n., pl. hon-eys, adj., v., hon-eyed or honied, hon-ey-ing.—a sweet, viscid fluid produced by bees from the nectar collected from flowers, and stored in their nests or hives as food. 2. the nectar of flowers. 3. something sweet, delicious, or delightful. 4. (often cap.) darling; sweetheart (used as a term of endearment for a loved one). 5. informal. something of esp. high quality, degree of excellence, etc. 6. informal. (often fol. by up) to use flattery, endearing terms, etc. [Middle Eng. hony, Old Eng. hunig; Ger., Dutch honig; akin to Greek knekos pale yellow, tawny]

—Webster's Dictionary

What is honey?

Honey, by definition, only comes from honey bees. Honey is basically a sugar solution of two simple sugars, glucose (dextrose) and fructose (levulose). Honey does not occur naturally; it is solely a product of the honey bee. Honey is produced from nectar, a sugary plant secretion high in moisture content, collected and converted by bees into honey (Figure 17-2).

Figure 17-2
A piece of natural comb, newly made, and being filled with nectar being ripened into honey.

Contrary to what many people believe, honey is not a mixture of nectar and pollen though both may be collected by bees from flowers. Liquid (extracted or crushed) honey frequently has pollen grains incorporated during processing. Such pollen helps to identify nectar sources for floral labeling of honey.

Both a physical and a chemical change occur in conversion of nectar to honey. To change nectar into honey, the bees (1) convert the nectar sugars to the two principal sugars of honey and (2) evaporate a majority of the water from the nectar.

The complex plant sugars (sucrose is the most common sugar but over a dozen others have been identified) are changed to their simplest six-carbon form by the addition of the **enzyme sucrase**. Worker bees produce the enzyme in their hypopharyngeal glands and thoroughly mix it with the nectar. The enzyme causes the complex nectar sugars to be reduced to the two **simple sugars, glucose and fructose**.

Diagrammatically, the chemical reaction is as follows:

$$C_{12}H_{22}O_{11} + H_2O \xrightarrow{\text{sucrase}} C_6H_{12}O_6 + C_6H_{12}O_6$$

sucrose   water   glucose   fructose

Glucose is less stable and its molecules reform into more complex sugars, though in small amounts. Bees also add another enzyme, glucose oxidase, which breaks some of the glucose into gluconic acid (the major acid of honey) and hydrogen peroxide (H_2O_2). Hydrogen peroxide is a mild anti-bacterial substance and, along with the glucose oxidase, is one of the reasons honey is a safe and digestible food, even when kept over a long time. Honey is more viscous and concentrated than nectar; both properties additionally help preserve honey from spoilage.

Honey bees, as well as humans and other animals, do not need to further digest the six-carbon sugars of honey. They are absorbed directly from the digestive tract. In contrast, sucrose, sugar produced from sugar cane (crystallized table sugar) or sugar beets (principally used in processed foods, soft drinks, etc.) and other plant sugars (agave syrup, maple syrup, etc.), must first be digested and converted to glucose and fructose before absorption.

Honey contains other components which naturally occur in nectar, including minerals, vitamins, acids, pigments, enzymes and aroma components. These materials pass, unchanged, from nectar to honey and, although they generally constitute less than 3% of the final product, they are largely responsible for giving honey its distinctive color, taste and aroma. Honey is more than a simple sugar solution.

To process nectar, hive bees take a portion of the nectar load of an incoming forager (Figures 17-1, 17-3, 17-4) then seek a quiet place in the hive to continue nectar conversion in a process called **active evaporation**. They regurgitate a portion of the nectar from their honey stomach to produce a bubble at the mouthparts (Figure 17-5). This creates a large surface-to-volume ratio, allowing the water to evaporate in the warm hive environment.

The bubble is taken back into the honey stomach and mixed with the remainder of the nectar and enzyme before producing another bubble. The hive bee continues this activity for several minutes with each stomach load.

The second phase of nectar ripening is termed **passive evaporation**. Following the bubble-blowing active evaporation, the hive bees begin storing the now ripening nectar ("green" or unripe honey) in beeswax cells (Figure 17-6). They initially hang droplets in beeswax cells to create a large surface for continued rapid evaporation. As the ripening process proceeds in the warm hive environment, sped up by bees circulating the air, bees consolidate the droplets.

Figure 17-4
Nectar forager (left) offers nectar drop to a hive bee (right).

Figure 17-5
Active nectar evaporation by a hive bee using her mouthparts to expose a bubble of nectar to the heated hive air. From O. W. Park, 1925.

Figure 17-3
Food exchange on newly constructed comb. L. Connor

While nectar varies from 5 to 80% water (most are in the 20 to 50% range) the final water content of honey is usually less than 20% (16-19%). When the cells are filled and sufficiently dehydrated, they are capped with a beeswax covering or capping (Figures 16-7, 16-8). In this form, honey lasts indefinitely, protected by its high sugar and acid content, thick viscosity and enzymatic activity inhibiting microorganism growth.

What can go wrong?

Honey, as produced by the bees, is a natural, pure product, but when taken from a colony, extracted and processed for sale it may be subject to mishandling. The addition of pollen during the extracting process is one example. Many feel this is a valuable addition and actively seek local, non-processed honey as they believe it is useful in treating allergies.

Honey, removed from the beehive, may **ferment**. This can occur because honey is hygroscopic, absorbing moisture from damp air. In a beehive, worker bees regulate the hive environment to ensure that stored honey does not ferment. Beekeepers harvesting honey need to take precautions that the percentage of moisture in the honey remains below the level where fermentation occurs (18.6%). This is done

Figure 17-6
Bees are drawing comb from foundation and using the cells to passively ripen nectar. L. Connor

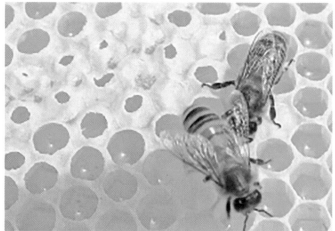

Figure 17-7
Workers capping cells of nearly ripened honey. L. Connor

by harvesting only honey that is fully capped and then processing the product without delay (Figure 17-8).

Liquid honey will eventually **granulate**. Granulation occurs because the sugar glucose is unstable as a liquid and naturally forms crystals. When honey granulates, excess water rises to the top layer and may ferment.

Granulation is a physical molecular change and not a biological spoilage. The exception is in the topmost fermenting liquid layer, making it less attractive to consumers. Too few consumers understand that granulated honey is not spoiled. In fact since honey may easily be adulterated, crystallization is considered by some as an indicator of pure honey.

Beekeepers, in processing liquid honey, can slow the granulation process. Processing, sometimes termed pasteurization, involves heating extracted honey while forcing it through a fine filter. Filtered honey appears bright and clear and will remain in the liquid state for a longer time. This increases shelf life and attractiveness of the product. Small-scale beekeepers often strain honey to remove large particles but usually lack the equipment to finely filter honey. Subsequently, their honey is likely to appear cloudy and granulate more rapidly.

Filtering removes particles of dirt, wax, already formed sugar crystals and air bubbles. Granulated honey can be liquefied by gently heating until the crystals are dissolved. Too much heat or prolonged heating, even gentle heating, darkens honey and reduces its high quality. Honey from floral sources with a higher glucose level granulate rapidly while honey with a high percentage of fructose may take several years to granulate.

Kinds of honey

Today, honey is available year round from local beekeepers and from around the world. The flowers from which bees gather nectar largely determine the color, flavor, and aroma of honey. Well known floral sources are orange blossom,

alfalfa, blackberry, buckwheat, sage and clover. When there is no designation of the flower source, the honey should be considered a blend of different floral types. Some beekeepers designate this blend as wildflower honey. Usually the lighter the color of honey, the milder the flavor and the greater its sales appeal. Consult the National Honey Board website www.honey.com for additional information on honey.

Honey is available in three styles: extracted, comb, and chunk. More than 75% of the US crop is sold as extracted honey (Figure 17-12). Extracted honey is the liquid honey separated from beeswax combs (Chapter 16). It is the type most often used for cooking, as a condiment, and to make mead.

In addition to being available as a liquid, extracted honey may be marketed as creamed (crystallized) honey. Creamed honey is extracted liquid honey that has been prepared in a semisolid state (Box 41, Figure 17-9).

Figure 17-8
A full frame of capped honey ready to harvest.

FINE CRYSTALLIZATION

The market quality of crystallized or granulated honey (Figure 17-9) is influenced by the size of crystals. Honey with fine crystals is more palatable than honey with coarse, gritty crystals. Honey to be marketed successfully in granulated form should have fine crystals and must be prepared using special methods. Honey that crystallizes naturally will not produce the desired fine crystal form. The inadequate control of fermentation and crystallization was a serious handicap in the successful marketing of crystallized honey until what is commonly known as the Dyce method was developed.

The Dyce process heats honey to destroy yeasts and melt crystals, filters it, then mixes it with small seed crystals. It is then placed at the proper temperature to form microscopically small crystals. The resulting product has a uniform creamy smoothness not found in ordinary granulated honey because the resulting crystals are very small. Chemically, the honey is not modified in any way by this process; only the physical size of the crystals is affected.

The following is a summary of the process: The honey should be heated until it is totally liquefied and until a temperature of about 150° F (66° C) is reached. The honey should then be thoroughly strained through several layers of fine nylon, a pressure filter press with diatomaceous earth or some other medium that will remove all foreign particles.

The honey should be stirred constantly and sufficiently to prevent overheating. The agitation should be from below the surface of the honey in order to prevent air bubbles being incorporated.

The honey should be cooled as rapidly as possible to about 80° F (27° C), and agitated again without incorporating air. This will remove the cooled viscous honey from the sides of the tank.

When the temperature of the honey is between 70 and 80° F (21 and 27° C), 10.0% of starter, which consists of fine, creamy, previously processed honey, is thoroughly mixed with the honey which has been heated, strained and cooled. This starter, or 'seed,' should have been ground to reduce the crystal size. Do not mix in air bubbles.

The honey is then left to settle for an hour or two, thoroughly skimmed if necessary, and then placed into containers of the size desired for market and stored at a temperature not higher than 57° F (14° C) and not lower than 45° F (7° C) until completely crystallized. This usually requires about eight days. The reason for leaving the honey to settle for a while before putting it into containers is to allow the majority of the air bubbles to rise to the surface. This precaution helps eliminate a frothy ring on the surface of the containers.

Honey high in water content should be blended with honey low in water content, so the resulting honey is between 15.5% to 18% moisture. This precaution will usually result in a spreadable product which is not too hard or too soft. Once formed, the product has a stable shelf life unless exposed to continuous temperatures above 80° F (27° C). It may be frozen for storage.

Figure 17-9
Bottles of creamed, granulated, honey in a cool room in a small-scale apiary.
L. Connor

In some areas, such as Canada and Europe, beekeepers routinely market crystallized honey. Unlike the natural crystals that are coarse and gritty in the mouth, controlled granulation produces smooth-tasting crystals the consistency of butter. Proper preparation of this product necessitates heating, filtering and seeding with previously crystallized honey.

Comb honey is wax comb filled by bees with honey and sold in wood or plastic sections. Section-comb honey is produced in the hive in square wooden boxes (Chapter 16, Figure 16-26) or in circular plastic holders (Figure 17-11). Comb honey is fragile and hard to handle; it is more commonly available at farm markets and at roadside stands, especially in the late summer or fall at harvest time.

Alternately, beekeepers may cut pieces of filled comb and wrap it in plastic wrap or put the comb in a plastic container. This is called cut-comb honey (Figure 17-10, Chapter 16, Figure 16-27)). It is more common than section comb as it is a bit easier to manage colonies to produce cut-comb honey. Chunk honey consists of pieces of the honey-filled comb put in a wide-mouth container with extracted honey filled in around the chunks (Chapter 16, Figure 16-28).

The yield of honey from a beehive will vary from one location and season to the next. Some locations are very reliable sites year after year, consistently producing surplus honey. Most beehives eventually produce some surplus honey provided there is beeswax comb available for the bees to store and ripen honey. Generally, the more beeswax combs available for the bees, the more honey they store. Populous colonies and timing of management are important to maximize honey yield.

Other sources of honey

By definition in several state laws (there is no federal law), honey is pure. It cannot be mixed with other materials and be legally labeled as honey, though this is frequently violated. From time to time 'artificial' honey has been sold, although the name is not consistent with the definition. Items might be called honey or nectar but actually be a sweetener from another sugar source. They will have few of the properties of true honey.

Honey bees collect nectar from flower nectaries, but not all nectar is floral in origin. Honey bees may also collect plant sap from extra-floral nectaries and convert the liquid into honey. Both floral nectar and that from extra-floral nectaries taste the same. Nectar from blueberry and cotton is commonly collected at leaf extra-floral nectaries.

Honey bees also collect honeydew, the sweet excretion of aphids, scale insects, tree hoppers and other plant sucking insects (Figure 17-13). Honey from honeydew is high in mineral content and usually granulates rapidly.

Locally, it may be called forest honey. It is reported to be the favorite honey of some consumers in Europe, such as the Bavarian region of southern Germany, where honeydew may be a major sugar source available for bees.

In addition to honey bees, honey may be produced by bumble bees, harvester ants (one group is called honey ants), honey gathering wasps and from stingless bees in the tropics. Only the latter insect produces a quantity worthy of harvest. Unfortunately, the culture of stingless bees, meliponiculture (after the major genus of stingless bees), is disappearing as the harvest potential is not very good. Stingless bee honey is, however, highly sought after as a medicine. Stingless bee honey is more acidic and higher in water content and is principally the sugar trehalulose (previously mis-identified as maltose) but is otherwise quite similar to honey from honey bees (Figure 17-14).

Adulteration of honey with other sugar sources is a widespread concern of the beekeeping industry. Because honey commands a considerably higher market price than other sugar sources, there is a financial incentive to mix a small amount of honey with less expensive sugars. Such adulteration can only be detected by specific lab tests,

Figure 17-10
Cut comb draining on a food rack. L. Connor

Figure 17-11
The Ross Rounds system of comb honey production allows bees to put honey directly into the circular plastic frame. The beekeeper adds lids and a label. Ross Rounds

unlike what is suggested on certain Internet sites. With less than one-quarter of domestic consumption of honey being produced by United States beekeepers, the possibility that a jar of honey in the domestic market is not real honey is a distinct possibility. In some countries, adulterated 'honey' is extremely common (Figure 17-15).

Uses of honey

Honey is both a versatile food and a traditional medicine. It is most commonly used today as a dietary sweetener in drinks, in glazes for meats or vegetables, in desserts, in salad dressings or in other foods where a sweet taste is desired. Since it is immediately absorbed from the digestive tract without further digestion, it is used by young and old alike as an energy source. Honey is prized for aerobic exercise. Endurance athletes like it for ready digestibility and even release of its carbohydrates. Some athletes like to use honey to regulate blood sugar levels and to restore body sugars after strenuous activity.

Honey is especially useful in bread and baked goods since its moisture-absorbing quality helps keep baked goods fresher for a longer period of time. Honey can be blended with butter, combined with ice cream, or used with various extracts to yield a blended syrup taste.

Honey adds consumer appeal to a wide variety of processed foods—breakfast cereals, snack foods, sauces and glazes. Honey may be prominent on the label but might not be the principle sugar source in the product. Truth in labeling is a big concern.

Much of the world uses honey for medicinal rather than dietary purposes. Honey, especially darker varieties, is high in antioxidants. Manuka honey from New Zealand is especially prized for this quality; among North American honeys, buckwheat has a higher antioxidant content compared to other (lighter) varieties tested.

Not all medicinal claims for honey or other bee products should be accepted, as too few have been rigorously examined in controlled double-blind medical studies. Many reported uses are anecdotal rather than based on experimental testing.

Honey is widely accepted as a burn and human skin treatment, as relief for a sore throat, ear infections, periodontal disease and gingivitis (although the high acidity would potentially cause other mouth problems) and to relieve persistent coughing among children. A few additional uses, by no means exhaustive, include:

- vehicle for medicine
- medicine (sore throats, burn relief, etc.)
- allergy relief
- antiseptic and antibacterial wound dressing

Figure 17-13
Aphids secrete honeydew, a sweet liquid honey bees turn into honeydew honey, and ants collect as a food source. L. Connor

Figure 17-12
Three different packages by one beekeeper in Texas. L. Connor

Figure 17-14
Stingless bee honey in bottles.

Figure 17-15
Buying honey in a local market in Bolivia. Price is cheap, no label, no honey in comb—is this product really honey?

- ingredient in cosmetics, lotions, soap, shampoo
- ingredient in gum
- processing of cigarettes, pipe bowls
- golf ball center
- embalming fluid
- counteract alcohol effects in blood

Beeswax

Not all beekeepers keep bees to produce honey. Some beekeepers keep beehives for other products, such as beeswax. Beeswax is produced by worker bees from four pair of special glands on the underside of their abdomen (Chapter 4, Figure 4-7). The wax is secreted as translucent scales and molded by the bees' mouthparts into six-sided comb cells (Figure 17-16). Bees use beeswax to cap honey-filled (Figure 17-7) and pupal cells. Starting as white flakes, beeswax comb darkens as bees walk over, rear young in, and store honey and pollen in it.

Beeswax consists of fairly short, 16- to 34-hydrocarbon acid and alcohol chains. It is very stable and not subject to deterioration. It has a low melting point of 143-145° F (62-63° C) and a natural, very pleasant aroma.

Beeswax is only obtained from honey bees. As beekeepers remove the wax cappings of honey-filled comb to extract the liquid honey, they accumulate beeswax at the rate of one to two pounds per 100 lb of honey (one-half to one kg per 45 kg). Beekeepers also melt used comb, burr/brace comb and hive scrapings to obtain beeswax but this wax is of lower quality since it is darker in color and contains more impurities. Darker beeswax may be bleached lighter but it is expensive to process.

Figure 17-16
Bee adding wax to natural comb under construction against a sheet of glass. R. Williamson

Processing of cappings to obtain the highest quality wax is done by melting the wax and honey mixture to separate the two materials. The wax layer floats to the top and can be easily removed, then cleaned to remove particles of dirt and other debris (Figure 17-17). It may need to be further re-filtered before use in candles or cosmetics (Figures 17-18, 17-32).

Nearly one-half of the beeswax used in the world comes from Africa where destruct-harvest of honey bee colonies is practiced. In this management, honey bee swarms are captured/attracted in bait hives to establish a nest in darkened containers (rustic hives). Once hived, the bees construct comb, rear brood and store honey. These nests are robbed periodically by their owners for the honey and brood, which are consumed, and the wax, which is melted and sold for export. In tropical Africa, bees driven from their comb either migrate or return to rebuild and fill new beeswax combs with honey.

Uses of beeswax

Beeswax fragrance and purity has been utilized for centuries in candles, cosmetics and as a high quality polishing wax. The wax from the combs was as important as honey in daily life. Strips of clean linen dipped into melted wax were used to bind wounds. Other early uses included waterproofing of leather, smoothing sewing yarn, and to make a primitive chewing gum.

Beeswax was used to craft and mold art work and jewelry and then melted, when the finished product was ready, in the lost-wax technique. There is a graphic art form called encaustic painting that uses beeswax and pigments for painting. Candles made from beeswax were the preferred light source until modern times. It was specified for use in the Catholic church as a symbol of purity and virginity.

Figure 17-17
Beeswax solidified as it pours into a collecting tub from the wax melter. The wax will float to the top in the tub as it cools. L. Connor

Beeswax was also used to fill dental cavities. Although evidence of prehistoric dentistry is limited, the earliest direct evidence is from a 6,500-year-old human mandible from Slovenia whose left canine crown bears the traces of a filling with beeswax. The study indicated that if the filling was done when the person was still alive, the intervention was likely aimed to relieve tooth sensitivity derived from either exposed dentin and/or the pain resulting from chewing on a cracked tooth.

Today, beeswax is used in nearly equal amounts by the beekeeping supply business (to produce foundation), by the candle industry and in the cosmetic industry. Other historical and continuing uses of beeswax include:

- weld together loose ends of thread
- lubricate needles or nails
- dental impression wax
- ointments/pomades
- pill coatings
- floor and furniture waxes
- polishing (lenses for example)
- insulator in electrical connections
- industrial uses as lubricant
- carpenters' varnish or finish
- saltwater corrosion preventive
- metal castings and molds
- ski and snowshoe wax
- coat archers' bowstrings
- food processing
- crayons
- printing

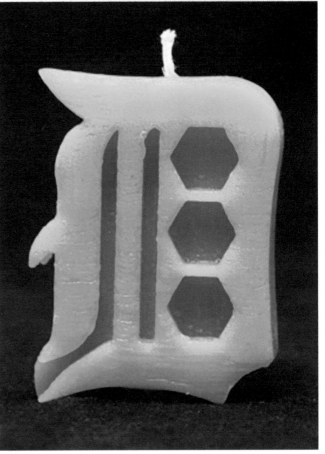

Figure 17-18
By modifying a popular Detroit sports logo with a hexagon design, beekeeper Rich Wieske created a popular beeswax candle. R. Wieske

Pollen

Honey bees collect pollen from a wide variety of flowering plants during the active season. Pollen is a source of protein for the bee diet since nectar offers little nourishment other than carbohydrates. All living organisms need protein to grow and develop. In honey bees, it is needed primarily by the larvae and newly-emerged adults. No single pollen source supplies all the amino acid need of bees; for example, dandelion pollen lacks L-arginine, an essential amino acid. Bees receive the necessary protein for growth and development by mixing pollens. Protein levels of pollen vary from 7 to 65%.

Bees pack the pollen into corbicular hairs creating corbicular pellets (pollen pellets). Pollen can be collected from honey bees by the use of a **pollen trap** (Figure 17-20, Chapter 13 Figure 13-44). A pollen trap is a hardware cloth device that is positioned before the beehive entrance. Bees must pass through the trap as they return to the hive from foraging trips. The corbicular pellets on the hind legs are knocked off by the wire mesh of the trap and fall into a collecting tray. Some bees are able to pass through the pollen traps with pollen basket loads intact as even the best pollen trap is no more than 85% efficient.

Box 42

COMB HONEY

At one time, eating honey directly from the comb was a guarantee of authenticity. Discovery of bee space and the movable frame hive led to development of an efficient extractor, and by the late 1800s liquid honey was produced in greater quantity. Quickly, two groups of beekeepers developed: the naturalists producing comb honey, and the commercial beekeepers, concentrating on extracted honey. Each group had their own hives, management style and advocates. Unscrupulous sellers adulterated the liquid honey with other cheaper sugars. Only the beekeepers selling honey in the comb could guarantee the purity of their product.

Passage of the 1906 Pure Food and Drug Act restored public confidence in honey and slowed the adulterators of liquid honey (adulteration remains a problem today, especially in the global market). Demand for comb honey has since decreased. In 1876, J.S. Harbison sent an entire train of boxcars completely filled with comb honey from California to the Philadelphia Exposition.

Beekeepers seeking to produce comb honey preferred the use of small hives. They captured swarms and put them to work producing and capping comb honey. Beekeepers realized swarm bees were more likely to quickly fill and cap honey-filled cells with light-colored cappings.

Comb honey producers championed Italian bees since they cap honey with bright white wax. Extracted-honey producers preferred larger hives to build strong, populous colonies. Those producers needed to control swarming or risk losing the majority of their yield.

Producing quality sections of comb honey is a challenging process to learn in beekeeping. Beekeepers need to know more about bees and need to manage colonies intensively to produce comb honey. Timing is critical. Colonies must be severely crowded, just at nectar flow, into a reduced brood nest to force the bees to work in the small sections of the comb honey super. Crowding means ventilation/swarming problems. The bees may not complete enough sections for harvest if you are late adding the supers, or if the honey flow is delayed or it ceases suddenly due to environmental conditions. Removal of completed sections needs to be prompt as continued bee travel on the cappings will darken them and make them less attractive.

Traditional basswood comb honey boxes are square or rectangular. They take time to prepare. When filled, they weigh one pound. Round plastic sections (holding 12 ounces) are easier to use and supers hold more sections.

Figure 17-19
A French beekeeper sells sealed frames of honey (covered in clear plastic film) in a small wooden stand at the village market. This allows the customer to cut sections of honey for use. The dish catches the dripping honey and is spooned into the morning espresso. L. Connor

Both sell for the same price. Both also require special, thin foundation.

Not all areas support comb honey production as only a predictable, intense nectar flow produces a good product. Completed sections do not store or ship well and need to be marketed quickly. Comb honey involves a lot of work and special management skills.

Hint: To produce some comb honey or cut-comb honey (Figure 17-19), collect one large swarm or put two or three swarms together in the same hive with drawn comb. As the bees fill the hive with brood, super with one or two section honey supers or shallow supers with thin surplus foundation. If your timing is right — on or just before nectar flow — and the colony is strong, the bees will draw comb, fill and cap the supers within a week.

Remove the filled supers as soon as they are capped and add another hive body for brood so the colony expands and has a chance to overwinter. Several publications detail the methods of producing comb honey.

Pollen should be trapped for only a portion of the time during the season because the bees need large amounts of pollen for proper nutrition and development of the colony. Beekeepers should avoid trapping pollen for human or bee consumption in areas of high agricultural activity or times of year (spring) when pesticide applications tend to be high.

As with nectar, some plants yield more pollen than others; seasons and locations vary greatly. Each beekeeper interested in collecting pollen needs to determine the best sources available for their location and the most appropriate season to trap. Avoid low protein content pollen like corn, which also may contain pesticides.

Uses of pollen

Pollen is consumed by humans as a food and dietary supplement (a protein source). Based on varying amounts of research, pollen has been advocated as a treatment for sterility, for prostate gland disorders, cancer and in allergy relief. Health food stores carry pollen, encapsulated in gelatin capsules or as pollen pellets.

Individuals use pollen as vitamin supplements in the diet and for skin care. Athletes have advocated pollen use, particularly for stamina, weight gain and body conditioning.

Before consumption of large quantities, individuals should test to be sure they can tolerate pollen in their diet. Allergic reactions, although not common, are possible. Pollens not only vary in color (Figure 17-21) but additionally in their potential nutritive and medicinal value. We do not know if all pollens can be tolerated so new pollen sources should likewise be tested before inclusion in the diet.

Pollen must be collected for use in manual human pollination of plants, or when pollen inserts are used. In these instances, plants are forced into early bloom and fresh pollen collected directly from the flowers. Bee-collected pollen is fed as a protein to other animals such as pet fish, reptiles or birds.

Beekeepers can trap pollen from disease-free colonies, store it frozen to maintain protein quality, and then re-feed it to colonies when natural pollen is in short supply, such as early spring, to stimulate colony expansion.

Royal jelly

Royal jelly (Figure 17-22) is another bee product. Royal jelly is the glandular brood food adult worker bees secrete from hypopharyngeal glands (located in the bee's head). The bees use royal jelly to feed queen larvae and, for the first half of development, also feed to worker and drone larvae.

Royal jelly is a pasty, creamy-white substance with a slightly pungent odor and a somewhat bitter taste. It is rich in vitamins and contains substantial amounts of sugars, proteins and certain organic acids. In spite of its high moisture content, it is highly resistant to spoilage by

Figure 17-20
Pollen traps on beehives. Extra cover helps keep moisture out of the trap.

Figure 17-21
Pollen pellets collected from pollen traps. U. Calif. Davis

Figure 17-22
Royal jelly from a queen cell. It may be collected from surplus queen cells and frozen. L. Connor

bacteria, yeasts or molds. Royal jelly protein, however, quickly decomposes at room temperature.

Although limited, there is demand for royal jelly to use as a dietary/food supplement, medicinally, as an ingredient in certain cosmetics, and as animal food. It is used in laboratory and clinical research. People may consume royal jelly directly, in gelatin capsules or in a mixture of royal jelly and honey.

There is evidence of antibiotic activity, benefit to the elderly, in healing of wounds and in reduction of cholesterol and triglycerides in humans. Some recommend it as beneficial to skin, general body and mental health.

Royal jelly is produced by following a schedule to produce queens in a colony. The best royal jelly yield occurs three days after grafting a worker larva into a queen cup, when the queen larva is fully grown. The royal jelly is often collected with a vacuum device after removal of the queen larva and strained to remove wax and the old larval skins. It takes 125 or more queen cells to yield an ounce (28 g) of jelly.

Royal jelly is stored under refrigeration or in the freezer prior to formulation in honey, in a lotion or in capsules for direct consumption. It is often sold at pharmacies, with honey, in small containers for a high price.

Bee brood

Direct consumption of bee brood is not common. Bee brood is high in protein, as well as vitamins A and D; it has no harmful ingredients. The protein content is slightly above

that of egg yolk, the fat content about the same as beef, and the ash content is only twice that of beef. Humans, animals kept by humans (caged birds, pet reptiles, small mammals, poultry and even fish), or other insects raised by humans (lady beetles, lacewings, etc.) can benefit from bee brood in the diet.

Human taste panels have tried bee brood prepared in a number of ways. Preparation methods include fried, brine pickled, smoked, baked and brandied. The fried brood were found to be the most tasty; deep-fat frying was judged the best preparation as there was less breakage of the pieces.

Their taste was compared to a number of foods including walnuts, pork cracklings, and Rice Krispies®. There was some reluctance to sample brood, especially when the final product looked like a bee (Figure 17-23).

In destruct-harvest, bee brood becomes part of the diet of the beekeeping family. Bee brood is very easy to obtain. It is possible to harvest three to four pounds (up to two kg) of brood from a standard colony. Late larvae and pupae are easily shaken from the frame (pupae can be removed only after their cell cappings have first been removed with a serrated knife) by bringing the frame down with a jolt over a collecting pan.

Bee brood has potential as a snack item, as a regular diet component or as a dietary supplement. Undoubtedly, some people will remain squeamish about eating an insect. Perhaps, in the future, bee brood might be utilized as an insect protein concentrate to help feed the increasing human population.

Propolis

In addition to collecting nectar, honeydew, water and pollen, bees collect propolis for use in the hive. Propolis is a sticky, resinous gum gathered from popular trees, flower buds and other sources for use as a sealant in the hive (Figure 17-24). Bees reduce the size of the hive entrance with propolis, coat surfaces inside the hive with it, use it to seal areas too small to permit comb construction, close holes and seal cracks with it and use it to entomb hive invaders too large to remove. Propolis has antibacterial, antifungal and antimicrobial properties and is key to keeping the bee nest a healthy place to live.

It can be collected with the use of a **propolis trap**, a plastic grid placed below the hive cover (Figure 17-25). As with pollen trapping, there is a favorable part of the season to collect propolis. It appears that propolis may vary chemically, probably depending upon plant source. Unfortunately we do not know which sources may be best for human medicinal use.

Propolis has been used for centuries to varnish, polish and waterproof, mainly wood. Violin makers, perhaps including Stradivarius, used propolis to finish the surface of their instruments. Around the world propolis is used topically and internally as a rural

Box 43

BEES AS FOOD

Humans in the so-called advanced countries eat relatively few insects. Although we consume fair amounts of sea and brackish water invertebrates such as crab, lobster and shrimp, we eat few of their dryland relatives — the insects. Most of the insects humans eat are consumed unknowingly.

A large variety of insects could be included in the human diet. Grasshoppers and locusts are common insects that are the most frequently consumed insects around the world. Many of the Western Plains Native Americans regularly ate grasshoppers and they distrusted European settlers who attempted to control the grasshopper plagues. Even the early western settlers were forced to eat grasshoppers more than once to survive. Locust plagues in Africa necessitate the eating of the locusts after the crops are destroyed.

Termites and ants have long been a part of the human diet. Termites and ants are very numerous and not very difficult to capture. Although small in size, they have a delicate taste. Whole native ceremonies are built around emergence of termite reproductives. Chocolate-covered ants are a novelty item in Mexican and Asian outlets.

In Mexico, a portion of the native population regularly eats the eggs of a large water bug (insect 'caviar'). They encourage the water bugs to lay eggs by placing straw on ponds for the females. The eggs are easily harvested from the straw just below the water line.

A large cicada has been a feature of the human diet. Aristotle apparently liked cicadas and regularly ate them. The Romans had a flour beetle they regularly consumed. It was fattened in vats of flour and wine. A number of caterpillars are also a regular feature of the diet of humans. Where the silkworm is cultivated, the pupae are dropped into hot water for silk separation and then the cooked pupae eaten.

Another favorite dietary caterpillar of humans is the bugong moth caterpillar of Asia and Australia. In many of the southeastern Asian countries, the natives injure a host plant to attract egg-laying female moths. The resulting caterpillar is allowed to grow and is eaten by children as an important source of protein in a diet that is otherwise very deficient in protein sources. For persons who like the alcoholic drink tequila, there is a caterpillar (mescal) that lives in the Agave plant, which is also the source for the tequila. Mescal caterpillars are available in some sections of the southwestern United States, packed in cans like sardines.

Figure 17-23
Uncapped worker bee pupae.

And honey bees? In a destructive harvest of brood, bee bread and honey, the bee brood is often the first part of the bee nest consumed since it would otherwise spoil. In some more northern areas, bee colonies are heavily harvested and hives restarted the next season with divides or package bee colonies. The bee brood (Figure 17-23) can be collected and consumed immediately or frozen and sold in the marketplace.

Bee brood and insects are potential dietary additions for humans because of their high levels of usable protein. Insects such as locusts, termites and ants are primary herbivores; food conversion efficiency of insects approaches that of chicken. Even the least efficient, like grasshoppers, are as good as cattle in converting plant material into usable human protein.

medicine, particularly in treatment of wounds, cuts and burns. A host of human aliments are treated with propolis, including cancer, anemia, and skin conditions as well as immune and cardiovascular system disorders. It has most recently been shown to have anti-viral properties to HIV and corona virus. It is popular in soaps, dental cream and cosmetics. Humans consume propolis as a dilute liquid or mixed into sugar or honey in the form of tablets or lozenges (Figure 17-26).

Venom

Bee venom is used to treat human allergic reactions to bee stings and as a relief from arthritis and serious human conditions such as multiple sclerosis. Neither the arthritis nor multiple sclerosis treatments are approved by most medical professionals. Practitioners, however, cite many individual testimonials as evidence of the effectiveness of bee venom therapy. The venom is harvested by having bees sting a plastic surface, after being shocked.

Live bees

Live bees have a number of expanding potential uses. Bees have been demonstrated to be useful in bio-assay monitoring. The adult bee is inexpensive, easy to condition, and relatively easy to maintain for use in such environmental detection experiments. Bees can be used as indicators of environmental pollution, warfare agents, drugs and perhaps human illnesses. Further uses of live bee as monitors are likely to be developed.

Mead (honey wine)

One final product, mead or honey wine (Figure 17-27), deserves special mention. Mead is an ancient alcoholic beverage, perhaps man's oldest fermented drink, brewed from a simple mixture of honey, water and yeast or made with common wine ingredients added to the brew, including grapes or other fruit. In mead, honey is the principle sugar for yeast fermentation. It may be made for personal use or sold with the proper permits.

After removal from the bees, honey ferments when diluted with water. Control of the process can produce an alcoholic beverage from a simple low-alcohol-content beer or ale to a highly prized wine or champaign-type beverage. The use of honey as a sugar source may have been discovered after rinsing beeswax with water following destruct-harvest or washing beeswax of its honey residue. By merely letting it stand, natural yeasts would ferment the residual honey; bacteria would eventually turn the mixture into vinegar.

In the making of mead, as in any wine, yeast cells attack sugar, releasing carbon dioxide and alcohol. A dilute solution of honey left at room temperature will ferment naturally, although the resulting product will likely be of low alcohol content and not very pleasant. To

Figure 17-24
This colony was established by a swarm that occupied a cavity in a tree. The bees deposited propolis in the cracks in the wood at the entrance and on the face of the trunk. R. Wieske

Figure 17-25
Propolis screen trap stimulates bees to deposit propolis. The plastic grid is frozen and then twisted to free propolis harvest.

make a quality honey wine, a mild-flavored honey, high quality wine yeasts and a few trace additives (acid blends more typical of familiar wines, additional yeast nutrients along with something to eliminate wild yeasts that might contaminate) are needed. The process is not complicated but the little details are important.

A **dry mead** (less sweet) may be secured by using less honey (3 to 3-1/2 lbs) mixed in one gallon of water; a sweeter wine is obtained by use of four lbs. of honey. Too little honey produces a thin product of low alcohol content that is difficult to keep, while greater amounts leave an excess of sugar and a sweeter final product. To be reasonably certain of the final product, use a hydrometer

Figure 17-26
Candy or medicine? Sugar and propolis mixtures are popular in many cultures.

to measure the sugar concentration of the honey-water mixture. A 22% solution with specific gravity of 1.095 yields a dry (non-sweet) wine while 25% or greater (specific gravity of 1.110) results in a sweeter product.

Mead making begins by diluting honey with water. Usually a dark honey, or one with a strong flavor, decreases the chances of producing a superior dry wine; likewise, water contaminated with heavy minerals, chlorine or other additions may detract from the delicateness or bouquet (smell) of the final product. Therefore, use a mild-flavored honey and pure, chlorine-free water.

Sourwood honey (Figure 17-27), or citrus honey are suitable mild-flavored honeys to use.

When making wine, most authorities recommend sterilization of the sugar source (in the case of mead: honey) to eliminate wild yeasts. Sterilization can be accomplished by boiling the sugar and water mixture for a couple of minutes. However, since honey can be adversely affected by such a procedure, boiling is not recommended to produce a decent honey wine. Instead, campden tablets or sodium bisulfite (from wine supply firms) should be added to the dilute honey solution (termed the 'must'). These liberate sulfur dioxide which will sterilize the must and kill foreign, low alcohol-tolerant yeasts.

The type of yeast used is probably the most critical factor affecting mead taste. Baking yeasts and non-cultured yeasts are not satisfactory. Suitable pure-yeast cultures can be obtained from wine supply firms or stores; an all purpose wine yeast (Madeira, tokay or sherry yeast), will give good results.

Yeast added to a honey-water mixture will ferment over a period of time; to hasten fermentation and increase the chances of a successful mead, yeast food (nutrient salts or urea and ammonium phosphate) and tannin (tea or cream of tartar) should be added to the must. Since most fruit wines are acidic, the addition of an acid in the form of tartaric or citric acid is recommended so the final product more closely resembles the wines most people enjoy.

Of course, it is possible to include fruit juices, fruit extracts or fruit itself as part of a recipe. Since these have sugars to contribute, it is important to measure and balance the sugar content of the mixture before starting the fermentation.

A non-metallic container that can be fitted with a fermentation lock should be used for fermenting the must. The lock prevents water, air or wild airborne yeasts from entering the fermenting mixture. Fermentation works best at 65° F (18° C) A constant temperature is better than a widely fluctuating temperature; temperatures lower

Two recipes for sweet mead

One

3-4 lbs. mild flavored honey

1 gal. water

1/4 oz. citric acid (level tsp.)

1/4 pint strong tea

yeast culture

yeast nutrient salts

1 campden tablet

Two

4 lbs. mild flavored honey

1 gal. water

4 grams (l/5 oz. or 3/4

Tsp.) cream of tartar

4 grams ammonium phosphate

4 grams tartaric or citric acid

4 grams urea

1 campden tablet

yeast culture

than 60° F (15° C) will lengthen fermentation time. Higher temperatures up to 85° F (30° C) produce a more rapid fermentation which does not present a problem, provided enough yeast nutrients are present in the mixture.

The must should be siphoned (racked) from the dead yeast cells and sediment after one month. Following all fermentation (cessation of foaming and carbon dioxide release), rack the wine again, being sure to siphon from the top so any residue is left behind. A cloudy wine will clarify with time but egg white (one egg white to ten gallons wine) beaten with a small amount of wine and then added to the remainder will hasten clarification. A fining agent such as gelatin or a commercial clay can be purchased from wine supply stores for the same purpose. Sterilizing the must mixture before beginning the fermentation definitely aids in obtaining a clear, non-cloudy (clarified) final product. The wine should be racked into sterilized bottles.

Bottles of honey wine, like wines, needs to be aged in a cool, dry place and left undisturbed in a horizontal position. Bottled sweet, cloudy wines might explode due to reactivation of yeast. One year is usually sufficient aging time but this is a matter of taste. Young wines are yeasty tasting, lack bouquet and are frequently cloudy. Mead can be sipped before, during or following a meal. It is a unique product from the bee colony. Enjoy!

Other ways to make money with bees

In addition to use of bee products in a wide variety of cosmetics and foods (Figures 17-29, 17-30, 17-31), beekeepers keep and manage their bee colonies to use in pollination rental. The original use of bees was in fruit pollination and many family farms had bee colonies as part of their livestock mix. Now, with intensive changes in agriculture, including large-scale commercial farming, bee colony rentals are needed in a growing number of fruit, vegetable, seed and fiber crops (Chapter 20).

Other beekeepers sell packages or nucs of bees. Package bees are shaken from strong colonies and sold by the pound in special wood and screen or plastic boxes. Nucs are assembled from strong, expanding spring colonies to both make up overwintering losses and to sell to 'newbees' (new beekeepers) starting a bee hobby. The nucs and packages need queens and a specialized business in rearing and selling queens, as part of the packages/nucs or to requeen colonies, is another way to generate income from bees

Figure 17-27
Freshly bottled sourwood honey mead. L. Connor

(Chapter 18). Special skills and specialized equipment are needed to produce bees and queens but the techniques are not too difficult to master.

Another income opportunity is the manufacture and sale of beekeeping supplies. Beekeepers keep their colonies in hives of wood, plastic or other materials and utilize items of metal and glass as well as a whole host of specialty items. Increasingly, sales are from on-line catalogs with prompt local delivery or from pickup at regional or national sales locations. Local and regional dealers may sell items from their basement or garage, handling items from one or more national manufacturers. Some of these dealers design and sell special beekeeping items.

Figure 17-30
For some, product diversification includes barbecue sauce, mustard and teriyaki sauces, all made with honey as the sweetener. L. Connor

Figure 17-31
Commercial beekeepers have invested in energy bars and drinks, working with the food manufacturing industry to produce a safe product accepted by the consumer.

Figure 17-28
Honey beer (left) and two commercial meads. Mead is a popular drink throughout the world.

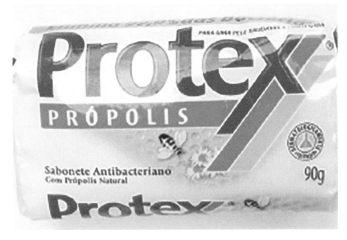

Figure 17-29
Colgate Palmolive offers soap with propolis (shown) and another with honey.

Not inconsequential is the education of new beekeepers or use of bees and bee products in artistic expression. Local bee associations offer beekeeping short courses and pay instructors in some instances. Writing about bees, photography of bees and development of artistic items with bee motifs are consistently popular sale themes.

Although used for various purposes world wide, pollen, royal jelly, bee bread, and propolis have had few peer-reviewed scientific research projects as they relate to use in humans and animals other than bees.

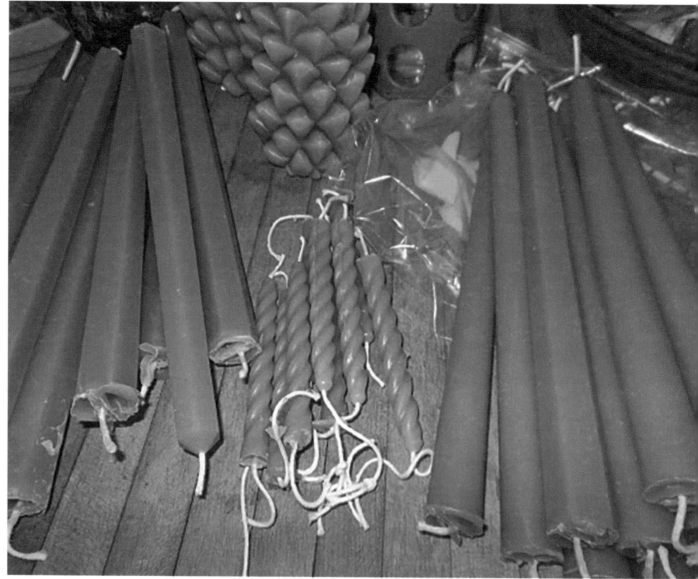

Figure 17-32
An assortment of pure beeswax candles produced for holiday sales and gifts. E. Forbes

key terms

1906 Pure Food and Drug Act	encaustic painting	granulation	pollen
adulterated honey	evaporation (active & passive)	honey stomach (crop)	pollen trap
batik		hydrogen peroxide	propolis
bee brood	extracted (liquid) honey	hygoscopic	royal jelly
beeswax	fermentation	invertase (sucrase)	rustic hive
comb honey	filtering honey	lost wax (jewelry crafting)	stingless bee honey
cut-comb honey	forest or pine honey	mead	sucrase (invertase)
crystallization (granulation)	foundation	meliponiculture	sucrose
destruct harvest	fructose (levulose)	National honey Board	
drawing comb	glucose (destrose)	nectar	
Dyce process	glucose oxidase	pasteurization	

discussion questions

The use of bee products has changed little over the ages. Honey is now more often used in the diet than as a medicine but other bee products still are more valued for their medicinal properties. Can you assess the value bee products had for man during the Dark Ages? In colonial America? In Europe versus the United States? How has honey come to be a part of the diet of western civilizations?

Why and how has honey been used as a medicine in the past? What are its uses today?

Imagine that you were going to raise bees. What would your target product(s) be? How would you equip yourself to raise such products?

Discuss how you might produce bee products, such as bee brood, pollen, beeswax, etc. What is mead? How is it produced?

exercises

Collect samples of honey from several floral sources and then attempt to describe the uniqueness of their taste. When you have had practice, have someone challenge your taste buds to a recognition test. Can you still tell them apart? See if other people, after appropriate training, can distinguish honey floral sources on the basis of taste and smell.

Survey the market and determine the type, quality and price of bee products. Include small neighborhood markets, large supermarkets, convenience stores, roadside markets and health food stores in your survey. In a supermarket, honey and bee products may be in two or three locations. What are the differences that dictate where it is featured and priced in the market? What are its neighbors? How convenient is it to locate?

In the fall, survey roadside markets, large and small, for bee products. How does their availability and price compare to the supermarket or convenience store? Ask market personnel where honey is not sold why they do not sell it. How well are bee products advertised, both inside and outside the facility?

Prepare bee brood and conduct a taste test with friends. How is it accepted? What form is best to get people to accept bee brood? Do you like bee brood?

Compare beeswax to other wax materials for use in art sculpturing and for decorative and functional candles (Figure 16-32). What are the unique properties of beeswax that make it easy/hard to use? Make something with beeswax or foundation sheets.

Make mead and/or bake/cook/prepare something with honey. What are the unique characteristics of such products when made with honey?

references

Ahnert, P. 2015. Beeswax Alchemy. Quarry Books: Beverly, MA

Ahnert, P. 2018. Beehive Alchemy. Quarry Books: Beverly MA

Berthold, R, Jr. 2002. Beeswax Crafting. Wicwas Press, Kalamazoo, MI

Conrad, R. 2017. Bee Venom Therapy (BVT). Bee Culture. June 2017

Crane, E. 1975. Honey: A Comprehensive Survey. Crane, Russak, New York

Fletcher, M.T. et al. 2020. Stingless bee honey, a novel source of trehalulose: a biologically active disaccharide with health benefits. Scientific reports 10: #12128.

https://lovelygreens.com/how-to-make-natural-beeswax-furniture/

https://woodandshop.com/make-a-historic-beeswax-oil-turpentine-furniture-polish-finish/

https://www.healthline.com/health/propolis-an-ancient-healer

https://www.healthline.com/nutrition/bee-pollen#section3 (pollen benefit to human health)

Marchese, M. and K. Flottum The Honey Connoisseur: Selecting, Tasting, and Pairing Honey, with a Guide to More Than 30 Varietals

Malone, F., 1979. Bees don't get arthritis. E.P. Dutton, NY

National Honey Board www.honey.com

Park, O.W. 1925. The storing and ripening of honey by honey bees. Jour. Econ. Enomol. 18:405-410.

Schramm, K. 2003. The Compleat Meadmaker. Brewers Publications, Boulder, CO

Morse, R.A. 1980. Making Mead (Honey Wine): History, Recipes, Methods and Equipment. Wicwas Press: Kalamazoo, MI

Traynor, J. 2002. Honey: The Gourmet Medicine. Kovak Books, New York

Taylor, R. 1996. The comb honey book. Linden Books, Interlaken, NY

Traynor, K.S. 2012. Two Million Blossoms. Discovering the Medicinal Benefits of Honey. Image Design, North Yorkshire, U.K.

Concepts

Queen rearing
    small-scale queen production
    Cloake board
    graftless cell production
    methods to raise queens

Drone rearing
    increasing desirable drones

Mating control

Introducing queens

Figure 18-1

Mated queens in cages on a holding frame, ready to be shipped to customers. Workers are feeding queens through the holes in the cages. L. Connor

Queen & drone rearing

In Chapter 10 we reviewed queen bee replacement biology (swarms, supersedure and emergency) and the mating biology of queens and drones in Drone Congregation Areas (DCA's). In this chapter we will discuss the beekeeping side of queen and drone rearing and mating. The two chapters should be reviewed together.

As mother of the honey bee colony (Figure 18-2), one of a queen bee's primary functions is to lay eggs. She also produces royal pheromones that keep the worker population working cohesively. We call such colonies **queenright**. As long as she has viable sperm stored in her body, a queen produces both fertilized and unfertilized eggs and the normal social life of the colony continues. When her pheromone production becomes insufficient, swarming or queen replacement (supersedure) occurs.

If a queen runs out of sperm, she becomes a **drone layer**, producing only unfertilized eggs. Without a queen in the hive, a **queenless colony**, the remaining brood emerges, worker bee populations decline, and worker bee's ovaries develop in the absence of queen and brood pheromones. This is a **laying worker colony**. A queenless colony eventually dies out unless a new queen is produced or one is successfully introduced by the beekeeper.

Queenlessness occurs for many reasons. Queens naturally meet with accidents, especially during mating flights. They may be eaten by predators or fly back to the wrong hive and killed. Early spring and late fall supersedure queens may experience a shortage of drones or poor flight weather for mating. In the apiary,

For I am a queen and I am a bee,
I'm devil-may-care and I'm fancy-free,
Love-in-air is the thing for me,
Oh, it's simply rare
In the beautiful air,
And I wish to state
That I'll always mate
With whatever drone I encounter.

—From *Song of the Queen Bee*
by E.B. White

Figure 18-2
Laying queen with abdomen enlarged by heavy egg production. L. Connor

beekeepers may accidentally harm or kill queens by causing them to be balled, dropping them on the ground during frame manipulations, or moving them to the wrong area in a hive where they are neglected.

If you remove a queen from a hive, within 15 to 30 minutes the level of queen pheromones drops, signaling to the workers that the queen is gone. The workers buzz louder than usual, producing what is called the **queenless roar**. Ten to 24 hours after a queen's removal, sharp-eyed beekeepers may observe the construction of **emergency queen cells**. Soon the beekeeper will notice that bees are storing pollen and nectar in the brood area where bees have emerged. Drones from neighboring colonies are accepted into the hive in higher numbers. Without a queen, the amount of open brood falls and the stimulus to collect and store pollen declines. Fewer and fewer foragers with pollen loads will be noted at the colony entrance.

Raising queens and drones

Beekeepers raise their own queens using the natural instincts of bees, having developed special methods to produce queens. These methods are discussed in this chapter.

For most beekeepers, drone production is often left to the natural conditions inside the bee colonies with no special 'drone rearing' methods. Large-scale queen producers provide **drone mother colonies**, drone-producing colonies with early nutritional feeding and drone-cell sized 'drone comb' to stimulate drone production.

Drone rearing becomes more complicated when beekeepers attempt to make crosses with a specific drone line or a desired race or queen line possessing specific traits. Such breeding and research programs prevent drones from flying from one colony to another by using queen excluders and cages. These beekeepers choose to produce these drones in isolated areas to obtain remote mating, or they use instrumental insemination.

Commercial U.S. queen breeders raise millions of queens annually that are sold throughout the world, primarily within North America. Beekeepers purchase queens to requeen existing colonies and to make new increase nucleus hives. They also keep queens in reserve in resource colonies whenever a production colony needs a replacement queen.

Learning the queen and drone rearing process increases one's understanding of bee reproductive biology, the inner workings of the hive, and may improve success as a beekeeper. It combines the joy of beekeeping with potentially stronger and healthier hives and potential income from selling queens. Raising quality queens requires competent training, strong attention to detail, and a small amount of special equipment.

Reasons to requeen

Queen problems are more easily solved when discovered early. Beekeepers use newly **mated queens** or **ready-to-emerge (ripe) queen cells** to requeen colonies that have lost their queen, or colonies that are performing significantly below the average productivity of other colonies, or colonies with *Nosema*, chalkbrood, European foulbrood, high mite levels, unacceptable defensive behavior or other undesirable traits.

Some beekeepers replace queens on a regular schedule, such as once every two years. Others replace queens whenever they see the need, often doing so when making increase colonies or while preparing the bees for the nectar flow or for winter.

Figure 18-3
Queen and worker bees. S. Weil

In general, colonies headed by older queens swarm more than colonies headed by young queens. However, when a colony is filled with young nurse bees and brood frames and all food cells are filled, young queens within their first few months of life have been observed to swarm. There are no absolutes.

During swarming (Chapter 10), half or more of the bees leave with the old queen while the remaining bees wait for a new queen to emerge from her cell, mature, mate, and begin laying eggs. The old colony can be without brood for weeks during a time when it could be producing bees that will gather next winter's stores. However, one advantage of such a break is the natural reduction in varroa mite populations. During this break in egg-laying, there are no cells ready for female mites to invade and reproduce.

Many beekeepers believe that a colony that swarms will not produce as much honey and may not produce any harvestable surplus for the beekeeper. Also, if either the swarm colony or the colony that produced it fails to thrive, it has a lower probability of surviving the winter.

Fortunately, the same seasonal patterns that favor swarming, predicting a food abundance that stimulates a colony to swarm, also support rapid regrowth (in the case of the parent hive), or expansion (in the swarm colony), so both colonies can become strong and vibrant just months after swarming. Keep in mind that all colonies simply respond to weather conditions. They have few, if any, mechanisms to predict future weather conditions.

New queens usually experience the greatest colony productivity because they lay the greatest number of eggs during their first season (Figure 18-3). These eggs turn into brood and then adult bees. Egg-laying decreases with each passing year. As the queen ages, pheromone production declines in both quantity and chemical quality. First-year queens have been shown to head healthier colonies with more bees and bigger honey harvests. Third year queens rarely meet these levels of productivity.

When to raise queens

Beekeepers in southern states begin queen rearing as early as February while northern beekeepers must wait until March or April. All queen cell production depends on two key determining factors—drone production and average nighttime temperatures. Queen production may continue all season as long as there no shortage of forage which inhibits quality drone production and maintenance.

Experienced beekeepers do not start to produce queen cells until drone brood has reached the purple-eyed stage, five days after cell sealing. Otherwise, the

Figure 18-4
A strong queen produces a strong colony. The beekeeper is inspecting the brood nest of a colony while seated on two supers.

virgins will not find mature drones within the Drone Congregation Areas.

There is a huge industry push for spring queens because requeening is easier when there are fewer bees in the colony. Colonies with smaller populations make finding and removing the old queen easier. In addition, early requeening gives the beekeeper more time to evaluate the queen's performance. Spring-produced queens are needed for making increase colonies from overwintered hives.

Many beekeepers raise their own queens during the late spring and summer nectar flows. Queens may be plentiful from breeders during June and July, but less plentiful in the late summer and early fall once rearing and mating conditions decline.

Requeening colonies after the nectar flow — ending in July, August or September, depending upon location — may reduce the likelihood of swarming the following spring while increasing colony productivity during the next honey season.

To ensure young queens in their hives, many beekeepers seek to requeen in the fall; unfortunately, if queen introduction fails, the colony may not be able to recover in time to prepare for winter. Robbing often develops while searching for the old queen inside colonies with large populations. If the honey flow is over, bees may also be more defensive.

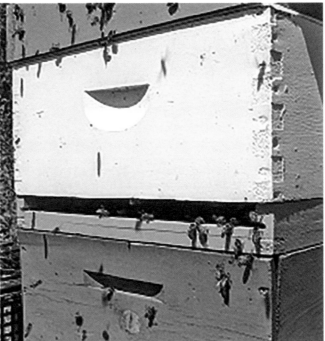

Figure 18-5
Cloake board without metal slide.

How to raise queens on a small scale

Here are three methods, in outline form, on how to raise a new queen. Each method is optimal for meeting different beekeepers' needs.

Raising a single queen using the emergency instinct

1. Select a colony with the most desirable characteristics from which to raise emergency queen cells. During swarm season, and as the main honey flow starts, elevate one or two combs containing eggs or very young worker larvae (open brood), along with the adhering bees, to a hive body above one or two honey supers. Leave the queen in the lower brood chamber.

Place one or two combs containing honey and pollen next to the selected brood and then fill the added hive body with empty comb. As an alternative, the frames you elevate can be frames containing developing queen cells from colonies preparing for swarming or supersedure.

2. Place a queen excluder between the lower brood chamber containing the queen and the honey supers. Put the new box over the supers. After you elevate the frames of open brood, wait a day so nurse-age bees from the brood chamber below have time to gather to care for the brood in the elevated frames of open brood.

3. Place a fully screened bottom board (Figure 18-5) or Cloake board (Box 44) between the honey supers and the hive body containing the raised open brood. The bees in the queenright part of the colony and honey supers

Box 44

USING THE CLOAKE BOARD

Queen rearing instructor Sue Cobey has popularized the Cloake board in rearing queen cells. She has also been able to import drone semen to breed her selection called the New World Carniolan strain of bees.

The Cloake board is named after Harry Cloake, a New Zealand queen breeder. He devised the board as a useful means of building a starter colony that converts into a finisher colony without the extra work of making up two different units.

The Cloake board (Figure 18-6) is basically a queen excluder in a slotted wooden frame. The frame's slot allows a 'temporary' thin metal or wooden sheet to be inserted, dividing a colony into a queenright lower colony and a queenless upper colony that will be used to start queen cells.

The Cloake board is used in a strong colony (Figure 18-7). The queen excluder ensures that the colony queen remains below. This colony is supered with one or two supers (boxes). Open-brood frames, with at least one frame of pollen and honey from the brood chamber are positioned in the box above the queen excluder. Attracted by the brood pheromone, young nurse bees will move above the excluder to care for the brood.

After a few days, much of the open brood will be in the capped stage. The nurse bees are then ready to be offered grafted queen cells or a frame of open brood from a selected colony. When ready to raise queens, the temporary floor—a piece of metal or thin plywood—is slid into the queen excluder rim so the brood area above becomes queenless. Within a few hours, without queen pheromone, the chamber is converted to a starter colony.

At this point, rotate the lower colony 180 degrees so that field bees returning to the hive enter the upper portion and augment the population in the upper brood chamber.

The slide-in floor is removed from the Cloake board after one day. The bees above continue to feed the developing queen cells started when the floor was in place.

The unit above now functions as a finisher colony. Before emergence of any queen, capped queen cells need to be removed and transferred to mating nucleus colonies. Following the removal of the ripe queen cells and subsequent hatching of all brood, the boxes above become supers.

Cobey, S. (2005). A versatile queen rearing and banking system-Part I the" Cloake Board Method" of queen rearing. American Bee Journal 145(4): 308-311 and (5) 385-386.

Figure 18-6
Cloake board with metal slide sitting at an angle on top of a board queen excluder.

Figure 18-7
Colony with Cloake board (with metal slide). The queen is in brood area below and new queens will be reared in top portion after the metal slide is added.

below will be unable to enter the upper chamber. There should be at least one honey super between the chamber containing the old queen and new one above in which the bees will rear a new queen.

4. Provide an entrance for bees in the top box. Entrances might be wedges, one inch (2.5 cm) wide and 3/8 inch (1 cm) high, cut into the rim of the ventilated division board, a one-inch auger hole drilled in the hive body, or wooden wedges inserted beneath the hive body and covers to create an entrance. Face the entrance toward the back of the hive, opposite the regular entrance.

5. Nine days after setup, carefully examine the box of raised brood for emergency queen cells. If you raised frames with existing queen cells, they should show evidence of queen emergence. Some beekeepers enter the rearing chamber after four or five days and destroy all of the developing queen cells except two, one capped and one uncapped. The first young queen that emerges will destroy the cell of the other one. Some prefer to leave all queen cells intact and let the bees do the selection.

6. When a virgin queen emerges in the top box, she will eliminate rivals within the first day. Within a week, she will take her orientation and mating flights. In a few more days, she will be laying eggs in the top box; by now, all brood raised will have hatched. Check her egg-laying pattern to determine mating success.

7. Once successfully mated, the new queen can then be used to replace the old queen in the lower portion of the hive. If requeening an existing colony, enter the lower brood chamber, find and kill the old queen. If you prefer, the new queen might be used to requeen another colony.

Find the queen you wish to replace, reduce this colony to a single brood box and then transfer the entire box with the new queen to the other hive with a sheet of newspaper in between. In both instances, check the colony in a week or two to be sure the colony remains queenright. If you mark the new queen at the time of requeening, it will be easier to confirm your requeening was successful.

Raising a few queens of a specific strain

1. During peak swarming season, or as the main nectar flow begins, put a second brood box above a strong colony if there is not one already there. Separate the two boxes with a queen excluder, placing the queen below the excluder, and add one or two supers. Place a screened bottom board or Cloake board modified queen excluder (Figure 18-6) above the honey supers.

Stock this new chamber with two frames of bee bread and honey and fill the box with additional frames, leaving a space in the middle for two frames.

2. Provide a flight entrance in the top box.

Figure 18-8
Gilbert Doolittle, author of *Scientific Queen Rearing* and leader in development of commercial queen production in the United States. From *History of American Beekeeping* by Frank Pellett, reprinted in 2013 by Wicwas Press.

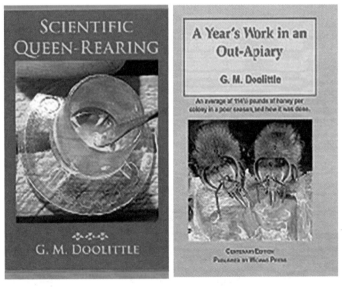

Figure 18-9
Gilbert Doolittle's *Scientific Queen Rearing* and *A Year's Work in an Out-Apiary*, reprinted by Wicwas Press.

3. From your best colony or breeder queen, select two frames of sealed and unsealed brood with clinging nurse bees and transfer the frames to the middle of the chamber above the double screen or Cloake board. If too few nurse-aged bees are transferred, shake additional bees from the selected colony into the rearing box. Locate the queen in the colony before you transfer frames or

Box 45

GRAFTLESS CELL PRODUCTION

Here are non-grafting queen cell production methods:

Miller method — A Miller frame is a standard frame in which medium brood or thin foundation is cut about midway in the frame length to form several downward V's. Or, use three to four pieces of foundation, about 3 inches (7.5 cm) wide, coming to a point about midway from the bottom bar.

Place this modified frame into the brood area of the selected breeder colony just before or during nectar flow. Bees will draw the comb and the queen should deposit fertilized eggs in the cells. The bees may make drone cells to anchor the foundation to the bottom bar.

After eggs appear, cut away the drone cells with a sharp knife or Exacto® knife so the lower edge of cells contains worker eggs or new larvae. Place the trimmed comb into the middle space of a starter colony; a closed broodless nucleus supplied with nurse-age bees. The bees will convert some of the lowest worker cells into vertical queen cells . In seven days, you will be able to cut and separate several capped queen cells for use in queenless mating nucs (Figure 18-10).

Alley, Case or Hopkins method — Henry Alley, a Massachusetts beekeeper, in 1883 described how to position a strip of egg-containing comb he had cut halfway down the frame. He trimmed the cell depth on one side close to the center midrib. Every two of three eggs were removed. The strip was then positioned facing downward on the bottom bar of a medium frame and put into a queenless starter colony.

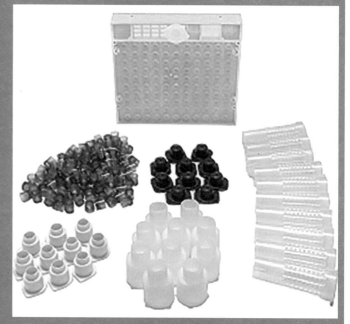

Figure 18-11
The comb box system eliminates grafting by having the queen lay directly in the cell cup. Mann Lake Ltd.

In the Case or Hopkins method, a complete frame with eggs or appropriate-age larvae from a selected breeder colony is laid on its side, supported and elevated an inch or two above the frames of a starter colony. The queenless starter feeds worker cells oriented vertically, and many queens can be produced.

Comb box (Jenter) system — In another popular non-graft system, the queen is confined to a plastic cage with plastic cups replacing foundation (Figure 18-11). The queen eventually lays eggs in the artificial cups. Once she lays eggs, the cups are removed from the apparatus and positioned vertically in special cup holders and given to a broodless starter colony. This grafting-free system, available as an entire kit, was developed by Jenter, an engineer-beekeeper. Various comb box caging systems are sold in generic versions by large bee supply dealers.

Cell punch — Using a cell punch, an entire worker cell, with an egg or appropriate age larva, is removed by cutting or coring it out. The whole cell is removed, and the larva is not touched; it is removed intact with its food supply uninterrupted. The punched cell is subsequently mounted on a bar, positioned vertically in a starter colony as described in the Doolittle method.

In all of these methods, capped queen cells need to be isolated and placed carefully into individual mating nuclei, one or two days before emergence of any queens.

Figure 18-10
The Miller method capped queen cells. R. Keller

shake nurse bees so you do not accidentally transfer the queen to the upper box.

4. As in the emergency queen rearing system described above, the queenless portion above the double screen will raise several emergency queen cells in the absence of their queen. Cut out and remove capped queen cells (being careful to not damage them) after seven days and subsequently isolate them into queenless mating nucs (see section on mating nucs). This may be difficult and cutting will cause damage to the frames.

See Box 45 for additional small scale methods to produce queen cells.

The grafting or Doolittle method

Grafting is term used to describe the **transfer of worker larvae** from worker cells to wax or plastic queen cups. This is a time-tested method to produce top quality queen cells. It is called the **Doolittle method** after Gilbert Doolittle, an upstate New York (Syracuse area) beekeeper (Figure 18-8). Doolittle, sometimes called the Father of Modern Queen Rearing, was a contemporary of Langstroth. He wrote extensively for the bee journals for many years.

He published his *Scientific Queen Rearing* in 1889. Doolittle, along with Langstroth, promoted adoption of Italian bee stock, writing how best to manage Italian bees (*A Year's Work in an Out-Apiary*).

In addition to Doolittle's books (Figure 18-9), there are two contemporary books on queen rearing using the grafting method. These are available from Wicwas Press, publisher of this book: Roger Morse's *Rearing Queen Honey Bee*s and Lawrence Connor's *Queen Rearing Essentials*.

The grafting (Doolittle) method is roughly as follows:

1. **Breeder colony**—Select a colony containing a queen of a desired strain. This is your cell **grafting mother**. It should have the most desirable characteristics you wish to perpetuate: wintering ability, honey production, gentleness and hygienic behavior. At grafting, find a frame with young larvae no more than 24 hours of age. Or, three and a half days prior to grafting you may place both the queen and a drawn, empty comb into a cage made of hardware cloth or queen excluder material, to force her to lay eggs. This will ensure a good supply of 12-hour old larvae for grafting.

2. **Starter colony**—In **cell starter colonies** bees receive dozens of newly grafted queen cells and feed them overnight (Figure 18-14). Use a standard five-frame nucleus box and fasten hardware cloth or window screen to the bottom for ventilation. Do not let the bees fly. Place a sponge soaked with clean water on the bottom of the starter. Add a frame of honey, a frame of bee bread

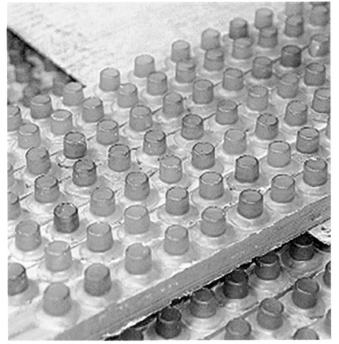

Figure 18-12
Empty plastic cells waxed on queen rearing bars.
L. Connor

Figure 18-13
Worker larva being transferred to a plastic cell cup on a stainless steel grafting tool. L. Connor

and a frame for cluster space. Have a cover ready to close the hive. An alternative starter is a standard box positioned over a queenright colony with a **double screen** or a closed Cloake board between the queenright portion below and starter hive above.

Figure 18-14
Bars of cells from a queenless, broodless cell starter. The starter was filled with nurse bees from a strong colony. The bees cannot fly or forage. This starter was used overnight to start cells, and then the bees were returned to their hive. The cells were moved to a cell builder (finisher)

Figure 18-15
Frame with two bars of started cells ready to be transferred into finisher colony, as in Figure 18-14. L. Connor

3. **Shake bees into the starter colony** — Enter a strong colony and find the queen. Temporarily cage her and set her in a safe place. Remove all the frames of sealed brood and shake the bees on these frames into the starter colony with the sponge and three frames from Step 2. Shake as many nurse bees into the starter colony as possible. Allow older field bees to fly back to their hive while you shake the bees. Once all the frames are shaken, gently place the lid on the starter. It now contains pollen and nectar that supports royal jelly production by the younger worker bees. The closed starter box is used overnight — it does not have an entrance, queen or brood.

Return the queen to the strong colony, releasing her from the cage.

4. **Prepare grafting cups** — Plastic or beeswax queen cups, grafting bars/frames and several variations of grafting tools are available commercially if you do not make your own. Place up to 12 to 20 empty beeswax or plastic queen cups on a single bar (Figure 18-12). Use fewer cups when nighttime temperatures are below 50° F (10° C) when the bees may be forced to cluster. On your first graft, use no more than two bars (24-40 cups).

5. **Grafting setup** — Return to your breeder colony and remove the frame of very young larvae you selected for grafting. Gently **brush the bees** from the comb and **wrap the frame in a moist towel** to protect the larvae from dehydration. Never shake the frame you graft from, or you may dislodge larvae from the cell bottom. Carry the frame to a work area to graft. This area should have good lighting (which can be a head-mounted light source) and some magnification.

If the grafting is done outside, keep the frame and newly grafted larvae covered to maintain humidity and to avoid direct sunlight. Position the frame so light reaches the bottom of the cells to provide maximum illumination.

6. **Grafting** — Select larvae between 12 and 24 hours old. Use a purchased grafting tool or make your own from a toothpick or metal rod (Figure 18-13). One option is to prime each cup with 1:1 water-diluted royal jelly or move some of the brood food from their original cells with each larva. Graft quickly at a temperature of 70° F (21° C) or warmer. Do not injure, chill, or let larvae dry out. Do not allow the larva to contact the side of the comb as it is removed from its worker cell nor when placed into the cup. Do not flip over larvae.

7. **Move graft to starter colony** — Before you introduce the cells gently pick up and drop the starter box about six inches to jar bees from the frames. Immediately place the completed grafting frames with the grafted cells into the center of the starter colony (Figure 18-14). Leave the cells in the starter overnight. The starter box is closed without foraging.

8. **Finisher colony** — A day or two before grafting, establish a finisher colony (Figure 18-16). Finisher colonies (also called **cell builders** because they do most of the cell construction), unlike starter colonies, can be queenright but the grafts need to be positioned in a queenless portion separated by a queen excluder.

Figure 18-16
Checking brood in a finisher builder before moving grafts from the starter colony. The queen is confined by an excluder below the pink queenless top box. L. Connor

Figure 18-17
A capped queen cell with abundant royal jelly, visible in the blue cup base above, pushed into the brood frame of a mating nucleus. L. Connor

Figure 18-18
Sealed queen cells on grafting frames. They are usually introduced into mating nuclei about 24 hours before expected emergence. C. Burkhead

The colony should be strong and have two hive bodies (deep or medium). The queen excluder confines the queen below in the lower box. The area above the excluder will receive all the eggs and larvae, called **open brood,** moved from the lower box to attract nurse bees into the upper box with brood pheromone. The upper box is filled out with frames of honey, pollen or sealed brood. Leave a space in the center for the transfer of queen cells. Finisher colonies may hold 100 or more developing queen cells, but start by giving them only one frame with two or three bars (24 or 60 cells).

9. **Moving grafted larvae** – The morning after you placed grafted cells into the starter colony, the queen cells that contain larvae (called 'the take' or successful starts) are moved to the finisher colony. *Very* gently use your finger tips or brush the nurse bees off the cells to get a count of the number of cells started (Figure 18-15). Put the started cells into the space in the middle of the finisher colony.

If the "take" is lower than expended or needed, you can reuse the closed starter box after transferring the first cycle of takes into the finishing colony The second graft will be 24 hours younger so mark the second graft distinct from the initial transfer.

10. **Cell emergence** – New queens will be ready to emerge after 11 or 12 days, provided larvae were less than one day old when grafted. If older larvae were grafted, the projected queen emergence will be earlier. Two days before the queens are due to hatch (the 10th day), the capped queen cells (Figure 18-18) should be transferred directly to mating nuclei or to colonies that are to be requeened. Failure to transfer ripe queen cells can be disastrous as one virgin queen will kill all remaining cells.

11. **Mating nucleus** – Prepare a mating nucleus for each ripe queen cell (See mating nuclei below in Mating queens section) and carefully install one cell to each nucleus. Following emergence, virgin queens will make orientation and then mating flights to DCA's (Chapter 10).

12. **Cell/virgin holding colony** – Some beekeepers use incubator hives to hold ripe queen cells. Or they set up colonies the same as cell builders, keeping brood next to caged ripe cells and eventually the virgin queens.

Unemerged cells may be caged (Figure 18-32). If you produce more ripe cells than the number of nuclei ready for the cells, place the ripe virgin queen cells into emergence cages or 'hair curler' cages. Virgin queens may be held for up to 14 days. Use caged virgins to replace queens that did not successfully emerge in mating nuclei. After 14 days, stored virgin queens experience a lower rate of mating success and lower sperm counts. They should not be used in a mating nucleus.

Figure 18-19
Green plastic drone frame from a drone mother colony for mating. D. Williams

Drone production & manipulations

Drones were briefly discussed in Chapter 10. Key aspect of drone biology is how drone developmental time impacts queen mating. Drones take 24 days to develop, while queens require only 16 days. This difference leads to the advise to wait to produce queens (by grafting or another method) until developing drone brood is in the **purple eyed stage**. That timing difference means the new drones will be sexually mature and taking mating flights to synchronize with beekeeper-raised queens.

Drone production starts in overwintered colonies only when a colony has a combination of abundant stored food and pollen and nectar entering the hive. Only the strongest overwintering hives will start drone production before the spring food supply becomes available.

In the spring, queens have a strong instinct to lay unfertilized eggs and the colony produce drones as soon as food conditions allow. This push to raise drones

Figure 18-20
Drone brood at the bottom of a medium frame placed into a deep hive body. D. Morgan

slows or stops once drone brood and drones are present, based on a queen's prior drone laying behavior. This mechanism prevents the further production of drones once a large cadre of drones have been started. After several weeks, new drone production usually restarts.

Beekeepers may take advantage of the spring instinct by introducing drawn drone comb (Figure 18-19), or a comb selected because of the large number or drone cells (Figure 18-21). Some beekeepers introduce a medium frame into a deep hive body, allowing the bees to quickly build drone comb in the empty space below the bottom bar of the medium frame (Figure 18-20).

Beekeepers engaged in commercial queen rearing add one to three drone combs to colonies designated for drone production (drone mother colonies). Add one frame every seven to ten days. Record the date of the first drone brood production to determine the earliest possible grafting date to produce new queens.

Trimming

Colonies regulate drone brood populations through trimming, removing developing drones when food supplies have declined. Eggs, developing larvae and even sealed drone brood are removed and body fluids consumed, apparently for hive nutrition. This often occurs after a cold snap in the spring, and bees have not been able to forage for several days.

Increasing desirable drones

Because queens and drones mate in the open, many beekeepers influence the number of 'desirable' or 'target' drones by promoting their production. Using multiple apiary locations, drone mothers (queens that produce the desired type of drone) are installed in all colonies. These colonies are given stimulative food and drone comb.

Figure 18-21
Sealed drone brood with typical 'bullet' cappings. TuckaBee

Colonies self-limit the number of drones they produce at any point in time, and beekeepers use this aspect of bee biology to increase the number of desirable drones. When Italian queens were first introduced to North America, queen producers like G. M. Doolittle reduced non-Italian drone production in colonies that did not have Italian queens. Doolittle simply removed a frame containing developing Italian drones from one of this Italian drone mother colonies and placed it into a non-Italian colony. The added frame of drones reduced new drone production by the non-Italian queen colonies.

Meanwhile, with the frame of Italian drones removed, the Italian colony is provided empty drawn drone comb so it will produce more Italian drones, increasing the total supply of desired Italian drones in the apiary.

Extending drone production

To prolong the mating period of queens, beekeepers feed colonies with protein and sugar mixtures to stimulate

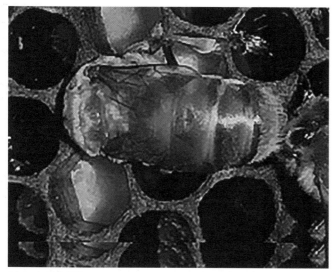

Figure 18-22
Drone feeding on pollen, indicating that it is a young adult drone that needs protein for sperm migration. Older drones making mating flights feed on stored honey. Tuckabee.

drone maintenance and new drone production. Rather than losing large numbers of drones due to a shortage of pollen (Figure 18-22), supplemental feeding maintains drones until fall. In Florida, drone numbers are maintained throughout October, or later, if conditions are favorable.

Drone holding colonies

The ability to produce and hold large numbers of drones for prolonged mating is discussed in *Bee Sex Essentials*. **Drone holding colonies** are the equivalent of a cell builder used for queens. Drone brood and worker brood frames are alternated in a otherwise queenless colony provided with a caged virgin. This creates excellent drone holding and feeding conditions. These colonies will support drones during a dearth when others are expelling them.

The same methods may be used to hold drones (for instrumental insemination) from desired bloodlines and ensure sperm viability. These colonies may be treated for varroa mite control as long as the treatment does not injure the drones or their sperm.

Mating queens

Mating (nucleus) colonies (nucs, nooks, nuclei) are either small (mini) colonies of about 1,000 bees in a special mating box (Figure 18-24), or larger, standard three- to five-frame nucleus box colonies with one frame of brood plus food frames (Figure 18-23, 18-25, 18-26). Larger and stronger colonies are more resistant to small hive beetles, wax moths and temperature extremes. Such mating colonies should be allowed to expand into standard nuclei after the queen has mated.

Mating (nucleus) colonies are prepared by the beekeeper to receive ripe queen cells. Young virgin queens hatch,

Figure 18-23
Three-frame mating nuclei in Florida, positioned on hive stands within a wooded area for protection from strong winds. Alternating entrance directions and bright box colors minimize queen loss due to drifting. L. Connor

are mated and then begin egg laying before they are caged for sale or transfered to full-sized colonies.

Caged virgin queens less than 14 days post-emergence may be installed in an introduction cage. Queens should be held for two or three days, and then the cork or plastic cap removed so the bees can eat through the candy plug. Do not direct release virgin queens as they often fly off!

Mating colonies are generally established the day before the capped queen cells are to be placed in them. They ideally contain some capped brood to ensure emerging young adults and adequate adult worker bee population. They also need include a frame containing honey and bee bread so the colony is never in danger of starvation. Small mini boxes are more difficult to establish and maintain than standard five-frame nucleus boxes but are used because they require fewer bees to establish (Figure 18-24).

Early in the season, when nighttime temperatures fall below 50° F. (10° C), bolster the colonies with more bees when they are established. As mating nuclei are made up, they should be placed in the shade and confined before transfer to a bee mating yard.

Mating nuclei may be as small in size as two frames or as large as five frames. Nucleus boxes can be standard hive boxes divided into two or three bee tight compartments (queen castles), each with a separate entrance (Figure 18-25), or they may be individual, stand-alone boxes (Figures 18-23, 18-26). Various sizes and shapes have been used and each has its adherents.

To stock a mating nucleus, carefully remove a ripe cell from the grafting bar and gently push the base of the cell in the area above the brood area (Figure 18-17). Nucs should have free flight but with small entrances

to conserve heat and reduce robbing by bees from other hives or pests like ants and yellowjackets. Small hive beetles can quickly destroy nucs and will make queen rearing virtually impossible where beetle populations are high.

Once established, leave mating colonies alone for 10 to 12 days after adding cells before checking to determine if the young queen is mated and laying eggs. If mated, she is now ready for transfer to a cage for sale or subsequent introduction to a colony that is to be requeened (Figures 18-28, 18-29). Within twelve hours, the same mating nucleus may be given another capped queen cell. Mating nuclei are often restocked with bees and brood to improve resulting queen mating.

The advantages of mating queens from nuclei are:

- reduced risk if the queen does not emerge from her cell, is deformed or is lost on her mating flight

- the inspection of a small colony is less time consuming

- less resource investment and apiary space is needed to prepare and house smaller mating nucs than use of full-sized colonies

- a mating nucleus permits evaluation of queens prior to their introduction to full-size colonies

Figure 18-25
Standard hive box converted into a 3-chambered mating nuc. Each of the three units are separate and distinct with their own individual covers (background) and entrances.

Figure 18-24
Many large-scale queen producers use mini mating nuclei that hold three small half width frames. They are useful for the production of one to two queens before the colony falls victim to small hive beetles or other problems.
L. Connor

Figure 18-26
Using a standard five-frame Langstroth nucleus box, frames of brood with bees removed are placed over a queen excluder that allows nurse bees to pass through to cover the brood. A queen cell, virgin queen (both for mating) or a mated queen is added to the unit, which is moved to a new location.

- a small queenless nucleus colony will accept a ripe queen cell or virgin queen more readily than a large colony

Mating control

While achieving some control of the mating process in nature would offer enormous benefits, mating accuracy is generally beyond the control of the average beekeeper. At best, it is possible to raise queens from a specific genetic stock and stimulate colonies to produce large numbers of drones of the desirable type to mate with queens.

Early attempts at mating control in confinement were unsuccessful, even inside large enclosures like athletic field houses and circus tents. Beekeepers have successfully controlled their bee stock in isolated areas, and by flooding their breeding area with the desired drone stock. They have their best success in isolated

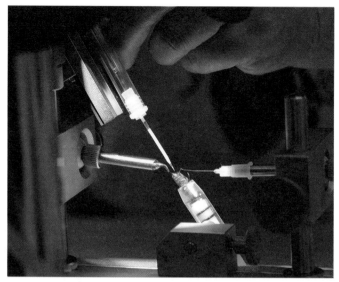

Figure 18-27
Queen bee undergoing instrumental insemination. She is held in a holder with a CO_2 gas feed. A syringe containing semen from multiple drones is inserted into the queen's median oviduct. D. Morgan

mating areas like islands or mountain valleys, yet these areas are sometimes poor beekeeping areas because of high winds, heavy moisture and low temperature. Few breeders have enough bee colonies to successfully flood a large enough area to effectively isolate their stock from unrelated colonies.

In areas with migratory beekeeping, isolation is virtually impossible as the number of colonies in a site may vary widely. Beekeepers seeking to breed survivor stock often seek the assistance of other beekeepers in their area to form an association of queen breeders. Individuals supply brood from their superior colonies and raise large drone populations of the desired types.

Instrumental insemination (sometimes called artificial) is a powerful but limited alternative for controlled mating. Early attempts at brushing the queen's abdomen with semen or immersing the tip of her abdomen in semen were not successful. In 1927, Lloyd Watson at Cornell University developed the first practical instrumental insemination device, but his success rate was low because his instrument did not ensure that the semen reached the queen's oviduct. Harry Laidlaw, Jr., discovered in the 1940s that the queen's valvefold needs to be moved out of the way to ensure semen reaches the oviduct.

Today, the techniques and instrumentation for instrumental insemination are readily available. By immobilizing the queen with CO_2 and positioning hooks to open her abdomen under a microscope and moving aside the valvefold that normally blocks passage to the oviduct, it is now feasible to place semen directly into the oviduct using a specially designed syringe (Figure

Figure 18-28
A queen in plastic cage with candy in the release tube. A plastic cap that keeps workers from eating the candy has been removed. This is usually three to five days after introduction into the colony. L. Connor

18-27). The semen migrates into the spermatheca of the queen as it does after natural mating. Multiple drone semen or semen from a single drone may be used.

Drones must be produced in closed, flight-proof hives, aged, and collected under controlled conditions before they are taken to the laboratory where they are ejaculated for their sperm.

Instrumental insemination is best learned from someone who regularly uses the technique; practice is needed to perfect insemination methodology. The equipment represents a considerable investment. It takes time to learn the process and even the best individuals only inseminate a dozen or so queens an hour. Methods for long-term semen storage are underway but are far from being available to beekeepers. Unfortunately, few beekeepers are willing to pay the price for instrumentally inseminated queens.

Queen introduction

Within the honey bee society, a single queen is normally present except during, or shortly after, natural queen rearing. Following supersedure events the mother may coexist with the newly-mated daughter queen for a short time. This is termed a mother-daughter queen colony (Chapter 10, Figure 10-10).

Since the welfare of the colony depends upon the queen, there are instances when beekeepers need to replace a queen or introduce a new queen into an established colony. Success in doing so begins with understanding essential queen biology.

Bees in an established colony recognize their own queen. An unrelated queen is usually considered an intruder. Beekeepers take precautions when introducing a queen to a different colony. During the introduction process, a new queen takes on the general hive odor and establishes her queen substance and queen retinue pheromones and the pheromones produced in her abdominal (tergal) and footprint glands. The different odor and behavior of a foreign queen presents challenges in introducing queens.

Requeening with virgins and mated queens

The processes of introducing queen cells, virgins, or mated queens are subject to the same odor issues as uniting bees of two colonies. Odor-disrupting techniques improve the successful introduction of queens to a new colony. If the colony to receive the queen is dequeened several hours before the new queen is introduced, the chance for successful introduction is improved because queenless worker honey bees are more readily attracted to and accepting of a new queen.

Introduction techniques that immediately release the queen are less successful because they do not provide the queen and the bees time to establish a common odor. When foraging conditions are very good, and if the queen is similar to her replacement in age, genetic background and behavior, the success rate of queen introduction is higher.

What is most useful, however, is to allow time for workers to become accustomed to the new queen's odor.

Bees obtain queen substance pheromone by physical contact. The pheromone is subsequently passed via food transmission and physical contact to other workers and shared with the hive population. Queens added to a colony without a proper introduction are balled by the workers, a behavior where the new queen is surrounded by worker bees and killed by suffocation and elevation of the temperature inside the ball.

Reliable queen introduction techniques allow bees contact with the queen's mouthparts and antennae but prevent the new hive's bees from stinging or balling her. Thus, the most reliable method to introduce new queens is via an introducing cage (Figures 18-28, 18-29, 18-33, 18-34). Bees touch the queen through the cage and by the time she is released among the bees (by bees or beekeeper), the workers are more likely to accept her.

There are a number of shipping cages that are very suitable for introducing queens. Plastic cages like those by Jz's-Bz's (Figure 18-28) are replacing the wooden variety. The standard wood queen shipping cage (Figure 18-29) can be used but are more effective if the mesh screening is one-tenth inch (2.5 mm) mesh.

Cages made solely of smooth wire mesh work very well (Figure 18-33). A hardware cloth or plastic push-in cage (Figure 18-34) gives good results as the queen can begin laying eggs in cells within the cage while the bees get accustomed to her odors. When the queen is caged over a patch of emerging brood, the newly emerged (naive) worker bees will aid in her pheromone transfer to bees outside the cage.

Not all bees need to touch the queen, but some must. Just the smell from a queen in a cage without mouthpart contact is not enough. If a queen is held in a group of bees where they can smell but not touch her, they exhibit queen replacement behavior and begin development of ovaries. But if some bees are allowed to contact a queen and they, in turn, mingle with the rest of the colony, queen rearing and worker ovary development is prevented.

Successful introduction of virgin queens requires more beekeeper attention than introduction of a mated queen. It is recommended to first introduce virgin queens into a mating nucleus to allow her to mate and lay worker eggs before caging her for introduction to a larger colony.

Requeening with brood

When a colony loses its queen, it uses the emergency queen replacement response to produce queen cells from young larvae originating from fertilized eggs. It takes a month before the colony will have a new queen laying eggs. The resulting colony obtains one-half of its genetic information from the original mother queen since one of her fertilized eggs develops into the new queen. The other half of the genetic information will come from her many drone partners.

During colony inspections, whenever a colony is found without (or apparently without) open brood, the beekeeper should add a frame of brood containing eggs and young larvae removed from a colony with desirable characteristics to facilitate raising of a new emergency queen. If the colony has a queen, (perhaps a newly-reared queen or brood was present, but not observed), then the transferred brood is readily accepted and cared for and will boost the colony population.

This technique, as old as beekeeping, was popularized by L.L. Langstroth. The major disadvantage with this method of requeening is the month-long interval before the colony has a new egg-laying queen. This is not a serious problem if done when there is sufficient time available for the colony to rebuild its population and honey stores before winter or a dearth period.

Requeening with queen cells

Queenless colonies usually accept a queen cell when provided with one. During swarm preparations, when the bees raise an excessive number of queen cells,

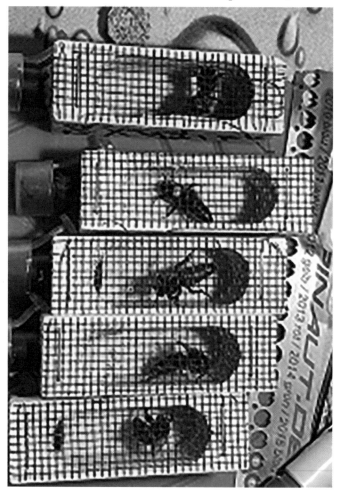

Figure 18-29
Mated queens (without attendant worker bees) in Benton mailing cages, ready to be introduced in hives or nuclei. D. Morgan

Figure 18-30
An extra queen cell produced during supersedure ready to be used by the beekeeper. L. Connor

Figure 18-31
Queen cells roughly 48 hours after grafting may be used to requeen queenless colonies and establish nuclei. L. Connor

several cells can be harvested and used to requeen other colonies. Extra supersedure cells may also be harvested for requeening (Figure 18-30).

Conventional wisdom is that requeening with swarm cells is the same as selection for swarming, which some consider undesirable. Supersedure might be the more favored natural queen rearing method to utilize as a source of producing queen cells, but it frequently only happens during the nectar flow when it is not often detected by the beekeeper. Supersedure, and subsequent production of 'natural' queen cells, can be forced by injuring the colony queen such as cutting off part of one of her front legs. Most beekeepers feel injuring a queen (along with killing one to dequeen) distasteful.

Removing a queen (dequeening) from a strong hive with desirable traits stimulates that hive's emergency queen cell production. Queen cells are usually produced on several frames. Such cells can be harvested by moving a frame with cells to a queenless or dequeened colony. The removed queen can be returned to her original colony after holding her in a cage for a day or so while her colony starts emergency replacement cells.

Rather than move the entire frame, the beekeeper may cut cells from the comb. There is some risk of damaging the cell itself in cutting or transfer. Cutting creates holes and leaves uneven worker comb. Because of differences in the incoming food supply, emergency cells are often smaller than swarm or supersedure cells, but the queens inside the cells are usually fully developed. Waiting until the cells are capped makes cutting easier but also lengthens the queenless period in the original colony and makes her subsequent re-acceptance less likely.

Most queen rearing techniques involve the emergency queen replacement response. For quality production and ease in handling developing cells, special techniques explained earlier in this chapter have been developed to ensure quality queen cell production under emergency (queenless) conditions.

Commercial queen breeders introduce queen cells to mating nuclei daily. The bees in the nuclei are prepared four to six hours in advance of cell introduction and heavily fed with sugar syrup. Ripe, ready-to-emerge queen cells are placed on the face of the comb about two inches (5 cm) below the frame top bar. The adjacent frame is carefully positioned to avoid dislodging or damaging the queen cell. Some beekeepers protect a ripe queen cell with a cell protector or put it in a queen cage (Figure 18-32).

When adding a queen cell to a large colony, remove the old queen a day before cell introduction. Leave a colony with a new queen, introduction cage or queen cell undisturbed for a few days after adding the queen cell to avoid worker bee or human damage to the cell.

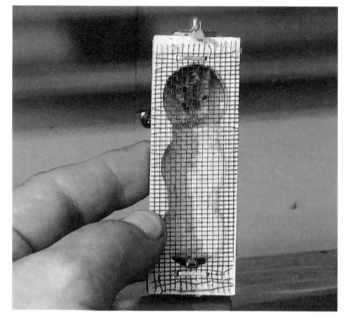

Figure 18-32
Ripe queen cell in an emergence cage made from a wood shipping cage with a large opening. D. Morgan

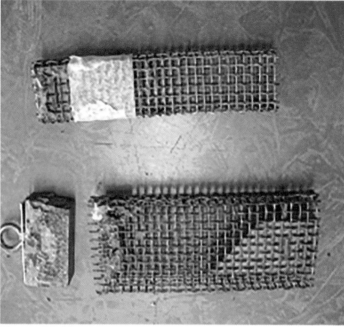

Figure 18-33
Hardware cloth introduction cages fit between two frames. Release the queen after three or more days of confinement.

Requeening with a ripe, ready-to-emerge queen cell means only a two- to three-week interval before a new queen will be laying eggs in comparison to a month or longer if the colony must raise its own queen.

48-hour queen cells

Recently beekeepers have adapted the method of using 48-hour old queen cells to requeen or establish a nucleus colony (Figure 18-31). Two days after grafting (using 12- to 24-hour old larvae), the developing queen is large enough to tolerate time outside of the hive (6 to 12 hours is typical), while floating on a bed of royal jelly. It is too small to move out of the cell, as older larvae can do. The method is a low-cost way to move desirable queen stock from one apiary to another. Each 48-hour old cell is placed in a queenless colony, where nurse bees complete feeding and cell construction.

Odor management during queen introduction

Beekeepers disrupt colony odor to improve the success rate of uniting two colonies. This disruption facilitates the mingling of bees from the two hives using the newspaper method, where one colony with a queen is added to another with a sheet of newspaper in between (Chapter 14, Figure 14-6).

The bees in the top box are not provided with an entrance and must go through the hive below, thus ensuring that the bees remove the newspaper between the two units and mingle. Relatively little fighting occurs between the once-separate but now more similar-smelling units. The bees decide which queen will becomes the colony's sole queen; the queen of the upper unit may enjoy an advantage.

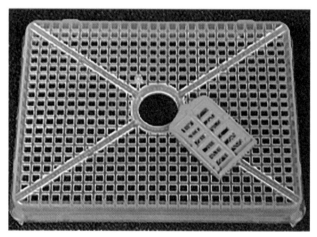

Figure 18-34
Plastic push-in cage. L. Connor

Uniting of bees and queen introductions work better under good foraging conditions when bees are more likely to mix. Feeding bees helps facilitate introduction.

Appreciating drones and queens

Many wonderful things are said about queens that are not said about drones. While the word drone has a strong negative meaning, drones should be seen as the loyal but momentary consorts, providing sexual service to the queen when needed. For most drones, this service is never needed. Yet in commercial queen rearing operations, thousands of drones may be called to service for successful mating. Any shortage of drones on those days results in queens with low sperm counts.

key terms

Alley method

breeder colony

breeder queen

cell punch

Cloake board

comb box system

Doolittle method

drone layer

drone production

emergency queen cells

fall requeening

finisher colony

grafting

grafting tool

graftless cell production

instrumental insemination

laying worker colony

mating control

Miller method

odor and queen introduction

plastic queen cage

push-in cage

queen introduction

queen production

queenless roar

queenlessness

queenright

quenless colony

raising queens of specific stock

ready-to-emerge cells

requeening

requeening during nectar flow

requeening with brood

requeening with queen cells

seasonal patterns

spring requeening

starter colony

discussion questions

How can you tell a colony is without a queen? Explain how to determine if the hive is experiencing an emergency situation, drone layer situation or laying worker condition? How might you tell if a colony has a virgin queen? Why would we want to replace a queen?

Why might bees accept or not accept a queen cell? A new virgin queen? A mated queen? Why is combining a nucleus with an established colony you wish to requeen a better technique than other methods?

Identify various means of raising queens. Describe the several means of obtaining capped queen cells and what we might do with capped queen cells to permit requeening of a colony.

What are the advantages of using a mating nucleus?

Describe nucleus colony management. How does making a mating nucleus in the summer differ from making a nucleus in the spring to keep a colony from swarming? Describe the preparation of a nucleus for overwintering in a northern climate. Compare these preparations with those of a beekeeper keeping bees in a southern state.

Raising queens is an excellent way to learn and experience beekeeping. The techniques are not complicated but you will need additional information and an apiary large enough to establish some mating nucs. Explain what you might need to raise queens.

exercises

Practice various techniques of introducing a queen to a colony. This could include the introduction of queen cells (capped and with larvae), virgin queens and mated queens with quick release versus a slower release technique.

Confirm that combining a nucleus with a dequeened colony is the safest, most reliable method of queen introduction.

Make a nucleus. Try doing so in different seasons and compare the outcome in terms of colony size, honey production and wintering success or failure.

references

Cobey, S. 2016. Instrumental/Artificial Insemination of Honey Bee Queens: 12 Most Frequently Asked Questions. American Bee Journal 156 (3): 339-342

Connor L.J. 2008, 2014. Bee Sex Essentials. Wicwas Press, Kalamazoo, MI

Connor L.J. 2006, 2014. Increase Essentials: Nuclei, management, wintering, Second edition. Wicwas Press, Kalamazoo, MI

Connor L.J. 2009, 2015. Queen Rearing Essentials, Second edition. Wicwas Press, Kalamazoo, MI

Doolittle, G.M. 1908, 2008 (Reprint). Scientific Queen Rearing. Wicwas Press, Kalamazoo, MI

Doolittle, G.M. 1908, 2005 (Reprint with additions). A year's work in the Out-Apiary. Wicwas Press, Kalamazoo, MI

Koeniger, G.N. et al. 2015. Mating Biology of Honey Bees Apis mellifera. Wicwas Press, Kalamazoo, MI

Morse, R.A. 1994. Rearing Queen Honey Bees, Second Edition. Wicwas Press, Kalamazoo, MI

Pellett, F. 2013 (Reprint). History of American Beekeeping. Root Candle Company, Medina, OH

Stahlman, D. 2013. A Queen Manual. https://www.ohiostatebeekeepers.org/wp-content/pdf/books/Queen_Manual.pdf

Figure 19-1
Increase colonies with jar feeders in Maryland. L. Connor

Concepts

Nucleus colonies

Making nuclei

Dividing spring colonies

Other ways to make increase colonies

Dividing spring colonies to make nuclei and reduce swarming

Making summer increase

Fall increase

Wintering nucleus hive

Nucleus colonies

We call them by many names. **Nucleus colonies**, divides, divisions, walk-away-splits, increase colonies, nucs, nooks, nukes and splits—they all are simply smaller colonies housed in smaller boxes (Figures, 19-1, 19-2). Many are five deep frames of bees, brood and honey, but they may be doubled up, five-frames over five-frames and managed like a thin standard hive. There are three- to six-frame variations and mini (baby) nucs used for mating

Many beekeepers enjoy great success using these smaller colonies. They are produced using different methods and used for different purposes. Because they are often used to increase a beekeeper's colony count, we often call them **increase colonies**. When they are used to supply additional mated queens or frames of brood or food, we call them **resource or support colonies**.

We have both written about how a nucleus colony fits into the concept of starting with **two and a half hives** during your first year of beekeeping. However you start—packages, swarms, or purchased nuclei—think about expanding your colony count by **one half colony**.

In the northern latitudes, beekeepers make increase hives from late March to August. In tropical climates, beekeepers make nucleus colonies timed with the next nectar flow, which may be linked to seasonal rainy periods.

When making an increase hive, the beekeeper must have a clear idea on how the colony will be used. Will it be an increase hive, used to replace a lost hive, or serve as a support hive? Will it be sold at a premium price as a nucleus hive because the bees are locally grown, and the queen is locally mated or of a mite-tolerant queen stock? The decision is up to you.

Nuclei can easily be managed as resource or support hives, producing brood, bees, queens and honey for use however you see fit. It serves as a backup hive—a 'Plan B' if something goes wrong with the hives you have.

Figure 19-2
Temporary nucleus hive assembled from April through August increase colony numbers and store new queens.

Figure 19-3
Type of brood comb for use in making an increase colony (nucleus). Removal reduces the swarming instinct. L. Connor

As a **resource hive**, the colony may be used first as a mating nuc, and later allowed to grow into a full-sized colony and used to make up winter losses. Producing resource hives may be part of your management plan to reduce the frequency of swarming. Or you may mate vigorous young queens, ready to replace a failing queen. Any nucleus colony may be allowed to grow and become full-sized.

Resource hives are often part of beekeeper's varroa mite management plan, a source of brood for a colony that needs it, a source of uncontaminated honey and bee bread, and a place where fresh new combs are drawn out.

More and more beekeepers use nuclei hives to evaluate queens, purchased or reared. Once installed in a nucleus hive, a new queen can be evaluated for her egg-laying ability and brood pattern. Once her bees have repopulated the colony, the beekeeper may be able to evaluate the hive's level of defensive behavior by counting stings.

If the queen and her bees meet your expectations, keep the queen in the nucleus and add additional hive bodies as the colony expands. Breeder queens are kept in smaller hives to extend their egg-laying life. Other beekeepers transfer hives into eight- or ten-frame units once they have evaluated the colonies and found them acceptable.

As you grow in beekeeping, keep at least half of your colony count as nucleus colonies. They become money in the bank, brood factories, and a source of replacement queens. In some years they may save your entire operation, or better yet, make it entirely profitable.

Making and using nuclei may provide the answer to a complicated challenge. When a large beekeeper from North Carolina bought a number of 'rustic hives' in log gums (non-movable comb) and transferred the bees to standard hives, the bees swarmed excessively. The beekeeper found it 'nearly impossible' to keep those bees in hives because they swarmed so frequently.

It turns out that the rustic colony beekeeper needed colonies to swarm each season to repopulate hives in his more primitive management system. Over the years he selected for intensive swarming behavior. Rather than letting bees swarm, the new beekeeper systematically made up nucleus hives to control the bees and requeen the stock. Nucs helped control the 'swarming problem' in the transferred colonies.

As an 'extra' hive, a resource hive provides backup for standard hives in the apiary. It is a fully functioning colony, only smaller in size and kept in a smaller box. Most nucleus hives function best when they use the same size frame as your production colonies (Figure 19-3).

Use same-sized (deep, medium, top-bar, or Warré) frames interchangeable in your efforts to boost, support, feed, and increase bee colonies. You trade the cost of the nucleus box and the bees for the freedom to save a colony when something goes wrong.

Nucs or nucleus colonies are a resource used to make up for failing colonies. They can quickly fill available equipment. Resource hives often provide a new queen, supply bees for an observation hive for bee product sales or exhibitions, showing bees in a most favorable light.

Smaller hives are easier to manipulate, lift and inspect. Compared to a full-sized hive, they can be opened on a hot summer day to show what is happening inside the hive to a group of 'mentees' and apiary visitors. Inspecting a small hive reduces the number of potentially defensive bees and the risk of stings. Having a small colony available for inspection leaves full-sized colonies undisturbed during nectar flows.

In summary, nucs are merely smaller versions of larger established colonies (Figure 19-4). You can purchase them to start a bee colony during the spring or make your own to do the same. As fully functioning but smaller versions of bee colonies, they are an excellent learning tool, enabling a novice to grow in knowledge and confidence as the colony grows in population. When well managed and given adequate growing space, nucs, when started early, provide a modest honey harvest.

Making nuclei

For many beekeepers, the removal of brood and bees from a strong, populous colony in the spring is **proactive swarm management**. One key to success is making nuclei responsibly, not weakening the donor hives by removing too much brood.

Dividing or weakening strong colonies is good bee management, especially if the colony is likely to build queen cells and swarm. Divides are a good way to build an apiary as they utilize bees with genetics suited for the area. Some beekeepers make up nuclei to mate queens (see Chapter 18) and then use the nucs as support hives.

Alternatively, some beekeepers select smaller colonies for nucleus making, arguing that these colonies are poor honey producers and are best used if converted into two or three new units headed by healthy, young, vigorous queens (Figure 19-5).

Divisions can be made at any time during the bee season (Figure 19-6). Depending upon the time of the local nectar flow, making early nuclei from strong over-wintered colonies may result in loss of honey production. This loss is offset by the value of new colonies and the reduction of swarming. Dividing bee colonies may require additional management to ensure the new colony properly builds up and stores enough honey for winter use.

To divide a colony, open the donor hive using as little smoke as possible. Find the frame containing the queen and set it aside to ensure that she does not move to another part of the hive. Remove two or three frames of mostly capped brood with adhering nurse-aged bees (Figures 19-7) and place them into a new hive body (Figure 19-6).

Figure 19-4
Beekeepers checking a four-frame nucleus hive.

Figure 19-5
Commercially raised nucleus colonies shipped to a northern location for distribution. S. Repasky

Figure 19-6
Making increase nucs is timed by the weather and the availability of frames of brood and ripe queen cells. C. Burkhead

Figure 19-7
Using primarily sealed brood in making increase colonies, the beekeeper ensures high bee population for growth.
C. Burkhead

Figure 19-8
The frame of brood has two ripe queen cells carefully pushed into the brood frame where brood was cut away to keep the cells warm and protect them from damage. C. Burkhead

Next, add a queen cell. Figure 19-8 shows use of two capped queen cells. Or install a new mated queen. Use queen cells reared by the bees (swarm or supersedure cells) or cells/mated queens purchased from a local producer selling locally-acclimatized stock.

Figure 19-9
Nucleus colonies do best when given frames of honey, often eliminating the need for syrup feeding. L. Connor

Some beekeepers use queen cells on brood frames from colonies preparing to swarm. Some argue that this propagates queens with a greater tendency to swarm, while others seek local queens adapted for local survival.

Add at least one frame containing honey and pollen to the hive body and fill the box with a full complement of frames (Figure 19-9). Return the old queen to the original colony and fill the empty spaces of the donor colony with drawn empty combs if available or frames with foundation. Some beekeepers leave the queen cells and move the original queen to the split, calling it an artificial swarm.

Use a standard hive box (deep or medium depth frames) or use a nucleus box holding four or five frames (Figure 19- 10). Standard boxes can be divided with solid boards and made into **queen castles** of two or three units (Chapter 18, Figure 18-25, Figure 19-12). In early or cooler seasons, stronger divides should be produced, containing more brood and worker bees.

Whenever you remove frames from a hive to establish a nucleus, replace the frames with drawn, empty combs from storage. If drawn comb is not available, frames with foundation or starter strips can be utilized. Foundation frames should be put together but frames with starter strips might be interchanged between drawn combs. Reduce the entrances of new divisions to prevent robbing.

When dividing colonies as a method of swarm control, the removal of brood and bees from those colonies should weaken them to the point where they will not raise new queens. Provide more brood rearing space, but do not weaken the original colony to the point where it will be unable to produce surplus honey.

Figure 19-10
Provided with three frames of brood, abundant nurse bees, ripe queen cells, and a frame of honey for food, this nucleus is ready to grow and expand. D. Morgan

Commercial beekeepers continually equalize colonies by moving frames of brood. They make nucleus colonies for increasing colony numbers (Figure 19-5) to sell to other beekeepers. With extensive colony numbers in apiaries there is little fighting among young bees when they are placed together since colonies often have similar hive odors. All colonies must be disease-free when frames are interchanged. New colonies should not be extensively manipulated.

Any divide that must rear a new queen cell should not be disturbed for three weeks. If there is no nectar flow, feed 1:1 sugar syrup to divides for the first few weeks. It may be necessary to continue feeding for a longer time. A rule of thumb is to feed until bees stop taking the syrup.

As their brood area increases, new bees emerge and the nuc population expands in size. Keep up with the bees and give them room before they become crowded.

Amount of brood—Most beekeepers build their increase colonies with either two or three frames of brood, removed

Figure 19-11
Late spring and summer nucleus colonies are an efficient way to increase colony numbers. L. Connor

from one or more strong, overwintered colonies. The brood and bees from different colonies are often mixed.

Bee coverage—It takes some skill to move the right number of bees needed to cover the brood when making a nucleus colony. Spot check new nuclei in the evening after assembly to make sure all the brood is covered with bees, as some older bees may return to their original hive.

Queen source—Purchase a queen or ripe queen cells from another beekeeper or raise your own queens. If the bees raise their own emergency queens it will take longer to have a serviceable nuc. One advantage of raising your own or having the bees raise a queen is that it maintains genetic diversity, results in a locally-raised queen and may be ideal if you are making these colonies for your own use.

Remember that when you are allowing bees to make and mate a queen, there will be additional loss. Figure on a 25% loss, that one quarter of your colonies will fail to produce a laying queen. Compare that with a mated queen from Hawaii or elsewhere with close to 100% introduction success rate unless the queens were overheated or chilled during shipment.

When to make the split?—Experience is often the key to knowing when to split a hive. It requires some knowledge of the future weather patterns as well as the expected bloom of bee flora. A mentor may be your best option, to ask when is the best time, especially if they have made increase nuclei for a number of seasons.

Figure 19-12
A look inside hives in Figure 19-11. Colonies are paired, each with a queen. Inner cover is a feed bag. L. Connor

Other methods to make increase hives
Walk-away-split

One option beekeepers use to make increase colonies is the classic walk-away-split. Brood and bees are removed from a strong colony and put into a nucleus box. A frame of food and empty comb fill the hive. The beekeeper lets the bees raise their own queen. About 75% of these units produce a queen that will successfully mate and start to lay. Queen quality may vary widely if the splits are weak.

In a follow-up visit to these colonies three or four weeks after setup, look for colonies with laying queens that can be moved into production equipment or kept as support or resource hives. Colonies that have not produced a queen can be combined with those that have new queens. Queens that are small, laying a poor brood pattern, or are otherwise unacceptable should be pinched and replaced with a laying queen with a better performance.

If colonies are maintained in two brood-right boxes, it is possible to divide by simply separating the two hive bodies, giving each one its own separate hive stand. These are sometimes called '**set-off' hives**. Four or more days after this separation, check the two parts. The queenless portion will have developed queen cells while the queenright portion will have a queen laying eggs.

Add a new queen to the queenless unit (the hive without eggs) using a cage introduction method or allow continued development of queen cells. This dividing method is not very refined. Neither the original colony nor the divide may produce any surplus honey, but this technique remains an easy method to increase colony numbers.

Make a resource colony over top of regular colony

One alternative is to build a resource hive over a strong colony, separated by a double-screen divider. This prevents bees in the two hives from making contact with their proboscises. It effectively separates the new colony from its parent.

Two or three frames of brood (including some eggs and larvae the proper age for queen cell construction) and adequate numbers of bees to cover the brood, will promote and support queen cell construction. The advantage of keeping the new hive over the bottom queenright hive is that it helps provide heat to support good queen rearing conditions. It also helps when you have a small apiary site.

Another advantage of this system, often called a **modified two-queen hive**, is it removes both bees and brood from strong hives, reducing their populations and the urge to swarm. Frames of foundation are often added to build new comb and to occupy the bees attention for a period of time.

These hives can become tall, especially when there is an early nectar flow and the bottom hive is supered. Once the unit above has a laying queen, it may be moved to a new beeyard location or the screen removed, newspaper added and the hive reunited. This system is ideal for beekeepers with a late spring and early summer nectar flow.

Whole hive reconstitution into nuclei

The idea of taking one or more strong hives and dividing them into nucs is not new. Langstroth was a fan of nuclei. Large scale commercial beekeepers continually make nuclei, working hive by hive. Many perform this splitting in the early spring, just as soon as the bees start to build up in population numbers.

Colonies are sent to California for almond pollination in February. When the colonies return (often in March), beekeepers make nuclei before the major spring nectar flow begins. Strong overwintered colonies are split into three or four nuclei by equalizing the frames of brood, bees and stored food.

Beekeepers use methods Henry Ford would recognize: an assembly line of crews tearing hives apart, separating bees, brood, honey and feeders into groups so they can be equalized and made into new nuclei colonies (Figures 19-13 and 19-14). At the end of this reconstruction, a ripe queen cell is added, the hive is closed up and the nuclei placed on pallets to be moved to a beeyard.

Each nucleus hive begins with three frames of brood and bees, a frame of honey (perhaps set aside from the previous season), and a purchased mated queen or a ripe queen cell. Frames of foundation may be added to fill a five-frame hive body.

Figure 19-15 diagrams a colony with 11 frames of brood and stored food. The frames were split into four nucs, each with three frames of brood (dark brown) and frames of drawn food comb (yellow frames) and filled out with foundation. In this example, one frame of brood was added from another colony. The original colony is completely split apart; the equipment is cleaned and stacked.

The use of a mated queen (often from a supplier in Hawaii, Florida or California) speeds the process of building a colony. Some beekeepers use **ripe queen cells** (those within a day or so of emerging), but allow for the added time it will take that young queen to reach sexual maturity, mate, let her ovaries swell up, and start laying eggs. This adds an additional 12 to 18 days to the schedule.

This method works best when the beekeeper has lots of experience with bees and local forage. A cold or wet March or April will cause a delay and slow nucleus development.

Later in the season, this system is used by beekeepers in southern locations who run bees for crop pollination and honey production. At the end of the nectar flow in northern states, the colonies are returned to the southern operation. Queens are reared and the colonies are split and fed during the fall for use as pollination units in the late-winter and early spring.

Once time has passed and the queens have mated and are laying, any 'blow outs' are combined so the adult bees are not lost.

There are as many versions of this as there are beekeepers. In Bolivia, one of us (DMC) regularly splits Africanized bee colonies occupying a full box into three hives a month ahead of anticipated nectar flow.

Dividing spring colonies to make nuclei and reduce swarming

Many beekeepers make spring nucleus colonies (mid-March into April and May) to replace colonies that died over the winter. They re-use the same frames and equipment after making sure the bees did not die from American foulbrood (see Chapter 21).

To house spring nucs, some beekeepers use standard boxes with a Masonite or thin plywood divider board (Figure 19-16). The two small units share heat, forming a thermal cluster on either side of the divider during cool spring weather. Other beekeepers establish a daughter colony next to the mother hive (Figure 19-17) so they can add brood and bees as needed while the nucleus grows.

Beekeepers may start colonies as mating nucs, and then shift their role to that of support hives. Those who are raising queens in areas of small hive beetles are increasingly using five-frame nucleus boxes (Figures 19-18, 19-19). As temperatures allow, they start the colonies in late winter or early spring with a single frame of brood and a frame of honey and bee bread. A frame feeder is provisioned with a small amount of 1:1 sugar syrup on a continuous basis.

The colonies are established with a ripe queen cell and are inspected every 14 days for queen harvest and restocking. With each queen harvest, the colonies are inspected and equalized. Additional frames of drawn comb are added for expansion while strong colonies may be adjusted by removing a frame of brood and bees, which is used to boost a nucleus where a queen failed to mate and produce brood. Once the mating season is over, the nuclei hives are

Figure 19-13.
Special holding box for eight frames of brood and bees. There is a screened bottom and top. The top nests into the enlarged box top. An eight frame spacer keeps the frames from crushing bees. These colonies are left in a cool room for 24 to 36 hours before being moved to the apiary and installed in nucs. L. Connor

Figure 19-14.
The boxes of eight frames each are stacked in a cool area for 36 hours to allow the bees to acclimate to each other and settle. The bees and brood are usually a mixture from several colonies. L. Connor

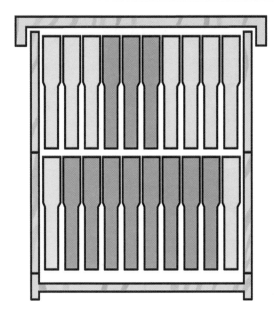

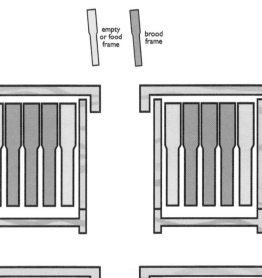

empty
or food
frame

brood
frame

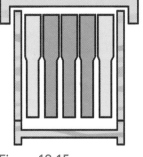

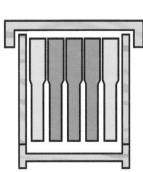

Figure 19-15
Some beekeepers divide an existing colony into four separate nucleus colonies. They may use an overwintered colony in the spring (especially following migratory pollination), or after the nectar flow. This reduces the honey these bees will produce but generates new colonies One of the four new units received a brood frame from a different colony Mated queens or ripe queen cells are added to each unit after they are set up. Use one frame of brood and bees for a mating nucleus, two frames for increase colonies and three frames for colonies that will produce honey the same season. J. Zawislak.

Figure 19-16.
Double mating nuclei in medium depth equipment. A piece of Masonite™ divides the unit from floorboard to cover. A Jz's-Bz's queen cage holds a queen in each unit. L. Connor

managed as five-frame support nucs to hold mated queens for late-season queen orders, or to winter as a nucleus to use for nuclei makeup the next spring.

Further division should be considered if new queen cells are built by the bees. The nucleus should have at least one frame of capped honey (and some cells of stored pollen) to help it get off to a good start and provide food in case nighttime temperatures drop too low especially if the colony is small (Figure 19-10).

Mid-spring and summer nuclei

An increasing number of beekeepers make new colonies in the early summer (Figure 19-11). In southern parts of the U.S., this is after the main nectar flow when there is just enough food for small colonies to develop over the summer months. In northern regions, beekeepers routinely remove brood and bees from colonies during the nectar flow to establish new colonies. The parent colonies experience a dip in bee populations as the flow is ending, but the nectar crop is not seriously impacted.

Summer nuclei are part of the natural cycle for new colonies, meaning that there must be ample nectar and pollen for the bees to collect. Queen introduction is easier under these conditions. Nucleus makeup follows spring pollination rentals and supering for the nectar flow.

Some beekeepers select weaker colonies to make into summer nuclei, breaking them apart into several smaller colonies, all getting new disease- and mite-tolerant queens. The simple act of dividing colonies creates a break in the brood cycle that reduces varroa mite development.

Nuclei made up early in the season often build so quickly that they need to be carefully managed as the season

Figure 19-17
Mother and daughter hives are often kept together in case the new daughter hive needs additional bees and brood. If there is enough brood but not enough worker bees, the positions of the two hives may be switched so the field bees boost the colony size in the nucleus unit.

Figure 19-18
Five frame nucleus hives in Georgia established in the spring with a single frame of bees and brood, empty drawn comb for expansion, and an internal frame feeder. As the season develops, additional frames are added and the colony built into a support hive used for mating queens. L. Connor

progresses, either by removing frames of brood to make up new colonies or by moving the colony into eight- or ten frame equipment. If a northern beekeeper plans to overwinter nuclei with young, mite-resistant queens, this is the time where the colony population is adjusted and the queen evaluated for brood laying pattern, temperment and other characteristics.

One method that works well is to use the **Doolittle increase method** to make new colonies during the months of May and June (Box 46). This produces a colony of nurse bees covering two or three frames of worker brood. A frame of honey prevents starvation.

As the colony matures, the queen mates and lays eggs, the initial brood emerges and the new adults care for the brood. The initial worker bees shift to foraging for food, and the colony grows rapidly. One of us (LJC) has used the Doolittle method to make five-frame nucs and kept them in five-frame equipment by simply adding a second

box of drawn frames and foundation. As a young colony, the bees will readily draw foundation if there is a nectar flow.

By July these colonies can be evaluated. They may be left as support hives to be overwintered. Or they may be moved to eight- or ten-frame equipment and become regular production hives.

When goldenrod blooms in August and September additional boxes may be added. Following aster bloom, the colonies may fill four or five nucleus boxes, where they may be prepared for winter.

Spring nuclei are frequently used to mate two or more queens. While larger in size, this reduces potential loss from small hive beetles. The last cycle of queens are allowed to stay in the hive and given adequate food to overwinter. Smaller colonies may be combined in the late summer to increase the chance one good colony survives the winter rather than losing two weaker hives.

Figure 19-19
Five frame nucleus box in Georgia established with an internal frame feeder, a frame of brood, a queen cell, and a food frame. If the colony grows, frames of brood are removed and added to weaker colonies. L. Connor

Fall increase

Beekeepers in areas with a history of a late summer nectar flow like goldenrod, purple loosestrive, bamboo (in the north) and composites, Brazilian pepper and eucalyptus (in the sun belt), have success making colonies in the late summer and fall. This helps replace colonies that have been lost over the summer from queen failures, disease, varroa mites, and pesticide exposure.

Northern beekeepers do not usually make mid-September or later increase colonies because there is not enough forage for the bees to prepare for winter. Some migratory beekeepers move full-sized colonies to southern locations and split them, making new colonies during September and October. This allows these new colonies to build in strength and be ready to move to California for the almond bloom which starts in February.

Fall nucleus colonies need to be built up, the queens checked, and heavily fed with both sugar and protein to build enough population to earn a decent pollination fee in California. This intensive beekeeping is not for the faint of heart but pays huge dividends if colonies are strong when the almond flowers open since growers handsomely reward beekeepers providing strong colonies.

During the fall management schedule, weak colonies can be combined with stronger colonies to improve their winter survival or, provided they have at least two frames of capped honey, overwintered as nucs. If a new queen was added to the divide, this queen may be used to head the united colonies as a method of requeening. Early fall feeding ensures sufficient time to provide adequate food reserves for colonies going into the winter months.

Overwintering nucleus colonies

Increasingly, beekeepers in cold climates are overwintering nucleus colonies to avoid the expense of package bees and to ensure quality hives in the spring. Beekeepers report that an overwintered nucleus colony will expand into two deep, eight- or ten-frame boxes by late March or early April and be a strong pollination unit for fruit bloom. They may then be allowed to grow strong enough for the nectar flow, used to make additional splits or to pull frames of brood and bees during the season to boost colonies.

There are several ways to winter nucleus colonies. Beekeepers place two nucleus colonies on top of a strong colony (Chapter 14, Figure 14-20; Chapter 19, Figures 19-20, 19-22). The bees are separated by wood or screen so they cannot mingle. Some beekeepers use a double screen while others simply set the two nucs on top of the colonies. All colonies each have a separate entrance. The heat from the colony below keeps the upper nucleus colonies at a more uniform temperature.

The second method eliminates the colony below. Two four- or five-frame nucleus boxes are placed on a hive stand next to each other to share heat. Two nucleus boxes, one below and one above, allow the bees to move upward as they consume winter stores. This also doubles the winter store of food. These are called double-double nucleus hives (Figure 19-26).

Figure 19-20
The colony on the right supports a double nucleus. There are two nuclei boxes, each with three boxes. Each colony has its own entrance. E. Forbes

Box 46

DOOLITTLE INCREASE

We discussed G. M. Doolittle in Chapter 18, when we shared his role in developing our contemporary queen rearing methods. He also provided beekeepers with a simple method of making new colonies.

His method allows a beekeeper to make a new colony within an apiary without moving it to a new location. It relieves the new or inexperienced beekeeper with the chore of finding the original queen before moving frames into a new hive.

It involves the use of a queen excluder. If making a increase nucleus, the queen excluder may be cut to fit a combining or conversion board (Figure 19-21).

The system relies on the biological attraction of frames of brood to nurse bees. The combination of brood pheromone and the impulse of nurse bees to feed larvae make this system work.

Select strong colonies for this method, perhaps colonies that have started to prepare swarm cells. Use brood frames from one colony and bees from another if neither colony is as strong as you want.

1. Select three to five frames of brood, ideally mostly older brood with emerging bees and at least one frame of younger brood containing eggs and larvae. This spreads out the age distribution of the emerging bees.

2. Shake or brush the worker bees off these brood frames and place the frames into a hive body or nucleus box above the queen excluder. The bees may be shaken at the entrance of the hive and the bees allowed to crawl inside. Replace removed frames with frames of drawn comb or foundation. This also reduces swarm pressure.

3. If the queen is not seen, don't be concerned, as she will be shaken or brushed off the frames. In the new colony introduce a mated queen, a virgin, a ripe queen cell, a 48-hour old queen cell or allow the bees to raise their own queen.

4. Fill the box with brood and food frames. Cover the hive and allow the bees to crawl through the excluder and onto the bee-less brood frames.

5. Later that day or the next day, move the increase box containing the brood frames and bees to a hive stand in your apiary.

6. If you have introduced a mated queen or a virgin, remove the cage cap or cork and allow the bees to chew the queen out of the queen candy in the cage.

7. Reduce the size of the entrance as there are few guard bees in the population of bees you have moved.

Figure 19-21
A conversion board, nucleus box, bee-less brood frames, a queen, and lid used to make a Doolittle Increase hive.
L. Connor

8. Make sure to have a frame or two containing honey and pollen in the box to provide adequate food. You may want to add a small feed container.

9. Check the hive every seven to ten days for strength and the condition of the queen.

This method reduces the swarming instinct in colonies and produces a new colony. First year beekeepers have success with this two to three months after starting a nucleus hive or a package colony.

Connor, L. 2014. Increase Essentials, Wicwas Press, Kalamazoo MI

Doolittle, G. M. 1908. A Year's Work in an Out-Apiary. Reprinted 2005, Wicwas Press, Kalamazoo, MI

Molded, five-frame polystyrene boxes were developed in Alberta, Canada for outside wintering (Figures 19-24, 19-25). They have the advantage that 100° F (38° C) sugar syrup may be fed at any time through the entrance of the hive, and the bees will take up the syrup from the bottom of the hive. The temperature of the syrup in combination with the well-insulated hive, allows the bees to break cluster even in the depth of winter. Wind protection is essential with these small units.

Another option is to move smaller colonies into controlled-atmosphere overwintering buildings. The honey frames are removed and the colonies heavily fed sugar syrup. The colonies are then moved into rooms

Figure 19-23
Mike Palmer inspecting a hive in December. The upper box is filled with four frames of honey with four frames of bees and honey below.

where the temperature is kept a constant 42° F. (5.6° C). Large fans disperse heat from the bee clusters and avoid CO_2 buildup in lower areas (Figure 19-27). Research this option carefully before adoption, weighing the risks and costs against the benefits.

Consult Project Apis m. 2021. Indoor Storage of Honey Bee Colonies in the United States.

Figure 19-22
Double nucleus (A and B) overwintered over colony.

Figure 19-24
Polystyrene nucleus box used to overwinter colonies in Canada and northern states. L. Connor

Figure 19-26
Double doubles—Two four-frame nuclei two boxes high, wrapped in roofing paper, sitting on an old hive body to raise it out of the Vermont snow. Each half has a lower and upper entrance. Cord ties the roofing paper and lid. L. Connor

Figure 19-25
Polystyrene nucleus box holding a nucleus made up, allowed to grow and was overwintered. L. Connor

Figure 19-27
Indoor wintering of single hive body colonies. Temperature, humidity, and oxygen are regulated. Steppler Farms

key terms

capped queen cell	double screen	nucs/nukes	set-off divide
combining (conversion) board	Hawaii queen	nucleus colonies	splits
commercial beekeeping	increase colony	queen castle	two and a half colonies
divides/divisions	mating nucs (mini nucs)	resource (support) colony	varroa mite
Doolittle increase method	nooks	rustic hive	walk-away splits

discussion questions

What would you use to construct a nucleus that would provide two or three cycles of queens in the spring, and then serve as a support hive (brood factory)?

How would you manage this colony for the fall and winter? What are the advantages and disadvantages of forming winter condos of nuclei hives to share heat and insulation?

Nucs might be two, three or four frames. When would you establish a two-frame nuc? What might be a negative of this nuc size? When might you make up a four-frame nuc? Why might we term a three-frame nuc a resource hive?

Describe nucleus colony management. How does making a nucleus in the summer differ from making a nucleus in the spring to keep a colony from swarming? Describe the preparation of a nucleus for overwintering in a northern climate. Compare these preparations with those of a beekeeper keeping bees in a southern state.

How might use of nucs differ between commercial beekeepers and those with backyard bees. Do you follow the concept of 2 1/2 hives? If not why might you change?

exercises

Build a chart showing the time needed to obtain emerging workers in an increase nucleus depending on if you make a walk away split, use a ripe queen cell, or buy a mated queen. Discuss the 'cost' of of each method in terms of time, money and hive outcome.

Confirm that combining a nucleus with a dequeened colony is the safest, most reliable method of queen introduction.

Make a nucleus. Try doing so in different seasons and compare the outcome in terms of colony size, honey production and wintering success or failure.

Make up different size nucs and compare success. Or try different methods of making nucs queenright and compare successes.

references

Bee Informed Partnership. 2019. Commercial Beekeeping A Field Guide.

Connor, L.J. 2019. Keeping Bees Alive. Wicwas Press, Kalamazoo, MI

Connor, L.J. 2014. Increase Essentials, Second edition. Wicwas Press, Kalamazoo, MI

Connor, L.J. 2015. Queen Rearing Essentials, Second edition. Wicwas Press, Kalamazoo, MI

Hoopingarner, R. 2014. The Hive and the Honey Bee Revisited: An Annotated Update of Langstroth's Classic. Wicwas Press, Kalamazoo, MI

Morse, R.A. 1983. Year in the Beeyard. Scribner, New York, NY

Chapter 20
Pollination

Figure 20-1
Apple flower showing five greenish pistils in center and multiple anthers (cream-white ovals on top of white filaments circling the pistils). L. Connor

Concepts

Pollination

Pollinating agents

Pollinating bees

Honey bee pollination

Colonies per acre

Moving bee colonies

Crop pollination requirements

Pollination

There are about 250,000 species of flowering plants on earth. For each, sexual reproduction requires that the male germ cell, pollen, be transferred to the female germ cell, the egg, and that their nuclei unite for a seed to develop. The first part of this process, the transfer of pollen grains, is **pollination**; and the union of germ cells is termed **fertilization**. For different plants, the movement of pollen can be accomplished in a number of ways. Bees are the pollinator in the vast majority of plants.

The first part of plant reproduction, **pollination**, occurs at the flower. In order to understand pollination, one must become familiar with the general structure of a flower. Figures 20-1 and 20-2 show two representative flowers, and Figure 20-3 diagrams the **essence of pollination**. The outermost part of a flower, consisting of **sepals**, is called the **calyx**. Sepals cover the flower (the bud stage) and are usually green. Inside the calyx is the **corolla** which is made up of **petals** (both white in Figures 20-1 and 20-2). They may be separate or fused and are often brightly colored to attract pollinators.

The inner sexual portions of the flower are the stamens and pistils. The male sex organs are the **stamens**. They vary greatly in number and arrangement with different species of flowers but most are prominently positioned above the petals. Each stamen has a slender stalk or **filament** with a sac-like **anther** at the top. It is here that the **pollen grains**, the male germ cells (the equivalent of sperm in animals), are produced.

The innermost part of the flower, the **pistil**, contains the female sex organs. It consists of three distinct parts: stigma, style, and ovary. The **stigma** is the top portion where pollen is captured. If the pollen grain is of the same species and environmental conditions are compatible, a tube grows through the style to carry the male germ cell into the ovary. The **ovary**, usually the most central

part of the flower, contains the **ovules** (eggs). Some flowers produce a single ovule, whereas other plants may produce over 1,000 ovules.

Fertilization is the union of the pollen nucleus (male germ cell) with the ovule (female egg) in the ovary. After fertilization, the ovules become the seed. In some plants the ovary tissue becomes a fruit or seed-carrying container of some sort to aid in seed dispersal.

Flowers may be either self- or cross-pollinated (Figure 20-3). With **self-pollinated flowers,** the pollen comes from same flower, same plant or from plants of identical genetic material. Flowers must be self-fertile or **self-compatible**. With **cross-pollinated flowers,** pollen is transferred from one flower to another. Flowers must be **cross-compatible**.

Many flowering plants have evolved various means to promote cross-pollination. Even plants with self-compatible pollen may benefit from cross-pollination. Cross-pollination is associated with plant vigor and survival of the species as it usually results in a mixing of genetic material. Cross-pollinated plants rely on an animal (Figure 20-3 and 20-5 shows a bee; Figure 20-4 shows a fly) or on physical forces, such as wind or water, to move the pollen from one flower to another.

Some plants have developed elaborate flower modifications to prevent pollen from the anther reaching the stigma in the same flower. Flowers exhibit maturing of pollen before the stigma of the same flower becomes receptive; others display self-incompatibility of pollen within a flower.

If the male pollen-producing anthers are absent but female parts function normally, the flower is a female

Figure 20-2
Almond flower showing a single pistil (greenish stalk in center) and multiple anthers (filaments white with anthers brownish color). L. Connor

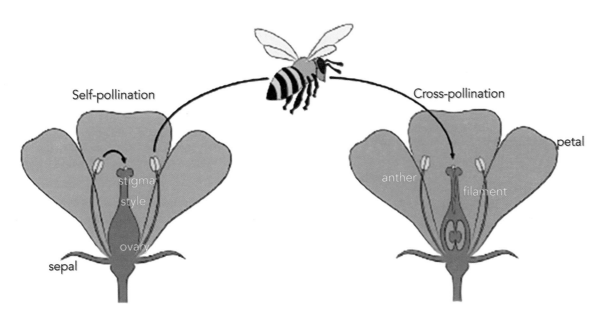

Figure 20-3
The pollination process and parts of the complete flower. J. Zawislak

Figure 20-4
Flower fly (Family Syrphidae), a honey-bee mimic, on an ornamental aster flower. L. Connor

Figure 20-5
Honey bee on apple flower, probing for nectar from the top of the reproductive structure. See text for a discussion of side-workers. L. Connor

or **pistillate flower**. If the female portion (the pistil) is absent, altered, or nonfunctional but anthers still produce pollen, it is a male or **staminate flower**.

Two variations may occur. The **monoecious plants** are plants that produce pollen on one portion of the plant while the pistil is located elsewhere on the same plant. Corn is a monoecious plant. Pollen is produced at the tassel on top of the plant, and the pistil, known as the silk, is where the ears develop. Cucumber is another example of a monoecious plant—male and female flowers are separate from different nodes on the same plant.

The second variation are the **dioecious plants** in which the sexes are on separate plants. Holly is a good example of a dioecious plant. Some trees produce only male (pollen producing) flowers and never have berries, while the female, berry producing trees, have only female flowers. Date flowers are another example of a dioecious plant.

Most flowers secrete **nectar**, a sugary, scented liquid, to help attract pollinators. Flower nectar is usually offered deep within the flower, near its base. Flowers additionally attract pollinators with brightly colored petals, intricate patterns, enticing aromas and other unique features. Many flowers entice pollinators with a variety of attractions.

Pollen also attracts visitors to flowers. It is a good source of protein. The flower may dust pollen on visitors or the pollinator may actively seek to dislodge and collect pollen from flower anthers during its visit. Flowers produce more than enough pollen to feed the visitor and be transferred to accomplish pollination. While most pollen

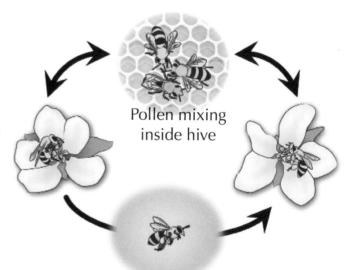

Pollen mixing inside hive

Tree to tree pollen transfer

Figure 20-6
While bees transfer considerable pollen directly from one flower to another, some pollen is mixed within the colony as bees brush against each other. From *BeeCabulary Essentials* by A. Connor. J. Zawislak.

transfer occurs at flowers it has been demonstrated there is also pollen transfer among honey bees in their hive. (Figure 20-6)

In seeking nectar and pollen, the insect accumulates pollen grains on body hairs. The grains are subsequently transferred to another flower as visits to the same flower species continue. Cross-pollination is not a deliberate animal behavior but an accidental transfer of pollen grains from anther to stigma adhering to body hairs.

Pollination does not merely accomplish greater seed or fruit yield. Increased pollination can induce a greater proportion of early flowers to set seed resulting in an earlier and more uniform crop. Pollination can also influence quality as well as quantity of resulting fruit. Sugar level, shape and form of fruit also have all been demonstrated to improve with adequate pollination.

Cross-pollination is essential for the commercial production of many fruit, vegetable and seed crops. Modern agricultural practices are creating new demands for pollination. The use of insecticides, herbicides, mowing of pastures and roadsides, and the overgrazing of pasture land has contributed to the decline in populations of major pollinators.

Pollinating agents

Cross-pollinated flowers must have some agent transfer the pollen from one flower to the next. There are a number of means for moving pollen:

insects	birds
wind	monkeys
water	bats
humans	snales & slugs
mammals	kangaroos
spiders	mites

Plants that produce pollen that is light and easily carried aloft are **wind-pollinated plants** (Figure 20-7). Some plants hold the anthers above the stigma and pollination is accomplished by gravity. A few aquatic plants use water currents to move pollen.

Other plants produce a heavy and sticky pollen that is not easily carried by wind or water from one flower to another so they must rely upon another method of transferring pollen. The vast majority of **cross-pollination** requires flying animals: common examples include bees (Figures 20-5, 20-8, 20-9, 20-10), flies (Figure 20-4), butterflies, beetles, birds, and bats.

A small number of animals, besides insects, are pollinators. Humans, as biological pollinating agents, are very expensive pollinators. Commercially, vanilla and date crops are **human hand-pollinated**. In greenhouse crops, and in situations where environmental conditions do not produce adequate cross-pollination, humans may need to temporarily assist plant pollination until more adequate and cheaper pollination can be arranged.

Humans hand-apply pollen by brush or pollination sticks made of chicken feathers and cigarette filters. Farmers in the Sichuan Province of China hand-pollinate apples and pears due to lack of natural pollinators. Mechanical devices such as vibrating toothbrushes are used in greenhouse pollination.

Growers use technical knowledge to accomplish pollination. Two examples are tomatoes and kiwi

Figure 20-7
Alder flowers are wind pollinated, producing large masses of pollen which bees collect. L. Connor

Figure 20-8
Bombus or bumble bee on squash flower. L. Connor

grown in greenhouses. Tomatoes and cucurbits (squash, cucumber and melons) formerly were hand-pollinated with a vibrating toothbrush but are now primarily pollinated by bumble bees (Figure 20-8). Bumble bees forage in such a way as to vibrate the flower which releases pollen (termed **buzz-pollination** from the vibratory action). Honey bees are poor pollinators in greenhouses; they orient poorly in the greenhouse and do not vibrate beneath the flowers like bumble bees. Figure 20-9 shows another buzz pollinating bee.

Insect pollination

Insects are involved in pollination of almost all flowers needing cross pollination. Virtually every major group of insects has been demonstrated to be involved in the pollination of some plant. Those insects identified as being involved in the production of one or more commercial crops are:

ants	flies and midges
aphids	mosquitoes
bees	moths
beetles	thrips
butterflies	wasps

Large-scale monoculture demands massive numbers of pollinators for a one- to three-week bloom period, but provides nothing to support the pollinators for the remainder of the season. Larger single-crop plantings need rental of honey bee colonies. Also needed are methods to conserve and augment native pollinators as fewer natural pollinators may be present in large monocultural landscapes, normally flowering deserts for the majority of the year.

It is estimated that over 3.5 million honey bee colonies are rented annually in the U.S. for nearly 90 crops grown on approximately 3.5 million acres. Total crop value is over $20 billion annually. Included are crops that represent about one-third of the total diet of the U.S. citizen; globally, about 10% of the human diet is insect pollination dependent.

The need for honey bees as pollinators is increasing, and the trend is likely to continue. Accelerated use of honey bee colonies in pollination is also present in developing countries. Presently there are barely enough bee colonies to meet demand.

Pollinating bees

Although the honey bee, *Apis mellifera*, is the most widely-used pollinator of insect-pollinated plants, four other bees are important on a more limited scale in planned pollination. These are bumble bees, mason (leafcutting and orchard) bees (Figures 20-10, 20-11) plus alkali bees.

Bumble bees are efficient pollinators but as a seasonally eusocial insect they are usually too few in numbers

Figure 20-9
Green bee (*Halictus*) buzz pollinating a tomato flower by hanging upside down and vibrating its thoracic muscles to release pollen. Honey bees do not do this. L. Connor

Figure 20-10
The alfalfa leafcutting bee is able to pollinate the alfafa flower without being hit by the flower's keel. USDA

Figure 20-11
Native mason bee pollinator the blue orchard bee (BOB)
(*Osmia lignaria*). USDA ARTZ

Figure 20-12
Honey bee colonies on a trailer frame, pollinating cucumbers
in Michigan. Michigan State University Entomology

to pollinate more than a small percentage of insect-pollinated plants. Their populations fluctuate widely from place to place and from year to year. Where relatively abundant one year, they may be scarce the next.

Bumble bees possess long tongues (**proboscis**), making them especially effective in pollinating deep, narrow tubular flowers such as squash (Figure 20-8). They also fly and orient better in greenhouses and in colder climates than honey bees.

It is possible to augment bumble bee populations. Conservation efforts are needed to preserve species richness and nesting densities. They are soil nesters so burying wooden/plastic nesting boxes in the ground is useful. Leaving hay bales or decaying plant debris at the margin of fields or in adjacent uncultivated areas helps provide nesting opportunities and cavities they can use to construct their nests.

Culture of bumble bees is expanding (Chapter 2, Box 3). Bumble bee quad nests are routinely purchased for greenhouse pollination, especially for tomato and kiwi which require buzz-pollination, and further advances in their culture will open yet other opportunities including field situations such as specialty seed or watermelon production. Bumble bee colony price, once $600 per colony, is now under $200, resulting in wider use of bumble bees.

The **alfalfa leafcutting bee**, *Megachile rotundata*, is a valuable pollinator of alfalfa, especially in the Western U.S. and Canada (Figure 20-10). This bee was introduced to the U.S. from Eastern Europe/Western Asia; it has subsequently been introduced elsewhere. It is a solitary bee but females build nests close to each other (they aggregate).

Female leafcutting bees build their nest as a series of cells in material such as beetle burrows and hollow stems,

but they readily adapt to nail holes, holes bored in logs or boards, and drinking straws (Chapter 2, Figure 2-7; Chapter 3, Figure 3-3).

The female leafcutting bee partitions cells in a hole of suitable diameter. Cells are made with pieces of cut leaves (hence their name). Each cell is provisioned with a ball made of pollen and nectar. Once she has built and provisioned a cell, the female lays an egg on this food mass. When one cell is sealed another is built in front of it, provisioned with nectar and pollen (often from only a select few or even one plant species), until five to ten cells are completed, depending on hole depth.

Completed nests, such as those of the alfalfa leafcutting bee, built in boxes of straws or boards with drilled holes, are saved from one season to the next. When adults emerge the subsequent season, fresh empty straws or boards are supplied to ensure large continuous populations. The leafcutting bee is not otherwise managed. They do not provide honey or other products.

The **alkali bee**, *Nomia melanderi,* is a native bee. It lives in arid and semiarid regions of the West. The alkali bee is confined in nature to localities where the soil is irrigated over a hard pan layer which leads to moist, relatively bare, alkali spots suitable for nest sites. On a commercial basis, large tubs of suitable soil are created and moved about to provide adequate population levels. More permanent soil conditions can be developed and seeded with a population for further development of an expanding population. See Chapter 3, Figure 3-7 for diagram of a typical nest of a soil-inhabiting bee.

Alkali bees are excellent alfalfa pollinators. They forage in somewhat cooler, windier weather than the leafcutting bee. Growers like to use the alkali bee because it forages in lower foliage that other pollinators

CONDITIONING/ARTIFICIALLY
ATTRACTING BEES TO CROPS

The idea of attracting and directing honey bees to a particular crop is an old one. Since bees live in a compact nest and display advanced communication, it is reasonable to believe it would be possible to stimulate the bees or somehow predispose them to concentrate on a certain plant.

Efforts to direct or lead bees to certain flowers, however, have generally not been successful. Immersing flowers in a sugar syrup and then feeding the bee colony this syrup or spraying the colony with the essence of target flower odors has not proven to be reliable, although it is a practiced in some regions of the world. One technique used is to feed a target-scented sugar syrup to a colony beginning a week before movement. Spraying blooming plants with sugar syrup, likewise, has failed to lead to better yield; at least one study found it counterproductive as the bees visited syrup droplets instead of the flowers, reducing the yield.

It is currently recommended that colonies not be moved to a crop until flowering starts, particularly for short blooming crops, so the bees do not establish foraging patterns on other flowers prior to bloom of the desired target plant. Waiting too long into the blooming period can be detrimental, however, as many plants produce better, bigger, sweeter fruits on dominant blooms (king

bloom of apple or early node flower of watermelon for example). Leaving colonies on target to the very last bloom likewise may not be an effective strategy as late bloom may not produce fruits or seeds.

An under-utilized but more effective method of improving crop yield is to select plants that are more attractive to pollinators and breed those qualities into the plant. It has been demonstrated that we can breed bees that collect higher proportions of pollen from a plant. Plants are bred for disease and insect resistance, desirable fruit qualities and other characteristics. Thus, it is not unreasonable to include pollinator attractiveness in a breeding program, although not extensively done.

More recently, the development and promotion of pheromone-based attractants has been shown to offer the possibility for improving honey bee pollination. Feeding synthetic queen substance within the hive has been demonstrated to increase worker foraging. Brood stimulates foraging too, and synthetic brood pheromone within a colony has been shown to increase pollen foraging. Pheromones can be particularly effective as they work with, not against, basic foraging biology.

Synthetic Nasonov scent-gland pheromone sprayed onto flowering plants has been shown to increase yields in pear, onions, and cantaloupes, though results have not been consistent. For example, studies in North Carolina showed no increase in cucumber yield when a commercial worker-pheromone material (Bee-Scent™) was used. It remains cost effective to rent another bee colony rather than to attempt the 'solution in the bottle' to achieve proper pollination.

may miss. Pathogens, predators and specific soil-nesting requirements are the major drawbacks to more extensive use by growers.

A native mason bee pollinator is **BOB**, the **blue orchard bee** (*Osmia lignaria*) (Figure 20-11). It is a tube nester that adapts easily to straws or holes bored in wood. It is currently being used extensively in Japan for orchard pollination; in the U.S. it is being used in almonds and fruit orchards. Another relative, the **horn-faced bee** (*O. cornifrons*), is similar but does better under more humid conditions. These two bees have yet to be widely adopted for crop pollination.

There undoubtedly are other **pollen bees**, as these may generally be labeled, that are also useful pollinators for other cultivated crops. Simply encouraging the conservation of natural pollinator populations is useful as we are discovering these insect helpers are suffering from many negative environmental conditions.

When a flower and foraging insect are not well adapted, a flower visit may not result in pollination. The insect may be too tiny, it may not have a body structure that facilitates pollen transport, or it may not exhibit foraging behaviors that will adequately transfer pollen. Nectar foragers are apt to be less efficient pollinators than pollen foragers.

Honey bee pollination
Providing honey bee colonies to pollinate flowers is by far the most common and easiest method of moving pollen from flower to flower for the vast majority of insect-pollinated crops. Humans have come to rely on the honey bee, an opportunistic forager, for pollination. Five reasons the honey bee is such a valuable pollinator are:

- perennial colony
- nectar and pollen are their only food
- plumose body hairs

- flower-constant behavior
- populations can be manipulated

Much is known about honey bee biology. Techniques and special equipment for management and movement of bee colonies have been developed. The honey bee is a generalist that visits many flowers (Figure 20-12) in an organized foraging behavior. It forages in all but the worst weather, and pollen and nectar are the only things it eats. We can even partially direct where and when it forages. We have been unable to design a machine or develop a chemical that can function better.

Managing bee colonies for pollination

It is important to provide strong colonies for pollination. Strong colonies not only supply more field bees, but the bees continue to forage when a weak colony will have ceased foraging activity. A strong colony forages at lower temperatures and in stronger winds than a weak colony. Colonies with an expanding brood pattern are better pollinating colonies because brood stimulates the collection of pollen.

Management of bee colonies for pollination rental is not much different from the management of colonies for honey production. The target for a strong, populous colony will be the projected bloom date of the plant needing pollination.

Colonies with only one brood box or a standard box and super are advantageous because they are smaller in size and weight, making them easier to move. Furthermore, the field bees will enter the hive directly into the brood nest, reinforcing the stimulus to gather pollen. However, many growers request larger colonies.

Figure 20-14
Strong colony in almonds. L. Connor

Figure 20-13
Apples with colonies on a pallet, moved at night. The colonies have brood in two boxes; an empty super reduces swarming. L. Connor

Bees rented for pollination for early-blooming crops, like almond and apples, need to be stimulated early by feeding sugar syrup or supplemental protein to yield large, expanding colonies at bloom time. Weak colonies should be bolstered by brood from stronger colonies, united with a nucleus or stronger colonies and boosted with a package of bees. Using package bees hived two to three weeks before pollination rental does not result in an effective pollinating unit.

While on pollination sites, beekeepers should continue to manage colonies. Weak units need to be strengthened and stronger colonies should be kept from swarming. Examining colonies is not always easy, as moving staples or bands (used to hold boxes together during movement) have to be removed for inspection and then reapplied to remove the colonies from the rental site at the end of the rental period.

For short-term results, feeding sugar syrup within the colony produces a higher proportion of pollen collectors among the foraging population of a colony. Trapping pollen at the hive entrance has not been shown to

Box 48

ONE COLONY PER ACRE

The advice to provide one beehive to an acre of plants in bloom (2.5 colony per hectare) was first recommended for fruit trees in 1916. The same standard has been repeatedly used for other crops without any research basis. What exactly is a colony of bees?

For adequate pollination, the foraging population of the pollinator colony is what is important. Forager numbers are determined by the size of the colony and conditions within the colony. Flight activity or number of boxes is not a valid assessment. Since it is so difficult to 'guesstimate' the adult population, we usually determine the number of frames occupied by bees or the area of the brood nest to provide a relative estimate of colony size. It is necessary to enter the colony to make this assessment.

When bee colonies are rented for pollination, it is important that they meet minimum size requirements. This varies with time of year and crop. Generally, minimum size is smaller for colonies rented early in the season, such as for almond or fruit tree pollination, than for later blooming plants like blueberry or cucumbers.

The most appropriate number of bees needed to adequately accomplish pollination depends on many variables. It is not unusual for published recommendations to be in conflict. Likewise, different assessment methods may not be in agreement. For example, published recommendations for cucumber pollination in the eastern part of the U.S. vary as follows:

1 colony for every 3 to 4 acres

1 to 3 colonies per acre

2 colonies per acre (high density planting)

1 bee per 100 flowers

1 colony per 50,000 plants

Estimates of the number of colonies necessary to pollinate a crop are usually based on experience and knowledge of growers and beekeepers rather than experimental study. The rate of one colony/acre (2.5 col/hectare) as mentioned above is usually quoted as the standard. In hard-to-pollinate or higher density crops, the number must be higher.

Figure 20-15
Cut-away staminate (male) gourd flower. A visiting bee becomes covered with pollen grains which may be transferred to a separate pistillate (female) flower. Just how many colonies are needed for adequate pollination depends on many factors. Growers are advised to use more colonies than less, or face the possibility of poor pollination and a short or deformed crop. L. Connor

improve pollination of a crop. In fact, the bee colony reduces brood rearing when pollen traps are used, which is the opposite desired effect.

Sometimes a special device termed a pollen insert, is used (Figure 20-20). The insert fits on the entrance of a colony; exiting bees walk through a pollen-filled tray. It is a temporary means of increasing cross pollination.

Pollen inserts have produced mixed results. Better results are obtained when the bees must walk through pollen dusted onto the hairs of a soft brush positioned at the entrance so bees contact it on exiting. The brush increases the chance of bees acquiring pollen grains from plants other than those being visited. Studies have shown there is some pollen exchange by bees within the

Box 49

Moving bee colonies

It is not difficult to move a colony of bees. Unauthorized movement (stealing of hives) is a hazard of commercial beekeeping where out-apiaries are not always secured locations. With migratory beekeeping, a beehive of a commercial beekeeper may be moved five or six times in a year (Figures 20-16 to 20-19).

Colonies are generally moved at night. This ensures the foraging population is within the hive when the hive is moved. (If weaker colonies are needed at a meeting or for teaching new beekeepers, moving them during the day will leave the foragers behind, resulting in a more reasonable-sized colony. An empty hive is then left at the old location to trap foragers which can subsequently be used to augment the population of another colony via the newspaper method). Colonies need to be securely fastened and closed with entrance screens before they are moved. Long staples are used to hold separate pieces together, as are metal or plastic straps which can be used to securely tie the entire hive together (Figure 20-16).

In warmer weather, a moving screen may replace the cover at the top of the hive. Covering entire truckloads of colonies with netting (Figure 20-17) and periodically spraying the load with water or using soaker hoses is good management, especially on warm, humid nights and during mandatory driver breaks when the move is a long one. Some beekeepers use refrigerated trucks for long hauls during the summer.

Beekeepers utilize and have adapted a number of ways to efficiently load and unload colonies for movement onto and within pollination sites. Many of the techniques were pioneered by beekeepers moving colonies for honey production. Initially, colonies were hand-carried but few beekeepers use manual labor in more developed countries today due to the high cost and unavailability of help.

Many commercial beekeepers and pollinators manage bee colonies on pallets, similar to those used to move commerce, modified to hold bees. Pallets hold four to eight colonies each, depending on their size. Mechanical devices like tractors or all-terrain forklift vehicles are used to load and move the pallets. Boom-type mechanical lifting devices or power tailgates are still in use, though their popularity has diminished. The Swinger® is a special loader developed specifically for beekeepers that is transported along with the stacked beehives (Figures 20-18, 20-19).

A cautionary note on moving. In a study comparing moving colonies vs. stationary colonies in pickling cucumbers, the moved colonies had reduced growth with lower yield cucumbers. Leave hives in a single location throughout the season or move hives at night time to avoid the loss of foraging workers.

https://www.canr.msu.edu/news/maximizing-honey-bee-pollination-in-pickling-cucumbers

Figure 20-16
Bees on a trailer, strapped down to move for crop pollination.

Figure 20-17
2,700 trucks of bee colonies are required for almonds.

Figure 20-18
Ready to move to orchard, including hauling the Swinger.

Figure 20-19
Beekeeper using a Swinger to load pollinating colonies. bees.

Figure 20-20
Pollen insert in pears.

hive. Forcing exiting bees to walk through a pollen filled tray or brush promotes additional transfer.

Breeding bees for better pollination is a distinct possibility. Bees have been selected to hoard honey and USDA researchers have demonstrated that they can breed a bee that collects a greater percentage of alfalfa pollen in only six generations. Research in Europe has demonstrated the feasibility of selecting bees for higher red and sweet clover pollen collection, as well as the ability to breed bees with longer proboscis length to reach into deeper flowers.

With a few crops like alfalfa seed, it is possible to assess pollination success and add additional colonies if results are below expectations during the actual bloom period. In melons and cucumbers with continual-pick harvest, pollination can likewise be evaluated, although failure to produce properly sized or adequate numbers of salable fruit may be environmentally linked (i.e. too high a temperature) or due to insufficient fertilizer, micro nutrient, or other reasons exclusive of pollination. For

most crops requiring pollination, it is not possible to determine pollination success from the appearance of the flowers until it is too late to take remedial actions.

Rental fees are normally standardized on a colony basis. In many instances, the strongest colony may be two or three times the size of the weakest. Are such colonies worth two or three times as much? In some pollination situations colonies are graded before delivery or at pollination sites with the rental fee adjusted accordingly. Base fee is centered around an ideal-sized standard colony.

With virtually all crops, it is not necessary (or desirable from a plant health viewpoint) to achieve 100% pollination to produce a commercially acceptable crop. If set is too heavy, it can be thinned later. Bee colony rental is really an insurance policy for poor flight weather or to help ensure more uniform ripening. Failure to set cannot be remedied later in the season.

Improving pollination results

To accurately determine the number of pollinators needed, growers and beekeepers should know factors such as: the rate flowers are visited, the number of visits per flower to achieve full pollination, pollinating efficiency per flower visitor (for each of the various pollinators), number of pollen grains deposited on stigmas (and number necessary for full fruit development), the effective pollination period (time per day and days per season), the proper conditions of stigma receptivity, movement pattern of major pollinators within the crop, number of flowers per area, daily pattern of flower attractiveness and other factors.

Crop requirements for pollination, even for commonly cultivated insect-pollination dependent crops, are not well understood. Plant breeders and pollination specialists too infrequently cooperate in studies. Knowledge of tropical plant pollination is in its infancy.

Honey bees can forage a considerable **distance from the hive**. Generally, they tend to stay close to home if suitable forage is available. Pollen foragers work closer to the hive and work faster than nectar gatherers. In one study, the value of placing colonies close to apple bloom was demonstrated by measuring the fruit crop. The researchers demonstrated only half the fruit yield when colonies were moved from adjacent to one mile (1.5-1.9 km) from the orchard.

Another study compared pollen collection on the first day after colonies were moved into or placed at various distances from flowering kale, fava beans and red clover. The percent pollen collection in all three plants was highest when colonies were located within the crop and decreased with distance of colony placement in kale and fava beans but not for red clover. The furthest distance was 1/2 mile (0.8 km).

In a Maryland study, the number of culls (nonstandard or non-saleable cucumbers) was reduced by half as the number of pollination colonies increased from zero to one and was further reduced, again in half, when plantings were supplied with two versus a single colony per acre. Misshapen, non-standard cucumbers have virtually no value on the fresh market for growers so inadequate pollination significantly reduces profits. The higher colony numbers are additionally desirable to yield a uniform set so that a greater percentage of the harvest are at the same developmental stage.

Bee colonies need to be distributed so pollination is uniform. Beekeepers, however, desire fewer locations, particularly if they need to continue to inspect their bees during the rental period. Often rental colony distribution is a compromise of conflicting beekeeper and grower needs and bee foraging behavior.

Honey bees obtain greater rewards of nectar or pollen from some plants than from others. Crops to be pollinated may be less attractive than other flowering plants such as weeds within flight distance. It is therefore best to move colonies of bees (Figures 20-16 to 20-19) to crops during or just before the main flowering period and to place them directly within or immediately adjacent to the area of flowering plants. This will ensure some pollination before the bees discover competing flowers and fly beyond the desired target crop.

At one time it was considered essential that competing bloom be removed by cutting weeds and clean cultivation. Herbicides might still be used to clear vegetation for machinery and to eliminate refuge sites for crop pests. Increasingly, the importance of fostering wild (native) pollinators has been demonstrated. Competition at flowers creates more movement of individual pollinators. Additionally, other floral sources benefit pollinator nutrition and provide additional forage opportunity that enhance, not diminish, the pollination of the target crop.

When renting bee colonies for pollination, a written agreement between the beekeeper and grower is desirable. Examples of contracts are provided in extension publications or use an Internet search engine to find samples. Too few beekeepers treat bee colony rental as a business contract and fewer still take the precaution of adequately insuring their business. Incredibly a few beekeepers even offer 'free' pollination services in exchange for an apiary site or the right to sell their bee products at the farmer's roadside stand. The contract should cover:

- number and strength of colonies to be used
- plan of colony distribution in the field
- time of delivery and removal of colonies
- the beekeeper's right of entry to service the colonies
- the degree of protection from pesticides
- plan of payment of the rental fee
- penalties for poor quality or service by the beekeeper
- breach of promise by the grower
- bonus for exceeding the minimum in quality service

Pollination of specific crops

Pollination is essential for farmers and growers to produce an abundance of safe, inexpensive food that helps to feed a growing human population. Since honey bees exist as perennial colonies, their populations can be efficiently managed for pollination. For their food, bees depend completely on nectar and pollen. While a bee is foraging, pollen is caught in the plumose (branched) hairs that cover the bee's body. Other bee species, native bees such as megachile (mason) bees are essential pollinators of crops and native plants.

Since honey bees usually collect from just one species on a foraging trip, the pollen adhering to an individual bee's body may brush off onto a subsequent flower and provide cross-pollination of that plant species. As a result, honey bees are considered efficient pollen transferring agents for a large variety of fruits and vegetables making bees an indispensable part of agriculture.

The majority of honey bee colonies that are rented for crop pollination in the U.S. are used on four crops: alfalfa seed, almonds, apples (and other fruits) and vegetables.

Figure 20-21
Honey bee forager visiting alfalfa flower. W. Nye

Figure 20-22
Bees unloaded from semitrailers, being staged in a holding yard before movement to the orchard.

Each offer different challenges and opportunities. Here is a further look into the pollination of these crops.

Alfalfa, *Medicago sativa*, is the world's most important forage crop. It is valued for its protein and soil-building qualities and by beekeepers as a honey plant. When it is grown as a forage crop, alfalfa is harvested before it blooms so bees do not benefit from it as a nectar plant. Farmers frequently fall behind in their harvest and many allow their alfalfa to bloom late in the season to secure some natural reseeding of their fields; it is then that bees may store a harvestable surplus.

Because of extensive use, alfalfa seed production is a very large business. Alfalfa flowers must be 'tripped' before cross-pollination and seed production can occur. To trip a flower, an insect must enter the flower and press its head against the large upper petal. This pressure releases a mechanism that frees the male and female flower parts, allowing pollination to take place. Only larger-bodied insects like bees pollinate alfalfa flowers (Figures 20-10, 20-21).

Honey bee foragers learn how to obtain nectar from alfalfa flowers without tripping them, perhaps because the release of the male and female sexual parts momentarily traps the bee's head and proboscis in the flower. After several foraging visits, honey bees learn how to access the nectar from the side of the flower without tripping. Individual bees are ineffective pollinators once they learn to modify their foraging behavior.

In the Pacific Northwest, honey bees are not considered as effective pollinators of alfalfa. The strong preference leafcutting and alkali bees show have for the collection of alfalfa pollen has been exploited, so these two species are preferred in more northerly areas. An entire industry of supply and service of leafcutting and alkali bees has developed for alfalfa pollination.

Almond, *Amygdalus communis*, is a major crop that requires pollination by honey bees. Commercial varieties are self-incompatible; therefore they need transfer of pollen from another compatible variety to produce nuts. Since almonds do not need thinning, and trees can support heavy nut set, growers attempt to obtain a maximum set. The expanding acreage of almond groves in California and Brazil require the rental of a recommended two colonies per acre (five per hectare). With newer varieties of higher-density plantings, where water (irrigation) is assured in California's Central Valley, even heavier stocking is occurring.

Since the flowering period of almond is very early in the season (February- March) when bee colonies are smaller and foraging weather is less predictable, beekeepers

Figure 20-23
Bees moved into almonds in California.

Figure 20-24
Pear blossoms with Mt. Hood in the background.

must use special measures to build colonies for adequate pollination service. Colony distribution is critical, as is proper timing and placement. Colonies come from all Western states, Texas and even from the East Coast. All out-of-state truckloads must pass through California border station checkpoint inspections prohibiting entry of small hive beetles, fire ants and other insect pests.

It is fair to say that almond pollination has changed U.S. beekeeping. Increasing acreage and a strong national and international market for almonds has led to a $14 billion dollar industry around this one crop alone. More than half of all the bee colonies in the U.S. are moved to California for almond pollination each spring. Some colonies are moved after fall harvest and winter into holding yards in southern California (Figure 20-22) but the majority arrive in time for movement directly into the bloom (Figure 20-23). These colonies then must be removed in four to six weeks.

Beekeepers are paid rental income by colony strength with the average colony centered on eight frames of brood with bees to cover (20,000 bees) (Figure 20-14). This is an unusually large colony for this time of year, achieved only via extensive stimulative feeding. Union of colonies, adding nucs to weaker colonies and for several years importing package bees from Australia (no longer permitted) are additional managements used to create such strong pollinating colonies. Numerous studies have demonstrated the value of eight-frame (compared to six- or seven-frame) colonies to profitability of the growers.

Figure 20-25
Bee colonies distributed by groups among pears, a hard-to-pollinate crop.

Figure 20-26
Set-down of hives in hybrid carrot seed production.

Rental fees have increased in the past decades, and now hover around $200/colony of standard strength, fully double the normal fees for all but blueberry and some specialty crops obtainable over the remainder of the season. Colonies additionally are further strengthened with the pollen and nectar obtained from the almond bloom so beekeepers need to reduce colony size to avoid swarming and collapse of colonies with too few floral sources following the almond bloom. Many beekeepers sell frames of brood to other beekeepers and market nucleus colonies to new beekeepers as additional income generators.

Fruit trees, especially apples and pears, were some of the earliest crops where honey bee pollination was recognized as important for commercial production. Bee colonies were used to pollinate pears before the 20th century and apple growers have used bees since the early 1900s. Bee colonies used in fruit pollination were, coincidently, the first reported instance of pesticide poisoning.

Pears, *Pyrus communis*, are one of the most difficult fruits to pollinate. The flowers (Figures 20-24, 20-25) have a very low nectar sugar content, they bloom very early when spring weather is often cold, and competing weeds are much easier to forage and more profitable for foraging honey bees. Commercially, virtually every production tree needs to be alongside a compatible pollen producing variety (pollenizer) to take advantage of the few bees that move from one tree to the next and colonies need to be widely distributed, not clumped, in orchard distribution. For **apples**, *Malus domestica*, pollination is a critical annual event. Most apples are grown in temperate regions and flower when weather is often unfavorable for bee flight, pollination, pollen tube growth, fertilization and fruit set. Growers therefore rent honey bees to secure adequate numbers of fruit set as an insurance for those seasons with poor weather conditions.

Unlike in pears, pollenizer varieties can be more widely spaced in the apple orchard and colonies are often clumped in distribution (Figure 20-13). One colony per acre (2.5 per hectare) is usually recommended to produce a commercially acceptable fruit set, but this level was established long ago without much basis. When weather and tree care conditions are favorable, the apple crop must be thinned for efficient annual production. Excess fruit can be removed by the thinning process but once bloom time passes, there is no way to add fruit to a tree.

Red Delicious, formerly the most commonly grown apple in the U.S., has structural variation not found in other apple varieties that allows foragers to obtain nectar without pollinating the flower (Chapter 10). Normal foraging requires bees to stand on the anthers to reach the nectary with their proboscis (Figure 20-5), but in Red Delicious variety Will Robinson discovered foragers position themselves on the petal and insert the proboscis between the base of the stamens to reach the nectary. Such foragers, termed 'side workers,' do little pollen transfer. Growers need to rent more colonies and intersperse additional pollenizer varieties to compensate for this behavior.

There is an effort to find alternative pollinators for fruit. BOB, the blue orchard bee, is one that seems to pollinate effectively, although the timing of when they emerge and fruit bloom is not always in sync. This species is stocked via filled tubes of the work of females of the past season. One bucket of 200 mason bee tubes can do the same pollination as a colony of honey bees. On the other hand, growers of both pears and apples in parts of southern China must hand pollinate their fruit as environmental degradation eliminated regional native pollinators.

Vegetables. Insects play a vital role in the pollination of several vegetable seed crops. Plant breeders attempt to develop hybrid strains of vegetables with male sterility (i.e. flowers that lack viable pollen) to facilitate development of higher-yielding, better-tasting varieties. Once discovered and cultivated, seed production is then dependent on cross pollination.

Seed crops include asparagus, onion (includes male sterile hybrids), carrot (includes male sterile hybrids) (Figure 20-26), parsnip, lettuce (includes male sterile hybrids), eggplant (includes male sterile hybrids), okra, tomato (very limited greenhouse pollination), and the cole crops (broccoli, cabbage, cauliflower, radish, rutabaga, turnip).

High numbers of bee colonies are rented to move the pollen from pollenizer (male fertile flowers) to the male sterile flowers to produce hybrid seed (Figure 20-26). These are high value crops and since the bees tend not to visit many of them, colony stocking is heavy (two to five colonies per acre or five to 15 colonies per hectare).

Rental fees are controlled by large multi-national companies or cooperatives and generally beekeepers are compensated by colony strength. The colonies however usually do not benefit and are often exposed to pesticide damage. Beekeepers report the need to extensively revitalize colonies, including feeding and uniting colonies, upon removal from seed pollination rentals.

In addition to essential pollination for seed production, several vegetable crops benefit from insect pollination for fruit production. These include: beans, pepper, cucurbits, eggplant and lima beans.

The most important, widely cultivated vegetables on this list are the various cucurbits (cucumber, squash, melons, etc.). Five of the shared characteristics of cucurbits that indicate co-evolution with insect pollinators are:

* Large showy flowers of yellow color are highly attractive to bees. Nectar, high in sucrose, is abundant in the large flowers and is secreted from numerous pores of a large nectar (Figure 20-8).

* Although flower bloom lasts only for one day, cucurbit plants produce numerous blooms. The plant is not a honey plant for the beekeeper, however, because the flower number is too low even in high-density plantings (Figure 20-12).

* Cucurbit pollen must be transferred by an insect because the pollen is heavy and sticky. Wind cannot transfer cucurbit pollen.

* Pollen of a plant is usually self-fertile but not self-pollinating because cucurbits are monoecious with male and female bloom.

* Cucurbit flowers need transfer to a lot of pollen as the ovule number may easily reach into the hundreds. Some cucurbits, like watermelon with a three-lobed flower, must have pollen on all three lobes for perfect fruit. Several pollinator visits are needed to realize perfect fruit in the cucurbits. Inadequate pollen transfer results in misshapen fruit of little value.

Most of the curcubits are grown in the summer season when forage conditions are better. Fields often are in locations where there is less competing bloom. Curcubits produced in small fields often attract sufficient natural pollinators. However, as they have become more popular in the diet and alternative uses have been developed for their fruit (and processing has become common), the acreage and size of cucurbit fields has increased, making planned pollination a more important part of their culture. They also have become part of the worldwide trade in agricultural products; the cucurbit in your local

Figure 20-27
Bee visiting raspberry blossom.

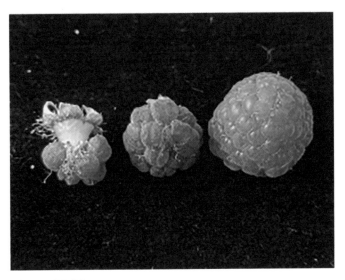

Figure 20-28
Normal (right) and poorly pollinated (left and center) raspberry. Poorly pollinated raspberries may average 8 to 23 druplets, compared to 45 to 90 in well pollinated fruits.

market may have been pollinated by bees half a planet away.

Small fruit pollination

Insects play a vital role in the production of a number of familiar wild, cultivated and homegrown fruits. Below is a listing of small fruits dependent on insect pollination for high yields and well-developed fruits:

raspberry	thimbleberry	elderberry
boysenberry	gooseberry	dewberry
loganberry	cloudberry	red currants
huckleberry	cranberry	black currants
strawberry	blueberry	grape

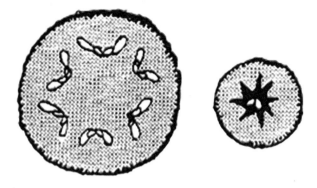

Figure 20-29
Cross section of blueberry showing well pollinated berry on left, and poorly pollinated berry on right.

Of all these small fruits, the role insects play in grape culture is the least understood. Some grape hybrids and cultivars require or benefit from insect pollination. Pollination requirements need better definition.

The remainder of the small fruits listed above all benefit from insect pollination (Figure 20-27). Adequate insect levels ensure high yields and well developed, full-fleshed berries. Figure 20-28 shows the size of properly pollinated of raspberry and Figure 20-29 represents a cross-section of properly and improperly pollinated blueberries.

Blackberry, also dewberry, loganberry and youngberry, are cultivated and wild-harvested in several growing areas worldwide. The white flowers are produced in 10- to 20-flower clusters. There are four petals with 50 to 100 stamens around an equal number of pistils.

Blackberry flowers secrete a significant volume of nectar at the base of the flower and are a nectar flow plant in some states in the mid-Atlantic, southeastern, and Pacific states in the U.S. Blackberry flowers produce a fine, much prized honey. Pollination of cultivated blackberry is usually not a problem because of the attractive nature of the flower. The cultivation practice of extensive monocultures, where numbers of native pollinators have been reduced, necessitate increasing honey bee colony rentals.

Honey bees are incorrectly blamed for causing damage to ripening grapes and small fruit by biting the fruit for the sweet juice. Honey bees, in fact, only visit damaged fruit. They lack mouthparts capable of directly injuring the fruit. The major culprit is usually yellowjackets, often generically termed a 'bee.'

Strawberry plants (Figure 20-30) may be **hermaphroditic** (i.e. having flowers with both the male stamens and female pistils) or distinctly gendered (i.e. the flowers of some plants having only the male stamens, and other plants having flowers with only

Figure 20-30
Strawberry flower at the end of blooming period. The anthers are depleted of pollen and the individual pistils are starting to darken after successful pollination. L. Connor

Figure 20-31
Where pollen grains have landed (via insect-, wind- or self-pollination) the ovules develop to form the achenes that simulate tissue growth and a berry. L. Connor

the female pistils). Plants with distinct genders are 'cross-pollinating;' that is, each plant requires another plant of the opposite gender in order for the plants to reproduce. Both hermaphroditic and distinctly gendered strawberry require transfer of pollen from male to female flower parts.

Flower stigmas are receptive before anthers offer pollen. The plant has a primary flower which yields the biggest and best berry. Subsequent berries are smaller because the first flower has a large number of pistils which, when pollinated, result in development of more achenes.

In commercial strawberry cultivars, the relative positions of stamen and pistil vary. Stamens shower viable pollen upon their own flower in some varieties, but others have stamens too short for the pollen to reach pistils. If too few pistils obtain pollen transfer, subsequent fertilization is inadequate and an irregularly shaped berry or 'nubbin' results. A large number of pistils at all locations on the flower must be fertilized for development of a large, well-shaped berry (Figure 20-31).

Research on strawberry pollination is of fairly recent vintage. One of the major findings has been to demonstrate the influence of stamen height on self-pollination. Short stamen varieties benefit most from honey bee visitation. The varieties with longer stamen length are less dependent on insects. In a study of 11 cultivars in Michigan, self-pollination was responsible for 53% seed (achene) development. Wind motion increased development to 67%, while insect pollination increased achene development to 91%. Strawberry growers generally do not rent honey bees for pollination as plantings are small, natural pollinators are often abundant, and the relationship of fruit development and pollination is not well known.

A decision to supplement pollination should take into account the size of the planting, abundance of wild

Figure 20-33
Honey bee colonies beside blueberry plants starting to bloom.

(non-*Apis*) bees, the abundance of feral honey bees, stamen length of varieties planted and history of fruit set and berry development. If two or more of these features are unfavorable, growers should strongly consider rental of honey bee colonies (Figure 20-31).

Cranberries have been one crop involved in tests of a concept in supplemental bee pollination: the **Disposable Pollination Unit or DPU**. Due to location and terrain where cranberries are grown, it is difficult to move and properly distribute bee colonies into large cranberry bogs for pollination. Thus, dropping temporary units of honey bees in plastic foam containers directly into cranberry bogs from an airplane has been investigated.

DPUs usually lack a queen but have comb with brood and pheromone substitutes to stabilize the unit and promote foraging for pollen. Although the technology is not yet adequately developed to put DPUs into practical use they hold potential as a pollination 'tool' of the future.

Figure 20-32
Cranberry bog—cranberries are like pears, a hard-to-pollinate crop.

Figure 20-34
Leafcutter bee on ornamental aster flower. L. Connor

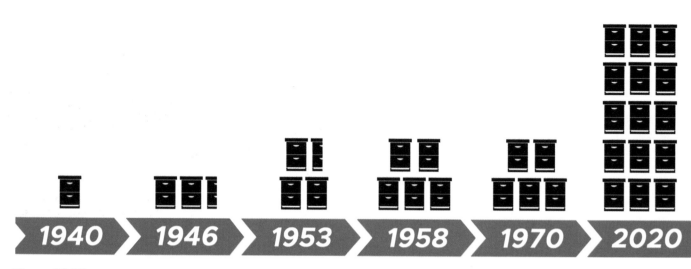

Figure 20-35
Increased number of colonies recommended for colony rental for five acres of cranberry from 1940 to 2020. J. Zawislak

Cranberry pollination demonstrates an interesting trend in the need for more honey bee colonies in pollination (Figure 20-32). The years and the published recommendations are shown in Figure 20-35. Difference in recommended number of pollination colonies is due to increased size of crop fields, decrease in size of natural pollinator populations and an increased understanding of pollinator-plant interrelationships. Pollination recommendations change as does crop culture and our understanding of the plant-pollinator interrelationship. The recommendations for many other crops have similar histories.

key terms

alfalfa	corolla	moving bees	raspberry
alfalfa leafcutting bee	cranberry	ovary	rental fees
alkali bee	cross-pollination	pears	self-pollination
almond	dioecious plants	pistil	side-workers
anthers	disposable pollination units	pistillate flower	small fruit
apples	essence of pollination	pollen grains	stamens
blue orchard bee	fertilization	pollen inserts	staminate flower
blueberry	fruit trees	pollination requirements	stigma
buzz pollination	human pollination	pollenizer	strawberry

discussion questions

Why are insects so essential in plant pollination (Figure 18-33) when physical factors like wind and water can also transfer pollen? What are some of the differences between a wind- and insect-pollinated flower? Give examples of both.

Why are honey bees the most commonly utilized insect in planned pollination? What are some of the other pollinating bees and the situations where they are the pollinator of choice? How was pollination accomplished prior to 1900?

What has happened that growers now must rent over two million colonies of honey bees in the U.S. for pollination?

Pick a cultivated crop that requires pollination and explain why pollination is needed and how growers of large plantings of that crop plan for pollination. How should a beekeeper manage bee colonies to ensure adequate numbers of bees available for the grower?

Describe the pollination requirements of a vegetable, a fruit and another crop.

Why are cucurbits dependent upon bees for pollination? What are some of the factors that demonstrate the co-evolution of plant and pollinator.

exercises

Visit an orchard, cucumber field, or other crop for which bees are rented for pollination during bloom time. Attempt to determine the foraging behavior of the bees. How many foragers are collecting pollen? How do they generally move about the field? What is the daily activity level of the colonies?

Interview both a grower and a beekeeper to understand the issue of pollination from each perspective. Write an essay or prepare a presentation on how grower and beekeeper differ or are the same and how the service of bee pollination might be improved for both.

There are some excellent films and videos about pollination. View and critique one or more of these.

Survey the literature for descriptions of how beekeepers move bee colonies. If possible, visit a beekeeper in your area.

Find a recent research paper on insect pollination and critique it. What did the study demonstrate? What techniques did the author use to demonstrate the value of the insect pollinator? What questions remain unanswered following this research? There are several technical books on how to document pollination research. Compare the study you have examined with one of these references to determine if the experimental procedure was appropriate.

Much more is known about temperate crops that require insect pollination than for tropical crops. Why is this so? Give some examples of the differences.

references

Calderone, N.W. 2012. Insect Pollinated Crops, Insect Pollinators and US Agriculture: Trend Analysis of Aggregate Data for the Period 1992–2009. PLos One. 2012; 7(5): e37235. doi: 10.1371/journal.pone.0037235

Caron, D.M. and R. Sagili. 2020. Honey Bee Pollination in Pacific Northwest. Amer Bee Jour. 160(5):575-577

Connor, L.J. and E.C. Martin. 1969. Honey bee pollination of cucumbers. Amer Bee Jour. 109:389

Delaplane, K.S. and D.F. Mayer 2000. Crop Pollination by Bees. CABI.

Free, J.B. 1972. Insect Pollination of Crops. Academic Press, London.

Garibaldi, L.A. et al. 2014. From research to action: enhancing crop yield through wild pollinators. Ecological Soc. America Frontiers 12(8): 439-447.https://doi.org/10.1890/130330

Mäder, E., et al. 2011. Attracting Native Pollinators. Story Publishing, North Adams, MA

McGregor, S.E. 1976 Insect Pollination of Cultivated Crop Plants. USDA AG Handbook 496. NOTE this is updated on an irregular basis on https://www.ars.usda.gov/ARSUserFiles/20220500/OnlinePollinationHandbook.pdf

Proctor, H. et al. 1996. The Natural History of Pollination. Timber Press, Portland, OR.

Robinson, W.S. 1979. Effects of apple cultivar on foraging behavior and pollen transfer by honey bees. Journal of the American Society for Horticultural Science 104: 596–598.

Steinhauer, A.L. 1971. Pollination of Cucumbers in Maryland. Amer Bee Jour. 111(6):224-225.

https://news.wsu.edu/2020/06/19/robotic-crop-pollination-goal-new-1-million-grant/

https://en.wikipedia.org/wiki/List_of_crop_plants_pollinated_by_bees

https://www.ars.usda.gov/pacific-west-area/logan-ut/pollinating-insect-biology-management-systematics-research/docs/blue-orchard-bee/

https://www.canr.msu.edu/news/maximizing-honey-bee-pollination-in-pickling-cucumbers

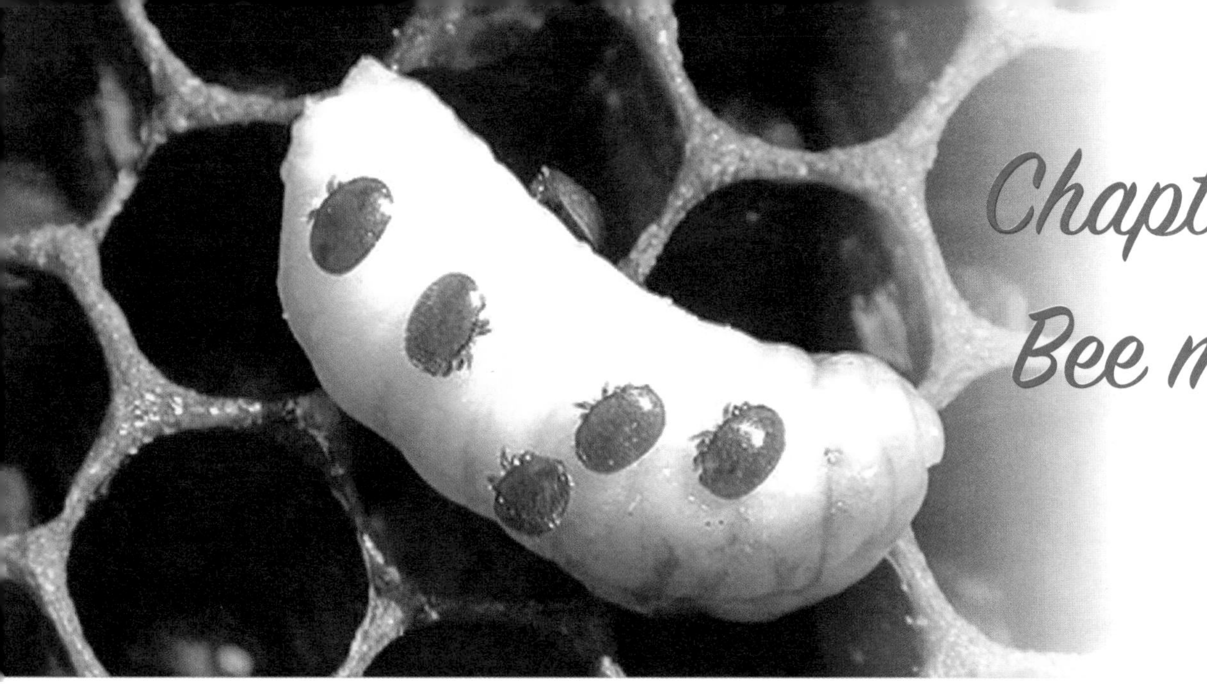

Figure 21-1
Six adult female varroa mites on a bee larva.

Concepts

Mite-related disorders

Honey bee tracheal mites

Varroa mites
> mite related disorders
> parastic mite brood syndrome
> colony collapse disorder

Control methods
> integrated pest management
> chemical control

Bee mites

Bee mites have completely changed beekeeping. Every year, around 30-40% of all managed bee colonies are lost overwinter with additional losses during the year. These losses are largely due to *Varroa* mite-transmitted viruses. Mite-weakened colonies that do survive will often collect less nectar and are less efficient pollinators.

Mites are eight-legged arthropod relatives of insects. They range from microscopic to 8 mm (0.3 inches) in size. Mites are common in and on soil, in water and in and around animals and plants. Some are parasitic. Over 40 different mite species have been found in pollen and in beehives; most are beneficial, not harmful.

Three parasitic honey bee mites are of major concern to beekeepers: the **honey bee tracheal mite**, **varroa mite** and *Tropilaelaps*. The latter is currently only found in Asia. **Annual survey** and sampling programs in the US and Canada actively seek to quickly detect if they (along with other exotic pests) have been accidentally introduced into the North American bee population. These ongoing surveys document bee health and track mite incidence.

Prior to their introduction to the US, bee mites were generally unknown. The tracheal mite was credited with causing the **Isle of Wight disease** in England before 1920, although not all specialists agree tracheal mites caused this mysterious disease. Discovery of mites, especially varroa mites, in the US led Canada in 1987 to close its borders to package bees and queens from the US; it was subsequently reopened in 1993 to permit the import of queens from the US.

Tracheal mites were first discovered in Texas in July of 1984, apparently spreading there from Mexico. A second population appeared in Florida, probably the result of illegal importation of queen and bees. Despite rapid regulatory actions, including the depopulation pupae, but also a **vector** for viral diseases. Varroa is the most significant deterrent to successful beekeeping, as failure to treat colonies leads to their collapse in a single season.

The third bee mite of concern is *Tropilaelaps* spp. It is similar to varroa in that it parasitizes both adults and brood. Its normal host is *Apis dorsata* but it has been found on *Apis mellifera* alongside varroa (Figure 21-2).

Accidental introduction into North America or elsewhere would be undesirable. It is widely considered to be more serious than varroa. Rather than a single feeding site it moves about host brood feeding at many sites. It is on adults a very short time, meaning there are fewer control options with tropilaelaps. The University of Florida has an informative fact sheet on tropilaelaps.

Mite-related disorders

With the advent of heavy mite infestations, two health disorders or syndromes have been recognized in honey bees. **Parasitic Mite Syndrome** (PMS) **or Parasitic Mite Brood Syndrome** (PMBS). Bee PMS was first described in 1994. Then in the spring of 2007 **Colony Collapse Disorder (CCD)** became of paramount concern for beekeepers.

Honey bee parasitic mite brood syndrome, PMBS (Box 50) symptoms are different from Colony Collapse Disorder, CCD (Box 51). With PMBS, at least some adult bees remain in a dead/dying colony. Colonies may survive the winter only to die in the spring. The adults perish while still in cluster, although cluster size and number of adults are small. In CCD, colonies die in the fall or early spring with an almost total lack of adult bee bodies.

In both syndromes, brood and stored honey and pollen are usually still present in the dead colony, ruling out starvation as the cause of death. Not all research authors or popular stories on colony death necessarily agree on strict adherence of the differing symptoms for the two syndromes. CCD has not continued to be a major issue, although still reported, if the original defining symptoms are used. Bee PMS is being renamed as PMBS as the major symptoms are the cruddy (snot-like) unhealthy brood.

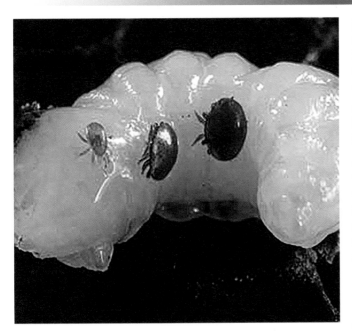

Figure 21-2
Tropilaelaps mite (left) and two varroa mites on *Apis mellifera* larva. Bee Informed Partnership

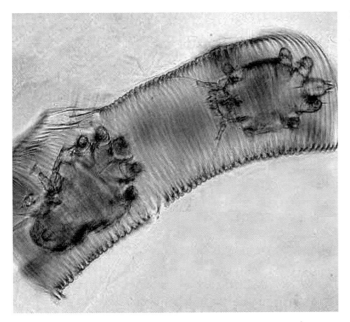

Figure 21-3
Honey bee tracheal mites in a worker bee trachea. Tracheal mites are tiny, oval, and whitish in color. B. Smith, USDA

or euthanasia (killing) of colonies, tracheal mites were found infesting colonies in other localities and too widespread for containment.

Varroa mites, on the other hand, are an extremely serious bee infesting mite of European (western) honey bees. Their original Asian host, *Apis cerana*, developed a balanced relationship with varroa, but European bees have not had the evolutionary time to adapt. Varroa is not only a **pest**, feeding on the fat body of adult and

Honey bee tracheal mite

The honey bee tracheal mite, *Acarapis woodi*, is one of three closely related *Acarapis* species of mites found on honey bees. *A. woodi* lives exclusively in the tracheal (respiratory) system of adult bees. The condition is termed **Acariosis or Acarine disease**. The remaining two species of *Acarapis* occur externally on the bee exoskeleton and are not considered harmful.

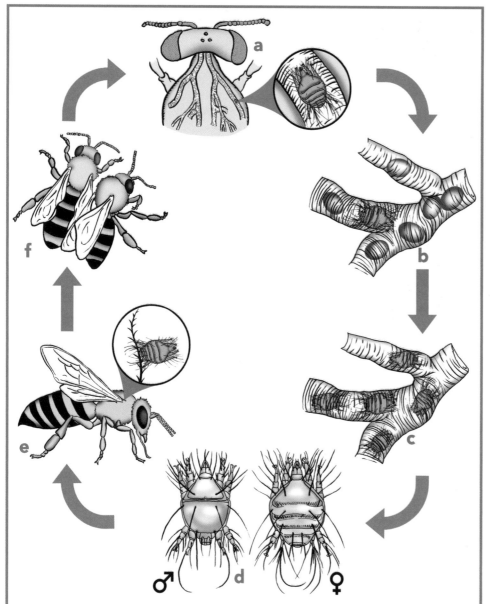

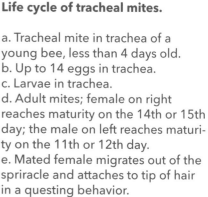

Figure 21-4

Life cycle of tracheal mites.

a. Tracheal mite in trachea of a young bee, less than 4 days old.
b. Up to 14 eggs in trachea.
c. Larvae in trachea.
d. Adult mites; female on right reaches maturity on the 14th or 15th day; the male on left reaches maturity on the 11th or 12th day.
e. Mated female migrates out of the spriracle and attaches to tip of hair in a questing behavior.
f. Close contact of bees permits exchange of female mite from an older infected bee into the first thoraxic spiracle of a young bee.
J. Zawislak

Figure 21-5
Positioning bee for dissection.

Tracheal mites are tiny, oval, and whitish in color. As in all mites, the adults have four pairs of legs (Figure 21-3). Newly emerged female tracheal mites exit the tracheal tube of adult bee hosts and crawl onto the tip of the bee's body hairs where it quests for the preferred host, a worker bee less than three days of age. Queens may also be invaded. The life cycle is illustrated in Figure 21-4.

A female mite enters the tracheal tube of her new host via one of the thoracic spiracles. She begins to produce eggs that are almost equal to her size. She lays about one egg a day for 8-12 days. Eggs hatch in three to four days into larvae and will then pass to a nymphal stage; they need 19-21 days to become an adult. The invading female and her immature mites live as parasites within the same tracheal tube. They need to puncture the tracheal wall to feed on bee hemolymph.

Tracheal mite populations vary seasonally. When colonies are populous and resources are abundant, the host infestation level is lower. Low levels of infestation make it more difficult to detect the mites. Upon initial introduction into the U.S., many colonies died from mite infestation, particularly in more northern apiary sites. Few do any longer.

Symptoms of tracheal mites are subtle and include: dwindling bee populations, weakened adult bees crawling in front of the hive, and the condition known as K-wing. This is a modification of how bees hold their wings while not flying. Normally the wings are folded one over the other but in heavy tracheal mite infestations adult wings remain partially opened in a K pattern (See Chapter 22 Figure 22-23). Infestation rates over 30% have been correlated with reduced worker healthfulness, decreased honey production and lower winter survival. These symptoms are not necessarily reserved for tracheal mites as they may indicate other disease (including virus) conditions.

To determine if a colony has a tracheal mite infestation it is necessary to sample adult bees to examine their thoracic tracheae. Older bees (from inner cover or entrance) will have the highest mite levels. The bees are collected into 70% alcohol. Of several detection methods, the most commonly used is to place a dead bee on its back and remove the head and first pair of legs by a forward-angled cut with scalpel or razor blade (Figure 21-5). A thin disc is removed from the exposed anterior face of the thorax and placed on a microscope slide. This thin disc can be examined directly but for greatest clarity a drop of 10% lactic acid solution is added to dissolve wing muscle for a day or so to facilitate examination of the trachea.

Figure 21-6
Crisco® patty is a mixture of vegetable fat and granulated sugar used in situations when honey bee tracheal mites are a concern.

Figure 21-7.
Buckfast bee developer Brother Adam in his queen yard. L. Connor

When examined under a microscope (40-100X), adult and immature mites can be seen within the trachea. The tracheal lining will show dark, discolored, crust-like lesions quite in contrast to a healthy tracheal tube.

An alternative is to arrange the bee on her back and pull off the head. Then with forceps or dissecting needle pull off the thoracic collar at the opening. This will usually expose the tracheal tube—you may need to tease a bit of muscle out of the way and even pull the tracheal tube outward. Infested tubes will look dark compared to uninfected trachea which appear white and shiny. Scar tissue will be evident and mites may even be visible inside the tubes (Figure 21-3).

Some state agriculture and university labs, and the Federal Bee Lab in Beltsville, Maryland, will do this analysis for you (check the USDA, Beltsville Bee Lab website for sample mailing directions and address). Oregon State University has a video that shows this dissection technique: https://catalog.extension. oregonstate.edu/em9145.

Control of tracheal mites

Soon after the discovery of tracheal mites in the U.S., beekeepers in the northern states experienced heavy winter losses. The 1922 federally enacted bee law banning importation of bees inadvertently resulted in the U.S. bee population having no exposure and little resistance to tracheal mites, perhaps explaining why bee losses were initially heavy. Today the mite causes minor annual loss and is not considered a major pest.

A number of chemical compounds and control strategies have been tested for tracheal mite control. The current varroa miticide **amitraz** is one that controls tracheal mites.

Menthol oil extract—1.8 ounces (50 g) of 98% purity, menthol, trade name **Mite-A-Thol®**, the same ingredient of menthol cigarettes and cough drops, reduces tracheal mite populations if colonies are fumigated in summer/early fall, after all honey stores have been removed from colonies. Menthol treatment is temperature dependent and may not be successful, especially if nighttime temperatures dip, resulting in too little evaporation of the menthol. Alternately, on hot days, menthol vapors may cause bees to exit the hive, rendering the treatment less effective.

Formic acid gel packs—Mite Away II®, sold as impregnated pads MAQS and time release Formic Pro® are effective organic chemical treatments for both tracheal and varroa mite control. It is especially useful as a fall treatment for tracheal/varroa mites when honey bee brood populations are lower (the acid may

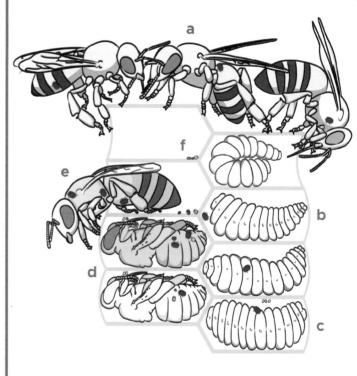

Figure 21-9
Life cycle of varroa mites.
a. Adult female phoretic mite feeds on worker bee fat body.
b. Female mite enters late larval cell just before sealing, hiding in brood food until cell is capped.
c-d. Female mite feeds on bee pupa. In 60 hours she lays her first egg, a male, and then produces female eggs at 30-hour intervals. Nymphs hatch and feed on bee pupa.
e. Adult bee emerges with original female and one or more fully developed daughters.
f. Male mites and immature female daughter mites die or are killed by bees once cell is opened.
J. Zawislak

damage bee brood). Formic acid may be incorporated in an integrated pest management (IPM) approach and is approved for organic honey production.

Essential oil treatments—**ApiLife Var®** and **Apiguard®** are also approved chemical controls. They are effective in varroa as well as tracheal mite control. Since many beekeepers are using formic acid and/or essential oils to control varroa, their use are likely reducing tracheal mites, perhaps a significant factor in tracheal mites currently being a less significant pest.

Grease patties—The combination of sugar and vegetable fat, with or without other additions, may reduce tracheal mite populations in the hive. It is thought that the fat interferes in some way with the young mites finding suitable hosts. Combine one part high-quality, solid vegetable shortening or coconut oil with two parts sugar to make patties; some like to add some honey to make

Figure 21-8
Two varroa on adult bee with deformed wings. Penn State

Figure 21-10
Varroa mite feeding on fat body of a worker bee. The mite is partially hidden by an anterior sternite where its mouthparts are feeding on the fat body. The fat body tissue flows into the digestive tract of the mite, as shown by the lighter, serpentine region of the mite. Inset: Mite has stopped feeding and has backed out of the feeding site. D. Morgan

the patty softer and more attractive to bees. Adding ten drops of an essential oil like peppermint or wintergreen, or the feeding stimulant **Honey-B-Healthy**® to the patty is also an option, resulting in prompt attention by house bees.

The mixture is formed into one-quarter pound (113 g) patties between waxed paper sheets and placed on top bars in cooler conditions or bottom boards during the summer (Figure 21-6). They can be stored in freezer before use. For best results, patties are used in the fall and winter. Take care if small hive beetles are a problem as the beetles will feed on grease patties in the hive.

Tolerant or hygienic bees—Tolerant bee stocks are widely recommended for varroa mite control and considered the best approach to keeping tracheal populations at low levels. Colonies found/suspected with higher tracheal mites should be requeened as a minimum, if not also treated to reduce the mite population.

One selection, the **Buckfast bee**, developed by Brother Adam of Buckfast Abbey, Devon, England (Figure 21-7), has been imported into the U.S. It is considered to be more resistant to tracheal mites. Once popular with beekeepers, the Buckfast stock purity has not been maintained in the U.S., though it remains of interest with its reported resistance. Although Brother Adam has died, the breeding program continues; there is a Buckfast breeding program in Ontario, Canada.

Varroa mite

The varroa mite, prophetically named *Varroa destructor* (formerly *Varroa jacobsonii*), is a large-bodied mite (1 mm

long by 1.4 mm wide—0.04 x 0.06 in) that can be seen without magnification (size of a large pinhead). It feeds and hitchhikes on the bodies of adult bees (Figure 21-8) and reproduces on pupae (Figure 21-1). This condition is termed **Varroosis**, the mite sometimes the **vampire mite**.

Varroa mites are oval, and pale to reddish-brown in body color. Varroa mites can be found on adult bees (Figure 21-8) but the majority (~90%) burrow between ventral abdominal sternite segments and are not readily visible (Figure 21-10). It was initially believed that the mites fed on bee hemolymph. However it has since been found that the mites on the bee abdomen puncture the soft membrane between segments to feed on fat body tissue of the bee adults.

The darker color adults, but not the white immatures, are easily visible against the white exoskeleton of the pupae. Cappings need be removed to see them (Figure 21-12). Female mites differentiate and prefer drone brood to worker brood, probably using brood pheromones to find an appropriate host.

The life history of varroa mites is reasonably well-known (Figure 21-9). In the **reproductive phase**, mated females enter larval cells shortly before capping stage and initially hide in the worker food in the bottom of the cell. The mite then must climb aboard the bee prepupae to avoid being entrapped in the silken cocoon constructed by the prepupa.

Within 60 to 70 hours, the mated female produces her first egg, a male. After an additional 30 hours she produces a fertile female egg, which will yield a daughter, followed by additional fertile eggs. The adult female pierces the exoskeleton of the bee pupa to open a feeding hole so she and daughters can feed on the body of the bee host.

As European bees have a 12-day average worker capping stage, the foundress female mite will produce one, rarely two, mature daughter mites. If the female mother entered a drone cell, two to three mature daughters can be produced, owing to the longer capped stage of the developing drone. The male is not parasitic and dies after mating.

If only one family of mites feed on the bee pupa, the bee will normally emerge, although it may have a shortened abdomen, misshapen (non-expanded) wings (Figure 21-8) and legs, lower body weight and reduced hemolymph volume. Infested pupae yield adult bees with a shorter lifespan (by one third or more) compared to non-infested bees. Infested drones will have less viable sperm for mating. If more than a single mite family is present in the cell, the pupae may not survive. Mites can transmit bee viruses so the adult bee that emerges may be diseased as well. Only a couple of the viruses show symptoms.

Foundress and mature daughter mites leave the cell attached to the adult host. This mite phase is termed

Figure 21-11
Wingless fly *Braula coeca* on queenbee. B. Smith, USDA

phoretic (technically the term means transport), or more properly **dispersal**. In this phase, the female mite seeks a younger-aged bee host to feed on fat body of the adult host (Figure 21-10). Younger-aged bee adults have a greater amount of fat body. Mite puncture holes leave the host susceptible to infestations of other diseases, including viruses. Hosts are located by touch, heat and smell as mite adults lack antennae or eyes.

Knowledge of the pest life cycle can help target control. Pests have different vulnerabilities to control interventions as they pass through their life cycle. For a pest such as varroa, both life cycle phases (phoretic/dispersal and reproductive) offer distinct and unique control opportunities as discussed further below under control.

NOTE: Varroa mites can be confused with a wingless fly commensal, *Braula coeca*. Braula, an insect, has six legs on the sides of a three-segmented body (Figure 21-11) whereas Varroa, a mite, has eight legs positioned forward on an oval, unsegmented body (Figure 21-1).

National survey data from **Bee Informed Partnership (BIP)** has documented overwinter losses averaging 28% for the past 14 post-CCD syndrome years (Figure 21-26). Traditionally, winter losses were around 10-15%. Summer losses average a bit less than 22% (ten BIP survey years). The excessive losses, initially labeled as CCD, but now characterized as PMBS, are considered to be largely, but not exclusively, due to varroa mites and their transmission of viruses.

Beekeepers who are proactive and control varroa mite buildup suffer fewer overwintering losses. One downside of heavy reliance on the use of chemical controls has been shortening of the productive life of queens and increased queen losses.

Extensive movement of colonies for pollination rental negatively affects queens; 10% queen loss is 'normal' with colony transport. The need to heavily feed colonies, equalize colony strength and extensive colony splitting to replace losses, plus stocking many colonies in one apiary beyond what natural vegetation can support, may also lead to higher in-season colony losses.

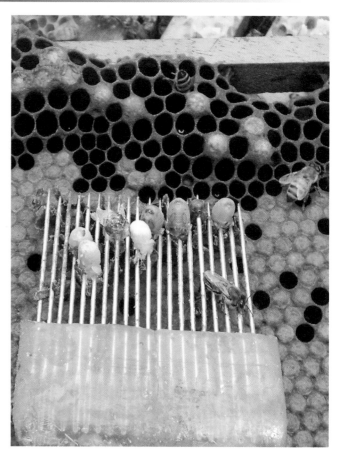

Figure 21-12
Using capping scratcher to determine if drone brood are infested; note mite on far left pupa. USDA, Beltsville, MD

Varroa mites are not a serious pest on *Apis cerana*, its Asian bee host, where they only infest drone brood. When the varroa mite transferred to *Apis mellifera*, perhaps as little as 70 years ago, European-race bees have proven less effective at removing mites from their hives. Subsequently varroa has become the most serious pest of *A. mellifera*.

Sampling for varroa mites

Sampling of varroa may be done by looking at brood, removing mites from adult bee bodies or by estimating number of mites in the whole colony. In heavy infestations, varroa mites can be seen on the bodies of adult bees (Figure 21-8). They are virtually impossible to see when they attach between ventral sternites of the host to feed on fat body. Mites are easier to spot when on lighter colored brood (Figure 21-1).

An objective of sampling colonies for varroa mites is to estimate how many mites are present. Simply looking for the mites on adult bees (Figure 21-8) or on drone brood (Figure 21-12) does not offer adequate precision on the size of the mite population. For greatest accuracy, removing mites from a known sample size of the adults provides a better estimate of mite numbers, and is recommended.

Figure 21-13
Collecting a sample of 300 bees directly into wide-mouthed sampling jar.

Sampling should begin in April/May and continue monthly. Consider more frequent sampling in the fall (August-November) as this is when mite numbers can increase rapidly. Pre-treatment sampling means using the mite numbers as a basis for decisions on mite control. If a control is used there should be a post-treatment sampling to confirm the treatment was effective in reducing mite numbers. Generally a post-treatment sampling should occur about a week following completion of the treatment itself.

In smaller apiaries with fewer than ten colonies consider sampling all hives, but in larger apiaries, sampling 7-10% of the colonies is recommended.

Brood Sampling

Capping scratcher — To sample the mite levels on drone brood you need to look at pupae at least two days past initial capping of their cells. Drone pupae are the easiest to sample via uncapping and pulling individual pupae from cells. The easiest way to sample is to impale pupae on a capping scratcher inserted at an angle, and then pull the pupae through the cappings (Figure 21-12).

Alternately, uncap a series of pupal cells and individually pull out drone pupae with tweezers or pointed stick or jar the frame sufficiently to drop the pupae onto a light-colored flat surface to allow easy viewing to count mites.

Figure 21-14
Collecting 300-bee sample (bees previously shaken from 2-3 frames into white bucket) to place in a Mason jar.

By counting the number of brood cells examined you can determine a percent infestation. Count the number of brood with mites not the number of mites.

Unfortunately efforts to equate percent brood infestation with the number of drones with mites have not been very successful. Thus you will only have a sense of infestation level. A big disadvantage of this sampling method is drone brood is not always available for sampling as colonies only rear drones under favorable conditions. This is especially the case in the fall when we wish to know the mite infestation for control decisions prior to colonies entering winter.

Adult sampling

Several methods of sampling adult worker bees are used to estimate the mite population and determine control.

Soapy water/alcohol — Numbers of mites on adult bees can be sampled by mechanically removing the mites. Collect around 300 bees by passing a wide-mouthed jar over the backs of bees on a frame (Figure 21-13) or by shaking the bees into a dishpan or bucket and then scooping out a one-half cup of bees (Figure 21-14). Add enough non-sudsing, grease-cutting soap or 70-95% alcohol to kill and cover the bees and then swirl the jar for one to two minutes. Pour the liquid portion through

Figure 21-15 (left)
Shaker jar developed in Alberta, Canada, uses alcohol or soapy water to dislodge varroa mites from the bodies of about 300 adult bees (top portion). L. Connor

Figure 21-16 (right)
Count mites collected in the liquid of the bottom jar or on filter paper. L. Connor

Figure 21-17
Bees in wide-mouth mason jar after shaking with about 1 tablespoon of powdered sugar.

a #4-8 coarse mesh screen (to trap adult bees) followed by a 50-mesh screen or coffee filter to trap mites. You can also count the mites in the liquid as shown in Figures 21-15 and 21-16.

Count the number of mites on the final filter surface. An estimated 90% of mites dislodge from host bees with this treatment. You can count (or estimate) the number of bees washed.

An alternative two-jar sampling device is available for purchase (Figure 21-15). It includes two plastic jars joined with the coarse hardware cloth screen between the lids. Adult bees are collected directly in one jar or one-half cup measure added, followed by alcohol or soapy water.

The sample is swirled for one to two minutes to dislodge the mites then inverted. The mites (and liquid) passes through the bee sample to the lower jar, leaving the bees in the upper jar. By counting mites in the liquid (Figure 21-16) and adult bees of the drained jar you have an estimate of the percent infestation.

Sugar shake — A non-destruct sampling method is to dislodge mites from a sample of adults using powdered sugar shake. As with above methods, a 300-adult-bee sample is collected into a wide-mouthed jar. The collection container lid is substituted with an eight-mesh hardware cloth screen. Add one to three tablespoons of powdered sugar through the mesh and shake the jar for 1-2 minutes (Figure 21-17).

Then place the jar in the sun to increase the temperature which helps dislodge mites. Re-shake the bees in the jar then invert the jar over a white surface to shake excess powdered sugar and dislodge mites onto the surface for counting (Figure 21-18). Sugar-coated bees in the sample can be released back into their hive.

This method works best with finely powdered sugar without impurities but is less accurate than alcohol wash. To determine an infestation level using sugar shake, alcohol, soapy water or ether, divide the number of mites by the number of bees in the sample. So, if you find nine mites in a 300-adult-bee sample that equals 3% (9/300).

For targeted up-to-date information on varroa mite sampling and control consult *Tools for Varroa Management*, a free download from Honey Bee Health

Figure 21-18
Shaking the mites and powdered sugar residue onto a white paper plate to count the mites. L. Connor

Coalition (HBHC) http://www.honeybeehealthcoalition.org/varroa.

Randy Oliver (www.scientific beekeeping.com) has described an inexpensive hand-made sampler of two clear cups and cloth mesh (Figure 21-19).

Ether roll — An older, no longer popular adult sampling method, is the ether roll technique. Collect adult bees into a glass container and then discharge a one to two second burst of ether into the container. Ether is sold in automobile stores as a quick-starting aerosol for automobile engines. The ether causes mites to get caught on the sticky (with regurgitated honey) inner surface. Count the number of mites of at least three rolls of the jar.

Carbon dioxide — An alternative is to dislodge mites from adults using carbon dioxide. Mites are collected as above into a special closable container with a plastic screen to hold the adult bees about one-half inch above the lower surface. Carbon dioxide is administered in short bursts until all adults are immobilized and then the container gently shaken. Mites are counted after they fall below the container screen. The bees can be released back into the colony. Be advised that both ether roll and carbon dioxide give less precise mite counts.

Whole hive sampling

Sticky boards for natural mite fall — An alternative non-destruct method of sampling involves collecting the hive debris from beneath the entire colony (Figure 21-20) and

Figure 21-19
Handmade mite sampler of two clear plastic cups with fabric mesh to hold adult bees—mites counted in liquid below.

count the number of varroa mites present (Figure 21-21). This allows for estimation of colony mite population size since hive debris also includes dead and dislodged mites that normally fall to the bottom board. For each mite multiply by 50 to estimate the total mite population.

Bee supply houses sell bottom boards modified to include sticky boards or you can modify the bottom screened board to place the counting board beneath it. Great Lakes IPM sells a sticky board with a sampling grid which requires only counting a third of the squares. Commercial boards come with pre-applied sticky material (Tanglefoot®).

Make your own sticky boards from stiff cardboard positioned below a wire screen. To trap mites, smear diluted Vaseline® or apply cooking spray on the cardboard. Scrape clean after mite count and reapply sticky material for reuse of the sampling board. To protect housecleaning bees from sticky material, the white paper or plastic board is placed beneath a slightly elevated eight-mesh screen.

Examine the debris for the presence of mites. Using a 10x hand lens and a strong light will make the search easier. Since debris accumulation is rapid, the collection paper/plastic is left beneath the colony for only one to three days. Divide total number of mites counted by number of sample days to obtain a mite drop/day figure. If a miticide, or other treatment, is added to the colony at the same time, mite fall will obviously be much heavier.

Threshold concept — Brood, adult bee and whole colony sampling should be used to help determine the number of mites (population size) present in a colony. Such a number, used as a threshold, helps form the basis for an integrated pest management (IPM) approach to mite control. Mite populations can soar rapidly, especially in the fall, and the entire colony collapse. If sampling is not done or produces an inaccurate estimate of total population or is not frequent enough to detect a rapid mite increase you can lose the colony.

Figure 21-20 (Left)
Sticky board for mite sampling.
Figure 21-21. (Right):
Mite on grid of a screened bottom board sampling sheet.

Using brood to estimate mite populations has not been found to be very reliable or reproducible. Sampling adults is more useful to determine a threshold level. From numerous studies, an alcohol wash is deemed the most reliable means of determining a threshold number followed by sugar shake. Beekeeper and author Randy Oliver, among others, suggests that mite infestation level should be maintained below 1-2% and never allowed to exceed 5%. See Oliver's web site www. scientificbeekeeping.com for a discussion of his mite population growth model and his studies on sampling and control (check date to be sure you have most recent report).

For entire colony sticky board sampling, the threshold is less a mite number and more a general estimate of how many mites fall onto the sticky board. Generally fewer than 12/day should be the baseline acceptable level. If there are a dozen or more mites consider applying a control or resampling (to determine if numbers are increasing) and if there are many more mites (dozens) then control is warranted. These numbers are valid for a mid-August/September sampling of a standard-size colony.

Sticky board sampling is useful to determine if your control application is having/had the desired result. Pre-monitor by counting the mite number, add another clean sticky board during treatment (number of mite drop should be elevated) and then do a third post-treatment sample, within a week of completing the treatment. Mite levels should be much reduced.

Looking at drone brood for reproducing mites or at adults for phoretic mites is not effective for determining a mite threshold. Looking at number of mites on drone

Figure 21-22.
Varroa mites on two drone pupae in burr comb between brood boxes–note mites on pupae but not larvae.

brood during colony spring buildup (Figures 21-12, 21-22) can provide an impression of how extensive the mite population is and key the decision to do a more reliable alcohol or sugar shake sample. If you see mites on adult bees it generally means the colony has too many mites and control needs to be done, or present control method is not effective.

Control of varroa mites

There is an intensive search for honey bees with resistance/tolerance to varroa mites. Some honey bees are more diligent at grooming the mites from their bodies while other bees are better at policing their brood. Workers will open capped cells with mites to disrupt mite reproduction. Such behaviors are grouped under the concept of hygienic bees. **Hygienic bees** help reduce mite numbers/mite reproduction in their colony.

Bees that develop faster as larvae, thus leaving too little time for foundress mites to produce offspring, is another means of reducing mite reproduction. Some bee stocks show reduced mite fertility, offering another means of resistance. So far, there is no one stock that provides the level of resistance needed, but the search continues.

In the absence of mite-tolerant bees, beekeepers are faced with the expensive, and often distasteful prospect of using a chemical inside their bee colonies. The alternative is equally distasteful -- watching colonies die from mites passing virus diseases or colonies die in the fall or overwinter with either Parasitic Mite Brood Syndrome (Box 50) or Colony Collapse Disorder (Box 51).

Reliance on chemicals for a control strategy is doomed to failure over the long term. A chemical that effectively controls a pest inside a beehive without potentially harming the host or contaminating the hive itself is probably unattainable. Natural materials such as acids or oils that occur in the environment or within bee bodies or bee products are usually in low concentrations. Quantities of such materials that might possibly control mites need be used at elevated levels such that negative effects and contamination are a distinct possibility. The dosage is the poison.

Chemical controls should be combined with non-chemical alternative control measures. This is an IPM approach. Cultural and physical-mechanical controls should be used to help prevent mite buildup. The chemicals are a last resort. Their use can lead to

'unintended consequences' such as damage to the bee host or contamination of the hive beeswax/stored reserves and can be harmful to the beekeeper applicator. (See discussion of IPM later in this chapter).

Numerous beekeepers have documented that colonies given a rest period following stressful pollination duties or monocultural floral source, experience better overwintering and respond better to spring stimulation with protein and sugar feeding than if they lack this summer/fall 'time out.' It is essential not to allow mite levels to increase unchecked during this period. Annual requeening with resistant stock also reduces negative virus effects.

Varroa chemical control

One of the earliest mite control strategies widely utilized was chemical control, although many beekeepers consider this distasteful and unsound. Several miticides have been developed and marketed that specifically target varroa. The sequence of chemicals approved for varroa mite control are summarized in Box 52.

The bee industry is relatively small in terms of pesticide sale volume so most of the compounds have been adapted from chemicals previously utilized for mite control on other animals. Formulation and application methods such as timed-release plastic strips based on the pet flea collar (Figure 21-23) have been developed that provide a margin of safety.

As with other pesticides, those utilized to kill bee mites may be synthetic or derived from natural compounds. At the cellular level where the kill occurs, it is immaterial if the chemical is natural or synthetic. The chemicals are meant to kill and are often needed at levels far exceeding their natural concentration. See Chapter 23 for discussion about how pesticides—those the beekeeper may use or which bees may encounter in the environment—negatively impact bees and bee colonies.

The first synthetic pesticide to be registered for varroa control was **tau-fluvalinate (Mavrik®)**, a pyrethroid compound. It was initially approved in 1987 under Section 18 (emergency use label) that had to then be approved by individual states before beekeepers could use it in that state. It utilized impregnated plywood strips. In 1990 a commercial product Apistan®, incorporating the pesticide in an impregnated plastic strip, replaced the plywood strips. It had a Section 3 registration, meaning it could be used following state approval.

Apistan was initially very effective in controlling mites. When correctly used it was relatively non-toxic to honey bees (although pyrethroids in general, are highly toxic to honey bees) due to rapid detoxification by the honey bee by cytochrome P450 monooxygenases. Subsequently, three additional synthetic compounds have been approved for varroa control. Only one of the three,

Figure 21-23
Plastic Apivar© pesticide strip inserted between adjacent frames. Photo courtesy of Scientific Beekeeping website.

Box 50

PARASITIC MITE BROOD SYNDROME

Bee colonies that are apparently healthy and productive suddenly experience a crash in adult population. Sounds like a plot for a bee horror movie but it is all too real a scenario for some beekeepers. Dead colonies have plenty of honey stores but few adults and a very spotty, unhealthy looking brood area. Death occurs primarily in the spring months. This condition was labeled Parasitic Mite Syndrome (PMS) in 1994 by the U.S.D.A. Bee lab in Beltsville, MD. Some individuals add BEE ahead of PMS but currently the term gaining wider use is Parasitic Mite Brood Syndrome, PMBS.

The term *Idiopathic Brood Disease Syndrome*, IDBS, has also been coined to describe this unhealthy brood condition. This references the unknown disease cause.

Honey bee PMBS colonies usually show high mite infestations in the fall. During fall brood inspections, unhealthy looking brood, sometimes referred to as 'snot' or 'crud' brood (from their physical appearance) is evident and the colony appears to have too few adults to adequately cover the amount of fall brood (Figure 21-24).

The poor brood condition is often the first detectable sign. Larvae die from a European-foulbrood-type field symptom but the specific pathogen of EFB, *Melissococcus plutonius*, is not always found in decomposing brood. Other dying larvae may have chalkbrood or sacbrood. The result is a very spotty fall brood pattern. Highly hygienic bee stock will also exhibit spotty brood as bees uncap brood cells with varroa mites. Spottiness, by itself, is not a definite diagnosis of this PMBS condition.

Adult populations likewise do not appear healthy in fall colonies. Various virus symptoms might be evident in adults, though virus symptoms are subtle and not easy to discern. With confinement, the colony population decreases as too few healthy brood are available to replace the aging adult population and the colony dies sometime in the early spring. Colonies are often reluctant to take sugar syrup in standard fall management or if administering fumagillin for nosema.

The signs of PMBS in adult bees include: varroa mites present, tracheal mites may or may not be present, significant reduction in adult bee population during the fall, queen supersedure, and crawling, unhealthy adult bees in the hive and at the entrance. Such symptoms may occur with other diseases.

Brood signs include: varroa mites present, spotty brood pattern, dead brood of all ages evident with a mixture of dead brood that may suggest AFB, EFB, or sacbrood, depending on which larvae are viewed. Younger-aged dead brood appear twisted and brownish in cells (typical of EFB infections), older dead brood may appear ropy (a symptom of AFB) but seldom elongated in their cells and dead/dying bodies are easily removed (unlike AFB). Dead brood has

Figure 21-24
Late October inspection reveals too few adults covering brood, early indication of BEE PMBS. Bee veils are always recommended.

a sour odor, not the characteristic odors of either AFB or EFB. As noted, brood condition is called snot or crud brood. PMBS mimics other diseases.

So far, no specific pathogen has been identified, so confirmation of field signs with lab analysis is not yet possible. It is too early to tell if some of the bee stocks reported to be resistant to mites are less susceptible to Parasitic Mite Brood Syndrome. Mites alone may not be the factor causing death. The role poor nutrition, size of the adult population, nosema infestation levels and even sugar and antibiotic feeding disrupting normal bee intestinal tract micro-organisms may play is uncertain.

Reducing varroa mite numbers, and their transmission of virus disease, may be the key to reversing the downward spiral but mite treatments need to be done early in fall. Treatments to reduce mites late in fall may be ineffective — colonies may be 'ghost' colonies, already too unhealthy to recover with rescue measures. Beekeepers who are using mite control and/or were feeding sugar syrup — with or without fumagillin, seem to have fewer colonies adversely affected.

BIP Blog Parastiic Mite Syndrome: https://beeinformed. org/2013/10/15/parasitic-mite-syndrome-pms/

Box 51

COLONY COLLAPSE DISORDER

Beginning in 2004 a new mysterious condition suddenly appeared as a killer of bee colonies. The term colony collapse disorder (CCD) was coined for this syndrome in 2006 by the Mid Atlantic Research and Extension Consortium (MAAREC) based on reports of Pennsylvania bee colonies that were suddenly dying when moved to Florida. The initial examinations of collapses, and subsequent CCD losses, have shared these symptoms:

• absence of adult bee population but honey, pollen and brood remain

• absence of bee bodies within or near the collapsed hives

• loss occurs in over 50% of colonies, independent of general apiary health

• collapse occurs rapidly, usually prior to wintering

CCD is characterized by an abrupt decline in adult bee population and a corresponding delay in attack of hive scavenging parasites such as wax moths, small hive beetles, or even robbing by other bees. If caught mid-collapse, colonies may have only a queen (Figure 21-25) and a small handful of young worker bees. Capped brood may be present but it has been neglected and /or cannibalized.

Subsequent studies have failed to identify any single factor or combination of factors that trigger CCD. A thorough examination of CCD published in 2009 concluded that CCD likely involves an interaction between pathogens and other stress factors. A more recent 2015 U.S.D.A. review of the numerous publications on CCD narrows the likely causes to interaction between pathogens, pesticides and bee nutrition.

CCD had some similarities to reports of sudden colony demise dating back over 150 years, given names such as disappearing disease, spring dwindle, May disease, autumn collapse, and fall dwindle disease. CCD continues to be identified as one of the significant factors in heavy fall/overwintering losses of bee colonies as documented by the BeeInformed Partnership annual survey (Figure 21-24).

Lacking a specific causation a large number of unusual causes have been postulated, with varying amounts of supporting evidence. These include:

• viral influences (mutated viruses, Israeli acute paralysis, significantly high viral loads)

• pesticides (chronic exposure, synergistic interactions, acute off-site poisoning, improper use of in-hive pesticides)

• agricultural influences (monocultures leading to poor general bee nutrition, declines in bee pasturage)

• solar radiation/magnetic field interruptions (vague implications of cell phone, radio tower or military experiments)

The effort toward unraveling the mysteries of CCD need recognize the differences between causation (factors proven to lead, necessarily, to a specific result) and correlation (factors that have been observed to change the signs we observe but may not actually be the specific trigger for a given outcome). In the absence of identification of a specific causation, personal biases and agendas seem to have taken the lead. The media has overused the CCD term; for beekeepers loss of colonies with few adult bodies continues the use of CCD term.

vanEngelsdorp, D. et al. "Colony Collapse Disorder Preliminary Report" (PDF). Mid-Atlantic Apiculture Research and Extension Consortium (MAAREC)

vanEngelsdorp, Dennis, et al. 2009. Colony Collapse Disorder: A Descriptive Study. PLoS One https://doi.org/10.1371/journal.pone.0006481

Goulson, D. et al. 2015. "Bee Declines Driven by Combined Stress from Parasites, Pesticides and Lack of Flowers" (PDF). Science. 347 (6229): 1255957.

Figure 21-25
This yellow-marked queen with a small handful of workers were the only survivors of a mid-November colony collapse. J. Larsen

Percent winter losses US Colonies 2007-2021

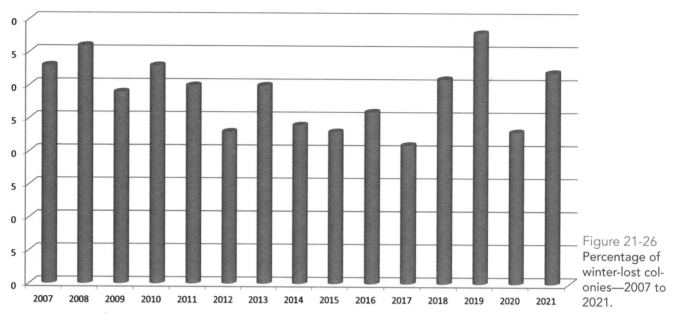

Figure 21-26 Percentage of winter-lost colonies—2007 to 2021.

amitraz, is currently widely utilized; all exhibit potential unintended negative side effects.

Eventually, varroa mites with their high reproductive rate can be expected to develop resistance to miticide chemicals. All four synthetic miticides have such demonstrated resistance, although mite resistance to the formamidine amitraz is not yet (by 2021) widespread. Illegal use may or may not have contributed to resistance development. Studies have demonstrated that individuals untrained in use of pesticides make frequent errors in correctly mixing and applying of pesticides. Under-dosing is one demonstrable route to development of pest resistance.

An uncomplicated field test, the Pettis test, was developed for individuals to determine if their bees have developed resistance. To test, collect 25 workers, place them in a jar with a piece of the plastic pesticide strip and compare mite drop at 6 or 24 hours to mite numbers remaining on bee bodies. If 50% or more mites remain on the bee bodies consider the mites to have resistance. It is recommended that this test be used first before application of a pesticide that has demonstrated resistance.

Only a couple of new (to bee mites) synthetic miticides are reportedly in the 'pipeline.' Two of the largest pesticide companies, Monsanto and Bayer (now one company), have hired bee specialists to help guide policy and coordinate the search for new pesticide compounds.

Varroa organic acid (natural) chemicals

Organic acid compounds and several essential oils have been shown to provide varroa control. They are not as convenient to use, are temperature dependent and, like synthetics, have negative side effects. They may also exhibit unpredictable levels of varroa control. Although organically/naturally derived, they are not necessarily safer to bees, hive contamination or beekeeper applicator.

Formic Acid — Registered as a Section 3 compound, formic acid is available as **Mite Away Quick Strips (MAQS®)** or as **Formic Pro®** (Figure 21-27). They are a unique biostrip with formic acid incorporated into a sugar-based material rather than plastic strip. MAQS and Formic Pro target mites within the brood cells and also kills mites on adult bees. Registration is unique in that use is permitted when bees are storing honey or supers are still on the colony being treated; it also is permitted at a one-half dosing application.

Formic acid is sanctioned under most organic honey production guidelines. It is a natural acid in honey and bee bodies but occurs at much lower levels than level needed to kill mites. Formic acid works as a fumigant. Illegally, some beekeepers continue to make and apply their own homemade formic acid product using the acid itself and a variety of absorbent materials.

Formic acid is a powerful acid and several beekeepers have experienced 'accidental burning' in their casual handling of this material. Side effects for bee colonies include shortening of adult bee life and/or colony queen loss. Use often results in open brood kill or temporary halt in egg laying by the queen.

Oxalic acid — This common acid is readily available as inexpensive wood bleach or as a Section 3 registered mite control (Api-bioxal). It is administered in two distinct ways. It can be mixed with sugar water to dribble between frames or as mist spray on package bees, or used as a fumigant. Direct contact is needed to kill mites.

Box 52

PESTICIDE SUCCESSION FOR VARROA MITE CONTROL

Beekeepers rapidly changed from being chemophobic (pesticides kill bees) to chemophilic (miticides are necessary to kill mites) once varroa mites invaded their colonies. A large numbers of beekeepers, including virtually all commercial and semi-commercial beekeepers, rapidly adopted chemical control.

Today there is a segment of beekeepers and environmentalists opposed to the use of chemicals to control mites. They self-label as treatment free, natural beekeepers, Api-centric or Darwinian beekeepers. The so-called hard chemicals—the synthetic miticides—have been the focus of this opposition, although any externalities, be it hard miticide, soft miticide, GMO-derived protein patty or even some sources of supplemental sugar, including use of high fructose corn syrup (HFCS), are anathema to some individuals; some even say irresponsible bee stewardship.

Fluvalinate—The first chemical compound tau-fluvalinate (Mavrik®), a pyrethroid, was approved (under section 18— emergency use) in only a few short months of discovery of varroa mites in the U.S. It was formulated in an easy-to-use strip to insert between frames in colonies with varroa mites. Mavrik was replaced by Apistan® and made available as a Section 3 (general use) compound.

Amitraz—It was soon joined by amitraz, a formamidine, trade name Miticur®, also only available under Section 18 registration. It also used the impregnated strip technology. However when it was implicated for causing bee losses, the manufacturer withdrew the material from the market. In 2011 Canada registered Amitraz for emergency use under

the trade name Apivar® and it has returned in the U.S. as Apivar, briefly under a Section 18 registration with a new manufacturer (Figure 21-23); currently it has a Section 3 general use registration.

NOTE: There is general acknowledgement that beekeepers continued to illegally use both these compounds by purchasing the compounds themselves and making their own application strips. Varroa mite resistance has also been found for both compounds. Illegal use may or may not include an 'acceptable' dosing as studies have shown that individuals untrained in use of pesticides make frequent errors in correctly mixing and applying of pesticides. How long the registered Apivar product will be useful is unknown.

Coumaphos—In 1999 a third organic insecticide was available to replace Apistan. This was coumaphos, an organophosphate, sold under Section 18 as Checkmite+®. It was also registered for in-hive control of small hive beetle. It too utilized plastic impregnated strips designed to hang between adjacent brood frames. Mite resistance to this material was reported within two years. It never achieved Section 3 approval and eventually states stopped requesting Section 18 use approval in light of EPA's intentions to discontinue registrations of all organophosphates. It seriously injured queens by lowering queen rearing success and new queen acceptance. It was also shown to cause low sperm viability among drones.

Hivastan—A fourth synthetic miticide, fenpyroximate, trade name Hivastan®, a pyrazole compound, was registered as a Section 18 in 2007. It was never been widely used as adult bee mortality was a serious drawback.

Oxalic acid is only effective on phoretic/dispersal mites so is most useful as a late season (November-December) cleanup of phoretic mites from adult bees once brood rearing has ceased. It can also be used in combination with the non-chemical brood break mite technique, applying it after older capped cells have hatched and new larvae have yet to be capped. It is more widely used in the north than in the south.

When used as a fumigant, a respirator with a chemical acid filter is necessary to avoid lung damage to applicator; gloves and eye protection are also highly recommended. It was initially not to be used when bees were storing honey but now has such approval. Unfortunately it is frequently improperly applied.

HopGuard®—This third organic acid is a derivative of hops beta acids, a by-product from the extraction of hops (for beer making). It provides good knockdown of mites on adult bees but does not penetrate capped cells.

It is impregnated on a cardboard strip placed between frames. It is messy and less effective when the cardboard strips dry out. It has not yet been widely adopted. Like formic acid, it can be used when supers are on colonies.

Acetic acid—Acetic acid has also been used illegally for varroa control. Vinegar, a dilute (5%) form of acetic acid, has reportedly been tried by beekeepers but this concentration is probably too low to be effective. Acetic acid would not seem to be of great benefit over formic or oxalic acid, and lacking approval, should not be used.

Essential oils

A large number of essential oil extracts have been tested as miticides and several such as pennyroyal, tea tree, patchouli, various mints and wintergreen have confirmed activity. Thymol, eucalyptol, menthol and lemongrass have the greatest utility and the greatest interest for use.

Figure 21-27
Formic acid pads.

Three essential oil products are properly registered as Section 3 use for mite control. Menthol has been utilized for tracheal mites (see Section on tracheal mite control in this chapter) while thymol is the material of choice for killing varroa mites.

Thymol — The essential oil thymol is the main ingredient in the slow-release gel **Apiguard®** (Figure 21-28) and the wafer application of **ApiLife Var®**. ApiLife Var also includes eucalyptol, menthol and camphor. Both have Section 3 registrations and fit within most organic honey guidelines. Both also give tracheal mite control and some control for the fungal disease chalkbrood (see Chapter 22).

Negative side effects of essential oil use include brood removal (especially if temperatures are elevated during application) and increased queen mortality. They are very temperature-dependent and work best when ambient temperatures are between 65° and 85° F (17-30° C). Essential oils provide less effective mite kill under lower temperatures and damage bees at higher temperatures. Bees often beard at the colony entrance when used.

Food additives/stimulants

Honey-B-Healthy® — HBH is a feeding additive/ stimulant that utilizes essential oils such as spearmint and lemon grass oil. An emulsifier lecithin is needed to allow the oil to be mixed into the sugar syrup. Honey-B-Healthy is not a legally registered treatment for mites (it lacks a sufficient amount of essential oil to kill mites) although some beekeepers reportedly use it for this purpose.

The Honey-B-Healthy (HBH) formulation has proven popular with some beekeepers. Syrup with HBH seems to increase syrup acceptance by bees and slows syrup feeders from developing mold or mildew. It is also used to introduce new queens by applying it to queens' body and spraying in the colony where new queens are being introduced. Some beekeepers like to use it as alternative to smoke during colony inspections, applied as a fine spray when opening and inspecting a hive.

Other feeding additive compounds — There are additional feeding additives available. Their exact role has not been determined and none have registrations as mite-killing agents. Some such as **ApiHerb®** adds plant compounds to sugar water, **ApiGo®** adds vitamins, **HiveAlive®** uses bio-active marine compounds from Western Ireland, **Vita Feed Gold®** and **Vita Feed Green®** are liquid bio-stimulant feeds based on the natural extracts of beets and molasses. There is even a suggested amino acid booster to feed to bees, in combination with Honey-B-Healthy. As long as they are not marketed as miticides, feeding additives are not subject to EPA registration approval. Most have not been independently tested for claimed effectiveness.

Microbials are another form of feeding supplement. Research is underway to see how they might be beneficial. If vitamins, minerals, microbials, additive compounds, etc. can boost colony and/or individual immunity, reduce stressor effects and lead to healthier bees, they will likely be quickly adopted.

There is a propensity for beekeepers to try untested methods for mite control or to use materials in an unlabelled manner. This is both potentially dangerous to bees and beekeeper and likely to be ineffective, giving a false sense of security, Most materials would have to be in highly concentrated amounts increasing the hazard. There is no magic bullet. All beekeepers would be better served to use the proven remedies in the recommended manner.

Powdered sugar and other dusts

Using **powdered sugar** to knock mites off adult bees is a popular but unreliable treatment (Figure 21-29). The fine powder may cause mites to lose their grip and fall to the bottom of a hive; or causes increased grooming resulting in increased mite fall. When used in combination with screen bottom boards, the powdered mites fall out of the colony or onto a sticky tray where they may be counted.

Powdering bees is impractical. Colonies should be powdered several times during a short time interval to reach mites as they emerge from the sealed brood cells. Efforts to shake all adults from the colony into a collection box to thoroughly powder them before return to their hive have not proven to be feasible. Powder sugar removes too few mites to justify the considerable effort involved. One exception might be the use of powdered sugar on broodless bees, such as package colonies prior to or just after installation.

Drying agents such as talc or diatomaceous earth have the same action. Comparison studies have shown mixed results.

Other chemical approaches

A product Sucrocide®, composed of sucrose octanoate esters, was briefly on the market as a mite killer. Bees had to be completely wetted to kill the mites and each frame had to be removed to spray the bees on both sides. Another chemical, mineral oil, has been advocated as a mite control alternative. A major disadvantage is the frames and beeswax combs become coated with the oil. Both these and other soaps and oils need be avoided.

New compounds are continually being evaluated, both chemicals for mite/pest control and materials that might be stimulants/additives/supplements to improve colony health. It seems that every few months a new material is touted as an effective mite control approach. Coconut oil, propolis, feeds provided to cattle, miticides used on other animals — the list seems endless. The potential market for such compounds is not really fully known. One research study suggests that mites compensate if applications are continuously repeated.

Varroa mites are a formidable foe. They are both pest and vector of disease pathogens. They were introduced to a new host, the European honey bee, which lacks the eons of coevolution between pest and target host. Isolated colonies in nature use distance, extensive propolis use, small guarded entrances, and other natural means that help ensure their survival. This concept, termed **Darwinian or apicentric beekeeping** has gained recent adherents. Colonies are managed less and kept in smaller hives so they swarm more. Swarming, with a subsequent brood break, does provide mite control.

Integrated pest management

Integrated Pest Managment, IPM, is a process that seeks to integrate more than just a chemical approach to pest control. The Food and Agriculture Organization (FAO) of the United Nations defines IPM as *'the careful consideration of all available pest control techniques and subsequent integration of appropriate measures that discourage the development of pest populations. [IPM] keeps pesticides and other interventions to levels that are economically justified to reduce or minimize risks to human health and the environment.'* IPM is not anti-chemical but rather implies a judicious use of chemicals integrated with other approaches to keep pest populations below economically damaging levels.

IPM, as applied to bee mites, does not seek total elimination of pest mites but rather is management of the pest to keep the mite population below an economic (or aesthetic) threshold. Management implies that the pest can victimize some of the colony members but not to the extent that it kills its host. It is an integration of sampling of the mite population followed by use of a variety of control methods to keep the mite population from exceeding a damaging level i.e. below a threshold level.

IPM requires accurate information on the pest population. Killing a colony to count the number of mites is, of course, silly, so we seek to find a method to accurately sample mite numbers. (See sampling discussion above). Current methods to estimate mite numbers in a bee colony vary in their accuracy and ease of use. Whole-colony sticky board counts give an entirely different sample of the population compared to counting adult mites removed from adult bee bodies. Some beekeepers dislike killing of bees (such as the alcohol

Figure 21-28
Essential oil (Apiguard) within rim feeder on top frames of bee colony.

Figure 21-29
Powder sugaring bees. A bee brush gently distributes sugar between frames, falling onto the adult bees.

wash method) so resist sample collection and use a less reliable method.

Knowing how many mites are in a hive, even when sampling is not entirely accurate, allows us to determine a risk threshold to target treatment decisions. If we know the rate of growth of mite populations, we may be able to predict population size. What we need to know is not if a colony has mites but rather how many mites are in a colony. We then can adopt a level we believe our colony can tolerate and still survive, produce honey or provide pollination.

A threshold number is a target, a number to keep mite populations beneath. A threshold is the point where if control is not applied, the return to the beekeeper will be below what might potentially have been gained, after accounting for the cost of applying a control. Since there are different objectives for keeping bees, this threshold will vary; beekeepers can factor in what they feel they can afford in terms of damage. For example, thresholds from 1-2% adult infestation to no more than 5% have been suggested. These are widely different target numbers.

For whole colony sampling, keeping mite populations below a daily mite drop of 12 mites/24 hours has been

one suggested threshold, but without much supporting evidence. Variables such as time of year, size of the colony population, previous treatment history, the bee stock and a major unknown on prevalence of viruses should all be factored into the decision of too many or if colony needs treatment.

IPM in honey bees utilizes an integrated approach of control methods that can lengthen the effective time period a chemical might be used before resistance renders that specific chemical less useful. IPM has also come to be understood, by that segment of beekeepers that are not seeking economic gain from bee colony stewardship, as a less toxic, host bee and environmental friendlier approach. IPM is termed by some as a more natural means of controlling the varroa mite.

Rotation of chemicals, a method to slow development of chemical resistance is part of an IPM approach. Resistance to synthetic chemicals has been repeatedly demonstrated. The beekeeping industry is considered too small and too specialized for large agricultural companies to be able to identify a potential profit to develop a new pesticide given the time and expense of developing control chemicals and getting them registered with the Environmental Protection Agency. Most miticides for varroa have been adaptions of

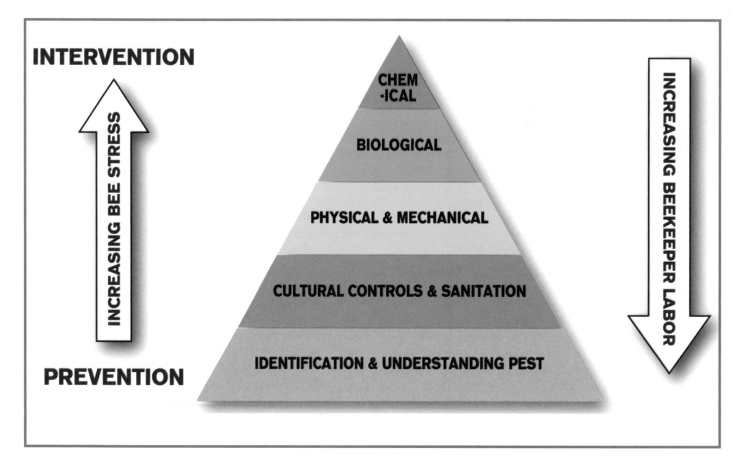

Figure 21-30
The IPM triangle. J. Zawislak.

other products, often with public funding, to enable the materials to be properly registered for use with honey bees.

IPM control options can be viewed as a triangle (Figure 21-30). It shows a broad base in sustainable approaches such as in cultural control methods and physical controls, like traps or temperature manipulations. These are preventive in nature, designed to keep the population of mite pests from exceeding a low, relatively harmless level. They are often low-tech, common-sense solutions that will not be as effective under higher mite pressure.

The IPM triangle peaks at intervention with chemical controls. Such materials are developed at considerable time and expense and are the high-tech, often high-cost solution. The level of toxicity of the triangle varies in sync with the preventive to intervention scale. Pesticide chemicals carry risks to non-targets, applicators, the environment, and host bee health, while promising to be highly effective in reducing the economic impact of the pest population.

One way to describe the triangle is the base offers 'smart solutions for thinking individuals' while the upper point provides 'dumb chemicals for non-thinking applicators.' An over-simplification to be sure but useful never-the-less to illustrate a dichotomy of approach to the difficult choices and sometimes lack of adequate information needed for effective control of a pest such as varroa.

Cultural control — Cultural control seeks to reduce outbreaks of pests by utilizing the best culture conditions to maintain healthy hosts and reduce pest incidence. Proper conditions begin with selecting a proper apiary site. Colonies exposed to more sun and with good internal hive ventilation have fewer varroa mites and small hive beetles (Figure 21-31).

Sunny, exposed (but wind-protected) apiaries help reduce stress; they should be coupled with management that improves seasonal success, particularly during periods of environmental challenge. Improved wintering conditions using entrance reduction, upper flight entrances, moisture wicking, assisting early spring development with feeding of protein, and movement to locations favoring early spring pollen, are part of good colony stewardship. (See discussions of seasonal management in earlier chapters).

Sanitation is of utmost importance in pest control in crops and animal care. It means avoiding transfer of diseases between colonies in an apiary, including drifting or robbing. Providing greater distance between colonies, as is seen in bee trees in nature, when feasible, is useful. Knowing that colonies closest to unhealthy colonies have a greater probably to become unhealthy, beekeepers should distinctively mark all colonies so they are individually distinctive to help reduce drifting.

Figure 21-31
Apiary site with good air circulation and in full sunlight helps reduce mite infestation level in colonies.

Figure 21-32
Breeding local queens to improve overwintering and mite control. Note soda bottle as syrup feeder and screwdriver as hive tool substitute.

Beekeepers should avoid moving infected material from one colony to the next. Most pests and diseases, including varroa mites, are readily transferred via beekeeper manipulations within and between apiaries. Culling older combs and replacing with new foundation is a useful means of reducing potential inoculum of pathogens and rids the colony of pesticides trapped by the beeswax comb cells.

Figure 21-33
Russian queen. From Russian Honeybee Breeders Association website.

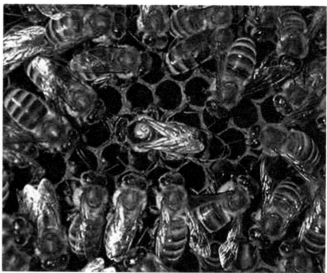

Figure 21-34
New World Carniolan queen. S. Cobey

In agricultural crops, cultural control includes the selection of pest-resistant varieties that do well within a particular farming operation. In bee culture, selection of mite resistant/tolerant lines of bees (sometimes defined as genetic control) is a method to develop healthier bees. Selection programs seek to develop lines that tolerate the mites. Survivor stock breeding programs have been started in many parts of the country, consisting of local beekeepers and beekeeper groups which seek to identify and breed from micro-habitat adapted survivor bees that resist varroa (Figure 21-32). These programs often seek to develop greater levels of winter survival.

New stock importations have been a successful method to improve beekeeping. When the northern European (German) bees were suffering from EFB in the early 1800s in the U.S., importation of and distribution of Italian bee stock reversed the downward spiral. Given our federal law prohibiting importation of bee germ plasma, stock selection is limited to bees currently in the country. Recently, the USDA's importation of mite-tolerant Russian bees, and the subsequent development of a Russian bee breeding group of private beekeepers to distribute this stock, has proven to be a successful application of a stock importation program (Figure 21-33).

An importation of drone semen has demonstrated promise for future stock improvement of Carniolan (New World) stock (Figure 21-34). Carniolan bees, though seriously degraded due to lack of isolation from Italian stock, are considered by many to be a better, more varroa resistant bee for cooler climate beekeeping conditions.

At the other temperature extreme, Africanized bees, common in the southern U.S., might provide another stock improvement approach. Although highly undesirable for their defensive behavior, Africanized bees resist serious varroa damage by exhibiting a more rapid larval development time. Foundress mites lack sufficient time to produce viable daughters in the shortened time frame, slowing mite population development. Only drone brood produces the next mite generation. Genes for shortened pupal development time could be identified (assuming it is genetically controlled) and inserted into European bee stock. (See discussion of Africanized bees in Chapter 2).

One other cultural control approach has been quarantines and legal sanctions (Figure 21-35). When tracheal mites first appeared this control was attempted. Colonies were confined to already infested regions and entire apiaries depopulated. Movement of bees out of infected areas was prohibited. These measures are often unpopular with free enterprise and globalization of markets. Quarantines are costly and therefore hard to implement and enforce by governmental agencies, particularly if they lack wide industry support. Such measures were not effective against either tracheal or varroa mites for a variety of reasons.

Movement of vast numbers of managed colonies for pollination and from north to south for overwintering is currently common for commercial U.S. beekeepers (Chapter 20). Colonies from several beekeepers co-mix in holding yards in crop pollination situations. How much this has contributed to the epidemic of bee losses is unknown. This and other managements, which can be considered unsafe practices from a sanitation standpoint, certainly might be a significant factor.

Physical (mechanical) control

Mechanical controls are efforts to create barriers or entrapment devices to prevent entry or reduce

Figure 21-35
Quarantines have not been effective in stopping mite movement.

population buildup of a pest. Beekeepers replace solid bottom boards with **screened bottom boards** (SBB). Mites that fall through the screen are trapped on sticky paper and are unable to reattach to another bee. Research on the effectiveness of screened bottoms show that they are only marginally effective, but they have become widely adopted as a sampling technique rather than control measure.

Heat (or cold) is an approach that works for some pests. Practical application of a thermal approach, adding heat (or cooling) has proven to be a challenge as we need to overcome bee temperature regulation behaviors. There are several devices that elevate hive temperature but they are costly. In general the temperature needs to be maintained at 104-108° F (40-42° C) for two to three hours to kill mites.

Overwintering at more or less constant temperatures (42° F, 6° C) with subsequent reduced brood rearing has been shown to be an effective cold treatment. Northern beekeepers move single story colonies into darkened buildings (indoor wintering) in the fall and then remove them to take to almond pollination in California or move them outside once warmer spring temperatures permit.

A shorter cooling period in refrigerated buildings during the season, such as following a pollination event, is being investigated and shows some promise of severely limiting normal mite population development.

A moderately successful but labor intensive method of reducing mite population buildup is to use **drone brood trapping**. Female mites prefer drone brood and this trapping method uses this preference to advantage. One or two frames with drone brood foundation (colored green for easier recognition; Figure 21-36) are inserted into the brood nest of expanding spring colonies. They are rapidly drawn into drone cells in the spring and queens will lay unfertilized eggs into them, even before completely drawn.

An alternative is to put a medium depth frame in a standard-sized brood box. The workers will build beeswax cells beneath the bottom bar, most likely drone cells (Figure 21-37). When the majority of the cells are

Figure 21-36
Inserting drone cell-sized comb foundation into brood

capped (ensuring female mites inside the pupal cells), the drone comb frame or cells beneath the bottom bar of the medium frame are removed from the colony. The drone brood can be killed (in a freezer) or cells opened and the drone pupae fed to chickens, fish, etc. Drone trapping technique only works in the spring when the bees rear the largest numbers of drones.

Management methods can be used to eliminate capped brood and use something to cleanse the adult bee population of phoretic/dispersal mites without brood present. Newly constituted colonies (without transfer of

Figure 21-37
An alternative method of trapping mites in a colony. Medium depth frame inserted into brood area of standard sized box leads to capped drone brood beneath bottom bar which can easily be removed and discarded.

brood), caging adults, treating newly captured swarms, treating colonies seasonally in late fall or early spring (when brood is minimal) all offer such an opportunity. Treatments might effectively utilize a desiccating agent, powdered sugar or natural chemical (HopGuard or oxalic acid).

A break in the brood cycle is an especially useful technique that stops both colony brood rearing and mite population growth. Inducing a brood break has shown such promise (especially when used with a miticide) that beekeepers are developing **queen sequestration** techniques. After bee colonies have produced honey or pollinated crops, their queens are either temporarily caged or replaced after an interval of 12-15 days with a mite-resistant queen. This break effectively reduces mite reproduction and gives workers time to groom themselves or combined with a chemical to help rid mites from the adults. This technique is an increasingly important tool in the IPM toolbox.

Biological control

There is no current biological control agent that effectively control varroa mite. Entomopathogenic fungi, genus *Metarhizium*, show promise in lab tests and several active projects to produce a product are underway. These fungi are often used in biological control of insects and other arthropod pests. Extracts from polypore mushroom mycelium of fungal species *Fomes* (amadou) and *Ganoderma* (reishi) fungi (a tree shelf fungus), both highly regarded in natural Oriental medicine, were shown to reduce the levels of honey bee deformed wing virus (DWV) and Lake Sinai virus (LSV). There is a current effort to bring this product to market.

Bacillus thuringiensis, the same bacteria used to control wax moth, but in a different strain, has been suggested as a candidate for mite control. Entomopathogenic protozoa and nematodes have also been examined and there is some possible development of one of them to control varroa. Nematodes are offered for sale for small hive beetle control.

Stratiolaelaps scimitus a predacious mite has been shown to feed on varroa mites in the lab but in-hive studies have failed to demonstrate they can establish a high population and reduce mites. Pseudoscorpions likewise have been viewed feeding on mites but they have not yet been demonstrated to be an effective biocontrol agent in the bee hive.

key terms

Acarapis woodi · acariosis · acarine disease · alcohol wash sampling · American foulbrod · amitraz (Apivar/Miticur) · Apis cerana · Apiguard (Thymol) · ApiLife Var (essential oils) · Apistan (tau-fluvalinate) · autumn collapse · Bacillus thuringiensis · Bee Informed project (BIP) · Biological control · Braula coeca · Brother Adam · Buckfast bee · capping scratcher · Carniolan bee · chemophobic/chemophilic · Colony Collapse Disorder (CCD)

Coumaphos · Crisco patties · crud brood · cultural control · depopulation (euthanize) · disappearing disease · drone brood trapping · debris(sticky) board · dwindle (spring/fall) disease · entomopathogenic fungi/protozoa · ether roll · European foulbrood (EFB) · feeding additives · fluvalinate · formic acid (MAQS/Formic Pro) · foundress mite · grease patties · Hivastan · Honey-B-Healthy · Hopguard

hygienic bees · Idiopathic Brood Disease Syndrome (IBDS) · indoor wintering · Integrated Pest Management (IPM) · Isle of Wright disease · K-wing · May disease · menthol (mite-a-Thol) · microbials · miticide · mite threshold · mushrooms (polypore/Metarhizium) · nematodes · overwinter/annual colony loss · oxalic acid · Parasitic Mite Syndrome (PMS) · phoretic (phorsey/phoresis) · physical-mechanical control · predatory mites

pseudoscorpion · quarantine (regulatory control) · queen sequestration · questing · Russian bees · sacbrood · sanitation · screen bottom board · snot brood · Sucrocide · sternite · sugar shake sampling method · threshold · thymol (Apiguard/ApiLife Var) · tracheal mites · tropilaelaps · vampire mite · varroa · varroa sampling · varroosis

discussion questions

Describe typical life history and pathology of mites that live on adult bees and bee brood. Where did they come from? Why have they become such a problem recently? What can be done to keep bees relatively mite free?

We describe mites as a relatively new pest on a host that has not had a long co-evolutionary history with the pest. Why is this significant? Should we seek to change the bee (make them stronger) or the pest (make mites weaker) or modify the hive somehow to create a brood break? What might be a more balanced relationship between introduced pest and host?

Differentiate between honey bee PMBS and CCD. If your colony is dead what specific signs might you look for to try to determine what happened? Can such information help avoid a repeat loss?

Control of varroa has initially been to use a chemical to kill the mite but why has this involved different chemicals? What is the chance that we will discover a 'magic bullet' to control mites? Why is an IPM approach a more sustainable means to control of varroa? Can prevention or physical mechanical control provide adequate control?

Describe current chemical and non-chemical varroa control options. If you keep bees or intend to start a new colony what control scheme would you employ to protect your bees and keep colonies alive and productive?

exercises

Sample a colony for mites using sticky boards and one of the adult sampling methods (powdered sugar, alcohol wash, etc.). How easy are they to use? How much did they cost? What do you need to properly take a sample? What problems did you encounter?

Sample for tracheal mites comparing cutting with scalpel or razor blade versus pulling collar off thorax of some worker bees. After sampling do you agree with most beekeepers that tracheal mites are not a significant problem? Prepare a grease patty or try another tracheal mite control. Would you prefer to use a control that is effective against both tracheal and varroa mites? Which one(s) will control both mites?

Compare and contrast time and expense of the various IPM techniques used to combat varroa and tracheal mites. Include chemical, mechanical, cultural, manipulative (physical) and genetic methods of control.

Perform the varroa control of drone trapping varroa control using either drone cell foundation frame or medium frame in a full-sized body. What problems did you encounter? Would you likely adopt this control technique? Why or why not?

references

CAPA. S. Pernal and H. Clay Ed. 2015. Honey Bee Diseases and Pests. Third CAPA, Beaverlodge, Alberta, Canada

Caron, D.M. 2020. Flatten the (mite) curve. Bee Culture. July

Hesbach, W. 2016 Varroa and splits. Northern Bee Books, West Yorkshire, UK

http://entnemdept.ufl.edu/creatures/misc/bees/tracheal_mite.htm

https://en.wikipedia.org/wiki/Colony_collapse_disorder

https://bee-health.extension.org/european-foulbrood-a-bacterial-disease-affecting-honey-bee-brood/

Honey Bee Health Coalition (HBHC) http://www.honeybeehealthcoalition.org/varroa (Varroa sampling and control)

Honey Bee Health Coalition. Best Management Practices 2019. https://honeybeehealthcoalition.org/wp-content/uploads/2019/01/HBHC_Hive_BMPs_v1.0_reduced.pdf

https://catalog.extension.oregonstate.edu/em9145 (Tracheal mite dissection video)

IFAS Tropilaelaps mite http://entnemdept.ufl.edu/creatures/MISC/BEES/Tropilaelaps.htm

Moore, P.A. et al. 2014. Honey Bee Viruses, the Deadly Varroa Mite Associates http://www.extension.org/pages/71172/honey-bee-viruses-the-deadly-varroa-mite-associates#.VbgmtLBFBjo

Pettis, J.S. et al. 2015. Diseases and Pests of Honey Bees. Chap 27 IN The Hive and the Honey Bee. Joe Graham Ed. Dadant and sons, Hamilton, IL

Sammataro, D. 2014. Diagnosing Bee Mites. Northern Bee Books, West Yorkshire, UK

Shimanuki, H. et al. 1994. Parasitic Mite Syndrome: the symptoms. Amer Bee Jour. 134: 827-828.

Stamets, P.E. et al. 2018. Extracts of Polypore Mushroom Mycelia Reduce Viruses in Honey Bees. Scientific Reports 8 # 13936.

UMN Bee Lab 2020. Varroa mites. https://www.beelab.umn.edu/bee-squad/resources-beekeepers/varroa

vanEngelsdorp, D. et al. 2013. Idiopathic brood disease syndrome and queen events as precursors of colony mortality in migratory beekeeping operations in the Eastern United States. Preventive Veterinary Medicine 108:225-233.

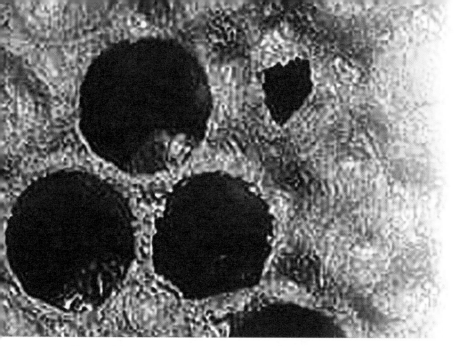

Figure 22-1
American foulbrood sunken capping and dry scale.
L. Connor

Concepts

Diseases

Brood diseases

    American foulbrood
    European foulbrood
    chalkbrood
    other brood diseases

Adult diseases

Diseases

Bees do not, on average, have more diseases or pests than other insects though more is known about them. Control of diseases has long been recognized as an integral part of beekeeping. Pests (mite pests were covered in Chapter 21), pesticides (discussed in Chapter 23), and problems with queens (Chapters 10 & 18) constitute very challenging situations beekeepers must confront to be successful.

Diagnosis of problems should begin as soon as the beekeeper enters the apiary, continue at the colony entrance and especially while inspecting a colony. When in the brood area, the brood should be examined for diseases and other problems.

Some governments provide apiary inspection services to inspect for diseases and provide diagnostic services. However, the beekeeper is always the first line of defense against diseases. Since the objective of many beekeepers is to ensure a harvest of honey and other products, or use of bees in pollination, good beekeeping requires maintenance of healthy, disease-, pest-, and pesticide-free bees.

Brood diseases

Bee brood inspection for disease symptoms is good bee stewardship. Every time the brood nest of a colony is entered, brood should be examined for disease. Beekeepers should make specific and intentional spring and fall inspections to confirm that colonies are in good health. They should recognize healthy brood (Figure 22-26). Proper diagnosis requires that beekeepers be able to recognize brood disease symptoms (Table 22-1).

Recognition of healthy brood in a colony is the first step. Brood should be organized in a solid and compact pattern. Ninety percent or more of the cells in the brood area should contain an egg, larva or pupa (capped cell) in the approximate ratio of twice as many larvae and four times as many capped cells as cells with eggs. Brood stages in

After a final molt to pupal stage movement ceases within the cell.

The beekeeper should look for any abnormal cappings and a spotty brood pattern (Figure 22-1; 22-2, Box 53, Figure 22-4). Abnormal does not necessarily indicate disease—chilled brood, starving brood, brood damaged by insecticides or plant poisoning, or abnormal queen genetic factors all have some resemblance to diseased brood.

Early disease detection allows the beekeeper more control options. Inexperienced beekeepers begin by learning to recognize that something is not right. In time, beekeepers should be able to tell one disease from another by using field symptoms. Do not be concerned if there is some confusion in reading these symptoms; the most important thing is to recognize a problem.

Diagnose a brood disease using trusted references containing detailed drawings and photographs. After field diagnosis, the disease should be confirmed by a beekeeper with more experience, such as an apiary inspector, or by sending a piece of comb to the USDA. Bee Lab in Beltsville, MD. Among the useful aids in disease symptom identification, the authors recommend: CAPA *Honey Bee*

Figure 22-2
AFB symptoms. Dark and greasy cells with holes in cappings. Diseased larvae at the bottom of the cells. R. Snyder

one area should be of similar age reflecting an organized, efficient egg laying behavior of the queen.

Newly emerged larvae and eggs are difficult to see, but all beekeepers need learn to see them. Larvae are distinctly white in color, should be centered in their cells and glisten in the light. With hand magnification, you should see larval movement and evidence of food in the cells. If something is wrong, you will see other symptoms.

It is easy to see the capped pupal stage when looking in a colony. The sealed brood caps of healthy cells should be a uniform light-brown in color, darkening a bit as they age. Healthy cell caps are distinctly six-sided and higher in the middle (convex). Some cells in the process of being capped may have an uncompleted center of the covering cap. At capping, larvae will move about the cell spinning a cocoon; they will be white, odorless and appear moist in the light.

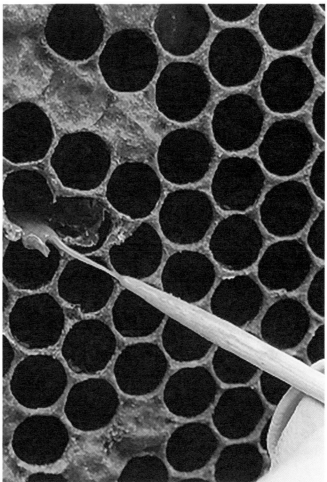

Figure 22-3
Ropy test. AFB will extend out like taffy, then snap back (other brood diseases do not).

Table 22-1. Field symptom comparison of various brood diseases of the honey bee. USDA

Characteristics to observe	American foulbrood	European foulbrood	Sacbrood
Appearance of brood comb	Sealed brood Discolored, sunken, or punctured cappings	Unsealed brood Some open brood in advanced cases with discolored, sunken or punctured cappings	Sealed brood Scattered cells with punctured cappings, often with two holes
Age of dead brood	Usually older sealed larvae or young pupae	Usually young, unsealed larvae; occasionally older	Usually older sealed larvae; occasionally young, unsealed larvae sealed larvae
Color of dead brood	Dull white, becoming light brown, coffee brown to dark brown, or almost black	Dull white, becoming yellowish white to brown, dark brown or almost black	Grayish or straw-colored becoming brown, grayish black or black; head end darker
Consistency of dead brood	Soft, becoming sticky to ropy	Watery to pasty; rarely sticky or ropy	Watery and granular; tough skin forms a sac
Odor of dead brood	Slight to pronounced 'dirty sock' odor	Slightly to penetratingly sour	None to slightly sour
Scale characteristics	Uniformly lies flat on lower side of the cell. Adheres tightly to cell wall. Fine, thread-like tongue of dead pupae adheres to cell roof. Head flat.	Usually twisted in cell Does not adhere tightly to cell wall Rubbery	Head prominently curled up. Does not adhere tightly to cell wall Rough texture, brittle

Diseases and Pests and Pennsylvania State Manual AGRS 116, *A Field Guide to Honey Bees and Their Maladies*. Both contain detailed information on how to recognize normal and examine suspect field symptoms.

American foulbrood (AFB)

The most serious brood disease for beekeepers world-wide is American foulbrood (AFB). When not controlled, it will kill an entire colony and be spread to other colonies in the apiary through robbing behavior. AFB is caused by the bacterium *Paenibacillus larvae* (formerly *Bacillus larvae*).

The vegetative or growing stage of AFB infects newborn up to two-day old larvae generally through their feeding. The bacterium is a slender rod, 2.5 to 5 microns in length by 0.5 microns wide that grows vegetatively in the larval gut then escapes to infect the entire larval body causing sepsis and cell death. Larvae do not die until just as the larvae are capped – at this stage infected larvae completely breakdown into a glue-like consistency.

When conditions become unfavorable for the vegetative form, this bacteria forms spores. Spores can survive decades. Spores are oval, approximately twice as long as wide. An estimated 2.5 billion spores exist in the dried remains (termed a scale) of a single larva killed by AFB.

AFB has very distinctive characteristics that assist in its identification (Figures 22-2, 22-3, 22-4). Capped pupal cells are sunken and many have one or more tiny perforations. The capping surface is sunken, appearing wet or greasy (Figure 22-2). The brood pattern, instead of being solid and compact, is spotty (shot-gun appearance) and not uniformly capped (Figures 22-4).

Larvae, dead from AFB, are positioned upright in their cells. With drying, dead larvae tightly adhere to the lower cell wall making them difficult to see or remove. Initially, larvae are an off-white becoming brown deepening to a caramel color with dehydration. They look unhealthy. The decaying odor is very distinctive (Box 54).

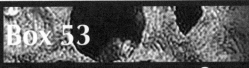

Box 53

BROOD PROBLEM?

Brood diseases attack developing larvae. Symptoms become apparent as larvae grow and as they approach the capped stage. Eggs are not affected; seeing eggs standing upright in their cells is evidence of a normal, queenright colony.

Begin by closely looking at the brood pattern. A spotty brood condition, termed a shotgun pattern, needs a close examination (Figure 22-4). Are there a number of cells that are not occupied by brood? If not brood, what is in the cells? They may be filled with pollen or nectar or they may have an egg or young larva in them. Look closely if you do not see a solid brood pattern.

Color, position, and the lack of normal appearance are key indicators something is wrong. Larvae infected with a disease pathogen appear off-white in color. They may not even resemble larvae once they dry out. They may not be positioned normally in the cell and do not glisten. You may see streaks of yellow or brown coloring.

Diseased brood in the capped stage has darker colored cappings, the cappings appear sunken, and have one or more punctures in them (Figure 20-2). Dead pupae will be tan or brown in color — very different from white, healthy pupae.

Look for all disease symptoms as a spotty brood pattern is not, in itself, confirmation. Spotty brood also appears when colonies reduce the brood area in fall, when bees use emptied brood cells to store honey or pollen, or brood was killed by sudden hot/cold weather, pesticide or toxic nectar.

New queens, or queens without enough empty cells for egg laying, may produce a spotty brood pattern around a more solid central core of brood. Colonies headed by queens of hygienic stock frequently have a spotty appearance as high mite numbers trigger their cell-cleaning behavior, causing bees to clear brood cells of infested pupae.

Never transfer known diseased brood frames to other colonies as this will introduce the disease to healthy colonies. Endeavor to reduce swarming, since swarms take diseases like AFB to their new home site. Bees drifting from one colony to another, as well as robbing behavior (the theft of stored honey by bees from another hive), should also be discouraged and guarded against — these are probable vehicles for AFB and other diseases to be spread horiontally from colony-to-colony.

Figure 22-4
Spotty or irregular brood pattern.

When death does not occur until the pupal stage, a pupal tongue may be visible extending from the remains of the decomposing body on the lower cell wall to the opposite wall. This is a positive diagnostic symptom of AFB but is not always present.

The most distinctive symptomatic characteristics of AFB in the hive are:

- irregular brood pattern (shotgun appearance) with many open cells among capped brood

- perforated, sunken (concave) capped cells, often greasy looking

- larvae have a sickly brown to caramel color, not white and shiny

- dead larvae rope out and snap back (ropy test)

- dehydrated scale tightly adheres to the lower cell wall

- distinctive odor (glue-pot or sulfurous chicken house or decomposition smell of 1000 dirty socks or gym locker long overdue for cleaning)

- pupal tongue may be present

Confirming disease — It is best to obtain confirmation of a diagnosis made on field symptoms. You can take a comb sample and send to the USDA or state laboratory. Such confirmations are usually free-of-charge. A honey-free sample of brood comb containing suspect symptoms, should be wrapped loosely in paper within a cardboard box. Do not enclose in plastic bags, aluminum foil, wax paper, metal or glass since it may promote fungal growth that will complicate confirmation. Include a short description, your diagnosis, name and return address.

Send to:

Bee Disease Diagnosis

Bee Research Laboratory

10300 Baltimore Ave BARC East

Bldg 302 Room 316

Beltsville, MD 20705

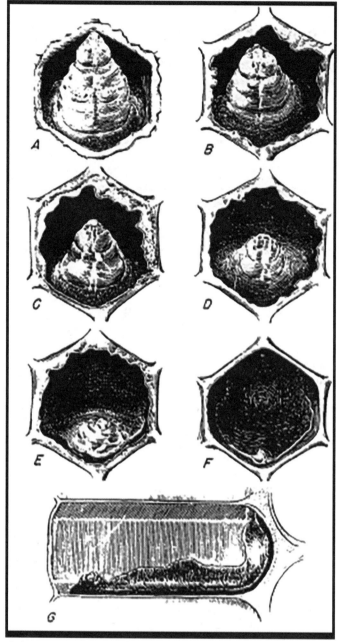

Figure 22-5
Field symptoms of honey bee larvae killed by American foulbrood. A. Healthy larvae at age when most brood dies of AFB; B to E. dead larvae in progressive stages of decomposition; F. top view and G. lateral view of scale. USDA

Larvae that have not fully decomposed have a sticky consistency and cannot be easily removed from the cell. With a toothpick, forceps or sharp stick mix the tissue and pull the remains out of their cell. If they rope out (Figure 22-3) like pulling taffy before snapping back into the cell (**ropy test**), you are likely looking at an AFB death.

With further dehydration of the larva, the dry remains (the **AFB scale**), is distinctive from other dried brood remains (Figures 22-5G). The scale tightly adheres to the lower cell wall, and is nearly impossible to remove.

Additional methods of confirmation include using the Vita Bee Health AFB Diagnostic Kit (Figure 22-6), the Holst Milk test or having a knowledgeable, experienced beekeeper look at the symptoms. If your state has an apiary inspector he or she would be the person to contact. You can check the Apiary Inspectors of America (AIA) website www. apiaryinspectors.org to find their contact information.

American foulbrood control — Treatment of AFB disease is subject to the specific laws of the state, province or country in which the colonies are located. It is the most serious brood disease and infected colonies must be aggressively handled, never dismissed. Because the bacterium forms a spore stage, non-specific treatments are often ineffective.

If inspection shows a few infected larvae, some colonies may survive once the frame with active disease symptoms

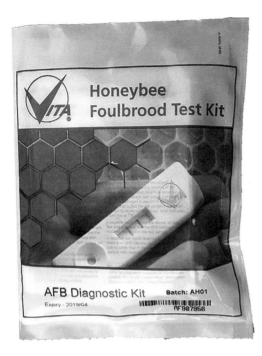

Figure 22-6
AFB diagnostic kit. Vita Bee Health

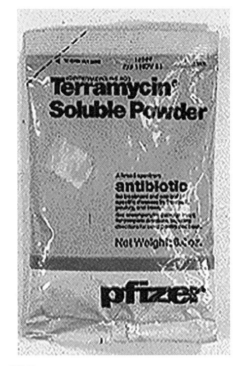

Figure 22-7
Terramycin antibiotic.

is destroyed. This occurs primarily in hygienic strains when the bees are diligent in removing infected larvae before spores are formed. A genetically-controlled behavior, hygienic bees remove larvae with active disease infestations, allowing larvae to outgrow the infectious period so that the colony may survive.

When tested, a surprising percentage of equipment, live colonies and harvested honey test positive for AFB, making their purchase and use without due diligence very risky. Avoid the purchase of used bee equipment, even those stored for a lengthy time period. When a colony dies from AFB, spores remain viable for many decades. If drawn comb is present, it should be carefully examined for dried scale. Before use, boxes, covers and bottom boards should be thoroughly scraped and even scorched with a torch. Frames are of greatest risk; when in doubt discard and replace with new frames and foundation.

Honey extracted from AFB-infested colonies is safe for human consumption but should not be fed to bees. Any honey of unknown origin carries a risk of infecting colonies with AFB.

Terramycin® — The antibiotic oxytetracycline, sold as Terramycin® (Figure 22-7), has been used for many years to treat AFB. Unfortunately, Terramycin does not kill the spores of the disease. It only masks the disease symptoms by killing the vegetative stage. As long as treatment continues, the symptoms do not appear. If treatment stops, colonies containing spores may 'breakdown' into an active AFB infestation. This is a common occurrence when a beekeeper, who has been treating, sells colonies, equipment or nucs; new beekeepers who do not know of previous

medication treatment or who do not continue the treatment may subsequently have a foulbrood problem.

Tylan® — Since the 1990s, AFB has been demonstrated to be resistant to Terramycin, prompting the search for other antibiotic treatments. **Tylan® soluble powder (tylosin tartrate)**, was approved in 2005 for treatment (Figure 22-8). It persists longer than terramycin.

Lincomix Soluble Powder® (lincomycin hydrochloride), was approved in 2012 but is not frequently used. Lincomix and Tylan remain biologically active much longer than oxytetracycline, increasing the risk of contaminating honey. If in doubt, consult an expert or bee inspection service for currently accepted treatment protocols for your area.

A veterinarian must prescribe use or provide a VFD (Vet. Feed Directive) before antibiotics can be purchased.

Burning — If colonies are heavily infected with AFB, the traditional treatment to eliminate the bacterium has been to burn and bury the bees, beeswax combs and equipment that cannot be effectively sanitized (Figure 22-9). Burning kills all stages of AFB, preventing further spread of the pathogen. Care must be taken to prevent robbing of the colony before and following burning since adult bees can pick up the spores and spread the disease. Bees are killed with a soapy water solution or gasoline and burned along with the brood and equipment. The safest way to do this is to dig a pit so remains can be buried following burning.

Some beekeepers attempt to save the adult bee population by shaking them into a cage and holding them without food to purge their system of spores, and then putting them on frames of foundation. A prophylactic Terramycin

Figure 22-8
Tylan for American foulbrood treatment.

treatment should be added when saved bees are rehived and the colony fed sugar syrup. This process is risky as it reduces the efficiency of the treatment. Rehived colonies must be carefully monitored for at last a year to be sure there is no further breakdown of disease.

Burning should be done in the evening, after bee flight ends, to ensure destruction of all bees in the infected

Figure 22-9
Burning AFB-infected beekeeping equipment.

colony. Since there are risks in moving the infested colony, burning is usually done in a pit dug in the apiary, though local burning laws may make this practice illegal. Double bagging dead bees and frames then burying in a landfill is permissible, provided the hives and frames will not become exposed in the future.

If wooden boxes, bottom and covers are not burned they should be thoroughly scraped to remove every trace of wax and propolis. The inner surfaces should then be scorched with a torch or in a fire chimney. If the equipment is in poor physical shape it should be burned or bagged and buried.

Lye bath — Beekeepers equipped to do the job may elect to boil the wooden pieces in a caustic lye bath (10% lye, boil for 20 minutes). Some beekeepers, in lieu of painting, coat the hive boxes, covers and tops in a mixture of paraffin and pine tar. Both materials are hazardous and should be done with proper precautions. Both have some risk of re-infestation.

Ethylene oxide — ETO is a sterilant gas that penetrates and kills the spore stage of AFB, but must be applied using heat and pressure to ensure penetration. Unfortunately, ETO is a known cancer-causing chemical and carries too many risks to allow individual beekeeper use. About a dozen states once approved ETO for treatment of equipment, but few do so today. Honey is not fumigated since ETO is not effective in eliminating AFB spores in honey.

Gamma radiation — Cobalt-60 radiation has shown promise for cleaning used bee equipment and frames of disease pathogen contamination. Imported food and medical equipment radiation facilities are used to treat bee equipment placed inside cardboard boxes or bags.

Regardless of the treatment method, beekeepers are wise to consider this rule of beekeeping: the whole is greater than the sum of its parts. With this in mind, it is wise to accept the loss and thoroughly eliminate the pathogen taking appropriate AFB control measures. Eliminating AFB by burning serves the greater good by protecting local bee populations. Partial efforts will merely extend the number of instances you and others might have to deal with AFB.

Apiary inspection programs

Most beekeeping regions of the world have apiary inspectors whose job it is to inspect bees for infectious diseases, though the enabling legislation varies from one jurisdiction to another. Inspectors do not look at every beehive and even the best-funded programs cannot look at the bee colonies of every beekeeper in their area. A number of states have disease laws on the books but increasingly lack funding to enforce the law or perform colony inspections.

In much of the world, apiary inspectors are veterinarians. In the U.S., inspectors are often biologists and technicians with some beekeeping experience. They are employed by state or county Departments of Agriculture. The only federal bee law in the U.S. forbids importation of bees or bee germ plasm; there is no national law specifically addressing bee diseases.

Apiary inspectors (and their 'helpers' — Box 54) look in beekeeper's colonies for symptoms of disease. State laws permit right of entry to inspect bee colonies, though most will welcome/invite the beekeeper be present during the inspection. Many of the programs have laboratories for confirmation of diseases or mites or they use the service of the USDA Beltsville MD Bee Lab.

Most laws require the destruction of AFB-infected colonies, though the inspectors often will work with the beekeeper to clean up an infestation. At one time the inspector would dig the pit and burn an AFB colony the same night but increasingly regulatory programs require that the beekeeper perform the chore.

Most apiary inspectors provide educational programs, along with their regulatory enforcement, in which they train beekeepers to look for the symptoms of disease. They may enforce other portions of the bee law, such as regulations on apiary site locations or honey house sanitation, though in some locations, a health department performs these duties. Apiary inspectors may certify bees and bee equipment as free of infectious disease for interstate transportation. Most agency inspectors concentrate their inspection efforts with the larger beekeepers.

Contact the **Apiary Inspectors of America (AIA)** or **Canadian Association of Professional Apiculturists (CAPA)** or search the Internet for a copy of your state, provincial or national apiary laws. Get to know the apiary inspector to learn about bee diseases and bee management. Inspectors have extensive experience opening colonies and looking at brood (Figure 22-10). Most welcome questions about bee diseases and management.

Other brood diseases

The remaining brood diseases are less serious than AFB, though field symptoms may be confused with AFB. See Table 22-1 for brood disease comparisons.

European foulbrood (EFB) — EFB is a non-spore-forming bacterial disease caused by the pathogen *Melissococcus plutonius* (formerly *Streptococcus pluton*). Other bacteria show up as the larva decomposes. *M. plutonius* is a short (0.5-0.7 microns by 1.0 micron thick), lancet-shaped bacteria. It infests worker, drone and even queen larvae.

The most typical symptomatic characteristics of EFB (Figures 22-12, 22-13) are:

- kills in larval stage before cell capped
- larva coiled (twisted) or in odd position in cell
- yellow streak of color in larvae which becomes brown over time
- trachea may be prominent in decaying larva

Figure 22-10
Inspecting bees with apiary inspector Don Hopkins of North Carolina.

- dead remains easily removed from cell with tweezers or pointed stick/toothpick
- sour decay odor (different from distinctive AFB odor)
- does not rope out or have pupal tongue as in AFB

Colonies with EFB have been unnecessarily destroyed because of an incorrect diagnosis. While both foulbrood diseases are caused by bacteria, each has different field symptoms. EFB kills younger larvae (Figure 22-13), so it is not detected by merely examining capped cells, which is the usual method of initial detection of AFB. The pupal tongue and ropy test diagnostic of AFB are not seen in EFB. It has a sour odor, different from AFB.

Many consider EFB to be a stress disease often appearing in spring colonies or in colonies moved for pollination. There is a genetic component with some colonies more prone to the disease than others. The snot or cruddy brood condition in Parasitic Mite Brood Syndrome (Box 50, Chapter 21) resembles EFB disease, but lab examination or

Box 54

GOING TO THE DOGS

American foulbrood has a very distinctive odor quite different from a winter-kill colony with decomposing adult bee bodies. Once beekeepers are exposed to the odor, they usually recognize it again. Many apiary inspectors use their noses to search for AFB, but in light infestations, other odors may mask the odor in a bee colony. Dogs with more sensitive noses, like that of Mack and Tukka, were trained to recognize the distinctive AFB smell.

Mack and Tukka work for the Maryland Apiary Inspection Service. They have capably demonstrated that a dog trained to detect the odor of AFB is a practical reality. Dogs have been trained to detect drugs, incendiary devices, environmental contamination sites, animal and plant poaching, insect infestations (such as termites and screwworm flies), human illnesses and AFB.

Mack is a Labrador retriever and Tukka a springer spaniel. Other dog breeds have also been used to detect AFB—a German shepard in Vermont and a beagle in Michigan. The breed influences concentration and work habits—a dog must train easily and have a high degree of reliability. On detection of the AFB odor, the dog receives a food reward (beagles) or a chance to play (Labrador retrievers).

Training is a never-ending requirement, involving providing positive reinforcement to improve detection abilities. Dogs are used only on empty equipment or during the winter because of the risk of stinging around active bees, but take their wages in dog food.

Figure 22-11
Maryland apiary inspector Cyril Preston, with AFB-sniffing dogs Mack (right) and Tukka (left). B. Ostendorf

use of an EFB diagnostic kit (similar to AFB kit Figure 22-5) will not be positive.

In EFB, the dead or dying larva are typically seen in an unusual twisted or coiled position in the cell (Figures 22-13, 22-12D), while AFB larvae are typically in the normal extended position (Figure 22-5 D-G). Dead EFB larvae, even when well desiccated, are relatively easy to remove with a toothpick or wooden match stick (i.e. they fail the ropy test).

Beekeepers sometimes opt to treat EFB infestations with the antibiotic, Terramycin® (Figure 22-7); Tylosin or lincoymcin are not effective medications. In virtually all instances, with or without treatment, bees remove EFB-infected brood and symptoms eventually disappear when seasonal and resource conditions improve. A break in the brood cycle (via requeening, for example), also helps the bees to clear the brood nest area of remaining bacterial contamination. Sugar-syrup feeding can also stimulate the colony to outgrow the disease.

The AFB pathogen produces an antibiotic that eliminates competition from other bacteria. Thus EFB is almost never found in a colony with AFB. Other disease pathogens, discussed below, are not suppressed and may be present. No single infected larva has been found with more than one disease pathogen.

Neglecting to obtain a free or inexpensive laboratory confirmation, especially if you are not familiar with bee diseases, can be a costly mistake. In addition to taking a sample and sending to a lab for confirmation, there are inexpensive field testing kits available for purchase for confirmation of both AFB and EFB diseases (Figure 22-6).

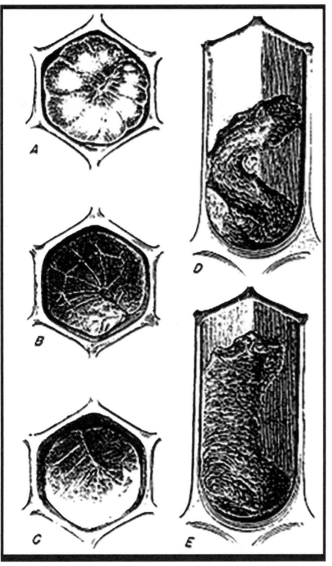

Figure 22-12
Honey bee larvae killed by European foulbrood. A. Healthy larva. B. Discolored larva with visible tracheae. C. One of several twisted positions of sick larvae prior to death. D and E. Longitudinal views of scales from larvae. Dehydrated larval scale is easily removed from its cell. USDA

Chalkbrood

Chalkbrood is an infection caused by the fungus *Ascosphaera apis*. Infected larvae are quickly overgrown by fungal mycelia and swell to fill the cell. Dead larvae look like a small nubbin of chalk, hence the common name.

The dead larvae, called **mummies**, may be off-white in color, marbled black and white or entirely black when spore cysts develop (Figure 22-14). The crusty, chalk-like mummies are found within sealed cells, on the bottom board, and outside the entrance of infested colonies where housecleaning bees have deposited them (Figure 22-15). First reported in the United States in 1972, chalkbrood is now common, quite often found during and after periods

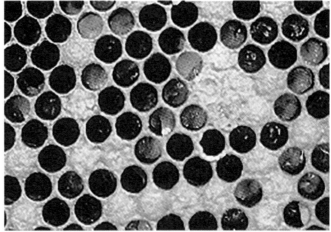

Figure 22-13.
European foulbrood infected larvae.

of cool, damp weather. It may also be seen in colonies used to trap pollen or colonies being fed contaminated pollen supplements. Chalkbrood does not usually kill a bee colony, even in heavy infestations, but will weaken them and slow buildup. Some bee stocks are more susceptible to this disease than others.

There is no treatment to control chalkbrood. Requeening, increasing ventilation of the brood chamber, siting colonies in sunny exposed locations, stimulative sugar syrup feeding and replacing old comb with new are sometimes effective deterrents to chalkbrood. As with EFB, colonies with chalkbrood during the spring often lack symptoms

Figure 22-14
Chalkbrood mummies on screen bottom board. L. Connor

Figure 22-15
Chalkbrood mummies on landing board at colony entrance. R. Synder

of the disease later in the season when weather and forage conditions improve.

A note of caution: if bees are fed a pollen supplement, be certain the colonies used to collect the pollen are free of chalkbrood. Chalkbrood mummies are collected in the pollen traps, and even as small, chewed pieces, infect other colonies when such trapped pollen is fed to them.

Another fungal brood disease, **stonebrood** (*Aspergillus flavus* and *A. fumigatus*) is rare. It also results in mummification of infected larvae, turning the larvae hard (difficult to crush) and black. Remedies are the same as for chalkbrood. Incidentally, this causative agent is used to produce the antibiotic fumagillin which is used to treat nosema disease in adult bees.

Bee viruses

Viruses are microscopic organisms that consist of genetic material (RNA or DNA) contained in a protein coat. They are the ultimate parasites. Our knowledge of the occurrence of viruses and their effects on bees is in its infancy. Some 20+ different viruses have been identified, but others will likely be discovered. It is not surprising that the helpless larval brood stage and social condition of a bee colony are ideal for several harmful viruses.

Sacbrood virus (SBV) is probably the best known of the brood bee viruses. It is caused by the virus *Morator aetatulas*. Sacbrood can be considered the bee equivalent to the common cold in humans. Adult nurse bees clean out infected brood cells and, in turn, contact the virus. Infected larvae die just before pupation. Dead brood are positioned upright in the cell, their bodies are dark white, grey, or brownish-black with the outermost portion (head) darker than the rest of the body (Figure 22-16). The dead, sac-like, leathery skinned larva is easily removed from the cell.

Infestations seen in the fall or spring disappear during the summer months. Since some colonies and locations exhibit more pronounced infestations, requeening or moving colonies may help reduce disease symptoms. There are no effective medications or treatments for sacbrood. Adults with the disease are symptomless.

Black queen cell virus (BQCV) kills capped queen larvae and prepupae (Figure 22-17). The infected larvae look like the sacbrood-infected workers with a tough, leathery, sac-like appearance that, over time, turns black. Capped cells containing infected prepupa are darker in color. It seems to have some commonality with nosema disease. At present there is no control other than requeening with different stock and perhaps improved nosema control.

Kashmir bee virus (KBV) and **acute bee paralysis virus (ABPV)**, two additional viruses found infesting brood, are both commonly noted with **Colony Collapse Disorder (CCD)** and believed to be transmitted by varroa mites. Symptoms are not especially distinctive in brood; adults with the viruses appear trembling and disoriented in front of an infested hive.

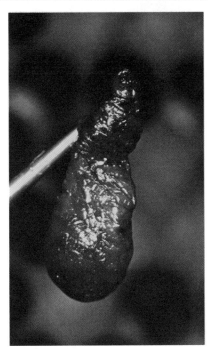

Figure 22-16
Sacbrood.
R. Williamson

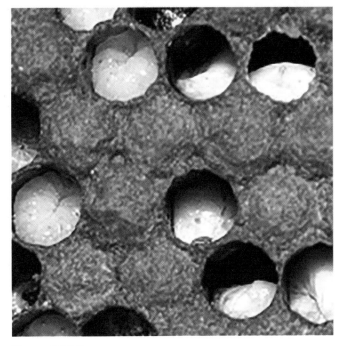

Figure 22-18
Idiopathic brood disease syndrome or IBDS, is found in colonies with rapidly declining adult bee populations. Often confused with European foulbrood. R. Snyder

Figure 22-17
Black queen cell virus (BQCV) kills queens in the sealed brood stage. R. Snyder

Idiopathic Brood disease syndrome (IBDS) — A continuing study of colony health of commercial beekeeper colonies found that a little-understood brood disease syndrome, labeled idiopathic brood disease syndrome or IBDS, is, along with colony queen replacement events, the largest risk factor for predicting the death of a bee colony (over 50% of colonies in the study did not survive a beekeeper season). IBDS is found in colonies with rapidly declining adult bees, a syndrome called Parasitic Mite Brood Syndrome (PMBS) (Chapter 21 Box 50). It is characterized by a high percentage of larval death in colonies where varroa mite levels and viruses are at lower than predicted levels.

Dead brood with IBDS was described as gooey, off-white, molten to the bottom of their cells. **Snot brood or crud/ cruddy brood** are other terms for the decomposing larvae (Figure 22-18).

Adult diseases

Most adult bee diseases are difficult to diagnose in the field since their symptoms resemble one another, and can even resemble non-disease factors that cause adult mortality

such as old age or insecticide poisoning. Little can be done to remedy most adult disease conditions, but their identification remains an important part of beekeeping practice.

Nosema — Nosemosis is the most serious of adult diseases. Nosema is a disease caused by a microsporidian, a type of fungus once considered a protozoan. There are two species of nosema in honey bees; the species *Nosema apis* has largely been replaced by *Nosema ceranae*. They are difficult to tell apart without advanced laboratory capability.

Spores of this single-celled organism are large, oval bodies, 4 to 6 microns long by 2-4 microns thick (Figure 22-20). The pathogen is found only within the epithelial cells lining the digestive tract midgut in adult bees. Infested bees show swollen midguts. The pathogen populations build up when bees are confined or stressed — as during winter confinement or when bees are shipped in a package. It is the most widespread of all bee diseases.

Symptoms of nosema are subtle. Nosema indicators include crawling, disoriented bees, K-wing adults (Figure 22-23), defensive bees, bees abandoning the brood to cluster elsewhere in the overwintering colony and colonies not consuming supplemental feed offered. Upon dissection, the midgut of heavily infested bees appears swollen, creamy-white in color, with less evident constrictions (Figure 22-19).

One of the *Nosema apis* symptoms is heavy concentrations of **bee feces** spotting hives, at hive entrances (Figure 22-21), on top bars, or on inner hive walls — this is not seen with *Nosema ceranae*. **Dysentery** is also found without

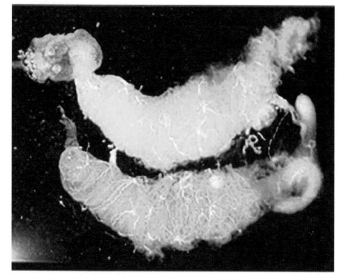

Figure 22-19
Nosema infected midgut above and normal below. Z. Huang

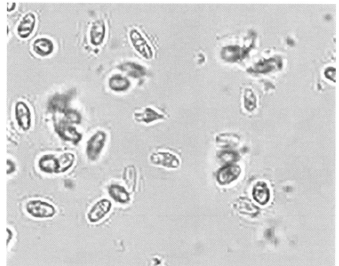

Figure 22-20
Nosema spores 400X.

nosema spores and has been linked to poor quality food stores and prolonged confinement in which the bees are unable to exit their hive.

To diagnose nosema, confirm the presence of spores with a microscope with 400X power (Figure 22-20). One method is to collect 25 bees from the colony entrance and squash them in a plastic bag with a rolling pin, adding 25 ml of water and examine the liquid under a microscope. Spores will be easier to view with the high-dry objective (400X) of a compound microscope. Independent bee researcher and journal author Randy Oliver (Figure 22-22) has excellent information on nosema sampling methods published in articles and on his website www.scientificbeekeeping.com.

Nosema can only be confirmed by examining adult bees. Limited surveys of nosema disease show that it is present in 50% or more of colonies sampled. Sampling methods that look only for spores may underestimate the actual pathogen incidence. Individual sick bees may have up to 30 million spores within the cells of their digestive tract. Bee colonies with heavy infestations show the following characteristics:

- crawling, disoriented bees outside colony, some with K-wing

- worker life span 20 to 50% shorter (begin foraging at younger age—precocious foragers)

- nurse bees have smaller hypopharyngeal glands and slower gland development

- produce less brood food and rear less brood

- higher supersedure rate

- heavier winter loss with poorer clustering, reduced food utilization v honey production reductions of up to 50%

Figure 22-21
Fecal spotting on the front of the hive. Z. Huang

Nosema treatment—Good apiary sites in sunny locations with winter protection are desirable, as is reducing stress on colonies. Young queens and comb rotation seem to help too. Preventive feeding of the drug **bicyclohexylammonium**, common name **fumagillin**, currently sold as **Fumidil-B®** has traditionally been advised but new data suggests the antibiotic may foster *N. ceranae* infections and make the condition worse.

The standard recommendation is to mix fumagillin in heavy syrup and feed colonies in the fall. If the bees do not take the syrup, try spraying it directly on the bees, when warm enough, to ensure ingestion of the compound. For the newer species, *Nosema ceranae*, the most effective drug treatment is still being determined. Treatment with fumagillin in spring and again after the honey harvest may be a more effective application timing with *N. ceranae*.

Nozevit, a natural product made from an oak bark extract, is sold for nosema control, but effectiveness data are not available. Essential oils may have limited control possibility and several of the additives, including Honey-B-Healthy, claim nosema control. Data are limited; they are not registered as antibiotics.

Adult virus diseases

While there are several important virus diseases of adult bees, studies of all the viruses that affect them are new. Varroa, and perhaps tracheal mites, are vectors of viruses or may facilitate pathogen entry into the honey bee host by creating feeding sites to allow viruses to enter the bee. Nurse bees, cleaning up dead brood, are known to spread viruses within a colony.

Figure 22-23
Deformed wing virus (DWV on left) and K-wing on right.

Adult bees may have sacbrood virus (SBV), better known in bee larvae than among adult bees. The virus is spread when an infected forager regurgitates nectar onto pollen being collected during flower visits. When stored, this pollen infects nurse bees that transfer the virus to larvae.

Three closely related viruses, transmitted by varroa mites, are Israeli acute paralysis virus (IAPV), acute bee paralysis virus (ABPV) and Kashmir bee virus (KBV); they also occur in larvae. All three viruses, in any combination, are frequently seen with colony collapse disorder (CCD) and high varroa mite numbers. They seem to be capable of rapid proliferation before subsiding just as rapidly. Higher viral levels in adults cause great harm to colonies including death.

Two viruses, apparently found only in adult bees, are chronic bee paralysis virus (CBPV) and deformed wing virus (DWV). Deformed wing virus is sometimes divided into A and B variants; The DWV B is also named Varroa

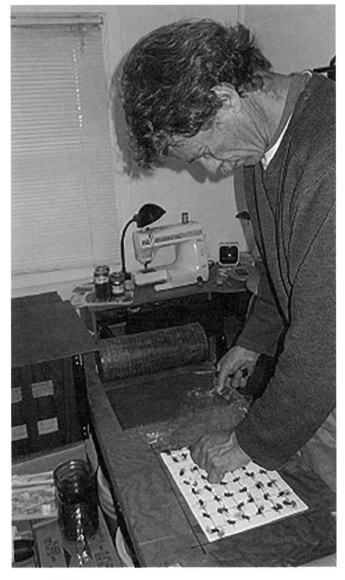

Figure 22-22
Randy Oliver crushing bees for nosema sampling.

Figure 22-24
Chronic bee paralysis virus (CBPV) is also called hairless black syndrome.

Figure 22-25
Deformed wing virus. DWV

destructor virus (VDV). CBPV presents as crawling and trembling bees at front of the hive unable to fly. They may have bloated abdomens.

A second expression of Chronic Bee Paralysis virus (type 2) is the condition called hairless black syndrome. Adult bees with CBPV lose body hairs and appear greasy (shiny) black Figure 22-24). Infected bees are driven from the hive and may be found struggling close to its entrance. Both CBPV types may occur in the same colony.

Deformed wing virus appeared in the United States after varroa mites began killing large numbers of colonies in the early 1990s. Its distinctive symptom, present in emerging adult workers, is stunted, twisted and otherwise deformed wings (Figure 22-25). The bees are underweight, discolored, and unhealthy looking, living only a few days. Their wings never become functional, and they are not effective as worker bees. DWV deformed wings are easily distinguished from K-wing symptoms.

Figure 22-26
Familiarity with healthy bees and brood are the foundation for early recognition of disease symptoms in the hive. P. Stromberg

DWV infected drones are also seen. Colonies exhibiting the symptoms of deformed wings often subsequently collapse. As varroa mites are the vectors for virus transmission, varroa mite control is key to DWV prevention.

More recent viruses are Lake Sinai viruses (LSV); several types have been found named LSV1, LSV2, etc. LSV1 and LSV2 are often one of the more common viruses found in bees. They appear in both weak and strong colonies and among migratory colonies often in association with Nosema and CCD. They do not have distinguishing characteristics.

Other adult diseases

In addition to the significant pathogens of nosema and viruses, there are other adult maladies but they are rarer. Some adult bees are found with unusually high numbers of amoeba (a protozoan) in the Malpighian tubules, the significance of which is presently unclear. Another adult malady is the bacterial infection called septicemia, caused by the bacteria *Pseudomonas apiseptica*. This, not the bacterial disease, causes breakdown of connective tissue inside the adult body. Adult bees dead from septicemia pull apart easily and have a putrid odor.

key terms

acute bee paralysis virus (ABPV)

AFB/EFB Test kit (Vita Bee Health)

ambush bugs/flies

American foulbrood (AFB)

amoeba

amphibians (frogs/toads/snakes)

apiary inspector

Apiary Inspectors of America (AIA)

Asian hornet (*Vespa velutina*)

Bacillus thuringiensis (Bt) Certan®

badgers

bears (brown/black)

bee eaters (*Merops* spp.)

birds (mockingbirds, swifts, kingbirds and thrushes)

black queen cell virus (BQCV)

Braula coeca (fly)

burning (AFB)

California buckeye

Canadian Association of Professional Apiculturists (CAPA)

chalkbrood

chilled brood

clandestine/stealth beekeeping

chlorinated hydrocarbons (DDT, Chlordane)

chronic bee paralysis virus (CBPV)

Coleoptera

cockroaches

deformed wing virus (DWV)

Diptera (flies) / predacious and scavenger

dragonflies

dried fruit moth

earwigs

electric bear fence

entrance reducers

ethylene oxide (ETO)

European foulbrood (EFB)

European hornet (*Vespa crabro*)

Fumagillin (fumidil-B)

fungicides

gamma radiation

giant marine toad

herbicides

Holst milk test

honeyguides (*Indicator* spp)

human vandalism/stealing beehives

Hymenoptera (ants/wasps/bees)

idiopathic Brood disease syndrome (IBDS)

Indian meal moth

inert pesticide ingredients

insect growth regulator (IGR)

Israeli acute paralysis virus (IAPV)

Kashmir bee virus (KBV)

larva(e)

Lincomycin (Lincomix)

lye bath

Mediterranean flour moth

mice

microencapsulated pesticide

Murder hornet (*Vespa mandarinia*)

naphthalene

neonicotinoid pesticide

Nosema

nosemosis

nozevit

organophophates (Chorpyrifos)

Paenibacillus larvae (AFB)

paradichlorobenzene (PDB) (Para Moth®)

parasitic Mite Brood Syndrome (PMBS)

Paris green pesticide

Pesticides/insecticides/herbicides

psocids

psuedoscorpion

pupa(e)

pupal tongue

ratel

robber flies

rodents

ropy test

sacbrood (SBV)

scale (AFB)

scavenger insects/mites

septicemia

Sevin insecticide

shrews/moles

skunk

small hive beetle (*Aethina tumida*)

spiders (crab and or-web weaver)

spotty brood pattern

spring- bristle-tails

starving brood

stonebrood

synergistic

systemic pesticide

termites

Terramycin (oxytetracycline)

Tropilaelaps mite

Tylan (tylosin tartrate)

USDA Bee Lab Beltsville

Varroa destructor virus (VDV)

Vita Bee Health Diagnostic kit

wax moth (greater & lesser)

woodpeckers

yellowjackets (*Vespula* spp)

zombie fly

discussion questions

What factors make AFB is the most serious bee disease? Why do we recommend that bees and frames in a colony with AFB be burned and buried? Why however is a colony with AFB more frequently treated with an antibiotic?

What are the other bee brood diseases and how do you recognize them? Since the other diseases are not as serious, should we even bother learning their symptoms?

How might you recognize nosema, the adult disease? What are probably reasons nosema is less serious than previously considered?

Brood and adult bees have a number of viruses. How can you recognize there might be a virus in your bees? What are controls for viral infections?

Describe the inter-relationships between virus, varroa mites and the syndromes of CCD and PMBS.

How should information about bee diseases best be conveyed to the new beginning beekeeper?

exercises

Determine the status of Apiary inspection for your state/province.

Examine adult bees for mites and nosema; check brood for diseases. Describe typical field symptoms and how you would confirm the existence of a disease pathogen in the laboratory.

Make sketches or take photographs of healthy and diseased bees and brood. Seek to verify/confirm disease symptom or mite identification.

There are a good number of Internet resources available to view brood and adult diseases (photos/videos/forums) but their quality/ usefulness varies widely. Look at and learn more about diseases using these aids. Provide a ranking on usefulness to beginners and more experienced/advanced beekeepers.

Determine if it would be possible to accompany an apiary inspector while he/she inspects colonies in your area. If not feasible, ask to interview the apiary inspector or if none in your area seek a beekeeper in your area who has had issues with diseases. Prepare a written or oral report on life of a bee inspector.

Accumulate literature available from extension or apiary inspection programs in your state/province, and neighboring areas where conditions are similar on recognition and control of bee diseases.

references

AIA https://apiaryinspectors.org/

BIP Diagnosis and Treatment of Honey Bee Disease. 2019 rev. Bee Informed Partnership. Univ. of Maryland

Burnham, A. 2019. Scientific Advances in Controlling Nosema ceranae (Microsporidia) Infections in Honey Bees (Apis mellifera). Front. Vet Sci 15: https://doi.org/10.3389/fvets.2019.00079

CAPA. 2015. Honey Bee Diseases and Pests. 3rd S. Pernal and Heather Clay Ed. CAPA Beaverlodge, AR

Frazier, M. et al. 2015. Rev. Field guide to honey bee maladies. Penn State Ext AGRS 116.

Moore, P.A. et al. 2014. Honey Bee Viruses, the Deadly Varroa Mite Associates http://www.extension.org/pages/71172/honey-bee-viruses-the-deadly-varroa-mite-associates#.VbgmtLBFBjo

Morse, R.A. and K. Flottum, Eds. 2013. Honey bee Pests Predators and Disease. Northern bee Books, West Yorkshire, UK

Pettis, J.S. et al. 2015. Diseases and Pests of Honey Bees. Chap 27 in The Hive and the Honey Bee. Joe Graham Ed. Dadant and Sons, Hamilton, IL

Stamets, P.E. et al. 2018. Extracts of Polypore Mushroom Mycelia Reduce Viruses in Honey Bees. Scientific Reports 8 #13936.

vanEngelsdorp, D. et al. 2013. Idiopathic brood disease syndrome and queen events as precursors of colony mortality in migratory beekeeping operations in the Eastern United States. Preventive Veterinary Medicine 108:225-233.

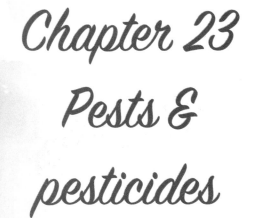

Chapter 23
Pests &
pesticides

Figure 23-1
Wax moth larva on comb. L. Connor

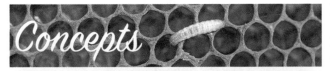

Concepts

Pests
   wax moth
   small hive beetle

Pesticides

Newest developments

Pollen or nectar toxic to bees

Pests

The bee colony has many pests and predators that attack adult honey bees, bee brood stages, materials stored in the hive, and even the hive itself. Major predators are other social insects like ants, wasps and other colony bees plus termites that attack colony domiciles. Some organisms simply use the hive as a place to live or as a shelter for their own young and nesting purposes. Others do harm by feeding on honey, pollen, brood remains or beeswax.

Pesticides have the potential to cause harm to bee colonies. Some beekeepers use a pesticide or antibiotic to control a pest or disease. Their use will continue to expand as we determine how bees can coexist with evolving pesticide use in agriculture and public health.

Mimics of pests and diseases complicate diagnosis. Some of these will be covered at the end of this chapter.

Insects — Insects are the most common life form on Earth. Many insects live and feed on adult honey bees and brood (dead or alive), honey and pollen, or live in the hive itself. Uncommon insects like springtails and bristletails, earwigs (Figure 23-2) and psocids (booklice) merely live inside the hive, feeding on debris or dead bodies and do no apparent harm. Cockroaches are harmless hive residents too.

Outside the hive, foraging workers are eaten by insects like larger bodied dragonflies, praying mantids and a host of predacious flies and bugs. In some special circumstances, such predators may reduce foraging numbers. Predatory insects feeding on queens captured on their nuptial flights are of special concern. Attacking hornets and yellow jacket wasps in the fall can weaken colony populations prior to the critical overwintering period.

Dead adult and brood bodies in front of the hive entrance and on the hive bottom board may attract a large number of different scavenger insects. Flies, beetles and insect

Figure 23-2
Earwig. Joseph Berger, Bugwood.org

relatives (such as mites and spiders) are among the most common. None are serious pests; few of these insects remain inside the hive unless the colony is very weak or dying.

Termites are a global pest of wooden hive equipment. In tropical and subtropical areas, it is not possible to maintain unprotected hives free of termite attack (Figure 23-3). Mud tunnels may be evident but may be concealed on the inside of the wooden hive bodies.

Breaking wood-to-ground contact and protecting hive stands and bottom boards with wood preservatives offers some protection from termites. Hives need be off the ground. Use a grease or oil barrier between the ground and the hive itself or suspend the hive above soil and vegetation contact (Figure 23-5). In regions of heavy termite pressure, non-wooden materials are used for hive stands. Some opt for cement bottom stands and even cement brood chamber boxes (Figure 23-4). Plastic hive equipment is another option.

Beetles (Order Coleoptera), the most common type of insect, may be found living in hives or around bees, especially dead brood or adult bodies. Most beetles are not pests but important recyclers of organic matter.

The **small hive beetle** (see below), once only found in Africa, was transported to the southeastern United States by 1998 and causes complete colony loss. It requires careful watching during hot, humid conditions.

Flies (Order Diptera) are seen in and around beehives. Many, like fruit flies, are attracted to sweet hive odors, especially fermenting honey, or to dead, rotting bees. Other flies, such as the **zombie (phorid) fly** parasitizes the adult workers. Predacious flies, such as **robber (ambush) flies** (Figure 23-6) capture foragers outside the hive and suck their body juices dry. Where populous, robber flies can be locally harmful to colonies.

Figure 23-3
Termite tubes on wooden hive bodies extend from ground outside cement blocks and metal hive stand.

Figure 23-4
Concrete bottom board and brood box.

Figure 23-5
Bee colonies on steel reinforcing bar hive stands with their legs in cans filled with motor oil designed to keep ants from entering. The lack of vegetation is another deterrent.

A wingless fly called the **bee louse** (*Braula coeca*), lives on the body of workers and queens (Chapter 21, Figure 21-11). Superficially, it may be confused with varroa mites but, unlike varroa, is usually harmless. Curiously, though they cluster onto queen bees; attendant workers who continually groom the queen's body do not remove the flies. With heavy use of pesticides for mite control, this fly is less commonly seen.

The zombie fly (*Apocephalus borealis*), deposits eggs into the body of an adult bee where they feed. When ready to pupate they exit the bee at the junction of head and thorax, decapitating their host. Up to 15 maggots may emerge from a single worker.

These flies were discovered by collecting dead bees attracted to lights near colonies. To see if you have "Zombees" collect dead bees seen below night lighting and put them into a screened container to watch for maggots emerging from the bee body to confirm their presence. There is no control.

Ants, hornets and wasps, of Order Hymenoptera may be serious pests of honey bees in some localities (Chapter 3). Ants are probably the most common bee pests; they nest in beehives and feed on honey. A few, like army and harvester ants, invade a colony and feed on brood, honey and adults that do not fly away. Tropical beekeepers often need to create barriers to nighttime ant entry (Figure 23-5) locating hives off the ground and using motor oil and grease around hive stands. Use of an insecticide for ant pest control has potential to harm the bees and contaminate the comb and honey.

Figure 23-6
Predacious robber (ambush) fly with prey.

Several hornets are bee pests. The largest species is the **Asian giant hornet (AGH)** *Vespa mandarinia*, or sometimes the **Japanese giant hornet** — media call it the murder hornet. Adults are two inches (5 cm) long (Figure 23-7). In Japan, beekeepers place traps at the colony entrance to keep the hornet from invading a colony; unprotected colonies may be completely destroyed.

Despite efforts to keep it within its normal range of temperate and tropical East Asia, in 2019 a nest and additional specimens were discovered in British Columbia (Vancouver area). In 2020, specimens were found in traps and a nest was located in northern Washington State. Efforts are underway to eradicate or at least contain its spread. Washington Department of Agriculture and Washington State University extension

Figure 23-7
AGH, the Asian giant hornet, called the murder hornet.

Figure 23-8
Yellowjacket adult on fruit.

Figure 23-10
Early stage (instar) wax moth. L. Connor

The **European hornet**, *Vespa crabro*, the initial 'true' hornet to be introduced into the U.S., is a pest in the eastern U.S. and is spreading into the Midwest (Chapter 3, Figure 3-14).

Hornet cousins, the widespread **yellowjackets** (Figure 23-8) are serious scavenger pests. They invade colonies to steal honey and feast on dead and dying adults Additionally, they interfere with fruit pickers and are a menace at outdoor restaurants, picnics or food events.

Yellowjacket control is difficult. Eliminating yellowjacket ground nests in the immediate vicinity of the hive may provide some relief. Beekeepers in the Pacific Northwest (Oregon, Washington and Idaho) use yellow jacket traps season-long in an attempt to reduce wasp numbers (Figure 23-9, Chapter 14 Figure 14-9). This might result in impressive catches, but trapping may not significantly reduce their predation, even at densities of one trap per colony. As in case for their larger cousins, the hornets, adding robber screens (Chapter 13, Figure 13-35) or reducing entrance size (Chapter 14, Figure 14-11) permits more effective entrance guarding by bees.

Wax moth

Traditionally, the most serious insect pest of bee colonies has been the **wax moth**. It occurs worldwide thriving in warmer regions. It attacks all *Apis* species' nests. The most destructive wax moth species is the greater wax moth, *Galleria mellonella*. Several other moths, such as the **lesser wax moth**, *Achroia grisella*; **dried-fruit moth**, *Vitula edmandsae* (in western U.S. *Vitula serratilineela*); the **Indian meal moth**, *Plodia interpunctella*; and **Mediterranean flour moth**, *Agnagasta kuehniella* are occasionally serious. The last two species are a major problem for beekeepers trapping pollen. Beekeeper losses due to moths exceed several million dollars annually.

Caterpillars of the greater wax moth (Figure 23-10) feed on beeswax combs, cast larval skins, pollen and honey. They can quickly reduce drawn brood comb to webbing

Figure 23-9
Yellowjacket trap. K. Ograin

provide excellent information on the AGH as an emerging North American pest.

An introduced **Asian hornet (***Vespa velutina)*** species, also known as the **yellow-legged hornet,** is spreading in France, Spain, Portugal and to Belgium and England. It is of concern to beekeepers in this region.

Both wasp species hover in front of bee colony entrances to grab and kill returning foragers; hive bees gather just outside their entrance reducing their flight from their colony when hovering wasps are present. The Asian Giant Hornet will even enter colonies, killing as many workers as it can and then afterwards cleans up the dead bodies. Both hornets feed on honey stomachs of bees and the thoracic wing muscles.

Figure 23-11
Greater wax moth larvae in webbing on drawn comb.

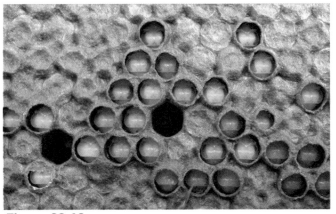

Figure 23-12
Bald brood (galleriasis). A. Mortensen, UFL.

and debris (Figure 23-11). They uncommonly tunnel in honey storage combs but can render comb honey unattractive if they tunnel beneath the cappings. As a scavenger, they can quickly reduce the beehive's most valuable asset, drawn beeswax combs, to total waste under the right temperature and humidity conditions.

A condition called **galleriasis** occurs when normal worker and drone bees are trapped inside their cell and are unable to emerge because they are webbed in by the silk produced by the wax moth. If the bee is removed, one or more wax moth larvae will be found at the base of the cell. When adult bees uncap adjacent cells apparently looking for the caterpillar to remove it creates a condition termed **bald brood** (Figure 23-12). It may resemble the uncapped brood that is seen in hygienic bees as they uncap cells to look for varroa mite, but with wax moth the uncapped cells are contiguous. Also, with the hygienic trait, the bees may be chewing both the comb and the bees themselves as they clean the cells.

Wax moths don't kill a colony. The usual scenario is that adult wax moth females find dying or weakened colonies, those with more comb than they can effectively protect, in which to lay their eggs. The weakened colony does not remove the caterpillars as normally occurs in strong, healthy colonies, and the caterpillars grow quickly, causing noticeable damage. Stored drawn brood comb, unless protected in storage, can quickly be reduced to debris. Honey storage comb offers no food for wax moths so it does not need to be protected in storage. Frames from dead colonies that have been used to rear brood or which contain stored pollen are especially attractive to the caterpillars since both provide the protein the caterpillars need to grow.

Wax moth control

In healthy colonies, the bees remove the caterpillars if they can access them. The best control for wax moth is to keep colonies strong and limit the amount of drawn comb in the colony to an amount that the bees can patrol.

Drawn comb in storage must be protected from wax moths. In the coldest months, freezing temperatures halt caterpillar development—thus storage of drawn comb in a freezer is very effective. Carbon dioxide fumigation, heat, and freezing temperatures each kill wax moths. For honey harvested in the comb, only CO_2 fumigation or freezing are acceptable. Freezing works best for empty brood comb.

Wax moths have some diseases and enemies that have been studied as possible wax moth biocontrol. Wax moths have a wasp parasite and a viral disease. A **bacterial control** (*Bacillus thuringiensis*) **Certan®** is an effective biological control weapon.

One interesting biocontrol used by beekeepers in the southern United States is placing boxes of combs infested with wax moth on the mounds of fire ants for a day or two. The ants quickly clean the infestation, feeding on wax moth caterpillars, eggs and pupae. They will also clean comb of other debris they can consume.

One material permitted for control of the wax moth is the chemical insecticide **paradichlorobenzene or PDB (Para Moth®)**. It is used to fumigate closed stacks of hive bodies with frames of drawn brood comb. PDB fumes kill all stages of the wax moth, except eggs, so continuous fumigation is needed if ambient temperature permits flight and re-infestation. Possibly carcinogenic, its use is being discouraged as detectable PDB residues lingers in beeswax.

A similar product, moth flakes containing the insecticide naphthalene, should never be substituted for PDB. It is deadly to bees.

Not everyone considers the wax moth a pest. It can be reared on an artificial diet and used by fishermen to catch fish, to feed birds and reptiles and is a common lab dissection insect in biology and entomology classes. Interestingly, the wax moth does not need wax for growth and development—in fact, it starves on a pure beeswax diet. It has been shown to digest polyethylene plastic.

Small hive beetle (SHB)

The **small hive beetle**, *Aethina tumida* (adult, Figure 23-13; larvae, Figure 23-14) is an aggressive and destructive scavenger pest of honey bee colonies and their comb. Adult beetles enter colonies and lay their eggs in cracks and crevices. Small hive beetle larvae develop in 7 to 10 days. Larvae leave the hive to pupate outside in the soil (Life cycle shown in Figure 23-15).

Once in the hive, adult beetles are difficult for bees to remove; the worker bees seek to imprison them in propolis chambers. If a beetle infestation is sufficiently heavy, beetle larvae rapidly become numerous. The larvae tunnel through combs of honey, feeding and defecating, creating slime, discoloration and fermentation in cells of honey. The fermenting honey and slime has the characteristic odor of decaying oranges. The slime and discoloration may even be seen staining the outside of the hive boxes.

Small hive beetles are attracted to pollen patties for supplemental food and even grease patties for tracheal mite control. Since these protein additives, frequently with sugar/honey, are commonly used on smaller colonies like mating nuclei, they may quickly become a beetle breeding ground to intensify the pressure on a colony.

Beetle attacks and the slime they produce cause bees to abandon their hive, leaving the comb unprotected. In addition to attacking living but weakened colonies, the beetles are also a pest of both stored comb and honey (in the comb) awaiting extraction. Honey runs out of comb, creating a mess in storage and extracting facilities. If any frames of honey for extracting contain brood, the deterioration is accelerated.

Although readily distributed with colony movement, small hive beetles are a major problem mainly along the U.S. eastern seaboard. Heavy organic, slowly draining soils, in contrast to lighter sandy soils, deter SHB life cycle. It is unknown why they have not become a more serious bee hive pest in the southwestern U.S. (where soils seemingly would be favorable) or along the West coast.

Small hive beetle control

The most effective control against the small hive beetle is maintaining colony strength. Colonies should have only the amount of comb and empty frames they can patrol. Careful use and monitoring of supplemental protein is necessary. To protect small colonies (such as nucs), a beetle trap can be used. There are several **beetle traps** on the market that use nontoxic mineral oil to suffocate the beetles (Figure 23-16). A floor **cleaning pad**, Swiffer® can be put beneath the inner cover to entangle adult beetles in the fabric. It needs to be periodically removed and discarded.

One chemical, **coumaphos**, originally used for varroa mites, will kill beetles but is not favored (Chapter 21) as it is absorbed by beeswax. Some prefer to treat the soil around the apiary with **Gardstar®** to poison beetles when they exit the hive to pupate. Do not use inside the hive. Various ground coverings have been tried to keep the larvae from reaching suitable soil to pupate, but without success.

Honey house sanitation is a must where beetle pressure is high. Empty drawn and honey-filled frames may be stored in a humidity controlled area. Giant dehumidifiers are used in Hawaii and other areas to reduce egg hatching and larval development. Relative humidity must be maintained below 50% to achieve this goal. Empty drawn comb that has been used to rear brood is highly attractive to beetles, and when possible, cold storage is an excellent protective measure; paradichlorobenzene fumigation is also effective.

Spiders, mites and ticks

Spiders, mites and ticks feed both inside (jumping spider) and outside the hive (**crab spiders or orb web weavers**, Figure 23-17), live on the bees (varroa and tracheal mites, covered in Chapter 21) or in hive debris (a host of other mite species). One

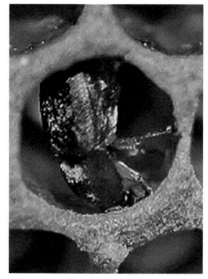

Figure 23-13
Small hive beetle in a worker cell. L. Connor

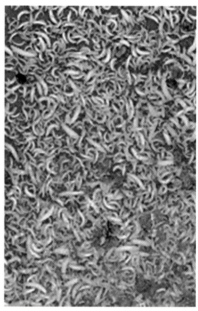

Figure 23-14
Small hive beetle larvae in cooking oil in a trap placed below a colony of bees in Hawaii. L. Connor

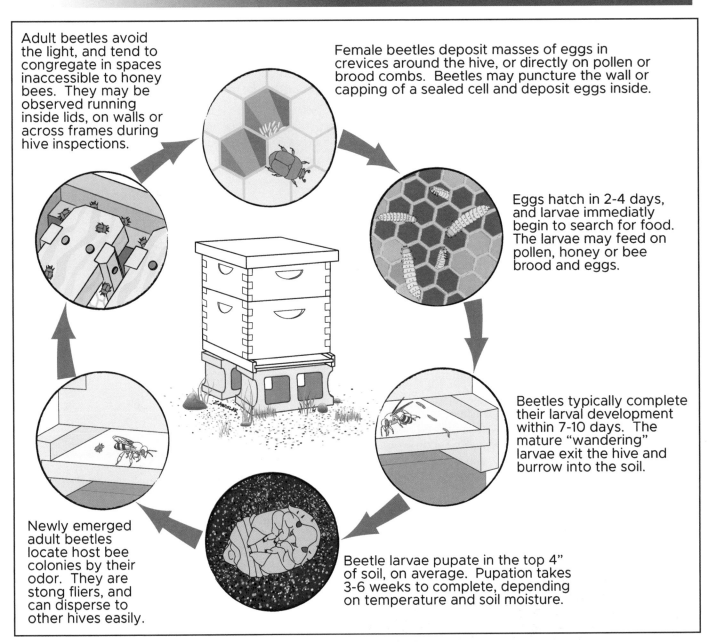

Adult beetles avoid the light, and tend to congregate in spaces inaccessible to honey bees. They may be observed running inside lids, on walls or across frames during hive inspections.

Female beetles deposit masses of eggs in crevices around the hive, or directly on pollen or brood combs. Beetles may puncture the wall or capping of a sealed cell and deposit eggs inside.

Eggs hatch in 2-4 days, and larvae immediatly begin to search for food. The larvae may feed on pollen, honey or bee brood and eggs.

Beetles typically complete their larval development within 7-10 days. The mature "wandering" larvae exit the hive and burrow into the soil.

Beetle larvae pupate in the top 4" of soil, on average. Pupation takes 3-6 weeks to complete, depending on temperature and soil moisture.

Newly emerged adult beetles locate host bee colonies by their odor. They are stong fliers, and can disperse to other hives easily.

Figure 23-15
Life cycle of small hive beetle (SHB). J. Zawislak

Figure 23-16
Several beetle traps are on the market that use nontoxic mineral oil to suffocate the beetles.

uncommon insect-relative and hive occupant is the **pseudoscorpion** (Figure 23-18). Most spiders and their relatives, with the exception of the varroa and tracheal mites, are not considered important pests, even when they occur on the flowers bees visit.

Though they like the cool shade and occasional meal offered by a beehive, black widow spiders and brown recluse spiders are more of a threat to beekeepers than the bees. They are commonly encountered in warm climates beneath, rarely on the outside of hives.

A third mite, *Tropilaelaps* spp, (Figure 23-19) is similar to varroa in that it parasitizes both adults and brood. *Tropilaelaps* is currently, confined to Asia, as varroa once was. Its normal host is *Apis dorsata* but it has been found on *Apis mellifera* alongside varroa (Chapter 21 Figure 21-2). Accidental introduction into the U.S. or elsewhere would be undesirable. Surveys are being conducted both to confirm it has not been accidentally introduced and as a means to deal with limiting spread if it is brought here.

Ticks will occasionally be seen in a hive, especially among bottom board debris. Of greater importance however is the possibility of ticks living in the apiary and their getting on the beekeeper.

Blacklegged ticks (*Ixodes* spp) (Figure 23-21) can transmit Anaplasmosis, Babesoides, Borrelia and lyme disease. Several ticks including **Rocky Mountain wood, American and brown dog tick** bites can transmit Colorado tick fever, Rocky Mountain spotted fever and Tularemia. **The lone star** Figure 23-20) and **Gulf Coast** ticks transmit several human diseases including Rickettsia, Heartland virus and Tularemia.

Lyme disease (Borreliosis) is of particular concern. It is a bacteria transmitted to humans by bites of **blacklegged ticks**. It is especially prevalent in the Northeast, Mid – Atlantic, upper Midwest and Northern California. This tick, about one quarter the size of a varroa mite, can be seen without magnification. It must feed for several (30+) hours before the bacteria are transferred.

The best control is to remove ticks before they embed in human skin and begin to feed. Bites often lead to a large circular rash. Unless treated early (with antibiotic) the disease will progress to joints, nervous system, and even

Figure 23-18
Illustration of pseudoscorpion.

Figure 23-19
Tropilaelaps spp.

Figure 23-17
Orb web spider—she built her nighttime web between two hives and captured a forager to provide food for her young.

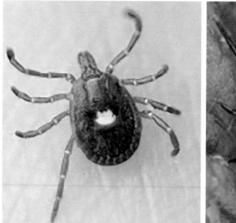

Figure 23-20
Lone star tick.

Figure 23-21
Black legged tick. U. ME.

the heart; individuals will feel fatigued with little energy. The website https://medlineplus.gov/lymedisease.html has details on human symptoms and treatment regimes.

Protecting against ticks is difficult. Out-apiaries where the grass or brush and the animals hosting these ticks are likely to be found are especially common areas to encounter ticks. Treating clothing and boots with products containing 0.5% permethrin or dusting/spraying pant legs/boots with insect repellents are recommended. Keeping pant legs tucked into boots (or socks) and doing a body check to spot any ticks crawling or settled on the body daily should be practiced.

Chiggers (also called harvest or red mites) are a mite that occurs in the same types of habitats as these ticks. The larvae irritate the skin and then feed at the injury site. They do not transmit a disease but their bites cause extensive skin irritation for several days, generally on legs, in the groin area or on arms. Treat clothing with permethrin, spray pants and boots with repellents and look for the red dots (they are tiny) at the end of the day. Use an over-the-counter itch relief but if scratching leads to infection of bite sites you may need an antibiotic.

Frogs, toads, lizards and snakes

Amphibians — like frogs, toads, lizards and snakes — rarely feed on bees, but may invade or live beneath an active hive to seek shelter and their food — the rodents and insects attracted to the beehive. An exception: the **giant marine toad**, *Bufo marinus*, sits at the entrance to a colony and eats foragers returning from the field.

Modifying hive entrances usually enables the bees to deal with these occasional pests in areas where they are likely to be a problem. Additionally, the favorable environment beneath the hive itself, where these animals live and hunt, may need to be modified. It is a good practice not to reach beneath an elevated hive without first checking for animals that might be occupying that space.

Birds

Generally, beekeepers outside the tropics have minimal problems with birds. Woodpeckers, in rare instances, attack the wooden hive, pecking holes in the hand holds and elsewhere (Figure 23-22). In Europe, colonies are sometimes protected with wire cages (Figure 23-23), especially during the migratory periods of the woodpeckers.

Insectivorous birds, like mockingbirds, swifts, kingbirds and thrushes, may eat adult honey bees but more commonly feed on other insects; some prey on slower-flying drones. If they pick off a queen flying to or returning from her mating flight it is more serious.

In African and Asian tropical areas, the **bee-eaters** (*Merops* spp.) and **honeyguides** (*Indicator* spp.) are more serious bee pests. Bee-eaters feed primarily on honey bees and stinging insects and beekeepers are often forced to move their hives out of areas where the birds occur. They migrate into southern Europe. Honeyguides seek beeswax and guide mammals (including humans) to a wild nest where they feed on brood and honey pieces after the nest has been torn apart.

Mammals

Mammals, tiny as mice, medium-sized like skunks and to a lesser degree raccoons (and their marsupial relative, the opossum), as well as larger mammals (baboons, livestock (cattle/horses/deer) and bears are all occasional bee pests. By a large margin, the most serious mammalian pest for the majority of beekeepers is other humans.

Human vandalism, such as tipping over colonies (Chapter 13 Figure 13-33), stealing of honey crops, theft of entire hives and, of course, use of pesticide chemicals in a manner which exposes hives and foraging bees to insecticide poisoning are all examples of human interference. Fear of neighbor overreactions in the urban/suburban environment creates many a clandestine/stealth urban beekeeper.

Figure 23-22
Woodpecker damage to beehive.

Figure 23-23
Cage to protect against woodpecker attack during spring migration in Southern England. J. Thomas

Figure 23-24
Field mouse found in bee hive. C. King.

Figure 23-25
Mouse nest with subsequent comb damage.

Figure 23-26
Comb repair of mouse damage; the new white cells are drone cells.

The smallest mammals, insectivorous shrews and moles, or rodents like mice, rats and squirrels, may seek shelter in a beehive or stacks of bee equipment. Of these, mice (Figure 23-24) are the most common mammalian bee pest. Apiary sites at the margin of wooded areas, where mice commonly nest, experience the highest pressure from mice.

Mice move into colonies when the bees begin to cluster with colder weather in the fall, coming and going when the bees are not active. They are most pestiferous when they build a nest within the colony. Their nests may extend for three or four frames (Figure 23-25). When mice-chewed combs are repaired, worker cells are often replaced by drone comb (Figures 22-26).

Mice should be excluded with entrance reducers early in the fall, though mice can slip into incredibly tiny openings. They have been observed chewing at wooden entrance reducers to regain entry. Elevation of the colony helps make the hive unattractive to mice as a nesting site.

Several larger-bodied mammalian carnivores feed on honey bees if given the opportunity. Nighttime visitors, like skunks (Figure 23-27), scratch on the hive body or entrance to draw a few guards outside. They roll the bees with their paw to avoid being stung and pop the bees into their mouth to suck like pieces of candy, discarding the bee remains in the area. They learn to avoid strong colonies as they return nightly to feast on bees. Stings do not seem to deter them—colonies often become defensive after such repeated nightly disturbances.

In Africa, **ratels, or honey badgers** are a persistent hunter of ground or low-hung bee nests. They have been known to tip colonies from hive stands. The ratel is sometimes led to bee nests by **honeyguide birds** where the ratels dig up and destroy the nest to eat honey and brood. The

Figure 23-27
Skunk.

Figure 23-28 Left
Bears present an increased risk to managed hives. C. John
Figure 23-29 Right
Hive frames scattered by a visiting bear.

Figure 23-30
Bear fence around bee hives.

Figure 23-31
Elevated platform to help protect against bears. Often they are more hazardous to the beekeeper than effective as a bear deterrent.

birds feast on the remains. Badgers, once common in Europe and North America but now infrequent, do the same, finding nests on their own without a bird to guide them.

Control of ratels, badgers, occasional weasels, martins, skunks and other medium-sized mammalian hive visitors is usually achieved by elevating the hive entrance. To reach raised hives, the animal must expose its chest and stomach where the fur is not as protective; after enough stings these pests turn to other, easier food sources.

Traps or exclusion screening can also be used against mammalian pests. When trapping, plan ahead to deal with the trapped animal, especially when trapping skunks. It may not be legal to release a trapped mammal except in designated areas. There are a host of cruel and inhumane traps or methods for dealing with mammalian pests, but even pests do not deserve such treatment. In more rustic management, colonies are often suspended in trees to deter all manner of pests such as ants (Chapter 3), rodents, ratels, elephants (Chapter 9, Figure 9-30), and humans.

The largest mammalian bee pest is one of the best known—the **bear** (Figure 23-28). Winnie-the-Pooh notwithstanding, bears prefer bee brood over honey.

Bears are not subtle in opening a hive to expose the brood. Their primary technique is to smash the hive and then carry brood frames away from stinging bees to eat bees, brood and honey (Figure 23-29). They tend to revisit an apiary where they have fed until all colonies are destroyed and will even show up in subsequent years.

Three different bear species in Asia seek feral and managed beehives but the brown bear of Europe and the black bear of North America are the most frequent beehive pests. Damage varies widely—apiary attacks were reported in 39 of 62 states and provinces in a survey. Attacks are becoming more commonplace as wild game programs seek to recover and restore bear populations.

Some states and provinces compensate beekeepers who build protective electric fences around their hives (Figure 23-30). Fences must be built prior to any instances of bear damage to be effective deterrents. A few states allow other measures, such as shooting. Many game officials cooperate in trapping and relocating problem bears to more remote regions. Efforts to elevate colonies on stands (Figure 23-31) or chaining of hives to trees have had limited success. Too often, the most effective measure in the long run is to simply move the apiary site.

Pesticides

There are over 500 pesticide chemicals used in agriculture, made into well over ten thousand formulations. The vast majority of these pesticides are considered harmless to honey bees, but about 10% can be very toxic and another 15% may cause moderate to severe damage to a colony of honey bees. Extension publication 591, available online from Oregon State University, provides detailed information on relative toxicity and measures to protect pollinators from unnecessary harm.

Bees and pesticides

Insecticide poisoning is nothing new to beekeepers. The first verified kill from an inorganic pesticide was to bees foraging in pears in 1881. Sometimes bees are exposed when they are in the wrong place at the wrong time, i.e. non-targets. Solving the dilemma of protecting beneficial organisms, like bees and biocontrol agents, while killing the damaging pests, is a challenging issue in agriculture.

Changing the formulation to better target pests and preserve beneficial insects was adopted early in insecticide development; unfortunately, some changes have rendered a pesticide more deadly to honey bees. In 1917, **Paris Green** insecticide (an inorganic of copper and arsenic), widely used in fruit orchards, was reformulated as a mixture with molasses bran. The sweet molasses odor was very attractive to honey bees, luring them to contact the poison and causing increased bee deaths.

In the late 60s, **Sevin®** insecticide, a carbamate synthetic organic insecticide commonly used (it was relatively safe to humans), was newly formulated in a molasses bait. The new formulation extensively damaged foraging honey bees when used for gypsy moth control in forests of the northeastern US.

The technical advance of **microencapsulation** (placing a pesticide within a polymer capsule) represents particular danger for bees since foragers readily pick up the capsules as they collect pollen and store them with honey-moistened pollen in cells. When that cell of pollen is used, the pesticide is released, killing the young hive bee engorging on pollen or the larva fed the pollen in its diet.

Companies developing pesticides continually seek to limit exposure of humans and human applicators. Systemic pesticides, materials that can be applied via seed treatments or onto plants at other than foraging times and then be translocated within the plants are such an example. However when the pesticide is moved into plant nectar, bees and pollinators are at greater risk.

Most insecticides kill by penetrating the insect exoskeleton, via ingestion into the digestive tract or when breathed into the tracheal system. A few chemicals degrade the exoskeleton itself causing the insect to dry out (desiccate). The majority of chemicals are nerve toxins and kill by interfering with nerve transmission, particularly at nerve synapses where the chemical

Figure 23-32
Pesticide kill. E. Topitzhofer

acetylcholine, carries the electrical transmission from one nerve ending to the next.

Pesticides may kill bees while foraging when they contact the material or the foragers bring the pesticide back to their hive. Then both older foragers and newly emerged bees may be killed. This shows as a sudden piling up of bee bodies in front of and on the bottom board of colonies (Figure 23-32). Pesticides may weaken the colony to the degree they don't survive the winter period. Distinguishing winter losses in weakened colonies as being due to pesticides or varroa mites or even starvation (in colonies weakened and unable to store sufficient winter reserves) is very difficult (Figures 23-33, 23-34)

Agricultural chemical usage has greatly increased since World War II. Synthetic chemical development has produced many more chemicals using different chemistries—what are described as families of chemicals. While a number of inorganic pesticides (the earliest pesticides in wide use) were highly toxic to bees, many of the synthetic pesticide families may have only one or a small number of chemicals hazardous to bees.

For example among the **chlorinated hydrocarbons**, DDT was not particularly hazardous but chlordane was; most of the chlorinated hydrocarbons have been removed from the market. The same is true for the **organophosphates** (these two chemical groups were originally developed for human warfare and following WW II were repurposed as insecticides). **Chlorpyrifos**, was only removed in a phase out from agricultural market use in 2021—it is among the top five chemical residues found in beeswax.

Losses from toxic poisoning are not confined to one family of pesticides or to certain crops or formulations of pesticides. Larger scale spray programs and application when flowering weeds are blooming present great hazards to honey bees. Applications, such as to forested areas or applying pesticides over agricultural crops or in mosquito control via airplane or powerful ground applicators, usually pose a greater risk to honey bees. Applications directly over or that might drift close to a beehive also are more hazardous (Figure 23-36).

Herbicides and fungicides have also both been shown to perturb beneficial gut microbes in honey bees. Used in great quantities, they have generally been considered relatively safe for foraging honey bees. The extensive use of herbicides and modern clean cultivation agriculture has

Figure 23-33
Dead bees over a small brood area. Disease, pests or pesticides?

Figure 23-34
Mold on dead bees complicates the 'reading of a dead colony.' The mold is a secondary aspect of the death of these bees by starvation, as evidenced by their bodies po-sitioned head first into the cells. This comb may be used in a strong colony as long as there is no American foulbrood scale present

Figure 23-35
Drone brood in worker cells caused by either a drone layer queen or laying workers.

resulted in loss of flowering weeds that beekeepers often depended upon for spring buildup and fall honey stores.

One negative consequence to fungicides may be **synergistic interactions**, whereby exposure to different pesticide compounds, such as some fungicides applied at the same time or following previous exposure to another pesticide, may result in elevated toxicity of the fungicide to bees.

Newest developments

Development and widespread use of genetically modified (GM) crops, such as cotton, corn, sugar beets and alfalfa have genetic information inserted into the crop seed to produce a pesticide within the growing plant. Depending upon the pesticide used, this may benefit foraging honey bees and pollinators. Beekeeper opinions are mixed in favor/opposition to use of this new selection tool.

Insect growth regulators (IGRs) are specific chemicals that can be applied to or genetically inserted into crop plants that send incorrect messages to insects that feed on the plant, preventing the pest from reaching the adult stage to reproduce. How IGRs may affect honey bee development is uncertain due in part to their possible detrimental effects on brood of honey bees is not required in registration of such materials. Following almonds, numbers of bee colonies lose a generation or more of brood due to use of an IGR applied in conjunction with a fungicide as the bloom period is finishing

Yet another approach toward safer, more **target-specific pesticides** has been the development of **systemic pesticides**. A systemic pesticide can be applied to seeds or added to the soil at planting, potentially reducing non-target exposure. The pesticide is subsequently taken up by the plant and distributed within the plant itself in sufficient quantities to kill a pest that feeds on it during the season.

Box 55

PESTICIDE POISONING SYMPTOMS

Pesticides that cause damage to, or near total loss of the foraging bee population, may be carried back to the hive before killing the foragers, leading to damage to both field and hive populations or, with certain compounds and significant exposure, kill the colony outright. In some instances, pesticide damage weakens a colony such that it fails to provide a honey crop or fails to store sufficient reserves to survive the winter.

The most readily apparent sign of pesticide poisoning is the sudden appearance of dead adult bees in front of the entrance (Figure 23-32). There will always be some dead bees in front of a colony, but with pesticide exposure, numbers will be much greater. If the exposure was fairly recent, crawling, trembling adults, along with dying adult bees with their proboscis extended will be evident. With some chemicals dead or dying larvae will also be evident.

It is difficult to detect insecticide loss due to chemical exposures that kill foraging bees before they return to the colony. With experience, it is possible to sometimes recognize that a colony has too few adult bees relative to its brood population. Heavy losses of field bees may lead to loss of brood or reduced brood expansion in the colony. Finding the dead foraging population in the field to document the cause is unlikely.

The most serious pesticide kills occur when bees bring back contaminated pollen and store it in the hive. Field bees, hive bees and brood will likely be affected. Contaminated pollen may continue to have detrimental effects for an extended time period as the bees use it. Since it is expensive to analyze for insecticides, testing dead bees for residues is not practical.

Chronic, long-term pesticide effects, in contrast to toxic (immediate) losses, are largely undocumented. Some pesticide compounds are capable of changing bee behavior. Bee colonies have amazing resiliency and often adjust for losses of adults and brood. However, pesticides that greatly alter normal worker (or queen) behavior or significantly shorten adult life present

considerable problems for hive stochasticity. As is case with any toxin, the dosage a colony receives may become significant the higher the exposure level.

Contamination of honey by pesticide residues is of particular concern since humans also consume this product; effects of beeswax contamination are largely unknown. Queens are less successfully reared in queen cups with elevated pesticide residue levels and drone sperm production may be adversely affected by pesticide exposure during their development.

In analysis of pesticide residues in bee bodies, honey and beeswax, the list of pesticides that contaminate some part of the hive is surprisingly large. Most materials show up at low detection levels, in part from use of highly sensitive detection equipment, but of particular note are the miticides beekeepers are using. These chemicals have been found in virtually all samples being tested, often at levels toxic (causing harm) to bees.

Figure 23-36
Air delivery of pesticides may produce bee losses.

Mullin, C.A. et al. 2010. High Levels of Miticides and Agrochemicals in North American Apiaries: Implications for Honey Bee Health PLoS One https://doi.org/10.1371/journal.pone.0009754.

Milbrath, M. and A. Jacquelyn. 2018. There's A Lot More Bad to Fungicide Exposure to Honey Bees Than You Thought. A Lot. Bee Culture July.

A new family of pesticide chemicals, the systemic **neonicotinoids**, formulated as seed coatings, ground or plant injection and even in direct application on pests, have been implicated as responsible for long-term chronic damage to bees. Lab studies have demonstrated shortening of adult bee life and effects on memory and

normal behaviors. Field studies are mixed. Measurable residues of neonicotinoids do not generally show up in beeswax or honey in bee colonies.

A neonicotinoid was responsible for killing 50,000+ bumble bees in Wilsonville, Oregon in 2013 when it was applied to flowering linden trees (*Tilia*) to control

Figure 23-37
Linden trees in bloom—black specs are dead bumble bees. Xerces

Figure 23-38
Bumble bee kill beneath the sprayed linden trees. Xerces

aphids (Figures 23-37, 23-38). The Oregon Department of Agriculture subsequently withdrew this usage for the material and fined the applicator, but similar accidents still occurred for the next two years.

There are some studies elucidating the danger of the other chemicals used to formulate the active ingredient, known as the killing compound, in pesticides. Formulation additives, the so-called inert ingredients, help compounds stick better to vegetation, activate the pesticide chemical or serve to help it better distribute after release. These so-called inert ingredients may themselves be toxic but, as inert ingredients, are not subject to the testing protocols used to license pesticides. Incredibly, pesticides applied to seeds prior to planting also are not subject to license testing protocols.

Many interdependent variables factor into whether or not bees will suffer from the application of a specific pesticide. The degree of toxicity of the chemical is one factor, as is risk with method and time of day of application. Other variables include the distance the bees are located from treated areas, the number of applications, the foraging behavior of the bees and weather conditions at application and post-application. Risk factors are often difficult to calculate in advance.

Generally, use of the least toxic compounds and locating colonies three or more miles from a pesticide application site are the best protective measures one can use to avoid a bee kill. It comes down to the beekeeper taking all the risk for their bees.

The damage caused by insecticides varies from one region to another, and even one year to the next. Agriculture is changing rapidly and compounds in use today have a short life span. Beekeepers have lobbied hard to seek government assistance in the widespread

belief the current licensing protocols of chemicals with the Environmental Protection Agency (EPA), the federal licensing agency, is not adequate, especially for chronic exposure situations.

Beekeepers, collectively and cooperatively working with entomologists, environmental scientists and the agricultural chemical industry, have sought to improve the situation. Expansion of insecticide use in developing countries and the need for increased harvests to feed the expanding world population necessitates a continuing effort. Grower adoption of Integrated Pest Management (IPM) is in the best interests of beekeepers both for bee and plant pests.

Conditions confused with disease

Plant poisoning

It is difficult to differentiate between bees killed by a pesticide and those poisoned by plants. Thankfully, only a small number of plant nectar or pollens are poisonous. The fact that nectar is dilute means individual exposure is usually so slight that the bees recover. Humans, too, face little risk from poisonous honey, although such occurrences have been noted historically (Chapter 1).

Two plants in the United States are known to possess poisonous pollen. These are **southern leatherwood**, *Cyrilla racemiflora*, also called titi. It causes larvae to turn purple and may kill enough to weaken a colony, and **California buckeye**, *Aesculus californica* (Figure 23-39) that kills adults and brood. In the case of the latter, beekeepers move their colonies away from the foothills of the Sierra Nevada Mountains of California, where the plant grows naturally, to avoid damage to their colonies.

Both **rhododendron and mountain laurel** from the heath family (Ericaceae) have grayanotoxin poisonous to bees and the honey to humans. Although widely distributed, reports of damage instances are very few. Their nectar, more favored by bumble bees than honey bees, is usually sufficiently diluted in honey that human poisonings are rare.

Honey from the South Carolina state flower, **Yellow jessamine** (*Gelsemium sempervirens*), has been more frequently implicated in human poisoning in the Southeastern U.S. Bees foraging on the flowers of yellow jessamine have appeared intoxicated, became paralyzed and died. *Tilia* (linden) nectar has been reported as toxic to bees, especially bumble bees; recent research has concluded that stressed bumble bees colonies may be further impaired when foraging on linden nectar.

Other flower nectar, and juices of some fruits, have been known to intoxicate foraging bees and wasps. This is thought due to ethanol fermentation of the diluted sugar source. It is difficult to pin down instances and many of the incidents do not apparently repeat in any frequency. Some of the pesticide chemicals produce symptoms that cause disoriented flight, bees buzzing in circles and inability to maintain sustained flight.

Exposure of beekeepers to plants that can lead to painful or toxic effects such as poison ivy, poison oak, the nettles, poison sumac and poison hemlock is also of concern.

Figure 23-39
California buckeye flowers.

Rashes and irritations should not be ignored until they become a more serious problem.

Disease, pest and pesticide mimics

There are several circumstances where colony non-productivity might be due to a mimic of a disease or poisoning symptom. Telling the mimics apart from pesticide, plant poisoning or diseases is difficult.

Low or high temperatures can cause brood death. Chilling of brood most often occurs with a sudden temperature change such as a cold spell in the spring or fall. Dead and dying brood will be primarily at the extremities of the brood area. Such brood becomes black and it may not be immediately removed by the house bees. Pesticide/disease brood losses are more apt to be seen throughout the brood chamber.

In early spring, the colony may expand too rapidly and colonies are set back during the cold spell. Dead brood and winter-killed brood will decompose and the resulting rapid growth of mold may complicate diagnosis and obscure other disease symptoms (Figure 23-34).

During a pollen dearth, larvae may be abandoned. Some might be seen trying to exit their cells. Larvae seeking to escape cells can also occur with sudden loss of adults, such as from pesticides and viral epidemics. Feeding sugar syrup and or pollen supplement might help a colony recover.

Dysentery

Dysentery is not a disease (Chapter 22 Figure 22-21). It is the result of poor quality food (fermented honey or contaminated fall feed), higher levels of moisture in the hive and extended confinement (in hives or a shipping package for example). It sometimes appears with the adult disease *Nosema apis* but is not seen with *Nosema ceranae* (see the nosema discussion in Chapter 22).

Wide-spread dysentery results in bees with distended abdomens that appear to be stumbling and sluggish in appearance. Providing quality winter stores, good air circulation and usable upper entrances are three remedies for dysentery.

Seeing dead or dying bees in the snow is actually a good sign during the winter. It demonstrates adults who need to void wastes being able to exit but subsequently becoming chilled and unable to return. When bringing nuclei or colonies inside a building for overwintering or other manipulations, it is important to seek to avoid dysentery. Dead bee bodies need to be promptly removed in enclosed structures.

Queen issues

A common disease/pesticide/pest mimic are issues with queens. Genetic abnormalities are possible but highly unlikely and would be difficult to diagnose. Drone laying queens will present an unusual and unique brood pattern, namely drones in worker cells (Figure 23-35), but so would the laying worker condition. The best distinction to diagnose is whether cells have multiple eggs (laying worker condition) versus a single egg (queen laid eggs).

Queens may lay too few or too many eggs, creating a brood imbalance. Some queens are more active than others and move about more, creating a brood pattern of all three stages mixed together. Likewise, during supersedure and swarming, queens lay fewer eggs but the presence of developing queen cells should be the key clue as to what is happening.

Spotty brood patterns (Figure 23-40; see Chapter 22 Figure 22-4). could have many root causes; one distinct possibility is that hygienic bees are removing and destroying mite-invested worker cells so a once solid brood pattern becomes mixed. Brood disease conditions or Parasitic Mite Brood Syndrome (PMBS) (Chapter 21, Box 50) are the usual causes of spotty patterns.

Heavy adult death would most likely be the result of pesticides or disease. Overwintering dead may accumulate on the bottom board or remain in the cluster position, and it will be difficult to discriminate between starvation, insufficient population to withstand a cold spell, virus or adult disease conditions.

Conditions that affect entire colonies, decreasing the performance of a colony, are sometimes nearly impossible to diagnose. Why did the colony not get strong enough? Why did it die over winter or during the season while others survived? Why did some colonies 'do nothing' compared to others that did very well? Skillful bee stewardship involves reading the colony, including those that don't perform as expected (Figure 23-41).

While sorting out probable causes will not bring a dead colony back or necessarily salvage a season of productivity for a non-productive colony, identifying the cause of bee problems and correcting the deficiencies or tweaking the management approach may help avoid repeat troubles in seasons to come. Dead and non-productive colonies have tales to tell—we have to improve our ability to recognize symptoms to progress as better, more experienced beekeepers.

Figure 23-40
Marked queen on a spotty area of brood. This is always a reason to look more closely at the hive and check to see if there are problems present.

Figure 23-41
Backyard apiary—keeping these colonies in good health and productive remains a challenge of bee stewardship.

key terms

ambush bugs/flies

amphibians (frogs/toads/snakes)

Asian giant hornet (AGH) (Japanese giant hornet)

Asian hornet (*Vespa velutina*)

Bacillus thuringiensis (Bt) (Certan®)

badgers

bald brood

bears (brown/black)

bee eaters (*Merops* spp.)

birds (mockingbirds, swifts, kingbirds and thrushes)

Braula coeca (fly)

bristletails

California buckeye

clandestine/stealth beekeeping

chlorinated hydrocarbons (DDT, Chlordane)

Coleoptera

cockroches

Diptera (flies) / predacious and scavenger

dragonflies

dysentery

dried fruit moth

earwigs

electric bear fence

entrance reducers)

European hornet (*Vespa crabro*)

Fumagillin (fumidil B)

fungicides

galleriasis

gamma radiation

giant marine toad

grayanotoxin

herbicides

honeyguides (*Indicator* spp)

human vandalism/stealing beehives

Hymenoptera (ants/wasps/ bees)

Indian meal moth

inert pesticide ingredients

insect growth regulator (IGR)

integrated pest management (IPM)

leatherwood (titi)

Lincomycin (Lincomix)

Lyme disease (Borreliosis)

Mediterranean flour moth

mice

microencapsulated pesticide

Murder hornet (*Vespa mandarinia*)

naphthalene

neonicotinoid pesticide

nozevit

organophophates (Chorpyrifos)

paradichlorobenzene (PDB) (Para Moth®)

parasitic mite brood syndrome (PMBS)

Paris green pesticide

pesticides/insecticides/ herbicides

preying mantis

psocids

psuedoscorpion

ratel

robber flies

rodents

scavenger insects/mites

septicemia

Sevin insecticide

shrews/moles

skunk

small hive beetle (*Aethina tumida*)

spiders (crab and/or web weaver)

spotty brood pattern

springtails

starving brood

synergistic

systemic pesticide

termites

tick associated illnesses

Tropilaelaps mite

USDA Bee Lab Beltsville

Varroa destructor virus (VDV)

Vita Bee Health Diagnostic kit

wax moth (greater & lesser)

woodpeckers

yellowjackets (Vespula spp)

yellow-legged hornet

zombie fly

discussion questions

Most of the bee pests described were insects. What are the four most serious insect pests? How does their control integrate with mite and disease control efforts? What is the distinction between scavenger and non-scavenger? Can you identify other insect pests of honey bees not included here?

How can fencing of a bee site serve to control human, bear, skunk etc. (i.e. mammal) pests?

If you have a weak colony how could you recognize that it could be due to a pest? Or to a pesticide? Or to a mimic? Where would you go to find help in identifying what pest (or pesticide or mimic) is causing damage to your bees?

Describe proactive preventive managements beekeepers should use to protect colonies from pests (or pesticides) and measures needed when a specific pest (or disease) is detected.

In the perfect world we need keep bees away from pesticides. Describe the typical means to detect pesticide damage to your colonies? Detecting damage to the bees themselves is more difficult– how can this damage be verified.

Distinguish between acute and toxic pesticide effects. Is one more potentially serious than the other?

Distinguish some of the things that might mimic pests or pesticides. Are there other mimics not identified here?

exercises

Some interactive computer programs cover pest problems in honey bees. Look at as many of these visual teaching aids as possible and critique them for information, effectiveness and visual quality. In particular check out The BeeMD.

Accumulate literature available from extension or other sources in your state/province, and neighboring areas where conditions are similar on recognition and control of bee pests. Put information together for pests not covered in this chapter.

Develop a program to use to educate a new beekeeper about pests that they might encounter and what the need to do for control.

How should beekeepers respond to the Save the bees from pesticides efforts of the numerous non-beekeeper organizations? ID organizations that are using bee-related information in a realistic manner as they seek to forward their agenda. What needs be done to help educate the anti-pesticide groups that bees and pollinators need be a part of the message regarding safer use of pesticides.

Seek a lobbying group and help provide them with good factual information on the effect pesticides have on honey bees (and other pollinators).

Look at Xerces, the largest and oldest group dedicated to conservation of invertebrates. How do you rate the information they have available?

references

https://en.wikipedia.org/wiki/Grayanotoxin

Akre, R.D. et al. 1980. Yellowjackets of America North of Mexico. U.S. Department of Agriculture, Agriculture Handbook No 552

CAPA. 2013. Honey Bee Diseases and Pests. 3rd edition. Ed by S. Pernal and Heater Clay Eds. CAPA, Beaverlodge, AB

Caron, D.M. 2017. It took 50,000+ dead bumble bees. Bee Culture, December

Frazier, M. et al. 2015. Field Guide to Honey Bees and their Maladies. Penn State AGRS-116.

Jack, C.J. and J.D. Ellis. 2018. Wax Moth control. IFAS Extension. https://edis.ifas.ufl.edu/aa141

Morse, R.A. and K. Flottum, eds. Honey Bee Pests, Predators and Diseases, 3rd Edition. Northern Bee Books, West Yorkshire, UK

Sallman, B. 2020. Is high fungicide use affecting bee health. BIP Blog https://beeinformed.org/2020/07/13/is-high-fungicide-use-affecting-bee-health/

Torgerson, K. et al. 2020. The Small Hive Beetle: A Potential Pest in Honey Bee Colonies. OSU EM 9143.

Gong, A.J. 2019. Invasion of the Bee Body-Snatchers. Bay Nature. https://baynature.org/2019/10/29/invasion-of-the-bee-body-snatchers/

Glossary

1906 Pure Food and Drug Act: First consumer protection law passed to protect food purity levels.

2-heptanone: Secreted from honey bee mandibular glands. Has been described as an alarm pheromone and/or a marker of enemies by guard biting; alternatively perhaps used to mark flowers visited by foragers or larvae fed or to anesthetize small enemies such as wax moth larvae and varroa mites.

24 methyl cholesterol: Plant steroid that honey bees cannot synthesize and must be obtained in the diet.

A

abdomen: Segmented, posterior (third) part of bee body internally containing heart, honey stomach, intestines, reproductive organs, and sting.

absconding: Abandonment of hive by total adult population, including leaving brood and honey, due to unfavorable conditions such as ants, starvation or other disturbances. Resembles swarming but lacking new queen production.

Acarapis woodi: Scientific name of honey bee tracheal (previously called acarine) mite. Infests tracheae of adult bees.

acarine disease (Acariosis): Caused by the mite *Acarapis woodi* that gets into the major tracheae of the thorax through its spiracles.

active evaporation: Systematic exposure of nectar via a bubble in the mouthparts of adult bee to mix enzyme sucrase and reduce water content for ripening nectar to honey.

active season: Time period when bees are actively foraging and rearing brood, not in cluster.

acute bee paralysis virus (ABPV): Virus infection of adult bees associated with trembling and hairlessness.

adult bee population: Bees in the final (4th) stage of their metamorphosis; includes nurse, house and field bees.

adulterated honey: Honey that has been artificially augmented by sugars or other ingredients other than floral nectar.

aedeagus: Reproductive organ of male insects through which they deliver sperm to females during copulation.

AFB/EFB Test kit (Vita Bee Health): Diagnostic kit that immediately shows the presence of antibodies to American foulbrood or European foulbrood.

Africanized Bee (AHB): A hybridized bee population in the Americas resulting from introduction of African bee race *Apis mellifera scutellata*, to Brazil mixing with European honey bees. AHB colonies defend and swarm excessively making management difficult. Popularly termed 'killer bee.'

afterswarm: Any swarm emerging from a colony after the primary swarm. Afterswarms contain one or more virgin queens.

aggregation: Grouping of one animal species, such as at food or nest site, otherwise without social interactions.

air sacs: Part of the tracheal system, abdominal air sacs allow for more air to be taken into the body for respiration.

alarm odor (chemical): Pheromone chemical (isopentyl acetate and other molecules) released by worker bee at time of stinging.

alfalfa: Also called lucerne (*Medicago sativa*), a perennial flowering plant in the legume family Fabaceae. It is cultivated as an important forage crop in many countries around the world; a major source of nectar for honey bees.

alfalfa leafcutting bee: *Megachile rotundata* is a solitary pollinator of alfalfa and other crops; naturally nests in plant stems, dead wood and cracks in walls. Artificial wooden bee blocks cultivated in pollination.

alkali bee: *Nomia melanderi* is a ground-nesting bee native to deserts and semi-arid desert basins of the western United States. This bee nests in salt-saturated, or alkaline soil. Managed as a pollinator of alfalfa.

allergic reaction: Hypersensitivity of the immune system to typically harmless substances in the environment. Honey bee sting allergic reactions occur in fewer than 1% of healthy individuals. See also anaphylaxis.

Alley method: Queen rearing method that uses cut pieces of comb cells of eggs or day-old worker larvae re-orientated to open vertically downward so bees can elaborate queen cells under queenless conditions.

almond: *Prunus dulcis* is an edible nutlike seed, grown extensively in California and requiring millions of colonies of honey bees for February-March pollination.

ambush bugs: Predatory bugs that frequent flowers; they use raptoral front legs to grasp prey, including foraging bees.

American Bee Journal: Beekeeping journal established in 1861. The oldest English language beekeeping publication in the world. Dadant and Sons, Inc. is the current publisher.

American foulbrood (AFB): Contagious disease of bee larvae caused by *Paenibacillus larvae*. See foulbrood diseases.

amino acid: Organic compounds, the basic building blocks of protein, that contain amine (-NH2) and carboxyl (-COOH) functional groups, along with a side chain (R group) specific to each amino acid. Provides key elements of carbon (C), hydrogen (H), oxygen (O), and nitrogen (N). Obtained by bees via pollen.

amitraz (Apivar/Miticur): A synthetic, non-systemic acaricide (pesticide) used to kill varroa mites.

amoeba: A single-celled animal that lives in damp environments or as parasites. One parasitic amoeba is uncommonly found in honey bee digestive tracts.

amphibians: Frogs and toads; often living in a variety of ecosystems. Some feed on honey bees.

anaphylaxis: A life-threatening allergic reaction of lowering of blood pressure, restriction of breathing and loss of consciousness. Requires prompt medical attention.

anatomy (morphology): The branch of biology concerned with the study of the structure of organisms and their parts.

andrenid (ae): A large group (family) of solitary, ground-nesting bees. Called mining bees.

antenna (ae): Paired, slender and jointed segmented appendages on bee head; primary taste, touch and smell receptors.

antenna cleaner: Structures on both front legs of *Apis* species that allow the bee to remove pollen and other material from the antennae.

antennation: Antennal contact between adult bees that passes queen substance and other messages.

anthers: The male part of the flower that produces and contains pollen; usually borne on a stalk (filament).

anus: The opening at the opposite end of an animal's digestive tract from the mouth through which solid wastes are discharged.

aorta: A simple tube that runs dorsally from the 5-chambered heart to carry hemolymph (blood) to the head/brain in insects.

apiary: The place where beehives (bee colonies) and beekeeping equipment are located. An out-apiary is a site away from the owner's residence. Also called a beeyard.

apiary inspector: Local or state official responsible for inspecting bees, usually for American foulbrood and varroa mites. They may provide surveys for potential pests.

Apiary Inspectors of America (AIA): A non-profit organization established to promote better beekeeping conditions in North America by inspecting for bee diseases, parasites and pests.

apiculture: The science and art of cultivating bees to benefit humans.

Apidae: The insect family of at least 5700 species of bees, including honey bees, bumble bees, stingless bees, carpenter bees, and others.

Apiguard: An essential oil treatment for varroa mites, producing Thymol vapor at temperatures above 15° C (59° F).

ApiLife Var: A combination of 74% thymol with the essential oils eucalyptol, menthol and camphor soaked in a fibrous wafer. Most effective when used at 18° C (64° F) or above.

Apis: Genus name for all the honey bee species.

Apis cerana: Scientific name of the Eastern honey bee, the cavity-nesting bee of Asia. Older name *Apis indica*.

Apis dorsata: Scientific name for the giant honey bee of Asia which builds single-comb nests suspended from tree branches or rocky ledges.

Apis florea: Scientific name for the small honey bee of Asia.

Apis mellifera: The scientific name given to the Western (European) honey bee by Linnaeus to distinguish it from all other insects. The word 'mellifera' means 'honey bearer.' A cavity-nesting bee.

Apistan (tau-fluvalinate): Synthetic pyrethroid acaricide used to control varroa mites but to which bees have developed resistance. Has an affinity for beeswax.

apitherapy: Medical use of honey bee products. This includes bee venom therapy.

apitoxin: Honey bee venom; main component is mellitin (52%)

apodemes: Ingrowth of the exoskeleton of arthropods that support internal organs and provide points of muscle attachment. Most prominent in thorax.

apples: Apple trees are cultivated worldwide and are the most widely grown species in the genus *Malus*. Most trees require cross pollination by honey bees, bumble bees, and orchard mason bees.

applied bee biology: Beekeeping.

Arnhart gland: Gland of last distal leg segment in all three adults, sometimes called arolium or tarsal gland. Secretes pheromone, called the footprint substance, deposited as bees walk on surface.

arolium: Median padlike structure between the tarsal claws of the pretarsus.

art and science of beekeeping: Integrating the theoretical science based data about bees with their proper stewardship. See applied bee biology.

Arthropoda: Phylum of invertebrate animals with exoskeleton and paired jointed appendages; includes insects, spiders, crustaceans and relatives.

artisanal: High quality honey bee products produced by local artisans in small quantities, using traditional methods.

Asian hornet: *Vespa velutina,* also called the yellow-legged hornet, an Asian predatory wasp indigenous to Southeast Asia. It is of concern as an invasive species in European countries from Spain to U.K.

asynchrony: Not simultaneous or concurrent in time.

attracting a swarm: Using brood comb, propolis, pheromones and/or floral scents to attract a swarm.

autumn collapse: Dwindling of hives for unknown reasons before winter sets in.

AZ hive: Also known as a Slovenian AZ hive, often kept within a building; hive frames are accessed from the back side rather than the top.

azimuth: An arc of the horizon fixing the intersection of the sun with the horizon; utilized by honey bees to fix sun's position in honey bee dance orientation.

B

B-complex vitamins: A class of water-soluble vitamins that play an important role in cell metabolism. Bees get their B vitamins from pollen, less so from nectar.

Bacillus thuringiensis **Bt (Certan®):** Common soil-dwelling bacterium, commonly used as a biological pesticide to control wax moth caterpillars in stored drawn comb.

bacteria: A type of biological cell. Bacteria were among the first life forms to appear on Earth, and are present in most habitats including soil, water, acidic hot springs, radioactive waste, and even the deep biosphere of the earth's crust. Most bacteria are harmless symbiotics but some are parasitic to plants and animals. American and European foulbrood are two examples of diseases caused by harmful bacteria in honey bees

badgers: Short-legged omnivores in the families Mustelidae; now uncommon pests of bee hives.

bait hive: An empty hive, bee box or structure with bee smell, pheromone or flower smell lure to attract a bee swarm. Following trapping, the new comb nest with bees is transferred into a standard bee hive.

baiting: Adding comb, propolis, pheromones or other compounds to swarm traps to attract scout and swarming bees. Also, process of enticing bees into supers.

ball-and-socket joint: A joint in which the rounded surface of a body part moves within a depression on another, allowing greater freedom of movement, as in the attachment of the scape of the antenna to the honey bee head.

balling: A behavior of worker bees whereby several workers gather (or ball) very tightly around the queen. Balling usually, but not always, results in the death of the queen.

bears (brown/black): Brown bears (Europe) and black bears (North America) are omnivores whose diet may include bee brood and honey from bee colonies.

bee apocalypse: A media-driven term, named after coining of the term colony collapse disorder (CCD) in 2006 to describe the extensive colony losses.

bee beard: A stunt where a caged queen bee/queen pheromone is tied around a person's neck to attract worker bees that are formed into a beard-like shape beneath chin.

bee blower: An electric or gasoline forced air blower used to remove bees from supers for honey harvest or requeening.

bee botany: The science of the relationship between flowering plants and their bee pollinators.

bee bread: A protein food of bees collected as pollen, processed by anaerobic fermentation and stored in beeswax cells.

Bee Culture: Formerly *Gleanings in Bee Culture*. Founded by A. I. Root in 1873 of what is now the Root Candle Company.

bee eaters (*Merops* spp.): Burrow nesting, bee feeding, birds of the savanna and open habitats of Africa, southern Europe and southern Asia.

bee escape: A device that uses a one-way passage of adult bees. Used to prevent reentry of bees into the honey supers so the honey-filled frames may be removed bee free.

bee gloves: Hand protection worn while inspecting bee colonies. Beekeeping cloth or leather versions often with gauntlets to additionally protect the wrists and forearms from bee stings.

bee gum: Usually a hollow log hive serving as the home of a honey bee colony in which bees construct combs without frames or other guides.

Bee Informed Partnership Inc. (BIP): A national 501(c)(3) nonprofit organization using science-based, data-driven approaches to improve the health and sustainability of honey bees by gathering survey data and field samples. Uses Tech Team specialists and other assets.

bee louse (*Braula coeca*): Relatively harmless, commensal fly living on adult honey bees (including queen). Larvae can cosmetically damage honeycomb cappings.

bee metamorphosis: The four-stage transformation (complete metamorphosis) of bees from egg to larva to pupa to adult stage.

bee space: A space (3/8 of an inch, 1 cm) big enough to permit unhindered passage for a bee but too small to encourage comb building or too large for use of propolis. Basic principal of moveable comb hive construction. Bee space occurs between parallel beeswax combs, between the outer comb and the hive walls and between boxes.

bee tree: A hollow in a tree occupied by a colony of bees. Called a bee gum when the tree section containing the bees is managed as separated section.

bee veil: Cloth and mesh head gear to protect head and face against bee stings.

beehive: An enclosable domicile in which a honey bee species of the subgenus *Apis* live and raise their young.

beekeeper: A person who keeps honey bees. Also called apiculturist, honey farmer or apiarist.

beeline: The shortest distance between two points. To follow a beeline or to line bees is to follow bees as they leave a feeding site and make their way back to their hive.

bees: Flying insects in Superfamily Apoidea, Order Hymenoptera, closely related to wasps and ants, known for their role in flower pollination.

beeswax: Natural animal wax composed of esters of fatty acids and various long-chain alcohols. Secreted from 4 paired glands on underside of abdomen of adult bees of genus *Apis*; molded to form honeycomb or cap pupal/honey-filled cells.

Benadryl: (Diphenhydramine). An antihistamine used to relieve symptoms of allergy, hay fever, and the common cold. May be used before or more often after being stung.

bilaterally symmetrical: Symmetrical arrangement of an organism along a central axis.

binominal: Organisms two-part latinized scientific name.

biological control: Method of controlling pests using other organisms. Relies on predation, parasitism or other natural mechanisms, including human management. An important component of integrated pest management (IPM) .

bird predators: Insect-feeding birds that feed on bees, including mockingbirds, swifts, kingbirds and thrushes.

bivouac (swarm cluster): A temporary intermediate encampment of swarming bees in an open area while scout bees decide on a permanent nestsite.

black queen cell virus (BQCV): A virus that infects the pupal stage of queen honey bees of genus *Apis*. Decomposing dead pupae distinctly black.

blue orchard bee: *Osmia lignaria*, BOB, also known as the orchard mason bee. A megachilid bee that makes nests in reeds and natural holes. Propagated to pollinate apple, almonds and for use in general pollination.

blueberry: Wild (lowbush) and cultivated (highbush) berry native to North America (*Vaccinium* spp). A southeastern blueberry bee (*Habropoda laboriosa*) and bumble bees are native pollinators; honey bees are used to supplement commercial production.

Boardman feeder: Beehive entrance syrup/water feeder.

bottom board: The lower piece or floor of the modern Langstroth beehive. Usually built to include hive entrance and frequently extends forward 1-2 inches (2.5-5 cm) for bee landing board. Screen may replace solid bottom for varroa and small hive beetle control.

bottom supering: Practice of adding empty supers under partially filled supers directly above brood boxes.

bounce and brush: A low-tech method of removing adult bees from frames during honey harvest. Frames are bounced before colony entrance and remaining clinging adult bees brushed from beeswax comb.

box (rustic) hive: Beehive made from irregular, unfinished lumber. Beeswax comb attached to box inner surfaces; not removable comb.

brace/burr comb: Comb built between frames, between boxes or in spaces where the bee space is not maintained.

branched (plumose) hairs: Bee feathery-like body hairs with branches or forks characteristic of pollen collecting bees.

Braula coeca (fly): A wingless fly that is a minor pest in bee colonies. See bee louse.

breaking (whirring) dance: See buzz run.

breeder queen: Queen selected for use to propagate daughters with similar desirable characteristics.

breeder colony: Colony housing a breeder queen.

brood: Immature bees; the egg, larval or pupal (sealed/capped) stages of development, confined to individual beeswax cells.

brood boxes: Hive bodies containing or used for brood. Often standard sized of 8 or 10 frames but can be other sizes (medium/shallow) or longitudinal (10+ frames).

brood chamber: The area of the hive where the brood is reared; usually the lowermost level of a hive. Also termed brood nest.

brood comb: Wax comb containing or used in past to rear brood.

brood population: The amount of brood in a hive, measured by frames or square inches.

brood separation: Moving brood frames away from the spherical/oval core of the brood nest.

Buckfast bees: An improved genetic bee stock initially of Italian carniolan cross developed by monk Brother Adam at Buckfast Abby in southwest England; developed to counter Isle of Wight disease. Bee best suited to UK.

buildup: Colony growth, usually in the spring or after a period of poor food intake.

bumble bee: Bee of the genus *Bombus*.

burning AFB: Destruct treatment to destroy frames, hive parts and bees infected with the disease American foulbrood.

buzz pollination (sonifiation): A type of pollination of flowers like tomatoes that require vibration by the pollinators. Honey bees do not buzz pollinate, while bumble bees do.

buzz run (breaking dance): Zig-zag running of scout bees in hive to initiate swarm departure or on swarm cluster to stimulate bivouac to depart for selected new home site.

C

California buckeye: (*Aesculus californica*). A horse-chestnut native to California that produces nectar toxic to honey bees. The seeds are toxic to humans.

Canadian Association of Professional Apiculturists (CAPA): An organization of bee researchers, educators and bee inspectors in Canada.

candy board: A sugar cake used to feed bees, used during winter.

capped brood: Brood cell at end of larval stage (prepupa) and during pupal stage that is covered with beeswax.

capped honey: Cells full of ripened honey, closed (capped) with beeswax.

capped queen cell: Capped (sealed) queen cell in pupal stage of metamorphosis.

capping scratcher: Devise used to open wax cappings of honey-filled cells and to check capped drone cells for varroa mites.

cappings: Beeswax covering of honey-filled honey cells which are removed before extracting honey.

Carniolan bees: A race of honey bees (*Apis mellifera carnica*) which originated in the southern part of the Austrian Alps and northern Slovenia. Also called Carnies.

carpenter bee: Bees of the genus *Xylocopa*; nearly all species burrow into dead wood or bamboo. Sometimes considered structural pest; often confused with a bumble bee

caste: In social insects, female adults physically distinct with different duties. In honey bees the queen lays eggs and worker honey bees do work.

caste differentiation: In honey bees a result of dietary quantity and quality differences that lead to a queen or worker.

caste system: Reproductive division of labor within female adults in eusocial insects; a single reproductive queen via pheromone secretions maintains more or less sterile female workers (and soldiers in ant societies).

Caucasian honey bees: (*Apis mellifera caucasia*). A gentle race of bees, dark in color, with heavy gluing (propolizing) tendencies. Originated in the Caucasus Mountains.

cell: Six-sided compartment of honeycomb used to raise brood and store honey and pollen (bee bread). Worker cells approximate five to the linear inch (about two per cm); drone cells are larger, averaging four to the linear inch (about 1-1/2 per cm).

cell bar: A wooden strip holding queen cups into which 1-day old worker larvae are grafted then inverted and placed in holder frame in queenless unit of young worker bees to start queen cells.

cell punch: Usually a metal ring that can be heated to use to cut out (punch) a single worker egg or larva intact within its cell for use in queen rearing.

Ceratina: The small carpenter bees, closely related to the more familiar large carpenter bees. Often metallic blue or black, they make nests in dead wood, stems, or pith.

chains of younger bees: See festooning.

chalkbrood: Brood disease caused by fungus *Ascophera apis*. Larvae turn whitish then gray or black drying to resemble tiny pieces of chalk. Heavy infestations detected on bottom board or at hive entrance.

chemical messages: Chemical messages (pheromones) transmitted by direct contact as a liquid or gas vapor.

chewing-lapping mouthparts: As in honey bees, proboscis to lap up liquids and functional mandibles to bite/mold beeswax.

chilled brood: Mortality of brood caused by a loss of brood heat, usually because there are not enough adult bees to cover the brood. Larvae lose color and turn black. Often seen after beekeeper manipulations of the hive.

chilling queens: Exposure of a queen bee during hive manipulation, shipping, and installation. Prolonged exposure to temperatures lower than 95° F. will impact introduction success and queen egg-laying ability.

chitin: Fibrous substance consisting of polysaccharides that is major constituent in the exoskeleton of arthropods.

chlorinated hydrocarbons: An organic compound containing chlorine, hydrogen, and carbon atoms; familiar examples are the neurotoxin pesticides DDT, Chlordane, and lindane. These chemicals have a wide range of uses, including pesticides, where they have caused environmental concerns. Many toxic to bees.

cholesterol: A sterol biosynthesized by all animal cells and an essential structural component of animal cell membranes.

chorion: Membrane covering of the bee egg.

chronic bee paralysis virus (CBPV): A virus infection of mainly adult honey bees with two infection types: Type I infected bees have a bloated abdomen and weak or trembling wings. The bees crawl on the ground and are unable to fly. Type II infected bees have complete abdominal hair loss, causing it to appear black and greasy. The virus is spread by symptom-free infected bees able to transmit the virus.

chunk honey: Type of honey containing both liquid (extracted) honey and a piece of comb with capped honey cells.

citrus greening disease (Huanglongbing (HLB) or yellow dragon disease): A bacterial disease spread by a citrus psyllids that yellows the veins and surrounding tissue of leaves, eventually killing the tree. This disease has had a profound impact on beekeeper's citrus honey production and colony health in Florida and elsewhere.

city bees: Bee colonies managed in urban situations, on rooftops, balconies and in protected sites.

clandestine/stealth beekeeping: Siting/managing bee colonies in such a way that they are not noticed by neighbors/the general public.

cleansing (cleaning) flight: Adult bees leaving the hive to void wastes.

Cloake board: A special piece of equipment used to facilitate raising queen bees. Invented by Harry Cloake.

cluster: Cohesive mass of bees clinging together, as during swarm bivouac or to conserve warmth during the colder months.

cockroaches: Aggregating/social Insects closely related to termites in order Blattodea; sometimes use a beehive to shelter; omnivores feed on organic matter.

cocoon: Protective silk envelope which an insect larva/pre-pupa forms about itself to pass the pupal stage.

Coleoptera: Largest insect order of beetles. Several beetles are beehive scavengers; one, the small hive beetle, a serious hive pest.

colony: An assembly of worker bees, drones and a queen living together as one social unit in a hive or other dwelling.

Colony Collapse Disorder (CCD): An abnormal event where most of the worker bees in a honey bee colony disappear in short time, leaving behind a queen, plenty of food, and a few nurse bees.

colony morale: A very general beekeeper term to describe the general demeanor of a colony that is not immediately attributable to specific health or vigor conditions.

colony population: A measurement of a colony's brood/adult growth and potential for pollination or honey production.

COLOSS organization (www.coloss.org): (Prevention of honey bee COlony LOSSes) non-profit headquartered in Bern, Switzerland that is focused on improving the well-being of bees at a global level.

comb: Also known as beeswax comb or honeycomb. The back-to-back arrangement of beeswax cells. Each cell is hexagonal and open at the top. When filled with honey or when brood reaches the pupal stage, the cell is capped (capped comb).

comb box system: Plastic container system that replaces grafting of larvae to produce queen cells. Also called Jenter or Nicot.

comb foundation: A thin sheet of beeswax embossed or stamped with the three-part base and hexagon of a normal worker cell. Worker bees add beeswax to draw into usable comb. May be molded from plastic, reinforced with or without wire.

comb honey: Honey produced and marketed in the comb. Section comb is honey in a wooden or plastic container as stored by the bee.

comb honey super: Hive body containing small wood or plastic sections to produce honey in the comb.

comb pheromone: Chemical beeswax odor stimulating foraging by worker bees and impacting other bee behavior.

combination (conversion) board: Wood board cut to fit different sized hive bodies for the purpose of making new colonies or combining two colonies housed in different sized hive bodies.

combining two colonies: The process of combining two colonies into one; usually through a newspaper or by shaking one colony's bees in front of another colony.

commercial beekeeping: Beekeeper(s) operating 50+ colonies for significant part-time (sometimes sideliner) or 500+ colonies for full-time income.

communication holes: Naturally-occurring openings in the honeycomb that allow bees to move from one side of the comb to the other. In movable frames, usually along the lower corners when full sheets of foundation are used.

compact brood pattern: Brood comb with nearly every cell occupied lacking brokenness in the laying pattern. Opposite is spotty.

compound eye: The large, multi-faceted paired insect eye.

constancy: Behavior of returning to the same flower species by foraging bees over subsequent trips and staying with that species during an individual foraging foray.

cooperative care of young: Sharing of the feeding of larvae by a group of females who may not be the mother of the larvae being fed.

corbicula (ae) (pollen basket): Area on hind leg of bee where body hairs are adapted for forming and carrying pollen.

corolla: Part of a flower that includes fused and/or separated petals.

Coumaphos: A nonvolatile, fat-soluble phosphorothioate pesticide that kills insects and mites. Used to control Varroa mites and small hive beetles but mites have developed resistance; considerable residual toxicity concerns in use

coveralls (bee suit): Loose-fitting, one-piece garment, often worn over other clothing during bee work. Some versions have Velcro wrist and ankle closures and a zip-in veil.

coxa: The first segment of insect and arthropod legs that attach to the thorax.

cranberry: Red, acid fruit of the genus *Vaccinium*, used as a juice, jelly or relish. Grows in bogs or acid soils.

creamed honey: A finely-granulated solidified honey made by seeding filtered liquid honey with 10 percent finely crystallized honey and storing at about 57° F (14° C). Sometimes referred to a Dyce process.

cross-pollination: Transfer of pollen from anther to stigma between plants which are not of identical genetic material.

crud brood: Unhealthy bee brood, also termed snot brood, recognized in Parasitic Mite Brood Syndrome (PMBS).

crystalized honey debris: Pieces of granulated honey removed by bees; seen as white specks in comb cells and on bottom board.

crystallization (granulation) of honey: Natural change of honey from liquid to sugar crystal form; not spoilage.

cull: Eliminate or remove. In beekeeping the term referring to the removal of older, damaged or unhealthy combs. It is also applied to removing or combining weak or queenless colonies with another colony.

cultivated crops: Any crop produced on cleared and planted on land that is used for commercial gain.

cultural control: Modifying the growing environment of a crop or animal to reduce the numbers of unwanted pests.

cut-comb honey: A piece of cut honey-filled comb marketed in a special container.

cutout: Term used by beekeepers to describe removal/transfer/harvest of bee colonies from trees and buildings.

D

dance language: Behavior used by honey bees to communicate the location of food or a nest site. Consists of repeated (dance) movements.

dancing: A series of repeated movements by bees on comb and in swarms. A means of dance language communication for food and home sites. Round, sickle and wagtail dances are the principal movements.

dead bees: In a healthy hive, dead bees are removed by undertaker bees and when possible flown about 15 feet from the hive. Excess dead bees at the entrance or bottom board, other than overnight, indicate pesticide exposure, starvation or some other health problem.

debris (frass): The material that accumulates below a hive.

defense: Defending from attack. In honey bees, guard bees are the primary agents of hive defense. Colony defense includes hitting the invader; stinging is the last resort.

defensive bees: Colonies that sting more often and/or more quickly that others to defend their nest. This may be a function of colony size, genetically influenced (as in Africanized bees) and other reasons.

deformed wing virus (DWV): An RNA virus infecting the honey bee, expressed as wing deformity in adult honey bees.

Demaree: Variation on swarm control devised by George Demaree in 1884; demareeing consists of separating queen from most of the brood.

depopulation (euthanize): Killing bees for disease or pest management, usually related to heightened defense, high mite numbers or American foulbrood.

dequeen: Removal of a queen from a colony; often done prior to requeening.

desensitization: Prevention or reduction of immediate hypersensitivity to honey bee stings by humans through administration of graded doses (shots) of allergen designed to build up immunity to the proteins in venom.

destruct harvest: Removal of honey comb and harvesting honey by pressure or heating. The wax comb is destroyed in the process.

detrose: Another name for sugar. See glucose.

dialects: In the honey bee dance language, different races or groups of honey bees vary in specifics of communication.

diet of pollen and nectar: The food of honey bees, plus water.

digger bees: Solitary bees that nest in the soil by excavating tunnels to build cells to rear offspring.

dioecious plants: Dioecious plant species have the male and female reproductive structures on separate plants.

diploid: A cell or an organism containing two sets of chromosomes (2n)—one from the mother and another set from the father. The normal female honey bee cell chromosome condition. Also called diploidy.

Diptera (predacious flies): Robber (assassin) two-winged flies (Asilidae). These bristly flies have a short, stout proboscis enclosing the sharp, sucking hypopharynx. With notoriously aggressive predatory habits; they feed mainly on other insects.

disappearing disease: See colony collapse disorder.

dispersal phase of varroa life cycle: Movement of varroa mites being carried on the body of honey bees.

disposable pollination units (DPUs): An artificial colony, with a queen or queen substance, in a disposable container; used for pollination. Colony not recovered following use.

divides/divisions: The result of removing brood and bees to weaken a populous colony and adding a queen or queen cell to establish a new colony.

division board feeder: Also known as a frame feeder. A wooden or plastic trough placed in the hive (often at edge of box); used to feed the colony supplemental honey or sugar syrup.

DNA methylation: A biological process in which methyl groups are added to the DNA molecule, changing the activity of a DNA segment without changing the sequence. DNA methylation acts to repress gene transcription.

dominance hierarchies: A type of social hierarchy that creates a ranking system. Relative rank is established between members of the same sex.

Doolittle increase: Establishing a new colony by elevating frames of brood above a queen excluder and allowing the nurse bees to cover the brood. A queen may then be added and the increase hive set off to a new location. A variation of a walk-away split.

Doolittle larval transfer (grafting): Transfer of very young worker larvae to plastic/wax queen cell cups that are then placed into a queenless environment for queen cell construction. Commercial method of producing large numbers of queen cells.

dormancy: A state of suspended or slowed physical activity; in honey bee winter cluster behavior. Period of slowed activity in which adult bees maintain temperatures adequate for survival and usually reduced brood rearing.

double boiler: An upper unit heated by boiling water. In beekeeping, double boilers are used to melt beeswax containing honey comb.

double screen: A hive separator of two pieces of screen or hardware cloth that prevents food sharing between two groups of bees, one below and one above the double screen.

dragonflies: Insects belonging to the order Odonata, characterized by large, multifaceted eyes, two pairs of strong, transparent wings, sometimes with colored patches, and an elongated body. Often predators of honey bees, especially of drones and queens during mating.

drawing comb (foundation): Comb building from foundation template (or naturally without foundation).

drawn comb: Comb having the hexagonal cells built out (drawn) by honey bees from a sheet of foundation or from top of nest cavity. Completed cells are about 1/2 inch (1 cm) deep angled upward slightly.

dried fruit moth: A snout moth in the genus *Cadra*. It thrives in warmer conditions and feeds on dried fruits, carobs, nuts and seeds and sometimes stored pollen in bee comb.

drifting: The movement of bees to another hive other than the one from which they originated.

drivert sugar: A dry partly inverted sugar used in icings and pan-coated confections. Used by some beekeepers as winter feed.

drone: The male bee, whose main function is the fertilization of a virgin queen bee. The male chromosome cell condition is haploid (1n).

drone brood trapping: A mechanical varroa mite control method utilizing capped drone brood to reduce reproducing female mites. Beekeeper removes and kills capped drone comb cells with mites.

drone cells: Larger (4 to linear inch) horizontal cells produced by worker bees for drone production but can also be used for honey storage.

drone congregation area (DCA): Sites outside the colonies where drones and queens mate. DCAs are high in the air and persist from one year to the net.

drone layer: A queen which lays only unfertilized, drone eggs. Results from improperly or non-mated queen or an older queen that has run out of sperm.

drone production: Part of the normal development of a colony during spring buildup. Drone cells appear before queen swarm cells.

drumming: Rhythmic pounding on side of hive to drive bees upward. Used to transfer bees from rustic (non-removal comb) hive into new hive body.

dry sugar: The solid form of sucrose (table or granulated sugar), a disaccharide compound of glucose and fructose. Used as dry bee feed, or mixed with water as a sugar syrup or hardened into sugar brick.

dwarf honey bee: *Apis florea*, species of small, single comb, wild honey bee of southern and southeastern Asia.

dwindle (spring/fall) disease: See colony collapse disorder. Also signifies a colony that slowly dwindles in adult population/strength at time other colonies are okay.

Dyce process: A patented process used to make creamed honey, known for very fine smooth sugar crystals. Developed by Dr. Elton Dyce in the mid 1930's.

dysbiosis: A condition when the bacteria in the gastrointestinal tract becomes unbalanced. Impaired microbiota.

dysentery: The discharge of fecal matter by adult bees within or immediately outside the hive. Common contributing conditions are *Nosema* spp. infections, excess moisture in the hive, starvation conditions and low quality food.

E

early spring: Period of early growth of the honey bee colony, usually reliant on food stores from the previous season, characterized by imbalance with older adult population predominant.

earwigs: Insect order Dermaptera. Often seen hiding in crevices of the bee hive. Considered harmless but in some areas may carry European foulbrood and may pierce cappings and ruin comb sections with excreta, food fragments and the skins of nymphs.

ecdysone: Prothoracic gland hormone secreted into blood; functions as epidermis-cell messenger to trigger molt.

eclose (eclosure): Correct term for emergence of an adult insect from a pupal case or an insect larva from an egg without rupture of covering membrane. Often incorrectly termed hatching.

ectothermic (cold blooded): An animal that is dependent on eternal sources of body heat; opposite is endothermic.

efficient supersedure: Queen replacement of failing original (mother) queen in which both the mother and daughter queens continue egg laying during transition.

egg: First stage of metamorphosis. Honey bee eggs are deposited at the base of the beeswax comb cell by the queen.

egg laying: The process of a queen laying eggs in beeswax comb cells.

egg laying rate: Number of eggs a queen lays in a certain time period, usually in one day.

electric bear fence: Electrified fence constructed around an apiary used to deter bear attacks.

emergency queen cell: The bees' method of replacing a colony that has suddenly lost its queen. Worker cells are modified to reorient horizontal worker cells into the vertical position.

emergency queen rearing: Queen replacement after sudden loss or removal of existing queen.

encaustic painting: Painting using heated and pigmented beeswax. Also called hot wax painting.

endopeptidase: Proteolytic peptidases that break peptide bonds from end-pieces of terminal amino acids.

endothermic: An animal capable of the internal generation of heat. Opposite is ecothermic.

engorgement: Behavior of worker bees filling (engorging) their honey stomachs with hive honey reserves, providing carbohydrates during the swarming and hive establishment process.

entomopathogenic fungi: Fungi (mycelia) that suppress significant insect/mite mortality. Adult bees are not impacted (because of their self-grooming) but may negatively impact brood.

entrance monitoring: Observational or electronic monitoring of hive entrance activity; used to determine bee flight, ingress of pollen, defensive behavior, removal of items and/or individuals from the hive.

entrance reducers: Devices designed to confine hive exiting and entering to a smaller area. Often used during the winter (as rodent deterrent), but also during periods of robbing.

Epipen (epinephrine) auto-injector: Auto-injector system containing epinephrine designed to be used in emergencies to treat allergic reactions to insect stings/bites (and also foods, drugs, or other substances). Emergency treatment to improve breathing, stimulate the heart, raise dropping blood pressure, reverse hives (body itching), and reduce swelling of the face, lips, and throat.

esophagus: Tube that passes food from the mouth (pharynx) to the honey crop of the honey bee.

ether roll: Using di-ethyl ether to sample percentage of adult bees with varroa mites.

ethylene oxide (ETO): Fumigant for used beekeeping equipment as an option to burning of equipment with confirmed/suspected American foul brood. No longer used as ETO is a flammable, carcinogenic, mutagenic, irritating and anesthetic gas.

European foulbrood (EFB): Bacterial disease of larval bees, non-spore forming. See foulbrood.

eusocial: Advanced level of social organization. Reproductive female (queen) caste tended by sterile worker caste, cooperative care of young and overlap of generations caring for young.

European hornet: *Vespa crabro*. True hornet accidently introduced into eastern U.S. over 100 years ago. Minor pest feeding on foraging honey bees.

evaporation (active & passive): Removal of excess water from nectar by actively exposing small droplets of ripening nectar at the mouthparts or (passively) hanging droplets of ripening nectar in the hive environment.

evolution: The change in heritable characteristics in a population of plants or animals. The process by which early life forms diversified into current species.

excessive swarming: Combined effect of prime swarm and afterswarms leaving the parent hive too weak to survive, or queenless.

exine: The decay-resistant outer coating of pollen or spores. Unique coat characteristics may be used for identification by palynology.

exocrine glands: Glands that secrete substances into an epithelial (outside) surface by a duct.

exoskeleton: External body covering (skeleton) of insects. Living portion (epidermis cells) with cuticle layers of chitin and sclerotin for strength. Outer epicuticle layer often waxy with extending body sensory hairs or hairy body covering.

expanding brood nest: Typical spring and summer expansion of the bee hive brood and adult hive population.

exposed nest: Constructed beeswax combs outside of a cavity; sometimes a swarm builds comb at temporary bivouac location when deterred from moving due to poor weather.

extra-floral nectary: Nectar-producing plant cells that secrete a sugary liquid from sites other than the flower.

extracted honey: Honey removed from the comb by an extractor via centrifugal motion and marketed in the liquid form.

extractor (radial & tangential): Manual or motorized machine that removes honey from uncapped combs by centrifugal motion. Radial removable extractors spins the honey from both sides at same time (perpendicular frame arrangement) while tangential extractors (frames horizontal) remove one side only requiring rotation of the frames 180 degrees to remove honey from other surface.

F

facet (of eye): The individual ommatidium of the compound eye in insects.

fall inspection: Pre-winter hive inspections between honey harvest and the start of winter. Often focused on feeding, if stores are low, queen replacement and mite sampling and treatment.

fall requeening: Replacement of a queen; sometimes due to supersedure failure or other late season queen issue: accomplished via mated queen or uniting resource nucleus.

fan experiment: Experiment of Professor Karl von Frisch designed to show the degree of directional accuracy of the bee dance.

fat (diutinus) bees: Bees prepared for winter. Individual adults have increased sugar and fats in the blood, enlarged food glands, larger fat bodies, lower levels of hormones, and the lack of brood rearing and foraging.

fat body (winter bees): Bees with large fat bodies distributed throughout the abdomen. Thought to help the winter bees to live until spring, providing the energy needed to heat the internal cluster.

feeder: A device to feed a bee colony sugar syrup; used to stimulate colonies in the spring or augment honey stores in the fall.

feeding additives: A wide range of vitamins, minerals, food compounds and items thought to augment honey bee nutrition and/or reduce varroa mite levels/development.

feeding pollen substitute: Standard nutritional practice by commercial and other beekeepers; designed to provide sugar, fat, protein and other essential components of honey bee nutrition.

feeding sugar syrup: Method of supplying sucrose to hives to stimulate growth or provide adequate overwintering honey stores.

feeders: A range of jars, containers, frame replacements and other devices used to feed honey bee colonies liquid or solid sugars.

femur: Largest region of an insect's leg, located between the trochanter and the tibia.

feral bees (hives, nests): A wild, non-managed nest of honey bees, as in a tree.

fermentation: Metabolic breakdown of a substance by bacteria, yeasts, or other microorganisms; activity of microorganisms that bring about a desired change to a food or beverage. In honey, spoilage.

fertilization: Action or process of fertilizing an egg, female animal, or plant, involving the fusion of male and female gametes to form a zygote.

festooning: A string of worker bees, usually observed during the process of secreting beeswax.

field bees: Worker bees who are mature enough to fly from the hive on foraging missions. Also termed forager bees.

filtering honey: Passing honey through fabric and screens—materials designed to remove large and small particles added to honey during human processing.

finisher colony: In queen rearing, a queen-right colony used to finish started queen cells produced in a starter colony.

fixing the location: Determination of the location of a nest or food source as shared by dancing bees.

flagellum (of antenna): Segmented terminal segments of an insect's antenna.

flight activity: Foraging and scouting behavior of bees, influenced by daylight, temperature, rain and wind.

flight path: The direction bees fly leaving their hive. Beekeepers should avoid obstructing/obstructions of the flight path.

floral designs: Flower patterns that assist foragers to associate in flower recognition; contributors to flower loyalty (constancy).

flow hive (super): Australian hive designed to harvest honey from frames by turning a lever; the frames contain a partially-formed plastic honeycomb lattice with vertical gaps.

flyway: Aerial flight conduit foraging bees use to reach food sources and drones to reach drone congregation areas for mating.

fondant: Icing sugar made from sugar, water, gelatin, vegetable fat or shortening, and glycerol. Cakes of fondant are used to feed bees.

food chamber: Hive body, positioned over brood chamber containing honey provided particularly for overwintering bees.

food hoarding: Storage of honey in beeswax comb, often in excess of what is needed for colony survival.

food transmission behavior: Exchange of nectar or honey from one bee to another; often seen in returning forager bees offering food to house bee who help convert the nectar to honey. Behavior passes pheromones.

forage cycle: The pattern of food gathering by a bee colony. Influenced by the flowering plant, weather conditions and hive biology.

forager: Usually an older worker bee that has completed hive duties and has moved on to nectar, pollen and propolis gathering behaviors outside the home.

foraging area: The location a forager is visiting to find food.

forelegs (front legs): The front legs; on the honey bee, the location of the antennae cleaners.

forest or pine honey: Honey produced by honey bees that gather honeydew from pines and other tree species.

formic acid: The simplest carboxylic acid; occurs naturally, most notably in some ants. It has a pungent, penetrating odor at room temperature, not unlike the related acetic acid. Also one of acids used to control varroa mites.

foulbrood (American and European): Bacterial diseases of honey bee brood noted for their strong odor. American foulbrood (AFB) is highly contagious and colonies contracting the pathogen *Paenibacillus larvae* (formerly *Bacillus larvae*) usually die from it. European foulbrood (EFB), caused by the pathogen *Melissococcus plutonius* (formerly *Streptococcus pluton*), is usually a spring disease from which most colonies recover.

foundation: See comb foundation.

foundress mite: The initial, or mother, mite that enters a larval comb cell at the time of larval pupation, to reproduce.

frame grip: Device that removes and holds a frame with one hand. Alternative to hive tool

frame holder: Device mounted on the side of a hive body to hold one or more frames outside the hive body during hive inspection.

frame spacer: Device used to space frames a certain distance apart. Used to ease removal of brood frames for inspection or make uncapping easier for honey storage frames.

frame: Four pieces of wood assembled as a rectangle to hold the beeswax comb. Modern frames (sometimes called Hoffman frames) have a thick top bar for support and end bars with shoulders to provide bee space between adjacent combs and sides of the hive.

fructose (levulose): Monosaccharide of honey produced in eternal digestion of nectar sugars. Also called fruit sugar; it is the sweetest of simple (6-carbon) sugars.

fruit trees: Members of the apple, pear, peach, almond and other tree species that require honey bee pollination.

Fumagillin (fumidil-B): Compound used to control nosema infections. Given to bees to control both species of nosema but may enhance, not control, *Nosema ceranae*.

fume board: Modified cover placed at the top of the hive where repellent chemicals are added; used to drive worker bees out of the supers for harvest.

fungicides: Pesticides that kill fungi. Some have been shown to impact honey bee growth and behavior.

G

gamma radiation: Penetrating form of radiation that has the shortest wavelength. Used to kill AFB spores.

ganglia: A structure containing a number of nerve cell bodies, linked by synapses, often forming a swelling on a nerve fiber. Located ventrally in insects.

gardening for bees: The practice of growing plants and trees that attract pollen and nectar foragers.

gaster: The part of the adult abdomen behind the petiole narrowing.

general food feeders (generalists): Animals that have a diet of a range of foods. Opposite is specialists.

giant honey bee: *Apis dorsata*, the honey bee of South and Southeast Asia; constructs a single brood comb.

giant marine toad: The cane toad (*Rhinella marina*); feeds on bees at the entrance. A large, terrestrial toad native to South and mainland Central America, but now found in Oceania and the Caribbean.

gloves: A covering for the hands worn for protection against cold or dirt. Beekeepers wear gloves to protect against bee stings or to handle caustic mite control chemicals.

gluconic acid: The carboxylic acid formed by the oxidation of the first carbon of glucose. Has antiseptic and chelating properties. Gluconic acid is found abundantly in plants, honey and wine.

glucose (dextrose): A simple monosaccharide (6 carbon) sugar with the molecular formula $C_6H_{12}O_6$. Glucose is the most abundant carbohydrate and most important source of energy in all organisms; most common sugar of honey.

glucose oxidase: Enzyme that catalyzes the oxidation of glucose into hydrogen peroxide and D-glucono-1,5-lactone, which then hydrolyzes to gluconic acid. Serves as preservative of liquid honey.

glycogen: A multibranched polysaccharide of glucose that serves as a form of energy storage in honey bees.

glyphosate: A broad-spectrum systemic herbicide; known as Round-up.

grafting: Transferring first instar larvae during queen rearing to produce queen cells and virgin queens; used in Doolittle queen rearing procedure.

grafting tool: Wood, plastic or metal tool used to transfer larvae.

graftless cell production: Production of queen cells by cutting strips, punching cells, or any other method to start cells without manually transferring the larvae.

granulation: A process whereby liquid honey solidifies as crystals. Termed crystallized or creamed honey when extracted-honey granulation is controlled and marketed as fine, smooth crystals.

gravity orientation (detection): Bees' use of gravity during the dance language to convey in dark hive the proper orientation to the angle of the sun for forager recruits.

grease/oil patty (Crisco® patty): A grease and sugar mixture used for tracheal mite control. Also termed extender patty when antibiotic terramycin is added as a foulbrood disease suppressor.

grooming (shaking) dance: A dance performed by a worker bee to stimulate another bee to remove dust, sugar power or mites from the dancing bee's body.

growing degree days (GDD): A measure of heat in accumulated ambient temperature used to predict plant and animal development rates such as the date that a flower will bloom or a pest might appear.

guard bees: Adult hive bees at the entrance of a hive that monitor the activity of returning foragers and defend against robbing bees and animal intruders.

H

hemolymph (blood): Circulating, free-floating cells in open circulation in a bee's body; carry hemocytes and chemicals to the bee's tissues.

hairy glossa: The hair-covered tongue of a bee.

hamuli: Tiny hooks linking the hind wing to front during flight.

haplodiploidy: The genetic condition whereby female workers and the queen have diploid body cells but drone males develop from unfertilized, haploid eggs and have haploid body cells.

haploid males: Normal male (drone) in which cells have only one set of chromosomes.

haploid: A cell or an organism containing only one set of chromosomes (1n)—normally results from meiosis in sperm or egg, but in Order Hymenoptera is the normal male body chromosome condition.

Hawaii queen: Honey bee queens produced in Hawaii and shipped over the world. Many are produced in one region of Kona on the big island.

headbutt: An aggressive thrust of the head of one animal to the head of another; honey bees use headbutting as a stop signal to warn of danger or halt competing dancers for alternative sites.

heart: Long, 5-chambered hemolymph-pumping organ at top (dorsal) of adult abdomen.

heat generation/conservation: A mantle of bees regulate cluster temperature. In the winter, temperature maintenance combines heat generation, conservation, and cooling, fueled by consumption of stored honey.

heater bees: Individual bees that press their body inside/against cell cappings while working their wing muscles to elevate body heat.

hemocytes: Blood cells that regulate homeostasis and the immune system.

hemolymph (haemolymph): Fluid in invertebrates equivalent to blood.

herbicide: A substance that is toxic to plants and used to kill unwanted vegetation.

heterothermic: Animal body temperature varies with environment; a variation of cold-blooded. Honey bees maintain a brood nest temperature optimized at 35° C.

hexagonal cell: Six-sided beeswax comb cell used by honey bees to rear brood and store food.

high fructose corn syrup (HFCS): A fructose syrup made from corn syrup; corn starch is broken down by enzymes. Used as a lower-cost carbohydrate food for bees by many beekeepers.

hind-legs: Third pair of legs of insects; attached to the thorax. In honey bee workers, the hind legs are noted for the corbiculae, or pollen basket structure.

Hivastan: A contact pyrazole miticide with a thick, pliable formulation used by beekeepers against *Varroa destructor* Discontinued due to bee deaths.

hive: A container domicile housing honey bees by humans. It may be in a skep, Langstroth, top bar or other form.

hive bee: An adult worker who performs duties in the hive (cleaning, nurse duties and guarding) before becoming a field bee.

hive body: A box, usually of wood, that holds 8 or 10 frames and serves as a home for bees. Standard depth (or deep super) is 9-5/8" and usually is used for brood. Shorter hive body boxes (supers) weight less and commonly used for honey storage (see super).

hive odor: Distinctive smell characteristic to individual colonies that results from food odors and body pheromones of adult bees.

hive stand: Wood, metal, concrete or other material support for bee hives to elevate hives above ground.

hive tool: A metal device used to break propolis seals to open hives, pry frames apart, lift frames, etc., while examining a hive.

Hoffman frame: A self-spacing frame where one part of the side bar is flat and the other is beveled, thus reducing surface contact. Developed by Julius Hoffman, a Polish immigrant working in New York state.

Holst milk test: Simple test using skim milk powder and macerated bee larvae to confirm American foulbrood.

homeostasis: Self-regulating process in which an individual maintains a stable physiological equilibrium. Social insects maintain collective activities in the colony's environment.

honey: A sweet, sticky fluid made by bees and other insects from nectar collected by bees from flowers. Consists mainly of the two simple sugars glucose and fructose with final moisture content below 18.6%.

honey or bees as weapons: In warfare, the use of honey from certain flowers that is toxic to humans. Often contains a poison grayanotoxin, a substance that disrupts the nerve cells. Also use of stinging insects to disrupt enemy forces

honey bee: Genus *Apis*, Family Apidae, Order Hymenoptera.

honey (nectar) flow: A time of year, perhaps more than once, when abundant nectar is available for collection and the field bees are sufficiently populous to store and ripen nectar for future use by bees or surplus for human harvest.

honey house: Building to extract and process honey.

honey plants: Plants that produce nectar and pollen collected by honey bees.

honey stomach (crop): An enlargement of the posterior end of the esophagus in the bee abdomen in which the bee carries nectar from flower to regurgitate at hive. Also known as the honey sac.

Honey-B-Healthy: Honey bee carbohydrate feeding stimulant; includes lemongrass and spearmint oil concentrate.

honeycomb: Honey bee-built food-storage and brood rearing structure with hexagonal back-to-back cells on a median midrib.

honeydew: A sweet fluid excreted by plant-sucking insects like aphids. Bees occasionally collect and ripen it into a type of honey marketed as pine or forest honey.

honeyguides (*Indicator* spp). Bird species in Africa that lead ground predators (including humans) to bee hives; they feed on honey and brood.

Hopguard: Miticide derived from beta acid aromatic hop processing compounds. Best used when no or little brood is preset.

horizontal (long) hive: Horizontal hive of one or more queen families with 16+ frames.

hormone: A chemical released by endocrine gland that sends messages (via hemolymph) to stimulate specific cells or tissues into action. See ecdysone or juvenile hormone, 2 major honey bee hormones affecting development.

house hunting: Behavior of scout bees to search for a new home before and during the swarming event.

Huber, Francois: Blind Swiss entomologist who used assistant, Francois Burnens, to study bee behavior. Discoveries included the fact the queens did not mate inside a hive, that queens are fed royal jelly, and workers also lay eggs.

human pollination: Transfer of pollen to stigmas by humans to pollinate crops including dates/tree fruits/greenhouse grown plants.

human theft of beehives: Stealing of bee hives from out-apiaries or pollination rental sites.

human vandalism: Criminal destruction/disturbance of colonies of bees.

hybrid (hybridization): Offspring resulting from two genetically different individuals or breeding (crossing) between populations (or sub-species) to produce strains with desirable characteristics.

hygroscopic: Taking up and retaining moisture; a property of honey.

hydrogen peroxide: H_2O_2, a chemical compound slightly more viscous than water. Used as an oxidizer, bleaching agent, and antiseptic. The enzyme glucose oxidase can break down honey into glucose and hydrogen peroxide resulting in the antibiotic property of honey or for treatment of human skin wounds.

hydroxymethylfurfural (HMF): Degradation of acidic sugars (such as HFCS) and honey as a result of heating in processing or storage at elevated temperatures. Used internationally as an indicator of overheating and/or improper/lengthy storage of honey.

hygienic bees: Bee population that describes a genetic predisposition to remove mite and disease infestations. Several hygienic tendencies include body grooming and detection/elimination of mites from capped brood cells.

Hymenoptera (ants/wasps/bees): Order to which all bees belong; includes ants, wasps, and certain parasitic insects.

hypopharyngeal glands: A pair of long glands coiled in the sides of the head consisting of about 550 oval acini attached to a collecting duct. Secretions are rich in proteins; in young workers they are an important component of royal jelly while in older workers they produce sucrose hydrolysis enzymes. Less developed in bees that are starved, exposed to varroa or poisoned with pesticides.

I

Idiopathic Brood Disease Syndrome (IBDS): Abnormal brood condition that resembles other diseases such as American foulbrood, European foulbrood and sacbrood. Dying brood appears liquefied (snot-like) at the bottom of their cells. Seen in condition Parasitic Mite Syndrome (PMS) or Parasitic Mite Brood syndrome (PMBS). No specific pathogen has been identified as responsible. See also crud brood.

increase nuclei colony: A colony produced by a beekeeper by splitting, removing brood and bees, or related method. Also called splits and divides.

Indian meal moth: A pyraloid moth of the family Pyralidae; minor pest of pollen in stored bee comb.

indirect flight muscles: Insect thoracic muscles connected to the upper (tergum) and lower (sternum) surfaces of the insect thorax. A second set of muscles attach to the front and back of each thoracic segment. Working alternatively, they cause insect flight.

inefficient supersedure: Queen replacement behavior of replacement of an old queen with a new queen with out overlap of both queens.

inert pesticide ingredients: Substances of formulated pesticides, (indicated as "inert or other ingredients" on the label); these proprietary ingredients may be emulsifiers, solvents, carriers, dyes, organosilicones, or other items. Some have biological properties.

inner cover: Internal cover used under the telescoping top cover on a Langstroth beehive.

insect ally: Any beneficial insect. Generally, insects that benefit humans, like lady bugs and honey bees.

insect growth regulator (IGR): Chemical that breaks the developmental cycle of an insect, often preventing molting.

instar: Developmental stage of arthropods; the interval between each molt (ecdysis), until adult stage.

instrumental (artificial) insemination (II/AI): The artificial depositing of semen into the oviduct of a queen by the use of an instrument; utilizes a microscope and hooks to open oviduct for insertion of syringe containing semen.

integrated pest management (IPM): Pest control technique that integrates several measures, including (but not primarily) chemicals, to keep pest population below economic injury level to minimize risks to bee, bee products, human health and the environment.

intercaste: Individual that has combination of queen and worker characteristics; intercastes do not ordinarily survive in social colony.

introduction cage: Small wood and wire (Benton and California) queen cage, or plastic (JzBz) of homemade wood and wire cage designed to introduce and release queens into the colony. Benton, California and JzBz cages used to ship queens from supplier to beekeeper.

invertase: Earlier term for enzyme that converts complex sugar of nectar to honey. See sucrase.

Isle of Wright disease: Disease of honey bees of English channel islands and England that was considered responsible for killing bees for over 20 years beginning in the early 1900's. Often linked to the tracheal mite *Acarapis woodi* (Acarine disease) but may have been a catch-all to describe excessive losses, perhaps due to nutritional deficiencies.

isopently acetate: Alarm pheromone released when bees sting.

Israeli acute paralysis virus (IAPV): Persistent RNA virus infecting honey bees; associated with colony collapse disorder (CCD).

Italian bees: Most widely used race of bee. Excellent honey producers and good brood producers. Originated in Northern Italy.

J

Johnston's organ: A collection of sensory cells found in the pedicel of the antennae that are used to perceive sounds by dancing honey bees to interpret distance to food. Also used in detection of electrical fields.

juvenile hormone (JH): Hormone secretion by the corpora allata in an insect brain. Functions in conjunction with ecdysone, to regulate larval molt to next larval stage. In adult bees, JH functions in egg maturing, queen longevity and worker behavior sequence.

K

K-wing: Appearance of bee wings with hind wing over front to resemble letter K; caused by tracheal mite infestation.

Kashmir bee virus (KBV): RNA virus infecting bees, including the brood and adults of honey bees. One of the viruses implicated in colony collapse disorder.

Kenyan top bar hive: A top bar hive with sloping side walls in which the beeswax comb hangs from removable bars. The bars form a continuous roof over the hive. Developed in 1971 by Drs. M.V. Smith and G. Townsend, Univ. of Guelph, for the Canadian International Development Agency (CIDA) as an inexpensive hive for African beekeepers.

Kingdom: One of the five taxonomic divisions in which living organisms are classified. For animals Kingdom Animalia.

L

labial (salvary) gland: The salivary gland system comprises two pairs of exocrine glands, one in the head (head salivary glands) and one in the thorax (thoracic salivary gland). Workers, queens and drones appear to have different functions for these glands.

labium: In honey bees, the labium forms the lower part of the proboscis.

labrum: The 'upper lip' or hardened exoskeleton plate on the lower center of the head; covers mandibles and flagellum beneath it.

landmarks: Physical elements observed outside the hive, used by honey bees during foraging orientation to and from home. May be part of the orientation to Drone Congregation Areas (DCAs).

Langstroth hive: Constructed domicile for a bee colony consisting of a bottom board, one or more hive bodies holding 8 or 10 frames, and a lid. Original design by the Rev. L.L. Langstroth (1852), modified early 1900s by A.I. Root Co (simplified Langstroth).

Langstroth, L. L.: A minister from Pennsylvania who patented the first removable frame hive incorporating bee space. The modern hive is frequently termed the Langstroth hive; it is a simplified version of similar dimensions as patented by Langstroth.

Large local reaction: Reactions to Hymenoptera stings that are exaggerated (large), but not life-threatening. Pain more intense, swelling more extensive, moves beyond the sting site, and itching persists for longer time.

larva (e): Feeding stage of development following egg prior to capping (pupal) stage.

laying worker colony: A colony without a queen and in which multiple workers are laying unfertilized eggs; colony in decline due to lack of new worker bees. Requeening laying worker colonies difficult.

laying workers: Worker bees which lay non-fertilized eggs, producing only drones in hopelessly queenless colonies. Not a drone layer.

leafcutting bee: Family Megachilidae. Bees collect pollen on hairs of lower abdomen; nest in the soil, a hollow plant stalk, or a cavity in wood. The solitary female lines nest tunnel with cut leaves. Some species commonly termed mason bees.

levulose: See fructose.

life cycle: The series of changes in the life of an organism, and in bees their colony population and reproduction.

Lincomycin (Lincomix): An antibiotic that is used to treat AFB bacterial infection in bees: Used to treat humans who cannot use penicillin antibiotics. Veterinary prescription needed for use.

liquid honey: Honey that has not granulated; as initially stored in the beehive and extracted by beekeepers.

locating hives: Placing an apiary in an area, following suggestions for safe placement.

locomotor: The power of moving from place to place.

long Langstroth hive: A horizontal Langstroth-style hive, holding 20 or more standard frames.

lost wax (jewelry crafting): Cire perdue is used to produce delicate metal sculpture. Voids are filled with pliable wax like beeswax then covered with clay or plaster and heated, hardening the outer wall and melting the wax. The voids where wax was first present is then filled with molten metal.

lye bath: A boiling lye water bath used to kill American foulbrood spores in bee equipment; Lye is caustic so eye and skin protection required.

M

making divides: See increase nuclei colony.

malpighian tubules: Excretory structures to remove nitrogenous waste from hemolymph; long tube-like vessels opening into the posterior part of the digestive tract.

mandibles: Mouthpart for biting, cutting and molding beeswax; Queen and drones have pointed mandibles to aid in cutting and biting, worker bee mandibles weakly biting, mainly used in the shaping of wax and construction of beeswax comb.

mandibular gland: Sac-like glands in the bee's head that produce 2-heptanone, an alarm chemical and anesthetic used to paralyze small hive intruders.

manipulation cloth: A heavy cloth used to cover frames exposed during hive inspection, exposing only the frame being inspected. Used during periods of robbing or cold weather.

marked queen: Queen with paint or glued disc on her thorax to make it easier to find her, document her age and confirm genetic history.

mason bee: Members of genus *Osmia*, of the family Megachilidae, named for use of mud nest partitions.

mated queen: The queen of the colony. She may live two to three years.

mating control: Any method used to control the queen mating to desired drones; methods include geographic isolation, temporal isolation, drone saturation, and instrumental insemination.

mating flight: The flight early in the life of a virgin queen during which time she mates with on average 15-20 drones during one or more mating flights.

mating nucs (mini nucs): Nuclei made with a small number of nurse bees, a small comb area, food and a queen cell.

maxilla: Part of mouthparts. In honey bees forms part of proboscis: paired usually with palpi for sensory purposes.

May disease: See colony collapse disease.

mead: A wine made with honey. If spices or herbs are added, the wine is usually termed metheglin.

mechanoreceptors: Organs or hairs that detect touch, electrical fields, sound flow and other stimuli.

medicinal honey: Honey used for animal or human medication, such as a burn, skin lesions or other surface wound injury; also for coughs and throat irritations.

Mediterranean flour moth: The stored grain pest (Mediterranean flour moth or mill moth) (*Ephestia kuehniella*) of the family Pyralidae. It is a common although minor pest of cereal grains and stored bee pollen.

medium (Illinois/western hive body or super): Hive box with a depth of 6 5⁄8 inches, and length and width dimensions of a Langstroth hive for eight to ten frames.

meliponiculture: Care and management of stingless bee colonies.

menthol (mite-a-thol): Essential oil treatment for tracheal mites.

metamorphosis: Change from egg to adult. See bee metamorphosis.

mice: Rodent of genus *Mus*, common pests of bee hives during the winter. Entrance reduction is major control management.

microbes: Bacteria, protozoa, fungi, algae, amoeba and slime molds. Found in most animals.

microbials: A microbe, mostly beneficial; some can cause potential problems.

microbiome: Microorganisms in an environment, such as in part of the body, usually in bee gut.

microencapsulated pesticide: A pesticide formulated as tiny particles or droplets surrounded by a coating.

mid-legs: Middle leg of insects; paired. Attach to the mesothorax.

mid-winter inspection: Usually a brief hive inspection held on a calm, sunny winter day, checking colony weight, cluster location and the need to supplement honey stores.

Midnite hybrid: A four-line hybrid developed by Dr. G.H. Cale Jr. for Dadant and Sons, Inc. Selected from dark race bees for gentleness and productivity. No longer available.

migratory beekeeping: Movement of colonies from one area to another to take advantage of different honey flows or for crop pollination.

Miller (tray) feeder: A hive top feeder with a space for the bees to crawl up a wood/plastic ladder to reach syrup.

Miller method: Queen rearing method developed by C.C. Miller; uses fertilized eggs laid by the queen on edge of comb to convert into queen cells.

minimum protective gear: The minimum protection a beekeeper needs during a hive inspection: often a veil, hive tool and smoker; beginners add bee suit and gloves.

mite-biting bees: Bees that bite varroa mite body parts, remove legs, and administer 2-heptanone (from mandibular glands) to control mites. Also called ankle biters or leg chewers. A form of grooming behavior.

mite threshold: The number of mites (per 100 bees or on sticky debris boards) that provides an estimate of risk of colony non-survival.

mite: Eight-legged arthropod relatives of insects. See *Acarapis woodi* and *Varroa destructor*.

miticide: A pesticide that kills mites.

monofloral diet: Bee feeding on pollen from a single plant course such as occurs in a monoculture crop like almonds.

morphology: The study of the form and structure of organisms and their specific structural (anatomical) features.

mortality rate: Death rate.

mother-daughter queens: When both the mother and daughter are present in a colony, a result of efficient supersedure.

moving bees: See migratory beekeeping.

multiple eggs: More than one egg in a beeswax cell; commonly seen in colonies with laying workers.

multiple mating: Queen bees mate with a large number of drones, providing advantage of increased genetic diversity of the resulting workers.

murder hornet (*Vespa mandarinia*): Asian giant hornet, native to temperate and tropical regions in China, Korea, Japan and northern India. Recently discovered in British Columbia, Canada and Washington state. Predators of honey bees.

mushrooms, polyphone (*Metarhizium*): Mushroom mycelia under investigation as a possible varroa mite control.

N

naphthalene: A moth control agent sold to the general public. Not suitable for beekeepers (only paradichlorobenzene (PDB) is recommended for wax moth control of stored bee equipment).

Nasonov (Nasanov) Pheromone: Pheromone released by scent gland at dorsal tip of abdomen assisting in orientation behaviors to hive, flowers, water and home sites of swarms.

National Honey Board: Federal government-industry program focused on the expansion of use of honey.

natural comb: Comb built by the bees in feral hives or outside of frames in hives or within frames without foundation.

nectar: A sweet secretion of flowers (from nectaries) of various plants; some secrete enough to provide excess for conversion to honey.

nectar collectors: In beekeeping, the bees that focus on nectar gathering rather than pollen foraging.

nectar guides: Marks on the flower visible to pollinators to guide them to the reproductive parts of the flower and nectary.

nectar flow: See honey flow.

nectar ripening: Bee conversion of nectar to honey.

nectar secretion: Release of nectar in the nectary of a flower.

nectar sugar concentration: The percentage of sugar found in nectar; will vary with environmental conditions and plant species.

nectary: A flower gland, usually base of sepal, whose cells secrete nectar. (See also extra-floral nectary).

neighbor concerns: Communicating with neighbors about the risks of stings, water supply and pesticide use.

nematodes: A worm of the animal phylum Nematoda, such as a roundworm or threadworm. Some nematodes are being used for the control of small hive beetles, others investigated for other bee pests.

neonicotinoid insecticide: A class of neuro-active insecticides chemically similar to nicotine. Imidacloprid is the most widely used insecticide in the world. Neonicotinoids are less toxic to birds and mammals than insects. Some are highly toxic to insects.

nest cavity: A sheltered, darkened cavity of the proper size and orientation for a honey bee colony to occupy and establish a hive.

nest consolidation: Natural colony reorganization of brood area and stored food as they prepare for colder weather.

newbees: Term used to describe people who are starting with beekeeping.

newspaper uniting: Combining two colonies using a sheet of newspaper with small slits in it. This allows bees to chew the paper and slowly merge the two colony scents.

nooks: Another term for nucleus colonies (nucs). See nucleus colony.

normal sting reaction: Swollen area of human tissue not extending over a joint with elevated wheal and redness; swelling and itching fade in a day or two. Not an allergic reaction.

Nosema: The microsporidian pathogens *Nosema apis* and *Nosema ceranae* that inhabit the bee gut.

nosema disease (nosemosis): A malady of adult bees affecting the intestinal tract. Results in poor queen performance and affects worker food production. Caused by the microsporidian pathogens *Nosema apis* and *Nosema ceranae*.

nozevit: An all natural plant polyphenol honey bee food supplement that is added to sugar syrup feed; often indicated for *Nosema control* but effectiveness undetermined.

nucleus (nuc/nook) colony: A colony of bees made by colony division; used to make new colonies, as support (resource) hives and in queen rearing (mating nuc).

nurse bees: Three- to ten-day-old adult house bees who feed the larvae and perform other tasks in the hive.

nutrition levels of legumes: Assessment of the protein level of legumes, often determined at harvest.

O

observation hive: A small colony of bees maintained in a single-comb-wide arrangement with glass or plastic sides for easy viewing of hive activities.

ocellus, ocelli: Three light-sensitive structures on top of the bee's head. Probably detects night and day and sets daily biological rhythms.

odor and queen introduction: Beekeepers may add odors to a hive during queen introduction in hope of increasing acceptance. Vanilla and other products are used.

opening brood nest: Manipulation of adding frames or re-spacing brood frames to introduce empty cells within the brood area to promote colony expansion/reduce chance of swarming.

optic flow pattern: The motion pattern generated in the compound eye that shows movement relative to the environment; may assist in communication of distance by dancing.

optic lobe: A major part of an insect's brain; optic lobes provide a link between the receptor surfaces of the eyes and the brain. Perform the first steps in interpreting visual information.

optimum foraging strategy: Concept, by Tom Seeley, of how bees maximize colony food-gathering activity.

Orders: Insects are divided into 29 different Orders based on morphology and genetics. The Order Hymenoptera includes sawflies, ants, bees and wasps.

organophosphates: A class of insecticides, easily absorbed through the skin and respiratory tract. Toxic exposures are common.

orientation flights: Increasingly distance flights made by new foragers as they become familiar with the hive's entrance and landmark surroundings. Also called play flights.

Osmia: Mason bees, a name commonly used for species of bees in the genus *Osmia*, of the family Megachilidae.

out-apiary: An apiary (beeyard) not at the beekeeper's residence.

outer cover: Protective hive cover used over an inner cover. One popular design is telescoping which covers top and overlaps sides.

ovarioles: Tubes of the ovaries where eggs develop. Honey bee queens will have 100 to 180 ovarioles per ovary; workers only a few undeveloped.

ovary: Egg-producing paired organs in abdomen of female.

over-heating queens: Anytime queens are kept at a temperature above 95° F., harm may occur to the queen.

overlapping generations: When the mother is in a nest with her sons and daughters. Characteristic of eusocial insects.

overwinter/annual colony loss: Colonies that die during the winter months compared to those that die during the active season.

overworking bees: An industry concept referring to extensive use of bee hives for multiple pollination rentals and honey production moves.

oviduct (lateral & median): The path of the egg from the end of the ovariole to the opening of the sting chamber.

ovipositor: Female egg-laying structure; in honey bees it is the modified sting.

oxen-borne bees: An ancient ritual whereby bees were supposedly produced from the rib-cage skeleton of an oxen; wasps came from horses.

oxalic acid: Poisonous crystalline acid with a sour taste, present in rhubarb leaves, wood sorrel, and other plants. Its uses include bleaching, cleansing and varroa treatment.

oxytetracycline: See terramycin.

P

package bees: A quantity of bees (2 to 3 lbs), usually with a queen, shipped in a wire and wood or plastic cage; used to start or boost colonies.

Paenibacillus larvae **(AFB):** Pathogen (bacteria) that causes American foulbrood.

painting hives: Practice of protecting exposed hive equipment by paint, stain or dipping in wood preservatives/hot wax.

palynology: The study of pollen grains and other spores.

palpi: Appendage attached to the oral (mouth) part and serving as an organ of sense in insects and crustaceans. In honey bees, the maxillae and labium both have palpi.

paper wasps: Vespid wasps that use dead wood fibers and saliva to construct nests made of gray or brown papery material in the ground or aerially. Most seasonally social. Some seek to rob honey at the end of the season.

paradichlorobenzene (PDB) (Para Moth®): A chlorinated aromatic hydrocarbon used as a fumigant insecticide and repellent (against moth caterpillars). Used to protect brood wax comb storage, but not comb containing honey.

parallel beeswax comb: Elaboration of beeswax comb with the bee space between parallel combs.

paralyzing wasps: Wasps that sting and paralyze prey to feed their offspring, usually in separate cells.

Parasitic Mite Brood Syndrome (PMBS): Symptoms observed in brood (snot/crud brood) when varroa mite populations high. See also PMS and IBDS.

Parasitic Mite Syndrome (PMS): Symptoms observed in colonies when mite populations high. See also PMBS.

parasitic wasps: Small, slender, hairless wasp relatives of bees with two pairs of clear to smoky membranous wings and long antennae; primarily lay eggs in insect larvae.

Paris green pesticide: A vivid green toxic crystalline salt of copper and arsenic; once a common insecticide and rodenticide.

parthenogenesis: Production of offspring without use of sperm, such as from a virgin female. Also termed haplodiploidy.

passive evaporation: Evaporation of a liquid, such as incompletely processed nectar, when stored in a warm and dry environment.

pasteurization of honey: Process of rapid heating, fine filtering, and cooling of honey with the purpose of killing natural yeasts and delaying crystallization.

pears: Fruit in the Genus *Pyrus*. Most varieties have low nectar sugar with odors attractive to flies but not honey bees.

pedicel (of antenna): Second segment of the antenna in class Insecta where the Johnston's organ is located.

perennial life cycles: Plants that grow year-round, surviving winter temperatures. May be herbaceous or woody. In honey bees social society continues through all seasons.

personal protection (against stings): Veils, suits, gloves. Also termed PPE (personal protective equipment).

pesticide exposure: Direct and indirect contact with a human-made pesticide.

phagostimulant: Stimulation of feeding by an organism. Sugar and pollen are common honey bee phagostimulants.

pharynx: Part of the insect digestive system; muscular for food uptake into the esophagus.

pheromone: A chemical substance released externally by an individual which stimulates a response in a second individual of the same species. Primer pheromones work long term; releaser pheromones elicit an immediate response.

phoretic (phorsey/phoresis): Movement of an organism on the body of a second (the host). Used to describe varroa mites being carried on the body of honey bees. More correctly labeled the dispersal phase of varroa life cycle.

photoperiod: Period of time each day an organism receives light; day length. Increasing photoperiod stimulates egg laying by queens during the winter.

phototactic: Individual response to light stimulus; adult worker (house) bees initially negatively phototactic (adverse to light) then positive (go towards light) by foraging age.

Phylum: A principal taxonomic category that ranks above class and below kingdom. Insects in Phylum Arthropoda.

physiology: Branch of biology that deals with the normal functions of living organisms and their parts.

piping: Audible sound made by confined queens. During emergence queen cell sound is called quacking while sound made by queen outside a queen cell is called tooting. Perceived by bees as cell vibrations; it serves to communicate a queen's presence to other queens and workers in the colony.

pistil: The combined female portion of stigma, style, and ovary of a flower. One or more carpels make up the pistil.

pistillate flower: Flowers containing the pistil (but not the male portion stamen); with pollination potentially setting the fruit or seed.

plaster (cellophane) bee: Members of the bee family Colletidae; females smooth the walls of their cells with mouth secretions.

plastic queen cage: Queen-holding cages for shipment and introduction. JZs-BZs are one popular design.

plumose: Branching as in body hairs covering bees; a feature of pollen-collection by bees.

plumose hairs: Hairs of bees that are feather-like or branched. Most body covering not sensory.

polarized light: Light in which individual light waves are aligned parallel to one another. Bees use outside the hive for orientation.

pollen: Usually a powdery substance consisting of pollen grains which are male microgametophytes of seed plants, which produce male gametes. Male reproductive cells of flowers collected at anthers and used by bees for rearing their young. It is the protein part of the diet; termed bee bread when processed and stored in cells in the colony.

pollen and nectar diet: Entire diet of bees.

pollen basket: See corbicula.

pollen bees: General term for non-*Apis*, non-eusocial bee species.

pollen collection and packing: Method used by honey bees to collect, pack and carry pollen.

pollen collectors (foragers): Forager bees that collect primarily pollen; some foragers of some flowers may collect both nectar and pollen.

pollen grains: Individual grain of pollen. Pollen grains are specific to species and their morphology is used to identify honey floral source.

pollen inserts: Device used at colony entrance to distribute compatible pollen during crop pollination.

pollen pellets: A clump of pollen grains collected by bees while foraging for pollen removed at colony entrance.

pollen substitute: Protein materials like soy flour and brewer's yeast used as a alternative to pollen and used as a protein food source for bees.

pollen supplement: Pollen substitute (as above) with pollen added.

pollen transport: Carrying pollen on special structures of a bee's body, such as the pollen basket, the corbiculae.

pollen trap: Devise that collects pollen pellets from hind legs of bees when they return to the hive following foraging.

pollen-collecting hairs: See plumose hairs.

pollinizer/pollinizer: The plant source of pollen used for pollination to produce a marketable crop.

pollination requirements: Necessary aspects of fertility of flowers of different plant species. For example: apples require cross-pollination while apricots are self-fruitful though cross pollination may boost yield.

pollination: The transfer of viable pollen grains from the anthers to receptive stigma of flowers.

pollinator: The agent which transfers pollen, such as a bee.

polyfloral diet: Mixed diet from several sources such as pollen from different floral sources.

postcerebral gland: Part of the salivary gland positioned in head.

pre-flow spring management: Beekeeper manipulations made before the nectar (honey) flow during spring build-up.

predatory mites: A mite species that seeks out and kills pest mites.

prepupa: Last developmental stage of the larvae form, just prior to molting into the pupa; in honey bees cocoon spinning stage beneath the beeswax cell capping.

primary swarm: The first (and often largest) swarm to issue from a colony; often includes the mother queen. See after-swarm

proboscis: Mouthparts made from the fused maxilla and labium used for liquid uptake of nectar and water.

professional beekeeper: Full-time commercial beekeeper deriving major source of income from honey bees.

progressive provisioning: Continuous feeding as the developing larva grows rather than massive provisioning or all at once.

propolis collectors (foragers): Bees that collect propolis and return with it to the hive.

propolis (bee glue): Resins collected from trees/plants; used to seal holes and surfaces in the hive; have anti-microbial properties for bees and humans.

proprioreceptors: Special nerve cells that coordinate neurologic and physiologic responses; helps the body determine where it is in space.

proventriculus: Structure that functions to engulf pollen in honey stomach and carry it into the digestive tract of a bee.

psocids (order Psocoptera): An order of insects that are commonly known as booklice, barklice or barkflies. Uncommonly found in bee hives.

pseudoscorpion: Unique arachnid found in leaf litter, humus and may hitchhike a ride on other insects. At least one species found in beehives but not believed harmful.

pupa(e): The non-feeding stage in the developing life of insect with complete (four-stage) metamorphosis. Also called capped stage.

pupal tongue: When pupae die of American foulbrood their tongues sometimes attach to the upper part of the cell. When it is observed positively confirms AFB but not always present.

push-in cage: Metal or plastic cage used to introduce a queen. Metal cages are made with 1/8" hardware cloth cut into roughly 3" x 3" squares.

Q

quarantine (regulatory control): Restriction on the movement of people and goods which is intended to prevent the spread of disease or pests.

quasisocial: Social characteristics of cooperative brood care but no caste system or overlap of generations.

queen: An adult honey bee female that lays eggs and produces pheromones. When newly emerged as an adult she is a young virgin queen; once mated and laying eggs, she is called a mated or fertile queen.

queen cage: See introduction cage; push-in cage.

queen cell: Occupied peanut-shaped beeswax cell containing a developing queen. Suspended, hanging vertically downward.

queen cup: Empty cup-like beeswax structure where the queen may lay a fertile egg to start rearing another queen.

queen excluder: Metal or plastic device which allows workers to pass through slots/wires, but spaced to keep the queen and drones from passing through.

queen fighting: Competitive fighting to the death of two same-aged queens.

queen introduction: The process of introducing a queen by caging and delayed release; many release methods are used.

queen marking scheme: International color scheme used to identify the year a queen emerged.

queen pheromone/queen substance: Chemical components secreted by the mandibular glands of a queen; also termed the social glue of a colony. Composed of several key chemical compounds and influences large number of activities.

queen pheromone distribution: Movement of queen pheromone from queen to bee and subsequently to the remainder of the colony by body contact and feeding.

queen production: Development of a new virgin queen by a colony stimulated by queenlessness or queen failure.

queen removal: Systematic removal (temporary or permanently) of a colony queen.

queen replacement: Removal of an old queen and installation of a new queen in bee colony.

queen retinue: Worker bees attending a queen by antennation, grooming, feeding and waste removal and picking up the queen's odor (queen substance) in the process.

queen sequestering: A varroa-mite control practice of confining the queen to create a break in the brood cycle.

queenless colony: Hive where the queen has been eliminated or removed.

queenless roar: Sound of a queenless colony.

queenlessness: The condition of lacking the queen.

queenright: A colony with a healthy, worker egg-laying queen. The opposite of queenless.

queenless colony: A colony lacking a queen.

questing: Searching for something; such as a tracheal mite searching for a young worker bee from body of an older one.

R

rabbet: A step-shaped recess cut into a Langstroth hive body to form a ledge for the frame to rest upon.

race: A population of bees geographically isolated that develops over time adaptions to area conditions.

raspberry: Edible fruit of the genus *Rubus*.

ratel/honey badger: *Mellivora capensis*, mammal native to Africa and Asia; major predator of honey bee colonies.

'reading' a colony: Process of hive and frame inspection to determine current bee activities and for diseases and pests.

ready-to-emerge cells: Queen cells that are in their final hours of pupal development; also called ripe cells.

record keeping: Process of recording hive activities and hive manipulations by beekeepers.

recruits: The forager-aged bees that respond to a dancing bee.

rectrum: Final portion of the intestine opening to the outside to void wastes; recovers water and minerals.

reducing stings: Methods used to manage bees using smoke, protection, and style of management to minimize honey bee defensive behavior.

regurgitation: Reversal of nectar/ripening honey from the honey stomach.

rental fees: Income from colony placement for pollination.

renting apiary location: Obtaining an outapiary site for bee foraging; often paid with honey rather than money.

requeen: To replace a queen. Often old queens are removed and replaced by a ripe queen cell, or a mated queen (via introduction cage).

requeening during nectar flow: Success usually improved in accepting a new queen while bees occupied gathering a nectar (honey) crop compared when requeening is attempted during a nectar dearth.

requeening with brood: The practice of giving a frame of eggs and young larvae to a queenless colony. Also referenced as making a walk away split.

requeening with queen cells: Using a 48-hour or ripe queen cell to establish a new queen in a colony.

resource (support) colony: A nucleus hive that provides a queen, brood frames or food frames. Some beekeepers call these hives brood factories.

resource abundance: The general concept to describe the amount of food available to foraging bees.

retinue: See queen retinue.

reversing brood nest: Process of swapping the position of hive bodies to help expand the brood nest in the spring.

robber bees/robbing behavior: Bees from other colonies stealing honey from another.

robber flies: Members of the fly family, Asilidae, that feed on insects. Powerfully built, with sharp, sucking mouthparts.

robbing screen: Device at the entrance that deflects the hive's bee flight while inhibiting entrance by robber bees.

robbing of honey: Removing honey from a colony by other bees, wasps and predators. Also refers to beekeeper harvest especially destruct harvest of non-removable comb hive.

ropy test: Simple procedure to check to see if a dead bee larva or pupa may have died of American foulbrood; the decomposing tissue will stretch out when pulled away with a toothpick or other device.

Rose hive (one size box): A different depth box of similar dimensions to a National hive in Europe.

round dance: A circular movement (dance) performed by scout bees that indicates food near the hive or nest site near the swarm bivouac.

royal jelly (bee milk): A protein-rich secretion of the worker's hypopharyngeal glands fed to young bee larvae. The queen receives this food throughout her larval period.

royalactin: One of the royal jelly proteins secreted by worker honey bees. Once incorrectly identified as specific substance to differentiate queen from worker caste in development

Russian bees: A stock imported by USDA from far Eastern Russia; selected for its tolerance to varroa and tracheal mites. Now propagated by a Russian bee breeders organization in the U.S.

rustic hive: Old-style, usually non-removable comb bee hive.

S

sacbrood: Commonly found larval virus disease, mostly nonfatal to the colony. Sometimes considered a stress disease.

save the bees: A movement to support efforts to conserve/restore bee populations considered threatened.

scale (AFB): The flattened dehydrated remains of a larva or pupa in beeswax cell that died from American foulbrood.

scape (of antenna): First antennal segment attached to its articulating base.

scavenger insects/mites: Animals that feeds on and recycles organic (dead) material or refuse in the hive.

scent gland (Nasanov gland): Gland on the upper tip of the worker bee's abdomen that produces a mixture of different chemicals (scent gland pheromone) that functions as attractant to other bees.

sclerite: Component exoskeleton plate or section covering a portion of the insect body. Examples include tergites covering top portion of gaster segments and sternites covering the bottom portion.

sclerotin: The structural protein of exoskeleton which forms the cuticles of insects; it hardens and darkens during the late pupal stage of development.

scout bees: Worker bees that search for pollen, nectar, water, propolis plus, during swarming, suitable nesting sites.

scrabbling: Foraging bee's rapid movement over a flower to dislodge and permit pollen collection.

sealed (capped) brood: Brood in the last larval (prepupal) and pupal stage when outer cell opening is sealed with a beeswax covering.

seasonal patterns: In beekeeping, the impact of seasonality on the production and collection of food and the resulting brood and bee production of colonies.

section honey: Where small pieces of honey have been drawn and filled in a wood or plastic container. Section honey includes basswood sections, Ross Rounds and Hogg cassettes.

self-pollination: Transfer of pollen from the anther to the stigma of a flower to the same flower. Compared to cross-pollination.

semisocial: Social species that display overlap of generations and cooperative brood care but lack a caste system.

sensilla(e): One or a few sense cells in the cuticle of the exoskeleton that detect odor, movement or other stimuli. Take many forms from hair-like, to peg and plate-like.

separating brood from queen: Manipulation used to create new brood area as means to control swarming or in making new colonies.

septicemia/sepsis: Blood poisoning by bacteria.

set-off divide: One of several methods of making increase

(nuc) colonies; involves movement of brood and bees to a new location to form a new colony. A queen may be provided or the bees allowed to raise their own queen.

settling tank: A container that allows air bubbles, wax particles and other debris to float to the surface following honey extraction.

Sevin (carbaryl) insecticide: A broad-spectrum carbamate insecticide potentially poisonous to honey bees and other pollinators.

sex attractant: A pheromone, in queen's 9 0DA, that attracts members of the opposite sex of the same species.

shallow super: Usually the shortest (5 ¾ inches) of the Langstroth honey supers; often used for cut-comb honey production.

shivering: Slight shaking movement of bees to keep warm by exercising thoracic wing muscles; occurs when temperature decreases.

shook swarming (shakedown method): A swarm prevention, disease and comb replacement manipulation; adult bees are shaken onto new equipment with foundation frames.

shrews/moles: Small mammal invaders of the hive once the wintering cluster has formed.

sickle dance: A repeated butterfly pattern dance of honey bees intermediate between round and waggle dance.

sideliner: Individuals who keep bees on part-time basis; bee income not their major form of employment.

side working foragers/side-workers: Bees and other pollinators that collect nectar from a gap in the anthers (in apple flowers) avoiding the anthers and stigma of the flower.

skep: Traditional icon of bee home from medieval times to present; a dome-shaped beehive of twisted straw. Beeswax combs are not removable.

skunk: Members of the mammal family Mephitidae that are nighttime visitors to bee hives to feed on bees.

slumgum: Dark residue consisting of brood cocoons, propolis, pollen and other debris after beeswax is rendered from honey harvest.

small hive beetle: Scavenger beetle (*Aethina tumida*) originally from South Africa; Currently a major pest of weak hives, primarily in the Southeastern U.S.

small-scale/hobby/backyard beekeeper: Person with a few colonies of honey bees, often kept in the backyard. Usually not commercially motivated in colony care.

smoker: Instrument used to examine colonies. Consists of a ventilated fire pot in which a smoldering fire is built that directs smoke onto the bees via a bellows.

smoker fuel: Flammable material that produces a cool, abundant smoke that does not irritate the bees as fuel in smoker.

snot brood: See crud brood.

social insects: Insects organized in a cooperative manner.

social wasps: Hornets, wasps and yellowjackets of Order Hymenoptera.

sociality: Group of animals organized in a cooperative manner. In insects, usually a family of related individuals.

solar wax melter: Glass-covered, often insulated, box heated by the sun to melt wax placed inside.

soldier (responder) bees: In certain species of bees, sometimes larger and heavier bees that defend a disturbed nest.

species: The most basic category in taxonomy; a group of organisms that can reproduce with one another in nature and produce fertile offspring.

spermatheca: A small, sac-like organ in the queen's abdomen in which sperm are stored after mating.

spiders (crab and orb-web): A large group of arthropod relatives of insects (2 body parts/8 legs) most of which are carnivores. Some spin silken traps to capture prey.

spiracles: External openings of the tracheal respiratory system tubes on the exoskeleton of the insect.

splits (divides): Other names for a colony division.

spotty brood pattern: Absence of consistent, solid sealed brood pattern in a frame; anything over 10% empty cells considered spotty.

spring dwindling: See colony collapse disease (syndrome).

springtails/bristle-tails: Small insects of the Order Collembola that feed on decaying matter. Generally harmless.

stamen: Male part of the flower on which pollen-producing anthers are borne.

staminate flower: A plant the produces male-only flowers with stamens but no functioning female pistil.

standard hive body: Regular deep Langstroth hive body of 9 5/8 inch depth of 8 or 10 frame width. Usually used for brood production.

Starline hybrid: A now defunct hybrid of four Italian-type inbred lines.

starter colony: A queenless, confined colony of young nurse bees that is given young larvae to start queen cell production.

starvation: Death caused by hunger when honey reserves are exhausted.

sternite: A sclerite making up the sternum (lower side) of an arthropod.

sticky (debris) boards: Stiff white cardboard or plastic tray placed beneath screened bottom board to trap/sample colony varroa mite levels/chewed mite percentage and assess other pests and diseases.

stigma: The receptive tip of the pistil of a flower that receives pollen during pollination.

stimulus (rewards): In behavior, a stimulus triggers a response. In physiology, a stimulus is a detectable change in the physical or chemical structure of an organism's internal or external environment.

sting: A sharp organ found in various animals (typically insects and other arthropods) capable of injecting venom, usually by piercing the epidermis of another animal. In bees, a modified female ovipositor.

sting glands: A series of glands associated with the sting apparatus. Includes venom or acid gland and the Dufour's (alkaline) gland plus pheromone glands.

sting reaction: Response of an organism to being stung. Humans show three sting responses: Allergic—A rapid, full-bodied response that can be fatal. Normal—Stays at the sting site but may have extensive pain and swelling. Toxic—Full-bodied response to too many stings at one time.

sting structure: The modified ovipositor of worker bees used to defend the colony or the individual. A complex protein is injected that causes pain, swelling and discomfort. An alarm odor is released to incite other bees to respond.

stingless bee honey: Honey produced by stingless bees of *Meliponini*. It has higher moisture content and slightly different chemical properties than honey from *Apis*.

stonebrood: A disease present worldwide caused by the fungus *Aspergillus flavus* or, less frequently, *Aspergillus fumigatus*, both found in the soil. Stonebrood can affect larvae as well as adult bees.

straining liquid honey: Removal of larger particulate material after extracting honey using screen or cloth.

strawberry: Fruit of the hybrid species of the genus *Fragaria*.

sucrase: Enzyme produced by bees that causes conversion of nectar sucrose to the glucose and fructose of honey (previously called invertase).

Sucrocide: Sucrose octanoate, introduced in January, 2004, as a treatment for Varroa mites on honey bees; not widely used.

sucrose: Cane or beet sugar; 12-carbon sugar of nectar before inversion into the simple, 6-carbon sugars glucose and fructose of honey.

sugar shake sampling method: A method of using dry powdered sugar to dislodge varroa mites to estimate colony mite population.

super: Any upper story hive box placed over the brood chamber for the purpose of storing (surplus) honey. A deep super is a standard hive body. Two common super sizes are the half-depth or Illinois (6-5/8 inches deep) and the shallow super (5-11/16 inches deep). Supers for comb section honey are 4-3/4 inches deep.

supering: Adding a super to colony. Top supering is placing newly added supers on top of existing supers; bottom supering is placing them above brood beneath existing supers; baiting means enticing bees into supers with sugar syrup or honey. Oversupering is practiced early in the nectar flow followed by undersupering as flow decreases.

superorganism: Colony of individuals where specialist bees work for the common good of the entire social unit and sum is more than just individual workers working together. Equated with the specialized cells of a single organism.

supersedure: The replacement of a weak or old queen in a colony by a daughter queen—a natural occurrence.

support hive: See Resource hive

surplus honey: A term generally used to indicate an excess amount of honey above that amount needed by the bees to survive the winter that might be harvested by the beekeeper.

swarm capture: Collecting a swarm from a temporary swarm bivouac site, hanging from vegetation or other structure prior to its moving into a permanent new nest site.

swarm cells: Queen cells produced under the swarming instinct; many positioned at bottom margin of comb.

swarm cups: Empty cup-like, vertically oriented beeswax comb cells; when queen places egg in one and metamorphosis continues it is then termed a queen cell.

swarm control: Management to keep colonies with developing queen cells from successful swarming. Numerous techniques are used that start with destroying the developing queens, then providing additional brood rearing space, removing brood, removing queen or other major management to keep the colony from re-starting new queens.

swarm prevention: Management of avoiding the development of queen cells in spring colonies; providing young-aged queens, proper ventilation, and adequate brood space for developing spring colonies are most effective prevention techniques.

swarm season: Period of the season, roughly a six week window nearing end of spring buildup, during which time swarm emergence is most common.

swarm: A temporary cluster of adult bees that have left a hive with the queen and full stomachs at a temporary bivouac site seeking to move to a new home. The first swarm with the old mated queen is called the primary swarm; additional swarms (with one or more virgin queens) are termed afterswarms.

swarming: The process of swarming or preparing to swarm. Swarming is reproductive division of a bee colony. The first indication for beekeepers is the presence of queen cells (swarm cells) in the brood area of a queenright colony.

sweat bee: Species of ground nesting Halictidae bees, many dark and small, attracted to human perspiration. They do not sting.

synergism/synergistic effects: Interaction or cooperation of two organizations, substances or other agents where the combined effect is greater than the sum of each of their separate efforts.

systemic pesticide: Molecules that kill pests when taken into plants and translocated to other tissues. May accidentally be secreted into nectar and negatively affect pollinators.

T

Tanzanian top bar hive: A top-bar hive with straight sides instead of sloping sides as in Kenyan top bar hive.

tarsus: Fifth segment of bee leg, often segmented.

temporary bivouac: Encampment in an unsheltered area. Honey bee swarms form temporary bivouacs hanging from vegetation and other structures before moving to a permanent location.

tergite glands: Found on the dorsal surface of the abdomen, these glands are considered the source of some pheromonal activity of the queen honey bee.

tergites: A sclerotized plate as part of the dorsal (top) part (tergum) of the bee's gaster.

tergum: Thickened dorsal (top part of body) plate on each segment of the body of an arthropod.

termites: Wood-eating eusocial insects once in the Order Isoptera now epifamily Termitoidae in Order of cockroaches (Blattodea).

Terramycin® (oxytetracycline): Medication given to bees in powder form for EFB disease condition. Also fed to colonies with AFB; it does not cure the colony, but suppresses AFB symptoms.

thelytoky: A form of parthenogenesis in which females are produced from unfertilized eggs.

thermoregulation: Ability of an organism to keep its body temperature within certain boundaries.

theromographic: Cameras able to detect thermal images.

thin surplus foundation: A thin, pure beeswax foundation used to produce section comb honey or cut-comb honey.

thoracic (salivary) glands: A pair of exocrine glands, one in the head and one in the thorax, of queens and worker bees.

thoracic spiracle: The largest trunk of pro-, meso-thoracic spiracle; houses tracheal mites.

thorax: The middle region of the adult bee body (the front part is the head and the last section is the abdomen). Consists of 3 segments . pro-, meso-, meta-thorax. Attachments include 3 pairs of legs and 2 pairs of wings.

threshold: The point at which a physiological or psychological effect begins to be produced. Also number of pest organisms (for example mites) that triggers decisions on control.

tibia: Insect leg part between the femur and the tarsus.

top bar hive: Horizontal comb hive of parallel combs started from v-shaped top bars lacking side or bottom bars.

top cover: Outermost cover enclosing hive at top. Many are telescoping and cover top and 2 inches (5 cm) on all 4 sides. Most have metal covering.

top insulation: Heat loss protection and moisture regulation material placed on the top of a hive in late fall for hive protection during the winter. Materials include industrial insulation, foam board, hay, straw, dry leaves, corn cobs and other products that collect moisture or slow heat loss from a wintering colony.

top supering: Placing new supers on the top of a hive's top box. Contrast with bottom supering (supers added directly above brood boxes).

tower supering: Placing one set of supers over two adjacent side-by-side colonies; supers are shared by both colonies.

toxic honey: A nectar or honey that has psychoactive or medical effects on humans. Sometimes called mad honey disease.

toxic reaction: Combined effect of multiple stings (too many in short time period). Not an allergic reaction. Also response to a chemical, such as a pesticide, by individual or bee colony.

trachea(e): Breathing tubes to deliver oxygen to cells and remove toxic gas by products such as CO_2. Tiniest branches are tracheoles.

tracheal mites: Tiny mite *Acarapis woodi*, that live and reproduce in the trachea of adult bees. Condition termed acariosis or acarine disease.

tracheoles: Fine respiratory terminal tubes of the trachea of an insect or a spider.

transfer of larvae, grafting: Process of moving a newly emerged larva to a queen cup. Initial action of queen rearing.

transferring bees: Moving bees from one hive to another. Term used to describe removal of bees from rustic hives, bee gums or buildings.

transition cells: Beeswax comb cells that are neither worker nor drone-sized.

travel stain: Darkened (stained) honey cell cappings caused by bees walking on them: undesirable for honey marketed in the comb.

trehalose: Sugar containing two molecules of glucose. Form of storage carbohydrate in fat bodies of bees.

tremble dance: Dance performed by forager honey bees to

recruit more receiver honey bees to collect nectar from the workers.

trichromatic (vision): Ability of animals to see different colors.

trimmed drone brood: Removal and death of drone brood from their cells by worker bee adults; most often occurs during a pollen dearth.

trochanter: Leg segment in insects located between the coxa and the femur; usually smallest segment.

trophyllaxis: Mutual exchange of regurgitated liquids between adult social insects.

Tropilaelaps **mites:** External parasitic mites that feed on the hemolymph of both drone and worker bee larvae, pupae and adult bees. Feeding causes stunting, damaged wings, legs and abdomens causing rapid colony decline. Not currently found in North America.

two and a half colonies: Management system of keeping a support nucleus hive (resource hive) for a supply of laying queens, or brood and food frames for every two full sized colonies. Recommended for beginners and small-scale beekeepers.

two-queen colony: Practice of establishing/keeping two brood areas each with queen divided by a double screen as a single unit; the two colonies with proper timing can be combined (removing the double screen) to produce a larger honey crop using less equipment.

Tylan (tylosin tartrate): Antibiotic used to treat bacterial infections in farm animals, including honey bees. For AFB treatment only.

U

Ulster hive: A five-frame nuc box modified with a top that holds a single frame between glass. When used as observation hive, a frame (usually one with queen) is elevated from nuc below to the position between the glass window.

uncapper: A device that removes cappings from frames of honey prior to being placed in the honey extractor.

uncapping knife (roller): Devise used to remove honey cell caps so honey can be extracted from frames. May be steam or electrically heated.

undertaker bees: Worker honey bees that recognize and remove dead bees from the hive using cuticular chemicals that decrease as bodies cool.

unemployed foragers: The available labor force in a hive, ready to be recruited to specific duties like foraging.

unfertilized egg: Egg that has not been united with sperm. In Hymenoptera such eggs develop into males.

unite: Combine one colony with another. Opposite of divide or split a colony.

unripe honey: partially ripened nectar not yet fully converted to honey.

unsealed (open) brood: Brood in egg and larval stages only.

USDA Bee Lab Beltsville: U.S. Federal facility that includes the Bee Disease Diagnosis Service, located outside Washington DC in Beltsville MD. Bee disease diagnosis has been a focus of this laboratory since its inception in 1891.

usurpation: Replacement of mother queen of an established colony by a (usurpation) queen from a small swarm that gathers on the outside the hive and moves inside. Swarm workers eliminate the mother queen. Relatively uncommon in European bees; one method Africanized bees take over European-race colonies.

V

vampire mites: Slang term for *Varroa destructor*. Research has shown that this mite feeds on fat bodies of adult bees and is not a blood sucking mite.

Varroa destructor **virus (VDV):** Originally Deformed Wing virus B. One of the most serious viruses reaching epidemic levels rapidly in fall, causing rapid colony death.

varroa mite, (*Varroa destructor***):** The most destructive mite pest of honey bees. Reproduces within capped brood and carried by adults (phoretic/dispersal phase). Condition is termed varroosis. Transmitter or several destructive viruses with mite feeding on brood/adults. Has resulted in extensive changes in beekeeping.

varroa sampling: One of several methods of detecting and counting varroa mites in a living bee colony. Two destructive methods (alcohol wash and ether roll) require the beekeeper to obtain a sample of live bees to wash (remove) mites from bee bodies. Powdered sugar and CO_2 dislodge the mites without killing the bees.

varroosis: Condition caused by varroa feeding.

veil: A pliable wire, nylon or cloth mesh worn over the face and head to avoid stings. Some beekeepers add gloves, coveralls and boots for maximum protection.

ventilation holes: Openings in the top and sides of bee colonies that increase air flow.

ventriculus (stomach/mid-gut): The functional stomach of the honey bee; it follows the honey stomach.

vibrating the queen: Behavior of workers designed to deny feeding and keep queen in motion so she loses weight prior to leaving her home with swarm.

virgin queen: Unmated queen.

visual clues: Orientation marks of flowers and landmarks bees use during foraging and hive orientation.

Vita Bee Health Diagnostic kit: A diagnostic kit that detects either AFB or EFB. Works by detecting specific antibodies.

vitamin C: Vitamin found in various foods, an essential nutrient involved in the repair of tissue and the enzymatic production of certain neurotransmitters. It is required for the functioning of several enzymes and is important for immune system function. It also functions as an antioxidant. Pollen supplies this (and other vitamins) for the bee diet.

vitellogenin: A protein found in blood and stored in fat body; related to egg development and in promoting adult longevity during winter.

varroa sensitive hygiene/VSH bees: A behavioral trait in which bees detect, uncap and remove or uncap and then recap bee pupae that are infested by the parasitic mite *Varroa destructor* (and other diseases) halting mite development in brood.

W

wagtail dance (waggling of abdomen): A distinctive figure-eight dance with vigorous side-to-side movement of abdomen (waggling) of the honey bee that communicates distance and direction to fly about a potential food or nesting site.

walk-away split: Term for splitting a colony; bees need raise their own queen in the queenless part or requeen once queenless portion determined.

Warré hive: Vertical top bar hive that uses top bars from which the bees build comb. Additional boxes added from below (nadired) not supered (except for modified Warré management). Named after its inventor, French monk Abbé Émile Warré.

wasp waist: In Hymenopteran insects, a narrow (petiolate) section in the abdomen.

water collectors: Foragers that find and collect water for hive use.

wax glands: Four pair of glands on underside of bee abdomen from which beeswax is secreted after bee has gorged on food.

wax melter: Container used to liquefy beeswax to separate honey and other components; often with a heat element and/or a water jacket.

wax moth (greater & lesser bee moth): A moth who enters beehives (at night) to lay eggs on the comb. Larvae (caterpillars) destroy the wax combs by boring through and chewing the wax, feeding on organic debris leaving behind waste matter and sunken tunnels.

wax pots in wax handling: A pot used to pour wax.

wax pots in social bees: Containers made of wax holding stored honey and pollen in colonies of bumble bees and stingless bees.

western (European) honey bee: *Apis mellifera* L., the most commonly managed honey bee species.

wet extracted frames: Combs that come out of the extractor with traces of honey on them. They may be placed outside to be robbed out, or placed on hives to be cleaned.

wheal: Following a sting, an area of the skin which is temporarily raised, typically reddened, and usually accompanied by itching.

whirring (breaking) dance: See buzz run.

White House bees: Bees placed and managed on the property of the White House during the Obama administration. Moved to Vice-President's home (Naval Observatory) during Trump presidency.

wild bees: Solitary or subsocial bees other than honey bees. Used to designate a (feral) honey bee nest in a tree or box.

wing veins: Raised veins in insect wings that strengthen the wing during fight and transport hemolymph.

winter bees: See fat bees and fat body.

winter cluster: Organization by closely packed colony of bees in winter to conserve heat.

winter wrapping: Roofing paper or insulation material used to wrap for winter insulation/wind protection.

wooden queen cage: Cages made to transport, store and introduce queens. The three-hole queen cages were developed by entomologist Frank Benton in 1905 to ship queens in the mail from counties in Europe.

woodpeckers: Birds feeding on wooden bee hives. May structurally weaken hive boxes.

worker bee: A female bee whose reproductive organs are only partially developed; responsible for carrying on all inside-hive duties except egg laying, and all outside foraging for food, water, and propolis.

worker comb: Comb with about 25 cells per square inch (4 per square centimeter). Drone comb has larger cells and results in about 16 cells per square inch.

Y-Z

yellowjackets (*Vespula* spp): Social wasps predatory on bee colonies.

zombie fly parasite: *Apocephalus borealis*. Larvae hatch from eggs placed on adult bees, causing unusual behavior of flying about lights at night. Larvae decapitate adults upon emergence to pupate.

Index

Third Edition

Metric conversions
1 inch = 2.54 cm
1 mile = 1.609 km
1 square mile = 2,590 square km = 640 acres
1 pound = 0.45 kg
1 U.S. ton = 0.9 metric ton = 2,000 lbs
1 kilometer = 0.621 mi
1 meter =39.37 in = 3.28 ft
1 centimeter = 10 millimeters (mm) = 0.394 in
1 hectare = 10,000 square meters = 2.471 acres
1 kilogram = 2.205 lbs

Reviews of the Third Edition

We are so lucky that Dr. Larry Connor is still publishing books about bees and beekeeping. His books are always fascinating and will teach you a lot of things you need to know. But they are fun to read and you will be glad you read it. The most recent Third Edition brings it right up to the latest and best information. You'll be glad you have it, and so will your bees!
— Dan O'Hanlon, West Virginia Queen Producers

Reviews of Earlier Editions

5.0 out of 5 stars
Most Valuable Bee Biology Book I Own
Reviewed in the United States on April 28, 2020

I've been keeping and studying Honey Bees for over 13 years.
If you're at all like me and must know every possible thing you can about honey bees, then this is a book that must occupy your bookshelf!
I study honey bees at the college level and this is my go-to book when doing research.
The pages are non-glossy, so you can make margin notes, or use your hi-lighter without smearing.
BUT, the bulk of the text is spot on and an exhaustive resource for any serious beekeeper.
I Highly recommend this book!
—Freddy The Frog

5.0 out of 5 stars
Best bee book ever!
Reviewed in the United States on May 24, 2017

I am used to purchasing the little soft back $15-$20 type of DIY beekeeping guide book(s) and this is not that. This book is more like an encyclopedia with way more info than I have ever been presented with, even after attending "bee school". I highly recommend this easy to read and comprehend title for those serious about becoming a student of bees instead of just having bees to steal some honey from. Get it, read it, reread it, refer back to it always and help save our lady bees!!!
— Mr. Anderson

3.0 out of 5 stars
Too expensive
Reviewed in the United States on September 1, 2020
Good book but WAY to much money. Good basic information, not to detailed, but pics are ok. All the information is available on the internet for free, sometimes even more complete than in the book. Granted it is nice to have it in hand and easily available.
—Michael Shepard

5.0 out of 5 stars
A must for EVERY BEEKEEPER.
Reviewed in the United States on March 24, 2019

Not only is it an absolutely beautiful hard cover book, it has amazing pictures for examples and loaded with knowledge. A must have when studying for the Journeyman and Master level in Beekeeping.
Every Beekeeper should have one band even just concerned people about our food crops pollination will want to read, look at the pictures and share......but probably not loan out.
—Anna Duncan

5.0 out of 5 stars
Stop now !! save yourself endless hours at the bookstore, tons of frustration and $$$ - All you need is this Book
Reviewed in the United States on October 27, 2014

I've never written a review on any product I've bought before because I tend to be a bit hard and critical on products. However with this product and my experience thus far with beekeeping I felt I should. I have ordered est. 7 books on the subject ($200.00) in the last 9 mos and found them all over priced and lacking in depth and knowledge. I was hopeful after reading the reviews on Honey Bee Biology but was still prepared to be disappointed and waste more money. To my great surprise I found the book amazingly well edited, easy to read and full of the education/knowledge that all the other books did not contain. The book could be priced for twice as much and still be worth it. This is my first year in the beekeeping hobby/business and I have abandoned/shelved all my other books and refer to this one only. Many thanks to all those that helped produce and bring this product to market. There is nothing negative I can say
—angie

5.0 out of 5 stars and perfect as an introductory text
Reviewed in the United States on February 13, 2017

I purchased this book because I was interested in teaching a basic course of honey bee biology and beekeeping to a small group of undergraduate students. The book is comprehensive in scope, very well organized, and perfect as an introductory text. All of the students have expressed how much they like this book. It is a small class but the consensus is unanimous. I agree that as an introductory text this is an outstanding choice, and I do not think there are other viable alternatives.

5.0 out of 5 stars
The best book in my bee library!
Reviewed in the United States on October 14, 2013

Clear, concise and engagingly written, this excellent look at bees, bee biology/physiology and behaviour is richly

illustrated and cleverly organized. I especially applaud the way in which the most recent research is presented, very readable and clear in its implications for the beekeeper. I was especially interested in the way the book explored foraging behaviours, and will use that information to plan my forage plantings next year (the country fields are so empty of bee forage now that you have to purpose-plant forage for them...). Meanwhile, all those of you city or country who want to give the bees a boost, plant up some spring flowering heather, some catmint (catmint, not catnip), some sunflowers and caryopteris (Bluebeard, very pretty). If we all put those in our gardens or on our balconies, it would really help build populations of all the pollinators! Great book, fascinating read.
— WesternWilson

5.0 out of 5 stars
Trying to learn how to keep the Honeybees alive
Reviewed in the United States on April 5, 2019

Still trying to learn how to keep the bees alive and this has a lot of information. I like this book as well as a few other books on beekeeping. I like it.
— Robert C

5.0 out of 5 stars
Wonderful textbook on Bees and Beekeeping
Reviewed in the United States on December 31, 2020

Great textbook for the novice and experienced beekeeper alike. There is so much detail, so much information. There is so much to learn about bees. They are truly fascinating creatures. We are lucky to have them in our world.
—Eileen Harvey